89TH CONGRESS, 2D SESSION
HOUSE DOCUMENT NO. 349

The Yearbook of
Agriculture
1966

THE UNITED STATES GOVERNMENT PRINTING OFFICE

PROTECTING

OUR FOOD

THE UNITED STATES, DEPARTMENT OF AGRICULTURE

THE UNITED STATES GOVERNMENT PRINTING OFFICE

FOR SALE BY THE SUPERINTENDENT OF DOCUMENTS, WASHINGTON, D.C. 20402 - PRICE $2.50

FOREWORD

ORVILLE L. FREEMAN, *Secretary of Agriculture*

As OUR SPACESHIPS soar towards the stars, we dare not forget that hunger still walks a thousand streets on our own planet, Earth.

For food shortages are an everyday fact in the developing countries. Malnutrition is common. A critical drought or a serious rampage by crop-devouring insects can result in widespread hunger and the threat of famine among millions of people.

We in the United States are fortunate. Our food abundance is one of the miracles of the age, with great gains in the last 20 years. In today's supermarkets the American housewife can choose among 7,000 to 8,000 items; two decades ago the food shopper could select from only 3,000 items. Our frozen food industry will produce 10 billion pounds in 1966, compared with 1.5 billion in 1946.

Freeze drying, aerosol containers for food, air delivery of fresh fruits and vegetables, all are among the new techniques that benefit the consumer. "Built-in chef service" in convenience foods often allows the housewife to bake better cakes, make better muffins, prepare more delicious stews—and save time too.

An hour's wages of a U.S. factory worker enables him to buy more of most foods today than he could in 1947–1949: 3.2 pounds of beef today compared to 1.9 pounds, 5.5 half gallons of milk at the store compared to 3.4, or 11 cans of peas compared to six. Frying chickens cost the consumer at least 15 cents a pound less.

We're spending about 60 percent more per person for food today than we did in 1946, but our after-tax incomes have more than doubled. As a result, the percentage of our income spent for food has dropped from 24 then to about 18 today. Besides, we now are getting higher quality—and higher valued—foods. Beef consumption per capita, for example, has jumped from 62 to 100 pounds a year.

We are a world leader in food. Our abundance has enabled us to share our food with others in foreign lands. During the past 12 years alone we have spent $18 billion in providing food and fiber aid

v

to 70 developing nations. And in the highly competitive world cash market during that time we were selling food and other farm products that brought to the United States $40 billion in foreign exchange.

Here at home, our abundance makes possible the food assistance programs that are helping close the nutrition gap for our own people. These programs benefit over 40 million Americans—children eating lunch or drinking milk at school with the help of the National School Lunch and Special Milk Programs; low-income families receiving direct donations of USDA foods or upgrading their diets with the self-help Food Stamp Program; and many needy children and adults in charitable institutions.

The 180 million tons of food aid we have sent since 1954 to needy people of other countries has done more than any other program in history to avert hunger and malnutrition. This aid has meant more to underfed families in the developing nations than a thousand spaceships, or hardware for a hundred armies.

Early in 1966 President Johnson proposed that the United States lead the world in a new *war against hunger*. Exploding populations are threatening the world anew with mass famine, because food production has not kept pace.

Hunger imperils world peace. It makes men desperate. Riots, the breakdown of government, chaos can result. And agents of enslaving philosophies are always at hand to scavenge in the ruins.

The new war against hunger is already underway. During 1966 the United States sent more food to India than any country had ever sent to another in all history.

But as President Johnson has firmly declared, self-help is the essential key to victory in the war on hunger. Under present trends, the time is not far off when all the production, on all the acres, of all the agriculturally productive nations on earth will not meet food needs of the developing nations. The developing nations must improve their own agricultures to survive.

The United States stands ready to assist by providing know-how as well as food. Food protection is an important part of both. The emerging nations need—beside food aid—to learn ways to overcome the hazards of pests, disease, weather, and spoilage.

Although we are a fortunate nation, our food abundance didn't just happen. The authors in this Yearbook of Agriculture point out that we have to fight 10,000 kinds of insects for our food. We have to combat 1,500 plant diseases, and 250 animal diseases. We have to fight spoilage and decay.

The result of this battle to protect our food is evident. In our own country, food quality is high, the abundance great, and the cost relatively low. Overseas, we have supplied 98 percent of food aid received by the less developed nations.

Protecting our food is a giant job, and a vital one for both America and the world.

How do we do it? The job has a thousand facets. Here are a few.

Federal inspectors check the health of more than 52 million animals at our stockyards each year. More than $2.5 billion is spent annually in the war against weeds.

Insects and other crop and livestock pests are being fought with chemicals, gamma radiation, light traps, viruses, predator insects, sound waves, microbial agents, and hormones. New advances are being made in developing crop varieties that resist pests.

The Agriculture Department participates in virtually every aspect of food protection, often working shoulder-to-shoulder with other Federal agencies, the States, local agencies and private organizations. Our research ranges from apples to zucchini. Our action programs include quarantine at ports, borders, and airports. Last year Department inspectors intercepted a dangerous alien plant pest every 16 minutes around the clock.

In our livestock health programs we hope to eliminate cattle brucellosis and hog cholera by 1972, and swine brucellosis by 1975. Cattle tuberculosis is just about wiped out. We have used atomic radiation techniques to virtually eliminate the screw-worm, a pest that can kill livestock.

The Agriculture Department inspects 60 billion pounds of poultry and meat products a year. Some 3.4 billion pounds of frozen fruits and vegetables are graded annually, and 225 million cases of canned products. More than 95 percent of our frozen orange juice is packed under continuous inspection by the Department.

These are a few elements of the "food protection" story. All of this the American people are inclined to take for granted. But with the support of the U.S. Congress, the Department continues to strengthen and improve these essential "food protection" services each year.

Many of these techniques can be modified and adopted by the developing nations to increase the quantity and quality of their own food supplies. We propose to help them do so.

As an American, I am proud of the great achievement of the American farmer and the food industry that has accomplished the greatest food abundance in history. As Secretary of Agriculture, I am proud of the USDA that has provided leadership for this great accomplishment.

Protecting our food is vital to a healthy and prosperous America. And without the food exports we are able to make from our abundance, our own economy would suffer severely and millions abroad would go hungry.

Food for America, food for a hungry world. This sums up the food protection job.

PREFACE

JACK HAYES, *Editor of the Yearbook of Agriculture*

OUR PURPOSE IS TO INFORM all Americans about the great scientific achievements that assure us a safe and plentiful supply of food.

This book is not only a record of accomplishment. It also is an explanation of how problems were solved and how we developed knowledge that will help solve future problems; a practical exposition of the proper way to handle foodstuffs from farm to table; an insight into procedures of chemistry, physics, marketing, and related disciplines; an overview of regulations and administration; and a reassurance.

The words above, adapted from the Prospectus for the 1966 Yearbook of Agriculture, served as "fence" lines from the planning of the Yearbook through its writing, editing, and production.

This book is witness to the remarkable teamwork between farmer, processor, transporter, wholesaler, retailer, and government (local, State, and Federal) in providing Americans with hundreds of millions of wholesome meals every day in every year.

A sunburned man on a tractor plants the seed that eventually sustains life for us all. As the farmer turns his furrows he uses every imaginable form of know-how to obtain the best and most from his land. His contoured fields and automated feedlots attain a productivity unmatched by nonfarm industry, and unmatched in recorded time. He has harnessed sun and soil and science and left his mark on history.

So vital in today's world is protecting our food that the Yearbook begins with the world and national food situations. The story continues through the battles for abundance against insects, decay, drought, and frost. It ranges from on-farm production to shipping and handling; from processing to packaging to refrigeration; from warehouse to supermarket to protecting food in the home and restaurant. The marketing marvel, military and space food problems, and safeguarding the sportsman's paradise are part of the story.

Some chapters take up government and industry roles in protecting our food. Safe use of chemicals is emphasized again and again throughout the book, and their tight regulation described from registration to monitoring. Nonchemical ways of pest control are explored in depth.

Protecting our food is important to every American, and touches on all aspects of the Nation's biggest industry—agriculture. It is reassuring to know that so many people and organizations are continually striving to keep our food the best in the world. Among them are thousands of scientists and hundreds of laboratories.

Authors make a Yearbook of Agriculture, and this one is no exception. The Nation is richer for their harvest of knowledge. Photographers, artists, and typographers add visual zest to the book.

The editor of the Yearbook was greatly aided by the work of the Yearbook Committee and the previous editor, Alfred Stefferud, who retired after planning the present volume following 20 years of distinguished service. The new editor was also fortunate in obtaining frequent counsel from W. T. Pentzer, Yearbook Committee Chairman. Others who helped are too numerous to mention. The editor thanks them all.

Members of the 1966 Yearbook Committee are:

W. T. Pentzer, *Agricultural Research Service*, Chairman
N. D. Bayley, *Agricultural Research Service*
John C. Blum, *Consumer and Marketing Service*
Arthur E. Browne, *Consumer and Marketing Service*
R. G. Garner, *Cooperative State Research Service*
L. C. Gibbs, *Federal Extension Service*
C. H. Hoffman, *Agricultural Research Service*
H. C. Knoblauch, *Cooperative State Research Service*
Ruth M. Leverton, *Agricultural Research Service*
John R. Matchett, *Agricultural Research Service*
Francis E. McLaughlin, *Department of Health, Education, and Welfare*
Jack P. Meiners, *Agricultural Research Service*
Ernest G. Moore, *Agricultural Research Service*
K. E. Ogren, *Economic Research Service*
Eugene P. Reagan, *Agricultural Research Service*
Edwin L. Ruppert, *Department of Health, Education, and Welfare*
Donald A. Spencer, *Agricultural Research Service*

CONTENTS

CHALLENGES

TOOLS OF PROTECTION

xi

GOVERNMENT AND INDUSTRY ROLES

THE ROAD AHEAD

PROTECTING

OUR FOOD

Protection and Plenty

A PHOTO PORTFOLIO

A 10,000-bird broiler house—poultry a'plenty.

The sun smiles on
the land, and harvest
prospects look good.

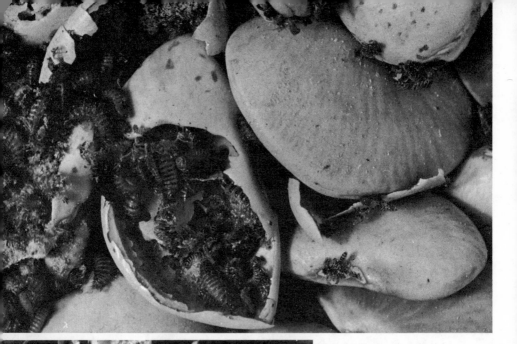

But insects, nematodes,
and other pests
attack crops both above
and below ground
and anywhere in the food line
from farm to table.

Among the victims are
lima beans, corn, and (right)
potato stems and roots
covered with
round nematode cysts.

Bacterial, chemical, and biological warfare is carried on against the pests that threaten our food.

A tiny electrode in a hypodermic needle measures the oxygen level in "blood" of a Japanese beetle grub infected with milky spore disease.

Housefly is tethered in a feeding stimulant test, aimed at practical control of this disease carrier.

Downwash created by helicopter rotors insures safe and effective penetration of spray material.

Grapes are sun-dried in an age-old technique to preserve food for future use. Processing, refrigeration, and fast transportation are some of the key areas in protecting our food.

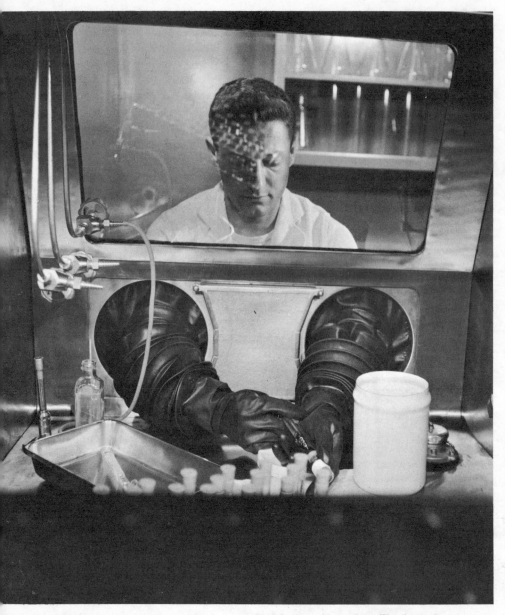

Safety hood protects technician in work with infectious viruses that afflict livestock.

Meat inspector checks retail label
to see that frankfurter ingredients agree
with those listed on
processor's rack for this lot.
Inspection assures that
meat products are wholesome.

The 500 careers in food protection range from the most complex scientific skills to the ancient art of sheepherding, where the grandeur of nature may help compensate for the rugged outdoor work.

Challenges

MAN'S HISTORIC STRUGGLE FOR FOOD

RAYMOND P. CHRISTENSEN

WORLD economic development was held in check for many centuries by man's inability to control the hazards of nature and expand his food supply.

Historical and archeological records indicate it took hundreds of thousands of years for world population to reach about 250 million by the time of Christ. It took 16 centuries more for that figure to double to 500 million. Food production increased slowly. Population growth was held to a small fraction of 1 percent a year by starvation, disease, and violence.

BEGINNING IN THE 1700's, new scientific discoveries vastly increased man's knowledge of agricultural production and marketing problems.

The land area under agricultural use was increased. Higher crop yields resulted from the use of crop rotations, improved varieties of crops, and better soil management practices. New breeds of livestock and better management practices increased the production of animal products.

New findings about how to prevent losses in crop and animal production from natural hazards—weather, weeds, insects, and diseases—became an integral part of the expanding fund of knowledge on agricultural technology.

Growth in food supplies resulting from these improvements in agriculture made it possible for world population to increase six times from the middle of the 17th century to the middle of the 20th. Moreover, the quality of diets was greatly improved. More nutritious and better quality food led to longer life and healthier people.

As output per farmworker increased, many farm people were released for work in other occupations. Rising productivity in agriculture helped make industrial development possible. Production of other goods besides food was increased.

Consumption levels for clothing, housing, and the many other things that people want in larger quantities were improved.

Famines and starvation were common before modern methods of preventing losses from natural hazards were developed.

The potato famine in Ireland in the middle of the 19th century is an example. Potatoes had become the main food crop. Potato blight almost wholly destroyed this crop in 1845 and 1846. Ireland lost almost a third of its population between 1845 and 1860 as a

* * *

Raymond P. Christensen is *Deputy Director*, Foreign Development and Trade Division, Economic Research Service.

2

direct result of the outbreak of late blight. About a million people died from starvation or from disease following malnutrition. A million and a half more Irish emigrated.

But large-scale famines have been reported even as recently as 1943, in India. Food shortages in Bengal in 1943 resulted from crop failure and reduction in imported food supplies due to the war. It is estimated that at least a million and a half people died from the famine and from the diseases connected with it.

WORLD FOOD SUPPLIES will need to increase at more rapid rates in the future than they have in the past if all people are to receive adequate diets. World population growth rates have gone up greatly in the last few decades. Average annual percentage increases since 1650 are as follows:

	Percent
1650–1750	0.3
1750–1950	0.4
1950–1960	1.5
1961–1965	2.0

According to estimates of the United Nations, world population will grow 2.1 percent a year between now and 1975 and 2.6 percent a year between 1975 and the year 2000.

It has taken all the vast reaches of time for the world population to reach a figure of 3 billion.

But it will take less than 35 years to add the next 3 billion if population growth rates do not decline.

Rapid population growth throughout much of the world raises questions about how food needs can be met. Can world food supplies be doubled by the year 2000? An even larger increase in food supplies would be necessary to provide nutritionally adequate diets for everyone.

New technological discoveries may be expected to increase agricultural production capacity. Moreover, application of currently known technology in the less advanced countries would greatly increase food production. But the world's land resources are limited. Obviously, population growth at 2 percent or more a year cannot continue indefinitely.

Dr. Philip Hauser, Director of the Population Research Training Center, University of Chicago, has pointed out that:

"One hundred people multiplying at 1 percent a year for 5,000 years of human history would have produced a contemporary population of 2.7 billion persons per square foot of land surface of the earth! Such an exercise in arithmetic, although admittedly dramatic and propagandistic, is also a conclusive way of demonstrating that a 1-percent-per-year increase in world population could not have taken place very long in the past; nor can it continue long in the future."

Historically, population growth rates have decreased with rising incomes, industrialization, and urbanization of countries. But reduction in population growth rates from over 2 percent a year to 1 percent or less will likely take a generation or longer. Meanwhile, ways must be found to expand world food supplies at record high rates.

THE "POPULATION EXPLOSION"

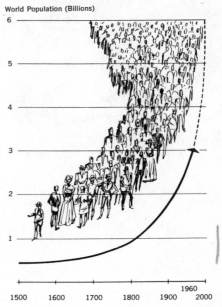

Flailing corn on a small farm in El Salvador.

The welfare of people in the United States and other economically advanced countries, where food supplies are abundant, will depend largely upon the success achieved in expanding food supplies to adequate levels in the economically underdeveloped countries. If food supplies do not keep pace with population growth, the peace and security of the entire world will be threatened.

FOOD SUPPLY CONDITIONS vary greatly among regions of the world.

Approximately a third of the world's population lives in economically developed countries where food supplies are ample for healthy and satisfactory diets for all, and only the lack of income and buying power limit a small proportion of the population to poor and inadequate diets.

But two-thirds of the world's population live in economically underdeveloped countries where many people do not get enough food to satisfy their hunger. In these countries, agriculture must be modernized and food production capacity greatly increased before national economic development is possible.

The diet-adequate areas include all of Europe, North America, Australia, and New Zealand, and a few countries like Japan and Israel.

In these areas per capita incomes average over $1,000 per year. People spend only 20 to 40 percent of their income for food. They have large amounts to spend for clothing, housing, education, and the many other things that help make life worth while.

Farmers market most of what they produce. Only small amounts are retained on farms for consumption by farm people. Food processing, storage, and transportation facilities in these countries are well developed. More than half the money consumers spend for food is for marketing services. Productivity on farms and in marketing industries is high.

Agriculture's share of the total population is small. It is less than 7 percent in the United States, 5 percent in the

United Kingdom, and 10 to 25 percent in most other European countries.

The diet-deficit areas include all of Asia except Japan and Israel and all but the southern tip of Africa. They also include the northern part of South America, and almost all of Central America and the Caribbean.

In these areas, diets average 300 Calories per day below standards considered essential for good health. They average 900 Calories per day below the level of the third of the world living in countries with nutritionally adequate average diets.

Daily consumption of protein in these areas is less than two-thirds of the level for the diet-adequate countries; fat consumption is less than a third.

DIET-DEFICIT COUNTRIES are struggling to achieve economic development. Per capita incomes in these countries average less than $100 a year. Farm products account for nearly half of all income produced.

Farm production is largely for subsistence purposes. Half or more of all food is consumed on the farms where it is produced.

Half or more of the food consumed is stored and processed on farms under primitive conditions. Commercial marketing, processing, storage, and transportation of food products are not well developed.

A large share of the total labor force, 60 to 80 percent, is engaged in farming.

The less developed countries depend heavily on low-cost food crops for energy.

Cereals and other starchy crops like potatoes, sweetpotatoes, yams, cassava, and other tropical root crops provide 65 to 80 percent of the calories in the diets of people in these countries compared with only 25 to 50 percent in the developed countries.

Diet-deficit countries consume small quantities of livestock products, the more expensive sources of food nutrients. For example, these areas consume only 20 to 50 pounds of meat, fish, and eggs per capita compared with 120

5

India's first grain storage elevator, built with U.S. aid.

to 290 pounds in the diet-adequate countries.

Population growth rates have gone up rapidly in the less developed countries in the last 30 years. They now average 2 to 3 percent a year or higher in some instances compared with 1.5 percent a year or less in most developed countries. Reduction in death rates resulting from improved health and sanitation measures, without comparable reductions in birth rates, accounts for these high population growth rates.

For many centuries, both death rates and birth rates in the low-income countries averaged around 40 per thousand of total population each year

and there was little net population growth. Famines and disease epidemics held down population growth.

Application of modern health and disease control measures has reduced death rates from over 40 per thousand of total population to 10 to 20 per thousand in many countries. Meanwhile, birth rates have continued relatively high at around 40 or more per thousand each year. This results in population growth rates of 2 to 3 percent a year.

Food needs in the less developed countries are expanding rapidly because of the record high rates of population growth. Population growth rates of 3 percent a year, plus allowance for gradual increases in food consumption per person accompanying higher income levels, mean that food supplies must increase 4 to 5 percent a year to keep pace with economic requirements.

India's experience during recent decades is typical of many of the less developed countries.

Total population increased only 5 percent in India during the 30 years from 1891 to 1921, or only one-sixth of 1 percent a year.

There was no growth during the 1891 to 1901 decade because of severe famines accompanying crop failure due to adverse weather and crop pests. Similarly, there was no growth from 1911 to 1921 because of the great influenza epidemic of 1918–19 which was especially severe in India.

But during the three decades from 1921 to 1951, population grew from 248 million to 357 million or by some 44 percent, over 1 percent a year. During these years, there were no severe nationwide famines or epidemics. Birth rates continued high at about 45 per thousand of population from 1891 to 1951 while death rates declined from 41 to 31 per thousand.

Since 1951, death rates have continued to fall. Consequently, population growth in India now exceeds 2 percent a year and the current population is about 490 million.

Contrary to what may be thought by many, the less developed countries have achieved outstanding increases in agricultural production in the last two decades.

Recently, the U.S. Department of Agriculture's Economic Research Service, in collaboration with the Agency for International Development, completed a new set of index numbers showing changes in crop production since 1948 for 26 of the less developed countries located in southern Europe, Asia, Africa, and Latin America. These 26 countries represent three-fourths of the people, the food, and income of all the less developed countries of the free world.

The index numbers show that total crop production increased at annual compound growth rates ranging from 1.6 percent in Tunisia to 9.7 percent in Israel. Many countries show increases of 3, 4, and 5 percent a year.

But the increases in agricultural production that have been taking place in many of the less developed countries are not large compared with those required for national economic development.

The upsurge in population growth is greatly expanding food requirements. In most of these countries, population is increasing at more than 2.5 percent a year, in many it is over 3 percent, and in some it is close to 4 percent.

Most of the less developed countries have increased food production as rapidly as population in the last 15 years. But merely keeping food production abreast of population growth is not enough. Most people in these countries are not eating enough food now. And very few are eating food of the type or quality they desire or need.

A granary at Togoniere, Ivory Coast.

ECONOMIC DEVELOPMENT sharply increases the total demand for food. It also brings about major changes in types of foods needed.

As people move from country to city, as they earn larger incomes, and—perhaps for the first time—have money in their hands, they are not content to sleep off famine periods. They are unable to forage from the land in periods of desperate food shortage. And they no longer are content to limit themselves to cereals and other starchy foods.

When incomes rise in the low-income countries, half or more of the additional income is spent for food compared with 20 percent or less in high-income countries. People who depend mainly upon cereals and other low-cost foods especially want to consume more of the higher priced foods such as sugar, meat, eggs, and milk when their incomes rise. Note in this connection that milk consumption in Puerto Rico has increased fourfold since 1953.

CROP PRODUCTION increased more rapidly than population in 21 of the 26 less developed countries studied during the 1948–63 period. But rates of increase in farm production have decreased in recent years. For all 26 countries, the compound annual rate of growth averaged 4.5 percent in the first half of the 1948–63 period compared to 3 percent in the second half. Percentage increases in population have been larger than for food production in many of these countries during the last 2 years.

When you add increased demands for food resulting from income growth to those resulting from population growth, you find that expansion in food production did not keep pace with expansion in total demand for food in 17 of the 26 study countries.

These calculations present the general picture. Food production has not kept pace with growth in economic demands for food in most of the less developed countries in recent years. Foreign trade data support this observation. Asia and Latin America had net exports of grain of over 10 million tons a year in the 1934–38 period, but in the last few years they have had net imports of 20 to 25 million tons.

AGRICULTURE MUST DO more than produce enough to meet rising economic requirements for food if it is to fulfill its role in national economic development.

Economic productivity in agriculture must increase so there will be an "economic surplus" which can be used for further production in agriculture or can be transferred out of agriculture to provide capital for industrial growth and to meet consumption needs of the urban population.

Rising productivity in agriculture is necessary to make possible the release of farmworkers and other resources for use by other sectors of the national economy. Increases in agricultural productivity also are needed to increase the purchasing power of rural people and create mass markets for industrial goods.

Agricultural commodity aid from the economically advanced countries can provide much needed resources for economic development to countries where agricultural production is not keeping pace with expanding economic demands. In fact, food aid may be worth just as much as other kinds of economic aid.

When the agricultural sectors of the less developed countries are not able to satisfy food demand, many serious consequences follow.

Countries may have to cut back sharply their industrial development programs in order to shift resources into food production or into food purchases from abroad. As national development is thus slowed down, people become frustrated and lose hope.

The government may decide, on the other hand, to fight it through on empty stomachs. It may attempt rationing, or other distributional activities to spread the food around more equally. This absorbs a great deal of the country's scarce administrative resources. It also leads to unhappiness

8

by the citizens, who may retaliate with strikes, riots, or forced changes of government.

To be most effective, agricultural commodity aid should be programed as a part of realistic, long-term, national economic development plans. Many countries need large amounts of food aid as well as other kinds of aid for several years in the future in order to accelerate economic growth rates. Food aid to meet emergency conditions that cannot be foreseen, of course, also can contribute to economic growth and human welfare.

Large numbers of people in the developing countries are not fully employed. Agricultural commodities can be used to pay labor that otherwise would be unemployed on capital improvement projects including construction of roads, schools, and land improvements for drainage, irrigation, and soil erosion control. Perhaps not enough effort has been made to use food aid in resource development projects.

THE UNITED STATES has supplied large amounts of food aid to the less developed countries. In recent years the total value of farm products shipped abroad under Food for Peace programs has averaged about $1.6 billion annually. Food aid accounts for nearly half of all economic aid the United States has given to foreign countries since 1956.

Food aid to the less developed countries comes chiefly from the United States. In fact, the United States has supplied 98 percent of the total.

Other developed countries also supply economic aid to the less developed countries. However, if food aid is included in economic aid, the United States has been the source of about half of world development assistance in the last few years.

FOOD SHIPMENTS under the U.S. Food for Peace programs have made significant contributions to economic development of the low-income countries. They have helped prevent food shortages and price inflation which disrupt industrialization plans and retard national economic growth.

Once economic development of low-income countries is achieved, these countries will become commercial customers for farm products from the developed countries. Japan, Taiwan, Israel, and Spain are examples of countries that have achieved rapid economic growth—partly as the result of food supplied by the United States under Food for Peace programs—and now have become important commercial importers of farm products.

WHAT ABOUT THE FUTURE of food aid? Can the low-income countries use larger amounts?

Marketing and distribution facilities limit the amount of food aid that can be used effectively in most countries.

Additional food aid probably can be used effectively for resource development projects in some countries. But careful planning is required. Administrative arrangements need to be made for employing workers and for paying them with food. In most instances, technical assistance must accompany food aid used directly for resource development projects. Moreover, workers cannot be paid entirely with food.

Tools and equipment and other materials are required for constructing roads, schools, storage and marketing facilities, or to carry out land improvement projects.

Some studies suggest that 30 to 40 percent of the total cost of development projects can be financed with food.

THERE ARE POTENTIALS for using larger amounts of food for development purposes in the less developed countries if other economic aid also is made available.

Certainly, many countries will require large amounts of food aid to maintain and improve consumption levels as long as population growth continues high. But the developing countries need to plan the use of food aid over the years ahead so they gradually become self-supporting and can

9

purchase food imports as well as other imports on a commercial basis.

Agricultural production capacity in the United States and other economically advanced countries of the free world has increased more rapidly than consumption needs during the past 20 years. Consequently, these countries have been able to expand agricultural exports to the less developed nations.

This has not been true of the Communist countries of eastern Europe, the Soviet Union, or Communist China. These countries have imported increasing quantities of farm products, especially food grains, from developed countries of the free world in the last few years.

ALTHOUGH FOOD IMPORTS have been important, the less developed countries have relied chiefly on increased production at home to meet growing food requirements. They will need to continue to do so in the future.

During the period from 1950 to 1960 grain consumption in the less developed countries increased from about 340 million to nearly 450 million metric tons, or by 110 million tons. Only 11 million tons of this increase came from larger net imports; nearly 100 million was increased production.

Total consumption requirements for grain in the less developed countries will increase by 250 million tons by 1980 if population growth continues at about present rates and per capita consumption rates do not change.

An increase in net imports by the less developed countries from 15 million tons in 1960 to 35 million tons in 1980 may be about as large as can be expected. In this case, the countries would need to expand grain production by about 230 million tons or 50 percent to maintain current consumption levels.

It is a mistake to think the less advanced countries can depend on the United States and other economically advanced countries for the bulk of their rapidly expanding food requirements.

There are several reasons why these countries will need to rely chiefly on home production. Transportation facilities are not available to move the additional quantities needed. Perhaps most important, the less developed countries have limited foreign exchange resources with which to purchase food from abroad.

Although food aid programs may increase in size, there are limits on the amounts the United States or other developed countries are willing to spend for these programs.

And as indicated by the data given for grains above, even a doubling of imports would not go far towards meeting the larger requirements expected by 1980.

Low levels of food consumption in the less developed countries result from low levels of productivity.

Food production per acre and per worker average relatively low in most of these countries. The farm value of food produced per farmworker averages less than $100 a year in the less developed countries compared with over $700 in the developed countries. Crop yields per acre average only about half as high.

Many of the low-income countries are densely populated. As a group, they have less than 1 acre of arable land per person compared with over 2 acres per person in the developed countries. Possibilities of expanding the land area under cultivation are limited.

In most countries larger food supplies must be obtained chiefly by increasing crop yields.

A larger food output per acre also will mean a larger food output per farmworker.

It might be expected that the densely populated, low-income countries would have relatively high crop yields since there are 5 to 10 times as many people to work each unit of land as in the developed countries. But the meager crop yields that prevail generally in the less developed countries result from low levels of technology, fertilizer, and other resources.

Grain combines move through a Washington State wheatfield.

CURRENT WHEAT YIELDS IN SELECTED COUNTRIES RELATED TO UNITED KINGDOM'S HISTORICAL TREND

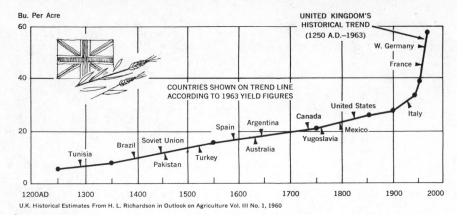

U.K. Historical Estimates From H. L. Richardson in Outlook on Agriculture Vol. III No. 1, 1960

CURRENT RICE YIELDS IN SELECTED COUNTRIES RELATED TO JAPAN'S HISTORICAL TREND

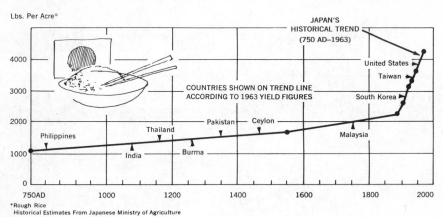

*Rough Rice
Historical Estimates From Japanese Ministry of Agriculture

CURRENT CORN YIELDS IN SELECTED COUNTRIES RELATED TO UNITED STATES' HISTORICAL TREND

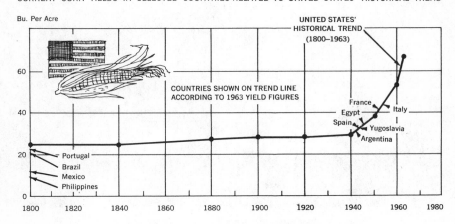

12

Fortunately, there are large potentials for increasing crop yields in these countries.

Rice yields average only a fourth as high in India and Pakistan as in Japan. Wheat yields average only a third as high in Tunisia and Turkey as in the United Kingdom. Corn yields average less than a fourth as high in Mexico, Brazil, and the Philippines as in the United States.

Improved varieties, better control of pests and diseases, increased use of chemical fertilizer, more irrigated land, and better tillage and harvesting methods have made possible rapidly increasing crop yields in the developed countries.

TODAY, FARMING METHODS in many of the less developed countries are similar to those that prevailed in Japan, the United Kingdom, and the United States one or two centuries ago when relatively little capital was employed in farm production, and land and labor were the main resources. Better farming methods and additional fertilizer and other materials are needed if the less developed countries are to improve their agricultural productivity.

The banishment of hunger and malnutrition from the world depends in large measure on how rapidly agricultural productivity can be increased in the less developed countries. If their crop yields can be doubled in the next 25 to 30 years, expanding food needs could be met even with rapid population growth.

Effective protection of plants and animals from the hazards of weather, disease, and pests has been necessary for the United States and other developed countries to provide their people with an abundant food supply.

Relatively little has been done to prevent losses to crop and animal production caused by insects and diseases in the less developed countries. The economically advanced countries use about 95 percent of pesticides consumed on farms while the less developed countries use only about 5 percent of the world total.

THE LESS DEVELOPED countries are located mainly in tropical zones where relatively little research has been conducted on how to combat the many natural hazards that reduce crop and animal production.

Not much is known about how to conserve and improve soil fertility in areas of high rainfall where soil erosion and leaching are serious problems. Effective alternatives to "slash-and-burn" systems of shifting cultivation need to be devised for rain forest regions.

Weeds take a heavy toll on crop production, especially over large areas where hand methods of agriculture still are practiced.

Much must be learned about how to improve agricultural production and marketing in the developing countries.

The United States, through the Agency for International Development, supports agricultural education

A Vietnamese farmer and a home economist inspect a stand of USDA 34 sweet corn.

and research programs in most of these countries. Other developed countries also give agricultural development assistance. Private agencies like the Ford and Rockefeller Foundations assist with agricultural education and research abroad.

The less developed countries also carry out agricultural education and research programs. But resources devoted to these activities still are small in most of these countries.

There is only one field extension agriculturalist for each 8,000 farmers in Chile and 17,000 in Thailand, compared with one for each 650 farmers in Japan and 500 in the United States. Expenditures for agricultural research average several times higher for each $100 of farm products produced in the developed countries than in the less developed.

THE TSETSE FLY makes large areas of Africa unsuitable for intensive agricultural use or for permanent farm settlement. It carries organisms that cause "sleeping sickness" which affects livestock. The fly inhabits brush in grassland areas where rainfall and soil conditions are excellent for crop production. Fortunately, measures are being developed to control and gradually eliminate this pest.

In east Africa, locusts once did much damage to growing crops but they have been brought under control. The Agricultural Research Service of the U.S. Department of Agriculture cooperated with the Desert Locust Control Organization for east Africa which includes Tanzania, Kenya, Uganda, Ethiopia, and Somalia to triumph over an insect that has plagued mankind since the beginning of history.

This activity was sponsored by the Agency for International Development. Locusts were carefully studied, U.S. insect control methods were adapted, and insect-fighting teams were trained.

For the past 2 years, desert locust populations have been lower than at any other time in history. There has not been a single locust outbreak during a 12-month period. Today, literally millions of people are being fed from crops previously sacrificed to the locust.

Rodents, especially rats, do much damage to crops in storage. In rural areas of India it is reported that there are 10 times as many rats as people. It is estimated that rodents destroy 25 to 30 percent of total crop production.

Estimates from other countries in southeast Asia are even higher. A study in Vietnam revealed that 35 to 40 percent of all agricultural production was destroyed by rats in 1962.

In Taiwan, a successful program of rat elimination is estimated to have increased food supplies made available for human use by 10 to 15 percent.

Protection measures are urgently needed to control the many natural hazards that reduce production of growing crops and animals, and that damage or destroy food materials in storage and marketing channels. These measures must be made as effective as those that have reduced human death rates. There are large potentials for expanding food supplies in the less developed countries by prevention of losses.

CONTROL MEASURES to combat the many hazards of food production and marketing involve economic costs for labor and materials. These costs may be large or small. Similarly, economic returns in the form of increased quantity and improved quality of food supplies vary greatly. So it is necessary to compare costs and returns in analyzing benefits.

Benefits to a nation from control measures can be considerable. Each dollar spent to apply pesticides to fruit trees may add $10 to the value of the fruit crop; in fact, little production of good quality may result without using pesticides. But materials for controlling losses are limited. They need to be used where economic returns are highest.

Methods of preventing loss, waste, and damage may not be known. Even if methods are known, they may be relatively expensive in terms of skilled labor and materials.

Vietnamese farmer displays produce to U.S. Secretary of Agriculture Orville L. Freeman (left) and Vietnam Minister of Agriculture Lam Van Tri (center). Extension demonstrations showed that vegetable production is practical in Vietnam with fertilization and pest control.

Research to find ways of preventing losses, and educational work to get them adopted, have made sizable contributions to human welfare in the developed countries. If it were not for these research discoveries and their application in food production and marketing, cost of food to consumers would be much higher, food supplies smaller, and food consumption lower.

The abundant supplies of food that the United States and other economically developed countries enjoy today result from the application of advanced methods of producing and marketing farm products. These methods can be improved. In fact, they will need to be improved to supply growing populations with the kinds and qualities of food they desire in large amounts.

But besides protecting our own food supply, we must seek ways to insure adequate diets for people in the underdeveloped regions of the world. Famines and starvation can no longer be tolerated. Peace and security in the modern world depend upon ample supplies of food for all.

15

OUR

FOOD

ABUNDANCE

GLEN T. BARTON

THE U.S. consumer has three interrelated blessings: His food abundance, his food bargain, and his high level of living. But without our great food abundance, he would not have the other two.

The total quantity of food eaten by 195 million Americans in 1965 staggers the imagination. It would fill eight freight trains with each train stretching all the way from New York City to San Francisco.

In 1965, an average-sized U.S. family of four persons consumed over 2½ tons of food. Meat, poultry, and fish eaten totaled nearly half a ton, and dairy products close to three-quarters of a ton. Fruits and vegetables accounted for well over half a ton. Flour and cereal products, sugar, potatoes, fats and oils, and eggs added up to over four-fifths of a ton.

We would not eat so well, nor so economically, without the use of modern methods for protecting our food supply from the ravages of insects, diseases, and other pests.

If chemicals could not be used for pest control, farmers' production of crops and livestock might decrease by 25 to 30 percent in a few years. Additional losses would occur from stored-product insects, ranging from 5 percent for vegetables to 15 or 20 percent for stored grains.

With such losses, most food items would be in short supply, and prices of food would rise greatly. Obviously, the U.S. consumer has a vital interest in full protection of his food abundance.

THE FORTUNATE POSITION of the U.S. consumer is underscored when our national average diet is compared with that of other countries. Adequacy of a country's diet can be gaged by how

Glen T. Barton is *Chief*, Production Adjustments Branch, Farm Production Economics Division, Economic Research Service.

16

per capita use of calories, protein, and fat exceeds recommended standards or falls short. Nutritional reference standards for regions, or groups of countries, have been developed. The standards represent minimum physiological requirements for normal activity and health. They allow for waste between retailing and final consumption, and recognize differences among regions in climate, occupation, stature and age of the population, and other factors affecting minimum food needs.

THE CALORIE LEVEL, per person per day, of the United States in the mid-1960's was about 3,200. This exceeded the calorie standard recommended for the United States by 20 percent. Only Australia and New Zealand outranked our country, by a slight margin. In comparison, the Soviet Union was above its calorie standard by 15 percent, but India and Communist China fell short by 7 and 19 percent, respectively.

Protein content, especially animal protein, is a widely accepted indicator of nutritional quality of the diet. The United States also ranked high on this score in the mid-1960's. It was above its standard for total protein per capita by 59 percent, and was surpassed only by Australia, New Zealand, Argentina, and Uruguay. The Soviet Union exceeded its standard for total protein by 47 percent, but Communist China was deficient by 14 percent.

The United States was 540 percent above its standard for animal protein and was outranked only by Canada, Australia, and New Zealand. Although the Soviet Union surpassed its standard for animal protein by 230 percent, Communist China had a deficit of 57 percent.

The United States topped the list of countries in fat consumption per person, exceeding its standard by 225 percent. The Soviet Union was above its standard by 60 percent, but Communist China was below by 40 percent.

The nutritional status of U.S. consumers is in general very good. But nutritional problems do exist.

The prevalence of obesity with its many hazards to health should concern us all. On the other hand, many individuals and groups in the United States still do not have adequate diets; low incomes and poor food habits are important causes.

However, we have sufficient kinds and quantities of food available to provide recommended amounts of nutrients and energy for all our people.

Food enough is not our problem. Improved distribution and better use of our food abundance can solve easily the nutritional problems which still exist in the United States.

NOT ONLY IS THE U.S. consumer well fed, he gets his food at the best bargain in history.

In 1965, we spent only about 18 percent of our take-home pay for food, compared with 26 percent in 1947–49. Consumers in Great Britain spend nearly 30 percent, Russians more than 40 percent. Food costs take half or more of income in the less developed countries of the world.

The U.S. consumer works less for more and better food than consumers in any other country. In the mid-1960's our industrial workers, for only an hour's pay, can buy a good meal for four persons. Workers in England put in 2 hours to buy the same meal. It takes 4 hours' work in Austria, 4½ in France, and more than 5 in Italy.

Our food also is a bargain in other ways—in quality, convenience, and food services.

We can get pure, high-quality food whenever we want it. Low-cost orange juice is available all year. New varieties and quick freezing give us vegetables and fruit of near-fresh quality in every season.

Precooked and other convenience foods lessen drudgery for the housewife. Meals eaten away from home take about $1 of every $4 we spend for food.

The big bargain in food makes possible other bargains for the U.S. consumer. Because of the high efficiency with which we can produce, process,

17

and market our food, the great bulk of the labor and other production resources of the United States is used to produce other goods and services. This adds up to our high level of living.

Agricultural marketing, the vital link between farmer and consumer, is playing an increasingly important role in providing food abundance to the U.S. consumer.

In colonial days nearly all our people lived on farms. At that time food was consumed chiefly on the farms where it was produced. "Farmer" and "consumer" most often were identical, and marketing had a limited role.

Only 6 percent of our people lived on farms in 1965. Marketing costs now account for about 70 cents out of each dollar the U.S. consumer spends for food. In contrast to colonial days, the job of agricultural marketing is large and complex.

If we had not made important gains in marketing efficiency and conserving food products after they leave the farm, our marketing bill would be much higher. Long-term growth in the size of the marketing bill is due partly to increases in the amount of services U.S. consumers have demanded along with their food purchases.

More packaging, more prepared foods, and more eating away from home have all added to the cost of marketing. But there have been important offsets to these increased costs. Inauguration of the supermarket era eliminated many costly services like home delivery of groceries and personal serving at stores.

Because of technological advances, many convenience foods are cheaper than their less highly processed counterparts. A can of frozen, concentrated orange juice is a better buy than the equivalent quantity of fresh oranges.

Modern methods of packaging and processing not only add consumer services, but also reduce losses of food between farm and consumer. Packaging, as opposed to bulk handling, protects food against pests and the elements.

U.S. food abundance at a supermarket, Silver Spring, Md.

Boxing of bananas and effective containers for fresh pineapple help preserve and protect these fruits during transportation. Replacement of wax-type milk cartons with a new plastic type prevents leaks and reduces loss of milk. Frozen turkeys prevent spoilage. A combination of a sanitary packing plant, icepack, and rapid transportation reduces spoilage of broilers.

Still other innovations in marketing help conserve food on its way from farm to consumer. Trimming, packing, and cooling fruits and vegetables near the scene of farm production help prevent spoilage. Vacuum cooling of lettuce right after harvest prevents rot and spoilage. New modern warehouse facilities of chainstores protect foods from rats and moisture, besides providing efficient handling of food.

SINCE MANY FARM PRODUCTS are bulky and are shipped long distances, transportation makes up an important part of their marketing costs. The transportation dollar today buys better and faster service because railroads and trucks have improved their facilities for moving farm products and the methods of handling them.

Railroads have shifted from steam locomotives to more efficient diesel engines. A major development, first used commercially in 1949, is the mechanical refrigerator car for transporting perishable foods. Another important innovation is the "piggyback" handling of loaded truck trailers on railroad flatcars.

Motortruck transportation has increased in efficiency with development of modern, high-speed highways on which larger loads can be carried.

Labor costs make up about half our bill for agricultural marketing. A chief reason for past improvements in marketing efficiency has been greater productivity of labor. Output per man-hour in food marketing in 1964 was 55 percent greater than in 1947–49. This about matches the increase in labor productivity in nonfarm production, but falls far short of the large gain in productivity of labor on U.S. farms.

THE NUMBER OF WORKERS on farms and ranches in the United States in 1965 was less than 7 percent of our total employment.

To be sure, the U.S. farmworker had plenty of help from his city cousins in providing consumers an abundance of farm products. For each worker on farms, more than two nonfarmworkers got paychecks for marketing farm products, or for manufacturing and supplying to farmers the machinery, petroleum products, fertilizer, and other nonfarm goods and services so crucial to modern farming.

The proportion of total workers employed on farms provides a good index of a nation's relative food abundance and level of living. In the mid-1960's, developed countries—like West Germany and France—reported 10 to 18 percent of their total workers on farms. Farm employment made up 70 to 75 percent of total workers in less developed countries like India and Pakistan. About 40 percent of all the Soviet Union's workers are on farms, compared with the U.S. figure of under 7 percent.

The sources of our abundant farm production are many, and have their roots in history. Four major sources can be listed:
• An endowment of good natural resources;
• Technology, based on research;
• Education; and
• Strong economic institutions.

Our food abundance is based on a rich endowment of land resources. The land area of the United States is located in the Temperate Zone and covers a broad range of climatic and soil conditions. This means a wide range in the capability of our land for agricultural use, and makes possible the production of a great variety of crop and livestock products.

The land area of the 50 States totals 2.3 billion acres. Forest land accounts for a third of this. More than a fourth is grassland pasture and range. About a fifth is classified as cropland. The remaining fifth includes urban areas and serves other purposes.

19

791–476 O–66–4

ADVANCED TECHNOLOGY is the cornerstone of modern farming and food abundance in the United States.

New technology stems from research. We spent $726 million for agricultural research in the United States in 1964. About $400 million was spent by private industry, and more than $300 million was public funds of the States and the Federal Government.

Nearly 15,000 professional scientists were employed by public agencies. Industry used an additional 12,000 scientists in research related to food and agriculture.

An important foundation for the present broad program of public research was laid more than a century ago. In 1862 the land-grant colleges and the U.S. Department of Agriculture were established. Our State agricultural experiment stations were started under the Hatch Act in 1887.

Over the years, public and private research has provided an increasing flow of new technology for use by U.S. farmers.

EDUCATION in its broadest sense is a necessary foundation for our present-day, highly efficient agriculture.

Since its early days, the United States has placed great emphasis on education. As a result of our long-established system of free public education, illiteracy is now a rarity.

The Federal-State Extension Service, which was started in 1914, was a major step in direct education for farmers. By the mid-1960's we had 6,600 county agents, 4,200 home economics agents, and 3,200 subject-matter specialists serving our farmers.

Another boost was given to agricultural education by the Smith-Hughes Act of 1917 which stimulated specialized vocational education. About 10,500 instructors were training 500,000 vocational agriculture students annually by the mid-1960's. This is an important source of education both for boys who will find their best economic opportunity in commercial farming, and young people headed for farm-related businesses and industry.

Our food abundance would not have been possible without our economic institutions.

The highly developed marketing and transportation system in the United States not only gives farmers assurance their products can be marketed quickly and efficiently, but also makes possible rapid and timely movement to farms of fertilizer, machinery, and other things needed in farm production.

Public and private credit agencies can provide promptly the production loans farmers need. The existing tenure system generally assures tenant operators a fair share in farming profits.

Perhaps most important of all, the preponderance of commercial family-sized farms in our agriculture provides an economic climate in which individual initiative and good management are rewarded.

Natural resources, technology, education, economic institutions—no one of these alone accounts for our present food abundance and food bargain. But the cumulative effect of these forces, in combination over a long period, does account for it.

OUR CURRENT SITUATION can be put in perspective by examining the highlights of changes in efficiency of farm production over the last century.

Farm output—total production of crops and livestock for human use—in the United States in 1965 was nearly six times as great as a century ago. The rise in output outran our population growth; U.S. population in 1965 was about five times that of a hundred years earlier. Although the volume of farm output expanded throughout the period, the efficiency with which it was produced changed greatly.

The end of World War I marked the beginning of substantial substitution of machinery and other purchased farm supplies for both farm labor and farmland. Use of farm labor reached a peak in 1920, and most of the expansion in farmland occurred by that date. Mechanization of farming was the

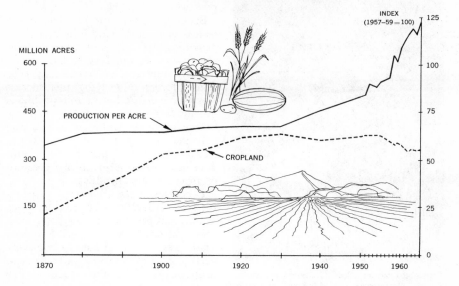

chief feature of the changes occurring from 1920 to 1940.

A major development was substitution of mechanical power of tractors, trucks, and automobiles for animal power of horses and mules. Purchased machinery and petroleum products became important production resources for agriculture.

Farmers shifted millions of acres of cropland plus substantial amounts of other resources from raising and maintaining horses and mules to producing crops and livestock for human use. This alone accounts for half the increase in farm output during the interwar period.

In contrast to the 50-year period before World War I, important average annual gains in production efficiency were recorded. Farm output increased moderately during the interwar period with a relatively small increase in use of total production resources. Our growing investment in research, education, and economic institutions began to yield a good return.

A NEW ERA in U.S. farming began in 1940.

Farm output expanded rapidly during World War II and the immediate postwar years when favorable price relationships encouraged farmers to rapidly adopt improved production practices.

Use of purchased farm supplies increased at a record annual rate from 1940 to 1950, and their substitution for farm labor and farmland was accelerated. Average crop yields rose about 10 percent during the 1940's.

Production efficiency—farm output per unit of production resources—rose at a much faster rate from 1940 to 1950 than in any previous decade.

Many observers at the time viewed the changes in U.S. farming during the 1940's as a "technological revolution." This term, however, more aptly describes the changes that occurred after 1950, when our growing investment in research and education paid off greatly.

Consider these changes from 1950 to the mid-1960's:

• 35 percent more farm output, with
• 11 percent fewer acres of cropland used;
• 45 percent less farm labor;
• 48 percent more purchased farm supplies; and
• little change in total production resources used.

21

Vegetable farmer Cecil Johnson of Island County, Washington, one of the contributors to our food abundance.

Three features of the technological revolution stand out:

(1) Overall production efficiency increased at a record rate.

(2) The rate of decline in use of farm labor far exceeded the large annual reduction from 1940 to 1950.

(3) A sharp upsurge in per acre yields of crops occurred.

Average crop yields rose by more than 45 percent from 1950 to 1965, compared with an increase of only 10 percent during the 1940's.

CHEMICALS HAD THEIR GREATEST impact on U.S. farm production after 1950. Greatly increased use of chemical fertilizers was a major factor in the sharp rise in crop yields.

Farmers in 1964 applied more than 8 million tons of the three principal plant nutrients—nitrogen, phosphorus, and potassium—to their crop and pasture lands. This was nearly three times the amount used in 1950 and almost seven times that in 1940.

Increased use of more effective pesticides to control insects, diseases, and weeds contributed importantly to a succession of record crop yields, as did

improved varieties and better cultural practices.

So farmers, drawing heavily on the results of research and education, are providing U.S. consumers with food abundance at the biggest bargain in history. But the technical and economic forces underlying this success story have created economic problems for our farmers.

One of these problems is that the capacity to produce farm products has outrun market demands for them. This has created a downward pressure on prices of farm products.

U.S. consumers, who account for 85 percent of our farmers' market, have such plentiful supplies of food that they will pay very little for additional quantities. Consequently, relatively small increases in farm production can drop prices of farm products to low levels.

On the other hand, lower prices for farm products have little effect in decreasing total farm output. As hundreds of thousands of farmers produce our major farm products, the production decision of an individual farmer has little influence on total output or the price he receives.

AS INDIVIDUALS, farmers plan on the basis of prevailing prices. Even at prices prevailing in the mid-1960's, it pays many farmers to use more fertilizer or more seed, or to adopt other improved practices. But results of these individual decisions increase total farm output and depress prices of farm products.

Thus, a technological revolution in farming and a rapid increase in farm output occurred in a period when farmers were faced with a cost-price squeeze. Farm output increased 35 percent from 1950 to the mid-1960's, while the ratio of prices farmers receive for their products to the prices they pay for things they buy dropped more than 20 percent.

Public policy has long recognized the economic plight of the U.S. commercial farmer. Each year, several billion dollars are spent on Federal farm programs designed to adjust production to market demand, to expand export outlets for farm products, and to improve farm incomes.

Even when we count the costs of farm programs, the U.S. consumer still gets his food abundance at a big bargain. Absence of these programs might mean cheaper food for consumers, but studies indicate it would spell economic ruin for commercial farmers.

Walter W. Wilcox of the Legislative Reference Service, Library of Congress, made a study which found that without price support and acreage diversion programs in 1961–63, farm output would have been 6 percent greater. Farm prices, he figured, would have been 22 percent lower, and net farm income 52 percent smaller. Wilcox's conclusions are generally supported by earlier studies at Iowa State University, Cornell University, the Pennsylvania State University, and Oklahoma State University.

Even with the aid of Federal programs, U.S. farmers generally have not shared fully in the economic fruits of our farm abundance. In 1964, for example, farm people received on the average only 55 percent as much income from all sources as did nonfarm people. Many operators of large, efficient, family-sized farms had incomes in 1964 that compared much more favorably with nonfarm incomes. However, in the absence of farm programs their economic status would quickly worsen.

Food abundance at a big bargain for U.S. consumers, but economic and adjustment problems for commercial farmers, summarizes our situation in the mid-1960's. But what of the future when we will have many more mouths to feed?

Let's look ahead to 1980—a decade and a half in the future, and a period of time equal to that of the agricultural revolution from 1950 to the mid-1960's.

U.S. population totaled 192 million in 1964, but is projected to rise to 245 million by 1980, an increase of 28 percent. Added to this likely large increase in demand for food and farm products by U.S. consumers is the prospect of a substantial rise in demand for exports from our farms.

If we protect the basic sources of our increasing agricultural productivity, food abundance at an even better bargain will be available to U.S. consumers in 1980 and beyond. Moreover, we should be able to share increasingly our abundance with less developed countries as an aid to their economic growth.

This future prospect is based on three major factors:

• In the mid-1960's, the production capacity of U.S. agriculture far exceeds the actual outturn of farm products.

• If needed, we can make much greater use of our rich endowment of land resources.

• Most important of all, we can expect public and private research to continue to turn out a large flow of new farm technologies.

Even though average crop yields were at record high levels in the mid-1960's, we already have the capacity to attain much larger yields.

This is illustrated in the central Illinois area where corn yields per acre average 80 to 90 bushels. A group of several hundred leading farmers in the area belong to a farm accounting service which supervises the farmers in keeping records of their farm business and provides consultation on improved methods of farming. These farmers produce average corn yields of 95 to 110 bushels, 15 to 20 bushels greater than the area level. The top 20 percent of the accounting service farmers, in turn, report corn yields 30 bushels above the area average.

Although the higher yields of these top farmers result partly from better land, the chief reason is greater use of fertilizer and other improved farming practices.

This story can be repeated for most of our other crops. Achievements of leading farmers today reflect what average farmers will do tomorrow. This is increasingly so as larger, more efficient, family-sized farms continue to grow in number and importance in U.S. agriculture. Operators of these farms adopt improved production practices quickly.

WE COULD ADD substantially to our annual farm output, if needed, by increasing the acreage of land used for crop production.

About 55 million acres of cropland were withheld from production in 1964 through Government programs aimed at adjusting farm output to market needs. In addition, millions of acres of potentially productive land could be diverted from other uses to crop production.

If required, in a few years we could easily add 100 million acres to crop production, or 30 percent more than the 334 million acres used in 1964. This is reassuring, and underscores the need for wise conservation and protection of all our land resources. However, prospects are that needs for farm production in 1980 can be met with about the same acreage of cropland used in 1964.

OUR CHIEF ASSURANCE of food abundance in the future rests on a continuing flow of new farm technologies. Protection of this key source of agricultural productivity will require further substantial investments in public and private research.

We will need to devise new and more efficient ways of protecting our increasing crop and livestock output from the ravages of weather, insects, diseases, and weeds.

Lack of sufficient water may prove much more of a bottleneck to increased crop production than will a limitation of land resources. Development of better and more efficient methods of conserving and managing our water resources will be a major challenge to agricultural research in the future.

Protecting our future food abundance also calls for further investment in education.

Commercial farming is becoming increasingly complex. Operators of the efficient family farms of the future will need a high level of managerial and technical competence. Likewise, good management and high technical competence will be prerequisites for the farm-related industries and businesses that serve farmers.

Increasing use will be made of electronic computers in management decisions on farms and in farm-related industries and business. Computers will aid agricultural marketing firms in more efficient control of food inventories. Greater use will be made of computers in servicing record systems of farmers.

Farm supply firms will develop computerized weather programs that will pinpoint the kind of farming conditions farmers face during their planting periods. This will aid management decisions on what crops to plant, what seeding rate to use, and what fertilizer and pest-control practices to follow.

To insure continued food abundance at a bargain, we also must strengthen and adapt our economic institutions to changing conditions. If food along with the increasing amount of services attached to it is to continue to be a good buy, further advances in marketing efficiency will be needed.

Public and private credit agencies will face a challenge in helping farmers acquire control of the increasingly greater amounts of production resources needed to operate larger, more efficient farms.

There also will be continued need for farm programs that protect commercial farmers from the economic disaster which lurks in their increasing production capacity.

Efficient commercial farmers deserve a fair return on their management, labor, and investment.

Prospects are that U.S. consumers will continue to eat well, and economically, for many years to come. To insure this, however, we must strengthen and protect the many sources of our food abundance.

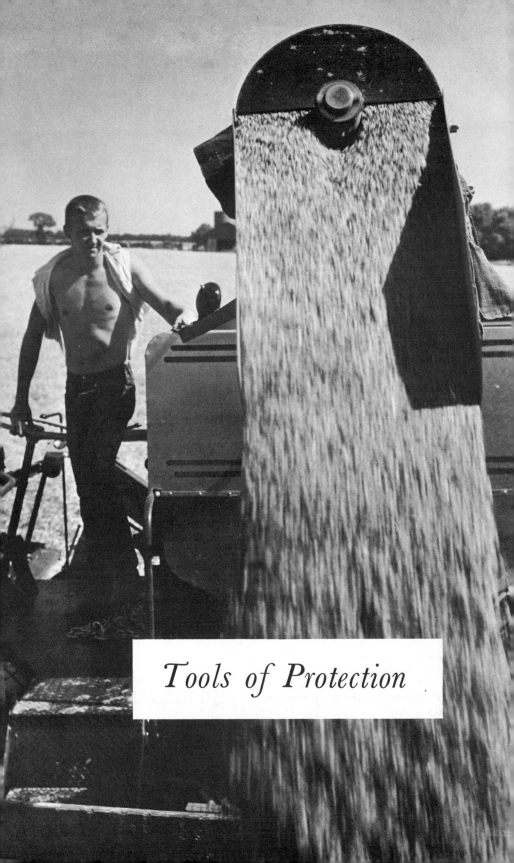

Tools of Protection

THE FIGHT AGAINST INSECTS

C. H. HOFFMANN and L. S. HENDERSON

HISTORY, from ancient times to the present, is filled with examples of man's fight against insects. He had to battle insects to grow food. Man also has fought them because they carried deadly or weakening diseases.

Insects were present on earth long before man. Through the centuries they have adapted themselves to changing environments and more recently even to changing agricultural practices.

Man's need to produce a wide variety of food in huge quantities has enabled insects to multiply in equally huge quantities to compete for the food grown. There is no end to their destruction. Even after the crops are harvested, insects attack them in storage.

In spite of man's most diligent efforts to control insects, he continues to be plagued by many species that compete for his food supply.

Today some people think that if the balance of nature is not disturbed, man won't have severe problems with insects. Perhaps the best answer is that man's way of life and his needs are such that a true balance of nature cannot exist.

All through the years man has bent nature to serve himself, has utilized plants and animals for his own benefit. He has had to fight the elements of nature that interfered with his food supply, health, or comfort.

In the United States man has greatly altered the land in using natural resources for his benefit. He cut forests to make room for houses and roads. He plowed prairies and cleared trees to grow crops. He has developed cities and industrial areas. These major changes have profoundly influenced the balance of nature.

With the number of human beings constantly increasing, the areas where a single crop is grown have become larger and larger.

This great change to monoculture has resulted in heavy populations of destructive species. The introduced European corn borer has spread throughout the U.S. Corn Belt, and borer populations have exceeded 60,000 per acre in some counties. Estimated losses to grain corn in 1963 amounted to 120,648,000 bushels.

Man has transported crops—like cotton and corn—to other areas. He

* * *

C. H. Hoffmann is *Associate Director*, Entomology Research Division, Agricultural Research Service.

L. S. Henderson is *Chief*, Stored-Product Insects Research Branch, Market Quality Research Division, Agricultural Research Service.

has also shipped animals from one area to another. In doing so he has unintentionally introduced insect pests.

These introduced species multiplied at a rapid rate in the large fields, which provided an almost unrestricted supply of food. Hence, some of the most destructive insect enemies were able to flourish.

The early settlers had no dependable methods of insect control; they were forced to sharecrop with insects.

Later, as farming became more complex and competitive, farmers began to use many different measures to control insects. These measures were essential if farmers were to produce adequate amounts of crops that would measure up to standards of marketing prescribed by law and that the public would accept.

Control measures made it more difficult not to harm the parasites and predators that are beneficial, because they destroy insect pests. And the measures required, especially those for controlling insects and weeds, often harmed honey bees and other insects essential for pollinating many fruits and other crops.

SCIENTISTS ESTIMATE there are from 625,000 to 1,500,000 different kinds of insects on earth. More than 82,500 occur in North America above Mexico.

In the United States some 10,000 species of insects are classed as public enemies. Of these, several hundred species are particularly destructive and require some degree of control. The estimated cost of insect control measures to protect our food and fiber is close to $704 million a year.

Insects must be controlled if man is to produce the food he needs and maintain high standards of health. They destroy food as well as the forage, pasture, and grain needed to produce livestock. They carry and transmit many diseases of plants and animals that further limit the food supply.

Our expanding population will require that we produce more and more food. And we must continue to fight insects for it.

THIS NATION can be proud of how it has learned to control insect pests; that knowledge has helped us maintain an abundant supply of high quality food at home and for other countries as well.

Progress in protecting our food would not have been possible without the hundreds of measures for controlling the many kinds of insects found wherever crops are produced, and in their processing, transporting, and storage. We have utilized insecticides, biological control, crop varieties resistant to insects, and various other nonchemical control measures fully.

Without insecticides, production of livestock would soon drop about 25 percent and production of crops about 30 percent. Food prices might then go up as much as 50 to 75 percent and the food still not be of high quality.

Insecticides have been used for many years. Very likely they will continue to be used in large amounts to control the most injurious insects. Sales of insecticides and miticides in 1964 amounted to about $218 million. The demand depends primarily on how often a species attacks and how severe the infestation is.

King Cotton accounts for about a third of the insecticides purchased. Cotton—which is both a fiber and a food crop—must be protected from the ravages of the boll weevil (*Anthonomus grandis*), cotton leafworm (*Alabama argillacea*), cotton bollworm (*Heliothis zea*), and a variety of other pests.

Insects affecting apples, corn, livestock, and citrus each account for more than 5 percent of spending for insecticides in the United States.

INSECTICIDES ARE IMPORTANT to agriculture, and in general they are effective, cheap, and safe. However, the great good derived from them can sometimes be partially offset by adverse effects.

The chlorinated hydrocarbon insecticides may leave toxic residues. Some of these insecticides turn up in meat and milk, persist in the soil, and under certain conditions may harm beneficial insects, fish, and other wildlife.

Another problem is the resistance that builds up in certain species of insects to chlorinated hydrocarbon, organic phosphate, and carbamate insecticides.

Problems like these have caused scientists in industry, the Federal Government, and the States to continue their search for new insecticides and ways to use them efficiently and safely. Nonchemical measures of insect control also are being explored, and will be discussed later.

Each year researchers test thousands of new chemicals for their toxicity to insects, with the hope of finding new ones that will control the pests but not affect other life. By their efforts they have produced a wide range of organophosphate and carbamate materials that are less persistent than many of the earlier chlorinated hydrocarbon insecticides.

THE NEWER MATERIALS can be applied to avoid most of the critical problems pertaining to residues. For example, two of them—malathion and carbaryl—are now used to control many insects in areas where it is essential not to treat crops or livestock with materials that persist and may show up in meat or milk.

These chemicals can also be used in areas where fish and wildlife should be protected from undue hazards.

Both malathion and carbaryl are toxic to many insect pests. Unlike the chlorinated hydrocarbon materials, they do not accumulate in animal tissues. Thus they can be applied up to or within a day or so of harvest on many human food and forage crops.

FOR MANY YEARS scientists have worked cooperatively to develop effective insecticides and methods of applying them without creating hazards. Some insecticides are effective in very small amounts if handled properly.

A new method developed in 1964 promises to revolutionize application of insecticides. Specially designed equipment permits dispersal of low volumes of undiluted chemicals. Sometimes efficiency of the insecticide is increased—with the cost of application much less than formerly.

Excellent results have been obtained by using only 6 to 16 ounces of malathion per acre against grasshoppers, the boll weevil, the cereal leaf beetle (*Oulema melanopa*), mosquitoes, and the beet leafhopper (*Circulifer tenellus*). This insecticide is of low toxicity to man and animals. Researchers are now trying to find out whether other insecticides can be used this way.

Answers also are being sought to questions like these: How safe is it to disperse the potent, undiluted insecticides from airplanes? What are their effects on beneficial insects, fish, and other wildlife?

In making these investigations it is hoped that tests with these sprays will show not nearly as much chemical required as with older methods. The prospect of reducing in such a simple way the total amount of insecticides within the environment is exciting.

STUDIES TO IMPROVE formulations go on continuously. Insecticides in granule form are popular with growers, who use them often.

A small amount of DDT in granules can be placed in the whorl of the corn plant where it is most effective against young larvae of the European corn borer (*Ostrinia nubilalis*) and greatly reduces the amount of insecticide that otherwise would be required in sprays.

Boll weevil on a cotton plant.

Chlorinated hydrocarbons in granules control mosquitoes that attack livestock as well as rootworms, wireworms, and other insects in the soil. Use of granules may also avoid or lessen adverse effects on beneficial insects, including honey bees, and on fish and other wildlife.

SEVERAL ORGANIC PHOSPHATES that act systemically (the plant absorbs the insecticide and moves it to the leaf or stem) can be used to control certain insects attacking cotton, vegetables, and forage crops.

Seeds are treated with the chemical, or granules containing it are placed in the furrow at planting time. The chemical is taken up by the plant and when an insect feeds on the leaf or stem it dies. Yet beneficial insects in the vicinity, because they do not feed on the plant but only on live insects, may entirely escape the systemic.

Di-Syston (0,0-diethyl S-2-(ethylthio) ethyl phosphorodithioate), phorate, and dimethoate are systemic insecticides that control sucking insects, particularly those that transmit plant diseases.

Systemic insecticides, such as ronnel, Ruelene^R (4-tert-butyl-2-chlorophenyl methyl methylphosphoramidate), coumaphos, and trichlorfon, with restrictions, are recommended for control of cattle grubs in beef cattle.

Today new insecticides, like Ciodrin^R (Alpha-methylbenzyl 3-hydroxycrotonate dimethyl phosphate) and dichlorvos, will control flies in dairy barns and milking establishments, or may be used directly on livestock without contaminating meat or milk.

FOR A LONG TIME a good insecticide has been needed in warehouses where food is stored. Many compounds otherwise effective leave an objectionable odor, flavor, stain, or toxic residue.

Pyrethrum is safe enough but only moderately effective; it must be applied frequently, and is expensive. These drawbacks prevent its wide use for commercial purposes.

Three years of intensive research with dichlorvos show it is effective in minute quantities. The residue is so short-lived it can't accumulate to high levels, even when applications are frequent. The Food and Drug Administration has been petitioned to approve use of dichlorvos in warehouses where food is stored.

The studies with dichlorvos may be a breakthrough in protecting food stored in warehouses against destructive or contaminating insects.

SOME NEW COMPOUNDS related to dichlorvos are also highly effective in small amounts and their residues disappear rapidly, but further tests are required. Some of these will be especially interesting since they have extremely low toxicity to man.

During studies with dichlorvos, researchers discovered that applying it in vapor was more effective and provided better distribution in the warehouse than as an aerosol or in mist sprays. And residues on the packages of food were less. Researchers then designed new, simple equipment to vaporize and dispense the insecticide.

Many of the other new compounds can be vaporized as easily as dichlorvos.

FUMIGANTS ARE widely used to control many kinds of insects, but always under special conditions.

All fumigants now available are highly toxic to man, at least in the concentrations needed for effective action. Precautions must be strictly observed to insure they are used safely. Care should be taken to aerate treated food and commodities.

Numerous types are available for treating a wide variety of products. The right fumigant must be selected for the specific job, then applied properly in the correct amount. Violate the rules and you can start a fire, cause an explosion, corrode metals, or ruin the product being treated. These are reasons why fumigation should be conducted only by trained and experienced operators.

Fumigants will control insects when nothing else can do the job. The new insecticides so effective in vaporized form kill insects that are exposed and out in the open, and are fine for a preventive program to kill invading insects before they become established, or to kill off superficial infestations. But the vapor cannot penetrate into stacks of packaged food in a warehouse, or into the mass of grain in an elevator bin. The penetration of a fumigant gas is needed to reach insects in these locations and stop them from multiplying to damaging numbers.

Fumigants are also applied to soil, especially in seedbeds and coldframes, to kill root-feeding insects and give young plants a chance to get started.

Fumigants play an important role in quarantine activities. Commodities can be fumigated and moved into commercial channels without spreading dangerous insects. Of even greater value is the fumigation of imported products to prevent the introduction of destructive pests that do not now exist in this country.

Present fumigants keep insects from destroying or damaging large quantities of grain and food, but better ones are needed.

The ideal gas would be specific in its action against insects but not toxic to warmblooded animals. It would penetrate rapidly, thoroughly, and uniformly into large bulks of commodities. It would air out just as rapidly after fumigation, not leaving any chemical residue in the product treated. It would not cause chemical or physical reactions affecting the quality of commodities.

We are far from finding such an ideal chemical, even from among the multitude of those being produced. Therefore alternate measures are being developed—the nonchemical or biological methods, which are discussed later.

Physical and mechanical ways of controlling insects have long been recommended by entomologists. Screens on windows and doors are standard equipment in many parts of the world

to prevent entry of flies, wasps, mosquitoes, and other insects.

Various types of devices that electrocute flies, mosquitoes, and other insects have been marketed. Although under some conditions these devices are useful, they do not usually provide enough control to be satisfactory.

FOR YEARS evaluations have been made of the effectiveness of light traps equipped with different kinds of lamps—blacklight, ultraviolet, and the like—for control of insect pests of fruits, vegetables, cotton, corn, tobacco, and livestock. Early work with the codling moth (*Carpocapsa pomonella*) was particularly promising. The traps provided control equivalent to that obtained with two applications of a spray containing lead arsenate.

However, most of the evaluations were conducted on a limited scale. Results were too inconclusive to warrant recommending light traps for control of these pests.

In 1962 more interest in light traps developed when traps equipped with blacklight and installed over large areas blocked invasion of strong-flying hornworm moths from outside a treated area.

Tobacco growers became interested in these light traps to help control tobacco hornworms (*Protoparce sexta*) and thereby cut down on the use of chemicals and limit residues.

Their interest was whetted by the promising results Federal-State workers obtained in an experiment with light traps in North Carolina. In the center of an area 113 miles square with about three light traps per square mile, nearly 50 percent control of hornworms was obtained in 1962 and almost 80 percent in 1963 and 1964. Growers who cut down the stalks of their plants in the fall prevented late-season breeding of hornworms, and probably contributed substantially to the control during the second and third years.

In several States other large-scale tests are being conducted to evaluate the effectiveness against the tobacco hornworm of using these blacklight traps along with cutting stalks after harvest. Such large-scale experimentation suggests light traps may become an important tool in controlling certain insects if used over a wide area.

Use of reflective aluminum strips is another method being tested. They are placed like a mulch in vegetable fields to reduce attack by disease-carrying aphids.

This material may supplant insecticides which frequently do not kill aphids quickly enough to prevent serious crop losses from their transmission of viruses.

Preliminary studies showed the aluminum mulches prevented aphid attack and thus protected cucumbers, squash, and watermelons from mosaic diseases.

PHYSICAL MEANS are already used to a limited extent against stored-product insects.

Refrigeration is one of the most common methods currently used. The temperatures, although not low enough to kill insects, prevent feeding and reproduction. Fortunately, the low temperatures also help preserve quality of product. But because of its cost, refrigeration cannot be used except for small amounts of high-value commodities like dried fruits and shelled nuts.

Sometimes it is possible to take advantage of natural cold. An old practice among managers of flour mills in the Northern States is to open the doors and windows for a few days during zero weather. The cold air kills the insects in the mill and fumigation becomes unnecessary.

Reserve food supplies have been stored in large limestone caves where the air is cool enough to prevent insect development.

In many large grain storage bins, cold air is forced through the grain to reduce the temperature below the level favorable to insects. Researchers are exploring the possibility of forcing refrigerated air through grain stored in areas with warm climates.

HEAT CAN SOMETIMES be used against insects that damage stored products.

Infrared radiation or heat, used to dry grain artificially, can also kill insects brought into the storage area from the field.

Another practice in flour mills is to raise the temperature high enough to kill insects. As with refrigeration, however, the cost is great. And the difficulty in treating large quantities of products makes the method impractical. There is also the danger of harming product quality. However, in many cases heat used to process products will kill any insects present.

IN 1964 A POTENTIALLY significant discovery was made. Researchers found that exposing adult Indian-meal moths (*Plodia interpunctella*) to certain sound waves during the egg-laying period reduced their reproduction by about 75 percent.

In the next generation larvae took longer to become full grown and adults that emerged tended to die sooner than usual.

The sound waves had a similar effect on flour beetles (*Tribolium* spp.).

This was a whole new field of investigation. What specific wavelength should be used? What other characteristics of sound are important? What is the nature of the physiological effect on the insect? These are questions the investigators hope to answer. This research could lead to a new kind of nonchemical control.

OTHER TYPES of physical energy can also kill insects or be incorporated into control programs. Light waves, high frequency electrical fields, high-intensity radiofrequencies and gamma radiation are some of the physical properties being investigated for this purpose.

In early 1966 a machine for irradiating large quantities of grain was built on a pilot scale. The Atomic Energy Commission made this facility available to the U.S. Department of Agriculture.

It is the first irradiator especially designed to handle grain in bulk and provides for new research not possible before. The same equipment also permits irradiation of packaged products.

Changing the proportion of components present in the atmosphere may prove a simple way to prevent infestations in stored grain or foods. This method is already being used for fresh fruit.

Research in 1965 indicates insects may be controlled without reducing the oxygen nearly as much as first believed. The secret may lie in establishing the right ratio between nitrogen and carbon dioxide while increasing the amount of these gases to reduce the oxygen content.

Cultural control can prevent or reduce insect damage to food crops. Such practices include sanitation, destruction of crop refuse, deep plowing, crop rotation, use of fertilizers, stripcropping, irrigation, and planting according to a schedule. Many of these practices are very useful but only a few can be relied on to combat severe infestations.

BIOLOGICAL CONTROL AGENTS, particularly insect parasites, predators, and diseases, as well as protozoa and nematodes that attack insects, have always intrigued the public.

People are now more interested than ever. Some mistakenly believe biological control can entirely supplant insecticides and thereby overcome such serious problems as insect resistance, unwanted residues on food and forage crops, and possibly the harm to beneficial insects, fish, and other wildlife.

But people forget that nature provides for the survival of both beneficial and destructive insects.

Before the population of a parasite or predator can expand, a high population of the host species must also be present.

Insect populations fluctuate from large to small depending in large part on many variables constantly at play in the environment. Frequently biological control agents are far outnumbered by the pest insect, and great damage to crops results.

Polyhedrosis virus disease applied to cabbage plants infects and kills the cabbage looper. Top, a healthy looper. Center, looper in an advanced stage of the disease. Bottom, dead looper with toes up.

For more than 75 years scientists of the Agriculture Department and co-operating States have searched for and introduced parasites and predators that attack insect pests. Over 650 kinds of these beneficial insects were introduced into the United States. A hundred became established.

They have furnished very good control of the Japanese beetle (*Popillia japonica*), European corn borer (*Pyrausta nubilalis*), spotted alfalfa aphid (*Therioaphis maculata*), alfalfa weevil (*Hypera postica*), wooly apple aphid (*Eriosoma lanigerum*), and several scales and mealybugs.

Undoubtedly better ways can be found to use parasites and predators. In past years research devoted to this type of control has been small compared with chemical control research.

The Agriculture Department plans to increase research on biological control agents, including their mass rearing and release, and ways of integrating biological control with chemical and other methods. Basic investigations will be conducted in the new Biological Control of Insects Research Laboratory to be built at Columbia, Mo.

MICROBIAL AGENTS can be used to regulate insect populations. Insect pathologists have recorded about 1,100 viruses, bacteria, fungi, protozoa, rickettsiae, and nematodes that parasitize insects.

Such an array is a real challenge to entomologists looking for ways to use them to control insects. Many pathogens are specific to a particular insect and, as far as known, without hazard to man and animals.

A pathogen that attacks the Japanese beetle is the milky spore disease, caused by a bacterium discovered in 1933 and now commercially available. Applied to turf in the eastern part of the country, it has provided good control of this beetle that ravages vegetables, fruit, corn, and forage.

DIPEL

Another bacterium, *Bacillus thuringiensis* var. *thuringiensis*, is pathogenic to 110 species of moths and 8 of flies. The Agriculture Department recommends it for control of the cabbage looper (*Trichoplusia ni*), the alfalfa caterpillar (*Colias eurytheme*), and the tobacco hornworm. Its potential use against moths that attack grain and cereal foods is being investigated.

Alligator-like larva of the lady beetle eating an aphid. Other aphids can be seen on plant stem. A common predator of many injurious insects, the lady beetle larva may consume 300 to 400 aphids before changing to the pupal stage.

As yet growers have not widely accepted *B. thuringiensis*. Standardizing the commercial product has been difficult and may account for some of the variable results when it was used in the field. But the grower will now be able to buy a new and more satisfactory formulation that has been developed by industry.

Some fungi exert control on insect populations. For example, under moist weather conditions naturally occurring fungi proved helpful in controlling the spotted alfalfa aphid.

SEVERAL OF THE 200 KNOWN insect viruses have shown great promise in controlling important insects like the alfalfa caterpillar, cabbage looper, bollworm (*Heliothis zea*), tobacco budworm (*Heliothis virescens*), gypsy moth (*Porthetria dispar*), corn earworm (*Heliothis zea*), tent caterpillars, California red scale (*Aonidiella aurantii*), and citrus red mite (*Pananychus citri*).

Experiments with the alfalfa caterpillar, the cabbage looper, and the gypsy moth showed that a composite of pathogens, such as *B. thuringiensis* along with the specific virus for the insect, gave faster and more effective control than either of the organisms used alone.

There is an excellent chance that insect pathogens can be produced, packaged, distributed, and applied essentially the same way as insecticides. This possibility plus the fact that insect diseases perpetuate themselves under certain conditions is ample reason to strengthen research efforts.

CROP VARIETIES resistant to insect attack provide the ideal solution to insect control. Their use is effective, cheap, and without hazard. Of course, desirable agronomic qualities must be retained as much as possible.

Varieties resistant to insects are popular with growers. Their built-in protection against pests makes insecticides unnecessary and avoids any worry about residues.

The greatest drawback is that entomologists and plant breeders usually

need 10 to 25 years to develop suitable varieties. In addition, varieties that can be adapted to different regions of the country must be developed.

Growers cannot wait so long for a solution to their important insect problems. Thus, they must utilize other measures until the long-term research is completed.

PAST SUCCESSES clearly indicate the many opportunities to develop crops resistant to insects.

Federal and State researchers developed and arranged for growers to obtain certified seed of 17 varieties of winter wheat resistant to the hessian fly (*Phytophaga destructor*), 2 varieties of wheat resistant to the wheat stem sawfly (*Cephus cinctus*), 5 varieties of alfalfa resistant to the spotted alfalfa aphid, many corn inbreds resistant to the European corn borer and the corn earworm, and several barleys and wheats resistant to the greenbug (*Toxoptera graminum*).

The varieties of wheat resistant to the hessian fly, which also possess other desirable qualities, are now being grown on 4½ million acres in 26 States.

Farmers using hessian fly-resistant varieties can now plant their wheat earlier, obtain needed growth for fall and winter pasture for livestock, and avoid hessian fly damage the following spring.

Previously, the only method for controlling the fly in winter wheats was to delay planting seed and this was effective only for the fall generation.

Some varieties of grains are naturally resistant to insect attack during storage, although this has been realized only recently.

Preliminary testing showed significant differences in the amount of insect attack among different varieties of rice. Researchers are now beginning to look over wheat and sorghum. A little more work has been done with corn, in cooperation with geneticists developing new varieties. Striking differences have shown up.

Kernels from some test crosses of corn are almost completely eaten up by insects within a few weeks after storing. Kernels from other crosses, which were exposed to insects constantly for more than a year, have not even been nibbled on.

Unfortunately, the resistant strains have other characteristics that are not desirable. However, the geneticists may be able to transfer the resistance factor so as to produce entirely desirable strains.

Undoubtedly more attention will be paid to finding resistant varieties among all our major crops. One question we are trying hard to answer is: What are the properties, physical or chemical, that make a kernel of grain resistant to damage by an insect?

STERILIZATION of male insects by gamma radiation and their release into a wild population of insects is a most promising approach to insect control or eradication.

Large populations of destructive insects and widespread distribution of well-established species restrict use of this method. In some cases, however, sterile insects can be released when pest populations are for one reason or another at a low ebb. Or releases may be especially effective when integrated with other methods of control. Under these circumstances sterilization should be of great value in controlling major insect pests that threaten our food supply.

Current methods of pest control, involving outright destruction of organisms with chemicals, are especially efficient when the pest population is high, but inefficient when it's low. In contrast, the sterile insect release method is generally inefficient when the pest population is high but very efficient when it is low.

Using the two methods together is better than using either alone.

After years of studying the use of sterility to control or eradicate the screw-worm (Cochliomyia hominivorax), some principles were established to show how this method might be used successfully against other insect pests. In 1964, Edward F. Knipling of the Agriculture Department worked out hypothetical models to illustrate how the sterility method might be employed against the boll weevil (Anthonomus grandis), tobacco hornworm, and tsetse flies.

SUCCESSES WITH GAMMA radiation as the sterilizing agent include eradication of the screw-worm from the island of Curaçao and from the Southeastern United States.

Screw-worms have been reduced about 99.9 percent by the huge sterile-fly release program currently conducted in the Southwestern States and adjacent northern Mexico. The cooperative program was begun in 1962 against this serious pest of livestock.

Another success was eradication in 1963 of the melon fly (Dacus cucurbitae), a pest of fruits and vegetables, in a pilot experiment on the 33-square-mile Pacific island of Rota. Malathion-protein hydrolysate baits sprayed on the most heavily infested farms reduced the number of wild melon flies. These areas were then overflooded with flies sterilized by gamma radiation.

An eradication campaign on Guam involved release of sterile oriental fruit flies (Dacus dorsalis). Two typhoons had first destroyed most of the host fruits, which resulted in a very low natural population. By taking advantage of this condition, eradication was accomplished with release of relatively few sterile flies.

MASS REARING and release of sterile Mexican fruit flies (Anastrepha ludens) has replaced the use of sprays to prevent establishment of this insect in the Western United States. Flies are sterilized with a chemical before release.

In 1964 more than 4.7 million sterile males of the Mexican fruit fly were liberated along the Mexico-California border, to prevent reproduction and spread of this pest to the fruit-growing areas of California. Sterile flies were released so as to maintain a 1,000-to-1 ratio with wild flies. This successful

35

new type of program superseded use of insecticide sprays that were applied for many years.

Eradication and control of the screwworm by the sterile male technique was spectacular, and so were the successes with tropical fruit flies in the islands. Throughout the world, research workers, pest control officials, and government authorities are now studying whether this method can be used against many of their own insect pests.

STERILIZING INSECTS in their natural environment is another new approach.

Releasing insects sterilized by radiation or a chemosterilant is costly. But using chemosterilants to sterilize insects in their natural environment would be much less expensive, especially in large-scale programs.

Chemosterilants could make it unnecessary to rear and release millions of sterilized insects. The chemosterilants could be applied along with a bait or incorporated into a lure. Pest insects would be attracted to a central source, be sterilized, and eventually return to their natural habitat.

Possibly chemosterilants may be found one day that are safe and specific and can be used in the same way as regular insecticides. Then when insects come in contact with the residues on vegetation, they will be sterilized. But many precautions have to be taken in using the chemosterilants now available for experimental use. For practical insect control, elaborate precautions will doubtless be required— perhaps placing the chemosterilants in special traps or other safeguarded devices.

SINCE 1959 MORE THAN 5,000 potential chemosterilants have been evaluated by Entomology Research Division laboratories of the Agricultural Research Service. Over 200 have shown some effect on insect reproduction.

The three most widely tested chemosterilants are apholate, tepa, and metepa. Our most advanced studies, including some small field tests,

showed their effectiveness against the boll weevil, pink bollworm, and Mexican fruit fly.

Results of laboratory investigations warrant carefully controlled field tests with the following insects: Cabbage looper, *Drosophila* spp., codling moth, melon fly, oriental fruit fly, Mediterranean fruit fly (*Ceratitis capitata*), and house fly (*Musca domestica*).

These preliminary results are very encouraging. But many problems must be solved before any control measures that include chemosterilants can be recommended.

Other intriguing approaches that have received only passing attention include development of strains of sterile-male insects genetically selected for sustained liberation, and development of strains that are genetically inferior for sustained liberation so as to introduce inferior genes into the natural population.

ATTRACTANTS SHOW much promise. They can be used to control a given species so as to avoid or greatly curtail the need for insecticides, again eliminating the problems associated with residues.

In Florida during 1956–1957 a protein hydrolysate-bait was applied along with malathion in a spray to eradicate the Mediterranean fruit fly. The treatment required only about a fourth the malathion needed when the chemical is applied without the attractant.

This success spurred entomologists and chemists to give special attention to developing combinations of baits and insecticides that might be safely used to control other insect pests.

Chemists of the Entomology Research Division synthesized some attractants that entomologists found were extraordinarily effective against fruit flies. The powerful attractants siglure, medlure, and trimedlure are now available for luring the male Mediterranean fruit fly, and cue-lure for the melon fly. Minute quantities present in traps allow regulatory agents to detect infestations.

Sometimes this method is so successful that unintentionally introduced fruit flies are all trapped before they become established in this country.

New materials that will lure various species of destructive insects are greatly needed.

ANOTHER ACHIEVEMENT that made entomological history involved using an attractant along with killing off the male of the species. This is a safe and cheap technique.

In 1963, the Entomology Research Division, cooperating with the U.S. Navy and the Trust Territory of the Pacific Islands, conducted an experiment on the island of Rota. Methyl eugenol was used, a chemical strongly attractive to male oriental fruit flies. Once the flies were attracted to this lure, they could not resist gorging on it, even when it was mixed with an insecticide.

Small cane fiber squares were saturated with a solution containing methyl eugenol and the insecticide naled. Every 2 weeks planes flew over the island dropping about 125 of the treated cane fiber pieces every square mile.

In addition, pieces of the saturated cane fiber were suspended from trees in village areas, and replaced with freshly treated pieces each month.

The last male oriental fruit fly was caught about 5½ months (four generations) after the start of the experiment.

Can this method be used with other insects? We believe so.

Natural sex attractants are other materials that show much promise.

After years of painstaking research, chemists of the Entomology Research Division isolated in pure form and chemically identified the extremely potent sex attractant secreted by the female gypsy moth. Moreover, they successfully synthesized another sex attractant they named gyplure.

This lure is closely related to the one occurring naturally in the gypsy moth. It can be produced in quantity and at a reasonable cost to use in the control program now in progress.

Finding the sex attractant of the gypsy moth was a breakthrough. Entomologists and chemists began to look for sex attractants in other insects. And they found some. They envision using the attractants to draw insects into a trap where they can then be killed with a volatile chemical or some mechanical device.

In the few years since the search began, scientists have come up with sex attractants for the peach tree borer (*Sanninoidea exitiosa*), lesser peach tree borer (*Synanthedon pictipes*), tomato hornworm (*Protoparce quinquemaculata*), southern armyworm (*Prodenia eridania*), cabbage looper, bollworm, tobacco budworm, cotton leafworm (*Alabama argillacea*), salt-marsh caterpillar (*Estigmene acrea*), codling moth, pink bollworm, banded cucumber beetle (*Diabrotica balteata*), the fall armyworm (*Laphygma frugiperda*), and the black carpet beetle (*Attagenus piceus*).

INSECT HORMONES have a powerful influence on growth and reproduction.

Once their structure is determined, chemists should be able to synthesize these hormones or structurally related compounds in quantities large enough for the entomologists to find out whether they can be used to control certain species.

If hormones are specific in their activity and will not affect other organisms, it may be possible to use them as a control method that would be entirely safe. But much complex, basic research lies ahead.

INTEGRATED CONTROL, utilizing two or more methods of control together or consecutively, is a method touched on in other sections of this chapter. An outstanding success was achieved with this method in California against the spotted alfalfa aphid.

Demeton, a systemic insecticide, was applied to the alfalfa. The plants absorbed the chemical and aphids that fed on the plants were killed, but aphid parasites and predators were not affected. Thus, the beneficial insects survived and further reduced the aphids not killed by demeton. They also reduced buildup of the next generation of aphids.

Alfalfa growers throughout the area began to use varieties resistant to the aphid. These varieties were cooperatively developed by several Southwestern States and the Agriculture Department. Some assistance in control was also furnished by naturally occurring fungi.

By making use of integrated control, it was possible to greatly curtail or avoid a sustained spray schedule with parathion.

AGAINST FRUIT FLIES, and perhaps other pests, it may be possible to reduce heavy infestations with a chemical spray combined with a bait, and then use the sterile insect technique to further reduce the infestation so it is no longer a serious economic problem or is even eliminated entirely.

As more sex attractants are discovered and more ways found to use them in concentrated form or to produce them synthetically, their use can be coordinated with other methods.

Potent sex attractants in traps might provide a way to control some insects, if the traps were installed in a large area. Insecticides or chemosterilants might be placed along with sex attractants in specially designed traps or even in light traps.

Tobacco insect researchers have begun to utilize the sex attractant of the tobacco hornworm along with traps equipped with blacklight lamps. Their studies have already shown that presence of the traps in fields where growers destroy the tobacco stalks after harvest has provided good hornworm control.

USE OF DIFFERENT biological control agents—insect pathogens, parasites, and predators—as well as application of insecticides works well in obtaining economic control of some pests.

The future of this method will depend, of course, on additional research. The biology and the ecology or interrelationship with environment of each pest must be investigated. Then this information must be correlated with practices used to control insect pests on various crops in different parts of the country.

Some of these newer approaches will be effective only if growers band together and treat wide areas of crops as a single unit. In this way each grower will benefit and so will the public in getting a continuous supply of high-quality food. Moreover, reduction in use of insecticides may well bring the total load to a level no longer worrisome to regulatory officials and the public.

OUR FOOD SUPPLY and that of other nations of the world will always be subject to attack by thousands of insect pests. If agriculture is to feed our Nation and also help other countries, improved and safer methods of control must be developed.

Success will depend on how much can be learned about the biology, ecology, and physiology of our most important insect enemies. With this knowledge and some real imagination we should be able to combat tnese small but powerful enemies and protect our vital food supply.

For further reading:
Biological Control of Insect Pests and Weeds, Paul DeBach and E. I. Schlinger, editors. Reinhold Publishing Corporation, New York, 1964.
Cotton, Richard T., Pests of Stored Grain and Grain Products. Burgess Publishing Co., Minneapolis, Minn., 1963.
Jacobson, Martin, Insect Sex Attractants. John Wiley & Sons, Inc., New York, 1965.
Knipling, E. F., "The Eradication of the Screw-worm Fly." Scientific American, Vol. 203, No. 4, 1960.
Metcalf, Robert L., Organic Insecticides—Their Chemistry and Mode of Action. John Wiley & Sons, Inc., New York, 1955.
U.S. Department of Agriculture, The Potential Role of the Sterility Method for Insect Population Control With Special Reference to Combining This Method With Conventional Methods. ARS–33–98, 1964.
——— Suggested Guide for the Use of Insecticides To Control Insects Affecting Crops, Livestock, and Households. Agriculture Handbook 290, 1965.
——— The Use of Insecticides To Protect Stored Grains, Fruits, and Vegetables. ARS–20–9, 1960.

PLANT DISEASES AND NEMATODES

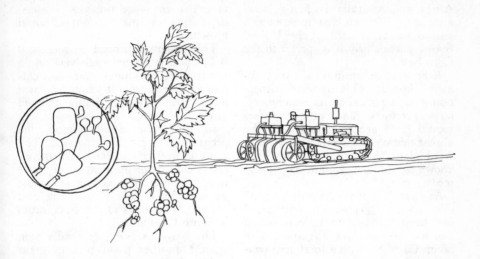

PLANT diseases and microscopic worms called nematodes are among the greatest hazards in man's continual struggle to feed himself.

Many diseases and nematodes have the potential of bringing about explosive outbreaks that can cause wholesale destruction of food crops, especially those grown in regions where the weather fluctuates widely.

U.S. Department of Agriculture figures show that for the period 1951–1960 the average annual cost to farmers for control of plant diseases and nematodes was over $135 million.

Because of the heavy damage they inflict, these plant pests sometimes even limit the kinds and varieties of crops that can be grown.

EPIDEMIC DISEASES, like cereal rusts and potato blight, are a constant menace to the profitable, orderly, and stable production of crops.

Without chemical control of scab on apples, approximately two-thirds of the Nation's apple crop would not be worth harvesting.

Plant diseases can greatly reduce yields, and cause losses in quality as well. Diseases induce poor coloration and flavor and blemishes or rots of fruit and vegetable crops. Grain may be lightweight, discolored, or shriveled. Oil content of peanuts, safflower, and soybeans may be lowered.

Many pests are debilitating rather than devastating. In fact, unfavorable soil or weather may be blamed for damage to cereal grains, corn, potatoes, sugarcane, and sorghum actually caused by nematodes and root rots.

DESPITE THE ENORMITY and complexity of the struggle against plant pests, recent advances in control have enabled us to hold the line or make gains against these enemies of our food.

A case in point is the battle with witchweed (*Striga asiatica*), a parasite on the roots of corn, sugarcane, sorghum, small grains, and many grasses.

* * *

Paul R. Miller is *Leader*, Epidemiology Investigations, Crops Research Division, Agricultural Research Service.

Hilde McGrath is a *Plant Pathologist*, Epidemiology Investigations, Crops Research Division.

Witchweed was discovered on corn in eight counties of North and South Carolina in 1956. This parasite had long been a serious pest in Asia, Africa, and Australia. Its first appearance in the Western Hemisphere was a serious threat to corn in the United States, particularly if it spread to the Corn Belt.

A Federal quarantine was immediately imposed. This required inspection and certification of machinery, farm products, and other carriers moved from areas infested with the almost microscopic seeds of the witchweed plant. A single plant has been known to produce as many as 500,000 seeds.

As a result of the quarantine, at the close of the 1964 season, witchweed had been confined to 24 counties of North Carolina and 10 counties of South Carolina, with a total area consisting of 270,000 acres.

IN 1958 THE Agriculture Department instituted a witchweed control program. The immediate objective was to kill the witchweed plant before it could produce seeds.

Previous tests had demonstrated that the herbicide 2,4-D, a weedkiller not toxic to fish, wildlife, bees, and other beneficial insects, was an effective killer of witchweed. It was applied as a spray at the rate of ½ to 1 pound per acre two or more times a season—depending on the amount of weed growth.

This program proved so successful it has been repeated each year. As a result of 7 continuous years of treatment, no evidence of witchweed was found on 1,500 previously infested farms.

In 1965, the eighth season, the program was greatly expanded. The Agriculture Department awarded contracts calling for application of 2,4-D to approximately 118,000 acres in the 24 counties in North Carolina and about 32,000 acres in the 10 counties of South Carolina.

The battle is being gradually won against another plant pest of great potential destructiveness, the golden nematode (*Heterodera rostochiensis*) of potatoes. This microscopic worm came to the United States in 1941 from Europe, and was found in potato fields in Nassau County, Long Island.

The nematode causes stunting and early death of the potato plant and reduces the size and yield of potatoes.

Applying nematocide DD to Long Island potato fields to control the golden nematode.

Pickett variety of soybean (right), which is resistant to the soybean cyst nematode, compared with a susceptible commercial variety of soybean on left.

This pest is one of the most difficult to control. The golden nematode has ruined so much of Europe's potato land that many countries limit potato growing to one crop every 4 years. Some areas abandoned potato growing altogether.

Shortly after the nematode was discovered on Long Island, the New York State Department of Agriculture and Markets took regulatory action to protect the potato industry. The hope was for eventual eradication, since the infestation was limited geographically and the nematode populations were relatively light.

The Pest Control Division of the Agricultural Research Service has been a full partner with New York State in supervising quarantine regula-tions that govern the movement of agricultural products, materials, and equipment likely to be contaminated.

Quarantine measures halted spread of the golden nematode for 5 years, but could not eliminate the pest. A chemical treatment was needed.

The first large-scale program of chemical control began in 1946 when 1,3-dichloropropene-1,2-dichloropro-pane (DD) was applied to infested land in the two Long Island counties. This fumigant has not entirely eliminated the golden nematode from the soil. But it has enabled the return of 2,000 acres of infested land to profitable potato production since 1946.

Even if the golden nematode was eliminated from this country, there would still be need for developing

41

resistant host varieties, in case the nematode got in again.

Since 1954, the Agriculture Department and the Agricultural Experiment Station of Cornell University have cooperated on a breeding program to develop commercially acceptable potato varieties that are highly resistant to the golden nematode or immune from its attack.

THE ORIGINAL SOURCE of resistance came from hybrid seed originating in Scotland and Holland. After two or more generations of backcrossing, several highly productive selections of potatoes of commercial promise are now available.

Unfortunately, when these resistant varieties are planted year after year on the same infested soil, new strains or types of the nematode develop capable of causing damage to the hitherto resistant potato plants.

A RECENT ADVANCE in control of an introduced disease is the development of a variety of soybean which is resistant to the cyst nematode.

Discovery in 1954 of the nematode attacking soybeans in North Carolina was the first report of this pest outside the Orient. It was causing severe damage to the crop and was a threat to the U.S. soybean industry.

Control of the soybean cyst nematode has been difficult. Multiple methods have been necessary. Application of chemical killers to the soil was not economically feasible for the farmer because cost of the chemicals was high and the treatment good for only one or two crop seasons.

CROP ROTATION of 2 to 3 years was also effective in controlling the nematode, but greatly limited production. Federal and State quarantines were only partially successful in controlling the nematode. Obviously, more effective control measures were needed, and the most promising line of research lay in developing resistant varieties.

In 1957, some 2,800 soybean varieties were screened for nematode resistance

in heavily infested fields. Four varieties were found on which the nematode did not reproduce.

ONE OF THESE VARIETIES, Peking, was backcrossed to transfer the resistance to the most popular commercial soybean variety in the Southwest, variety Lee. However, this resistance was associated with the undesirable quality of a black seedcoat.

The black seedcoat was bred out by making other backcrosses to a variety closely related to Lee, but which had the desirable yellow seedcoat. The new yellow-seeded variety, which is resistant to the soybean cyst nematode, was named Pickett.

This new variety was developed cooperatively by the Agricultural Research Service, and the Agricultural Experiment Stations of Arkansas, Missouri, North Carolina, Tennessee, and Virginia. Seed increase and distribution are being handled by the foundation seed organizations in these States. Seeds of the Pickett variety will be available to farmers in 1967.

GRASSES GROWN PRIMARILY for producing seed serve as hosts for many diseases which are difficult and expensive to control. A recent advance in control of these diseases is field burning. This is now the most important single method of reducing disease-producing organisms in grass seed fields.

The method consists simply of burning stubble and debris that remain in the field after harvest. It has resulted in good control of several seed and inflorescence (flower) diseases, among them blind seed disease, grass seed nematode, ergot, silver top, sheath spot, and leaf rusts of Kentucky bluegrass.

Once-a-year burning destroys the disease organism above ground and provides the basis for economical control by chemicals.

Every year about 100,000 acres of grass seed crops are burned over, including most fields of perennial ryegrass, Alta fescue, highland bentgrass,

Chewings fescue, red fescue, Kentucky bluegrass, and several wheatgrasses.

Another technique is applying propane gas flame to living plants as well as dead stubble. Two of the important diseases of peppermint, rust and wilt, are now being controlled in Oregon by this method.

Flaming controls rust by breaking the life cycle at these critical periods: Overwintering spores on the soil surface or on crop debris are killed; tips of the earliest emerging shoots, which are usually infected, are killed; and all of the susceptible foliage is removed at a time when the spores must infect leaves or perish.

To COMBAT WILT of peppermint, stubble is flamed after harvest with a propane burner. Fungus within the stem is killed without incinerating the stem. Sometimes green stems are not even charred externally.

Flaming also incinerates fallen leaves and other dried plant debris on the soil surface, eliminating them as infection sources.

Propane flaming may have wider application in the future than field burning, because the operator can control the amount of heat by regulating the speed of the mobile unit.

ANOTHER TYPE OF HEAT—in the form of hot air—is proving useful for control of ratoon stunting, a virus disease of sugarcane. A plant virus is a protein-like substance which can multiply in living tissue and produce disease. The disease was first reported in Australia in 1932. Since then it has been found in nearly all the world's sugarcane-growing regions, including the United States.

This virus disease was first identified in the United States in 1952 in Louisiana. Its identification solved the mystery of what was causing heavy losses suffered by the industry from yield decline of sugarcane varieties.

The disease is transmitted mechanically on cutting knives. Once established in the plant, the virus persists indefinitely.

Symptoms on diseased plants include reduced growth of cuttings and seedcanes, yellowing of foliage, and discoloration of portions of the stem—all of which result in greatly reduced yields. Based on some Australian work with hot-water treatment, plant pathologists in Louisiana have found that hot air is equally effective and in fact has several advantages.

LARGE-SCALE TREATMENT with hot water is only practicable on plantations with sugarcane mills, because of the amount of hot water needed. But electricity for operating hot-air ovens is available on all of the sugarcane farms in Louisiana.

Electrically heated ovens were developed by scientists of the Agriculture Department and the Louisiana Agricultural Experiment Station, in cooperation with industry. The diseased cuttings are placed in the ovens for 8 hours at an ingoing air temperature of 136° F. Five or six of the 8 hours are needed to bring the internal stalk temperature to 122° F.

The hot-air treatment brings a substantial increase in yields.

The $240 million peanut crop is subject to heavy losses from disease, but here, too, gains are being made.

Stem rot, or southern blight, which is caused by the soilborne fungus *Sclerotium rolfsii*, alone caused an estimated average annual loss to peanuts of 7.5 percent for the 1951–1960 period.

Until the past decade there was no satisfactory control for this disease. Crop rotation wasn't much help because the fungus attacks such a wide variety of crops, as well as many kinds of broad-leaved weeds. The nature of the fungus and its mode of attack made development of resistant varieties highly improbable. Chemical control had only mediocre success.

THE STEM ROT DISEASE organism lives more on dead matter than on living organic matter. Consequently research during the past decade has been directed toward reducing the organism in the soil.

Two techniques were developed. One is deep-covering dead plant debris on the soil surface at the time of seedbed preparation, and the other is nondirting cultivation.

Deep-covering is done by plowing under the trashy surface layer of the soil to a depth of at least 4 inches, which is below the effective infection zone for peanut plants.

Even more important than deep-covering is nondirting. This consists of planting peanuts on a slightly raised bed, then using a preemergence weed-killer in band treatments at the rate of 1.5 gallons of 53 percent active substance per acre. Only the areas between rows are cultivated.

Dirt shields are used to prevent soil from being thrown around the plant base during cultivation. With this method, only infrequent hand weeding is needed.

Nondirting has been consistently better than deep-covering in the control of stem rot.

However, a combination of the two methods is recommended.

The percentage of disease infection and yield of peanuts per acre for a 5-year test, as shown in an accompanying graph, illustrates the low level of infection and high yield from the deep-covering, nondirting procedure.

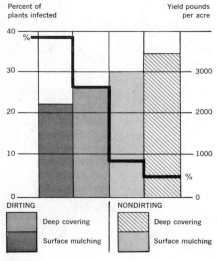

Percent of plants infected — Yield pounds per acre

DIRTING
Deep covering
Surface mulching

NONDIRTING
Deep covering
Surface mulching

ONE OF THE NEWEST and most promising nematode control methods consists of adding a chemical to the irrigation water for citrus trees.

The citrus nematode, *Tylenchulus semipenetrans*, is widely distributed in all U.S. citrus-growing regions. It greatly reduces citrus yields. The nematodes live in the soil and feed on roots of citrus trees. They seldom kill the trees, but growth and yield of heavily infected trees slowly decline.

Ideally, when new groves are set out, nematode-free planting stock should be used because planting stock is the most important source of infection. This is not always possible, since it is hard to detect the pest on nursery stock. There are no obvious early symptoms on the roots.

IN THE WESTERN citrus regions, good control of the nematode is obtained by putting 1,2-dibromo-3-chloropropane (DBCP) into the irrigation water. The solution of DBCP in water contains 25 percent by volume of DBCP per acre in 5 or 6 inches of irrigation water. The DBCP is added to the water by metering it into an engine-driven centrifugal pump. The mixture is then distributed evenly throughout the groves.

Soil samples before and after treatment show nematode populations are reduced by more than 99 percent and remain low for 2 or 3 years. During the 3 years following treatment, citrus fruit yields have been increased by as much as 12, 38, and 24 percent, respectively, over untreated trees. Increases of 22 and 11 percent in average fruit size have been recorded in the second and third crops after treatment.

Many formerly unproductive citrus groves have been restored to high production by this inexpensive method of controlling the nematode. This method of nematode control is limited to use in semiarid regions where all of the irrigation water percolates directly into the soil.

DBCP in irrigation water has also given good control of the citrus nematode in cotton, in sugarbeets, and in grapes.

Of all the diseases afflicting plants, those caused by viruses are the most difficult to control. The first record of a plant virus disease goes back almost 400 years, and these diseases today are counted in the thousands. Most major food crops are subject to infection by one or more destructive viruses.

MANY CONTROL MEASURES, often in combination, have been used in the past and are still being used. They include immune or resistant crop varieties, seed stock certification (especially for control of seedborne viruses), quarantines to prevent movement of infected plant material, roguing out of diseased plants, heat treatment and tip culture to eliminate the virus from propagating material, and insect vector control.

Breeding for resistance to virus diseases has met with only limited success. Seed stock certification and Federal and State quarantines are important and useful tools, and so are heat treatment and tip culture.

ALTHOUGH A FEW plant virus diseases are transmitted in infected seed or through mechanical means, the great majority are moved from plant to plant by insect carriers (vectors), like aphids, beetles, grasshoppers, leafhoppers, and thrips.

Many insects are able to transfer a virus disease by first feeding on infected plants and then on healthy ones. Aphids transmit infection of yellows virus to sugarbeets and strawberries, and carry cucumber mosaic and watermelon mosaic to cantaloup and other melons.

Insects also spread sugarcane mosaic and barley yellow dwarf of small grains.

The beet leafhopper transmits curly top virus to beans, cucumbers, pumpkins, squashes, sugarbeets, and tomatoes. The plum leafhopper carries peach yellows to peach trees, and other leafhoppers spread phony peach and other peach diseases.

Wheat curl mite transmits wheat streak mosaic, and the corn flea beetle spreads bacterial wilt in sweet corn.

AGRICULTURE DEPARTMENT scientists have been working on use of light and color to repel virus-carrying aphids from crops.

For a long time it was known that some colors attract and others repel certain insects. For example, traps painted yellow frequently are used to collect aphids, because yellow attracts them.

In one case where unpainted aluminum pans were placed around the yellow traps, aphids were repelled from them. The repulsion was believed due to reflection of light rays by the aluminum surface.

This observation led to research with aluminum as a foliage spray and in the form of strips laid on the soil surface for a mulch.

Sprays containing aluminum were applied directly to plant foliage. But even with stickers to make the aluminum adhere, the sprays were relatively ineffective.

The aluminum did not stick to the leaves long enough, became dull, or it reduced the growth of foliage.

In 1965 tests, aluminum foil was compared with a black plastic covering. Half the ground in fields planted to bush squash plants was covered with aluminum mulch, and the other half with black plastic.

Aphids trapped in yellow pans indicated a seasonal reduction of 93 percent for the aluminum mulch and 41 percent for the black plastic, compared with unmulched checks. Eleven weeks after planting, only 4.1 percent of the squash plants were infected with watermelon mosaic virus in the aluminum foil mulch. This compares with 51 percent infection in the black plastic mulch and 69 percent with no mulch.

More research is needed to determine the value of this control for specific virus diseases of crops. Other experiments show watermelons were not protected from early infection with

45

mosaic because the rapid growth of young vines covered the aluminum mulch early in the growing period so aphids were not repelled.

A TIP CULTURE TECHNIQUE in combination with heat therapy has given good control of virus diseases on a variety of crops.

Virus diseases have reduced vigor and fruiting of strawberry plants for 40 years. But State certification programs have made available propagating stock free of recognized viruses for the past 15 years.

Within the last few years USDA scientists have detected a previously unknown virus (latent A) in some certified strawberry stocks. They found that heating propagating stock to 100° F. and removing small shoot buds from the almost dead mother plants eradicated the virus in the buds. Vigor and fruit production were greatly restored in plants grown from the buds.

Another technique is growing entire strawberry plants from small bits of plant tissue in jars (tissue culture). Combined with heat treatment, this has enabled plant pathologists to eradicate other viruses which cannot be eliminated from plants by heat alone. Prospects are good that many varieties no longer grown because of lack of vigor due to viruses will be returned to profitable production.

THE OHIO Agricultural Experiment Station, working independently, has refined a technique to free apple clones from chlorotic leaf spot, stem pitting, and possibly other viruses. A clone is a group of plants derived from a single plant by means of vegetative propagation, as by grafting.

Trees infected with the viruses are grafted into 1-year apple seedlings. After 5 days the trees are pruned just above the dormant buds and placed in rooms where the temperature is maintained at 98° F. After about 42 days the trees are removed and the tip and uppermost usable bud of each shoot are grafted onto separate young apple seedlings. This material is then free of

all viruses and ready for propagation.

Similar heat treatment techniques are proving successful in research on eliminating viruses from grape and raspberry propagating stocks.

The Plant Quarantine Division of the Agricultural Research Service (ARS) keeps constant vigil for plant pests reaching our shores through the normal day-to-day flow of traffic. It also maintains a strict quarantine on plant material brought into the United States by Agriculture Department employees for experimental or scientific purposes.

Plant explorers and collectors continually search for resistant varieties from cultivated plants throughout the world, and it is important that this material be screened for disease before importation.

Quarantine regulations prohibit entry of several kinds of plants likely to be infected with virus diseases. The Agriculture Department is permitted to bring in plants in this category. But they must first undergo a period of detention and observation before their release for experimentation or crop improvement.

PLANT QUARANTINE STATIONS are maintained by the Plant Quarantine Division at the U.S. Plant Introduction Station, Glenn Dale, Md., in cooperation with the Crops Research Division of ARS. They are also maintained in California by the University of California Citrus Experiment Station at Riverside, and the Agricultural Experiment Station at Davis.

Quarantined plants are grown under controlled greenhouse conditions and thoroughly tested and observed for 2 to 8 years for detection of virus diseases.

Many viruses have long incubation periods. Symptoms caused by others show up only under special environmental conditions, including day length, temperature, and light.

A few examples illustrate the prevalence of intercepted viruses.

In an 8-year test period at Glenn Dale, 56 percent of 1,006 tests of potatoes revealed the presence of several important viruses, including one that had not been reported before in the United States.

Thirty-four percent of 125 tests of grapes showed the fan leaf virus, and 14 percent of 42 tests of sweetpotatoes showed sweetpotato yellow dwarf virus and internal cork virus.

The potato virus not previously reported in this country was the tobacco veinal necrosis strain. It was detected in quarantine at Glenn Dale in two of three potato introductions from Bolivia which were destined to be used in a breeding program for developing improved varieties at the U.S. Potato Breeding Station at Sturgeon Bay, Wis. The potatoes had to be destroyed as a result.

This aphid-transmitted virus strain can also infect tobacco, and causes devastating epidemics on tobacco in central Europe.

Development of resistant varieties is the most effective and economical way to control many plant diseases and nematodes.

Disease resistance has proved especially effective where acreage is large and the unit of value or profit margin of a crop so small as to make use of chemicals too costly. As a consequence, nearly all U.S. oat acreage is resistant to Victoria blight.

Black stem rust in the spring wheat belt has been reduced from one epidemic expected every 3 years to two epidemics in about 30 years.

Rice varieties resistant to the seed-borne nematode that causes white tip disease have almost eliminated the disease. Nova and Saturn, two medium-grain rice varieties, have been released. They are resistant to the destructive rice blast disease.

Another resistant long-grain variety is scheduled for naming and release in 1966.

Two bacterial wilt-resistant alfalfa varieties, Ranger and Vernal, are now grown on more than 12 million acres.

Sugarbeet varieties with a high degree of resistance to damage from the curly top virus are widely grown.

THERE ARE NOW two varieties of sweet sorghum, Wiley and Rio, whose resistance to anthracnose, the most serious disease of sorghum in the southeastern United States, amounts almost to immunity.

THE ANTHRACNOSE fungus aggressively attacks both leaves and stalks wherever rainfall is adequate for sorghum growing, and seriously reduces sugar content.

The very aggressiveness of the fungus has permitted development of resistant varieties with relative ease. Artificially induced disease epidemics of great uniformity can be produced at very little cost. Under such severe disease conditions, it is easy to select individual plants that show good resistance.

IN THE SEARCH for resistant breeding material, sometimes there is no source among native plant species. So plant explorers and collectors bring back from other countries cultivated plants and their wild progenitors that contain resistance to various diseases. These introduced plants are then crossed with our native varieties that contain preferred characteristics.

A good example of introduced resistance is the Benton variety of barley. The foreign collection from which this variety was ultimately derived originated as a plant introduction from Africa.

This barley was first grown in the United States at the Agriculture Department's Introduction Station in Chico, Calif., in 1917. It was later assigned and maintained in the Department's world barley collection. Its resistance to the barley yellow dwarf virus disease was first discovered in California tests in 1951. In 1958 the selection was introduced into Oregon, and found to have excellent resistance to virus strains there.

Benton was named and released by the Oregon Agricultural Experiment Station in 1965. It is adapted to the spring barley regions of Oregon and classed as a feed barley.

Since 1960, Benton has averaged 56

bushels compared with 49 for Hann-chen, the commonly grown variety in the area. The greatest difference in yield was noted in 1961, when the virus disease was very serious—51.4 bushels for Benton and only 20.6 bushels for Hannchen.

WITH THE CONSTANT evolvement of new diseases, and especially of new races of the disease-producing organisms, a parallel need has arisen for new reserves of breeding material for resistance. This need is being met with a gene bank for breeders maintained by the Agricultural Research Service.

This world seed collection serves also as a reservoir of new characteristics for crop improvement. Four regional ARS plant introduction stations are currently screening the world seed collection to determine sources of resistance to common diseases.

The gene-for-gene concept provides the necessary theoretical basis for this work.

This hypothesis was first conceived by an Agriculture Department plant scientist working on the breeding of flax varieties for resistance to flax rust. He speculated that parasites like the rust fungi which cannot survive apart from their hosts must have evolved in association with the hosts. If this is so, it could then be assumed that during their parallel evolution, host and parasite developed complementary gene systems.

THIS MEANS that for each gene conditioning resistance in the host there is a specific gene in the parasite that determines its ability to produce disease. Thus, before rust can develop there must be a gene in the pathogen for disease initiation and a corresponding gene for susceptibility in the host.

Based on this principle, flax breeders may now select the proper combination of genes to breed into new varieties confident they will provide a high degree of lasting protection.

Some diseases cannot be controlled effectively by any of the biological methods already discussed. Under

favorable weather conditions they become explosively destructive and spread rapidly in a short time.

Successful control of epidemic diseases depends on prompt application of pesticide sprays before the disease outbreak. The farmer must know when an epidemic is impending and therefore when to apply his sprays.

The Agriculture Department, in cooperation with the State experiment stations and extension services, operates a plant disease forecasting and warning service for farmers. Based on environmental factors, primarily temperature, rainfall, relative humidity, and dew, at the plant level, forecasts are made of outbreaks of several diseases which fluctuate greatly from one year to another.

WARNING LETTERS are sent throughout the growing season to growers and to manufacturers of pesticides and spray equipment. They may tell the growers of a community that disease outbreak conditions are such that control measures will result in economic gain. On the other hand, the letters may say the outbreak is unlikely to be serious enough to justify the time, energy, and money needed for control.

THE PLANT DISEASE forecasting program is credited with saving the lima bean industry and reducing the number of spray applications needed to control late blight of potatoes.

Downy mildew of lima beans once was very destructive in about 1 out of 3 years. Before the forecasts, growers had to make several routine fungicide sprays each year to guarantee a crop. Cost of spraying became so prohibitive the lima bean industry was on its way out.

Today, as a result of accurate, precise forecasts, growers only have to spray for lima bean downy mildew when an epidemic threatens.

In some Northeastern States the number of spray applications required for effective control of late blight of potatoes has been reduced 50 percent as a result of blight predictions.

48

PROTECTING THE SPORTSMAN'S

PARADISE

DONALD A. SPENCER

SETTLERS of the North American Continent placed great reliance on an abundant supply of fish and game. Establishment of colonies like Virginia and the westward trek of the pioneers could not have been possible without this wildlife.

The settlers prized deer, buffalo, elk, and antelope; wild turkey, grouse, quail, ducks, and geese; fish, lobsters, clams, and oysters; and they were not averse to trapping and snaring small animals and birds as well.

COOKBOOKS of America's first 200 years carried recipes for "roast larks," told how to cook "reed birds" and "snow birds," and gave tips on how eggs collected in the wild could be preserved for winter use. Rabbits and squirrels were supplemented with other field game like gophers and chipmunks.

Food gathered from the wild was a major component of the food supply of that bygone era.

Reliance on fish and wildlife as a major contribution to the food supply has continued in some parts of North America.

When I visited the island of Grand Manan (New Brunswick, Canada) in 1940, my breakfast eggs and a delicious egg custard dessert for dinner came from a winter store of 1,500 herring gull eggs preserved under water glass (sodium silicate).

At that time "egging" was a common practice on the gull nesting islands off the coast of eastern Canada. As long as the eggs are regularly removed from the nest, the herring gull will continue to lay.

To protect the species the Canadian Government set a cut-off date in June designed to allow the gulls to acquire a normal clutch of three eggs, hatch, and raise a yearly brood.

QUITE RECENTLY the Alaska Crippled Children's Association published a small "Eskimo Cook Book" prepared by the students of a day school in Shishmaref, Alaska.

* * *

Donald A. Spencer is *Chief Staff Officer*, Animal Biology Section, Pesticides Regulation Division, Agricultural Research Service. He served with the Fish and Wildlife Service, Department of the Interior, between 1927 and 1962.

The foods are almost exclusively from the Arctic wilds and include owls, loons, ptarmigan, bear, caribou, seal, walrus, and whale. Every part of the animal that is edible is utilized.

FISH AND GAME for food are just as frequently a matter of choice as of necessity. In February 1862, the wife of President Abraham Lincoln planned the following menu for a gala dinner at the White House:

Champagne Punch
Stewed and Scalloped Oysters
Boned, Truffle-Stuffed Turkey
Pate de Foie Gras
Aspic of Tongue
Canvasback Duck
Partridge
Fillet of Beef
Ham   Venison
Pheasant   Terrapin
Chicken Salad
Sandwiches and Jellies
Cakes   Ices

YET YOU DON'T HAVE TO return to the 1860's to find fish and game featured prominently as gourmet foods. Examine a menu the next time you dine at one of the larger restaurants or hotels. You will find an amazing number of dishes from the oceans, the rivers, the prairies, and the forests.

Perhaps you can start with a shrimp cocktail, follow with a bowl of green turtle soup, then select either an abalone steak or frog legs for an entree.

In other adventures in good eating, there are places in the United States where you can find channel catfish crisp-fried in cornmeal, or fried clams practically replacing the hamburger.

YOU MIGHT THINK our mushrooming human population would sound the death knell for native fish and wildlife. Cities, industries, roads, and cultivated fields have changed the face of the earth. Domestic livestock compete for pasture. Forests are used for timber and plastics. Civilization's wastes pollute lakes, rivers, and harbors.

But despite the march of man, the amounts of fish and game that come to the American table today may well exceed that harvested during any other period of American history.

The percentage in the average diet is nowhere near as great, but the aggregate in pounds of fish and game consumed in the United States is surprising—not millions but billions of pounds. This fish and game abundance is possible only through concerted efforts to manage and protect our wildlife resources.

Fish and game are a renewable resource if the annual harvest leaves breeding stock for the coming year, or provision is made for restocking.

During the summer biologists are sent into Canada and Alaska to learn how waterfowl are faring on their breeding grounds. This information is used to judge what numbers of ducks and geese may be taken by hunters as the migratory flights move south in the fall.

In each State similar studies of mammal and game bird populations are conducted as a guide to establishing the hunting season and the bag limits.

Such controls based on research and annual population surveys provide a continuing harvest from a resource that otherwise might very rapidly become depleted.

THE LAST National Survey of Fishing and Hunting, in 1960, shows that 21 million people in the United States participated in fresh water fishing, totaling 385 million days of recreation.

Even allowing for "the one that got away," this is far too great a drain on the natural reproductive capacity of fish in our streams, our lakes, and our reservoirs.

Natural foods for fish are abundant in late spring and summer and the solution has been to stock these waters with fry, fingerling, and even catchable-size fish from 104 national fish hatcheries, 481 State hatcheries, and 1,175 commercial hatcheries.

Salmon are hatched and reared in some 21 fish hatcheries in the Columbia River Basin in an attempt to offset disruption of the spawning runs caused by high dams.

Game farms as well as fish hatcheries can be employed to restore many wildlife populations that are seriously depleted by a natural catastrophe or overharvest.

Advancing civilization is constantly creating new problems in protecting our fish and wildlife.

Tall buildings, TV towers, and even the steady vertical beam of a ceilometer searchlight at weather stations may litter the ground with dead birds on stormy nights.

In one night near Macon, Ga., an estimated 50,000 birds died of exhaustion from circling around a ceilometer. This is now corrected either by the use of color filters or by rotating the ceilometer beam from horizon to horizon.

Hydroelectric and irrigation dams erected along the major river systems could have brought to an end the valuable salmon, shad, and rockfish resource. These fish spend their lives at sea but must return to the upper reaches of our fresh water streams to lay eggs (spawn). Costly bypass streams—called fishways—or giant staircases of low waterfalls—fish ladders—must be constructed at each dam to make it possible for fish to reach their breeding grounds.

THE BUREAU of Sport Fisheries and Wildlife, Department of the Interior, now administers some 28,559,382 acres of Federal wildlife refuges in the United States, including Alaska and Hawaii.

The National Parks and Monuments, State Parks, Wildlife Management Areas and Refuges, and a few outstanding privately endowed areas like the Welder Wildlife Foundation at Sinton, Tex., add to what is a vast outdoor laboratory and breeding ground for endangered species.

A hunter flushes a pheasant on a hunting preserve in Posey County, Indiana.

Refuges, while contributing to production, have a much more important role in protecting key habitats against change brought about by agricultural and commercial development.

This program receives important support from sportsmen. Purchase of a Duck Stamp costing $3 by each licensed waterfowl hunter provided $4.6 million during the fiscal year ending June 30, 1965 which was spent to acquire land and water for migratory waterfowl.

The plan is to preserve approximately 1.8 million acres of waterfowl breeding habitat, mostly in Minnesota, North Dakota, and South Dakota. Natural lakes, marshes, and potholes valuable to waterfowl production will be protected by direct purchase or easements against drainage.

THERE HAVE BEEN times in the late summer and fall, and particularly during periods of drought, when waterfowl by the tens of thousands died in the shallow waters of our western ponds and lakes. On Great Salt Lake in Utah windrows of dead ducks have lined the shores for miles.

The killer is avian botulism. Through intensive efforts of Government scientists, conditions favoring the multiplication of the botulinum bacillus and the deadly toxin it produces are now rather well understood. Some corrective measures are possible.

Rabies in foxes and bats, red tides that litter the beaches in Florida with dead fish, and a deadly dinoflagulate (plankton) on which oysters feed in certain northern waters are but a few of the serious disease problems under study to protect fish and wildlife.

PROTECTION OF fish and game resources frequently is the indirect result of agricultural programs with entirely different goals.

Eradication of the screw-worm in Florida and control of the cattle fever tick in east Texas were intended primarily to protect the domestic livestock industry. These programs also clearly benefited deer in those areas that are plagued by the same parasites.

In the Western States the control of coyotes, bobcats, and mountain lions to protect livestock and poultry is in no small way responsible for the abundance of game in that section.

SIMILARLY, manipulation of the plant cover for range improvement, or use of herbicides to clear vegetation-choked waterways, benefits fish and wildlife occupying the same habitat.

Man finds himself in competition with many natural predators within the ranks of wildlife. Like man, these predators may at times exert so much pressure on their prey as to endanger the species.

The sea lamprey was present for many years in the St. Lawrence River and Lake Ontario but was blocked from the other Great Lakes by Niagara Falls. With the building of the Welland Canal around the falls the lamprey finally reached Lake Huron by the late 1930's.

This blood-sucking eel flourished in Huron by feeding on the prized lake trout. It became so abundant that the commercial catch of lake trout fell from 6 million pounds in 1935 to 344,000 pounds in 1953.

In Lake Michigan the disaster was even more complete. The lake trout catch dropped from 6.9 million pounds in 1943 to 3,000 pounds in 1952.

In a classic research program the Interior Department's Bureau of Commercial Fisheries screened more than 8,000 organic chemical compounds to find one that would selectively kill the young (larval stage) of the lamprey during the 5-year development period spent in the bottom mud of streams tributary to the lakes. They found such a control chemical in TFM which is now in use to build back fisheries in the Great Lakes that once produced a commercial catch of over 100 million pounds annually.

Another predator poses a serious threat to oyster production.

So much fresh water is being diverted from our rivers for domestic and irrigation purposes that the oceanic

52

bays at the mouths of these rivers have an increasing salt content, from less dilution of sea water. Predators of the oyster—a marine snail called a "drill" and a sporozoan disease called MFX— were formerly repelled by the low salt content of the water, but can now move into the oyster producing areas.

A new chemical product of research called Polystream appears capable of controlling the oyster drill without harming the oysters.

GAME BIRDS and mammals frequently inflict losses on crops and other commercial enterprises.

Rabbits seriously damage orchards by girdling the base of fruit trees. Large flocks of migrating waterfowl can, in a matter of hours, consume and otherwise destroy a field of ripening grain. Deer, by repeated browsing on terminal shoots, suppress the growth in a forest plantation over periods of 10 to 20 years.

Progress has been made in protecting crops against wildlife by using scare devices, fencing, and chemical sprays and paints that repel rather than kill.

CHEMICAL PESTICIDES used to control insects, fungi, and weeds have on occasion killed wildlife. Commonly, these undesirable effects result because the wildlife species is peculiarly sensitive to the poison. It can also happen that a wildlife species in a treated area is not endangered until a persistent pesticide is accumulated—or stored in the tissues—by some species on which it preys.

Research on the hazard of an agricultural pesticide is a time-consuming and costly undertaking. The manufacturer is presently required to furnish

Pesticide residue study at the Patuxent Wildlife Research Center, Fish and Wildlife Service, Laurel, Md. Chemist Calvin Menzie checks battery of Soxhlet extractors in which pesticides are removed from macerated tissue by solvent extraction.

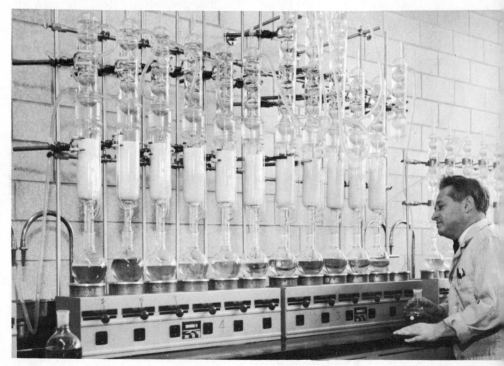

authoritative, documented pharmacological data bearing on possible hazard to humans and domestic animals, and residues in soils and food crops. In addition he must furnish toxicity data on a few representative species of fish and wildlife.

Helpful as this information is, species of fish and wildlife number in the tens of thousands and often have large differences in susceptibility.

RECOGNIZING the enormity of the task of evaluating the total effect of pesticides on fish and wildlife, Congress in 1958 authorized increased expenditures by the Fish and Wildlife Service to study the effect of pesticides on fish and wildlife and the food chain.

This program is presently providing much needed information on the acute and chronic toxicity of common pesticides. It is now possible to compare the relative hazard to fish of pesticides available for control of mosquitoes in marsh areas. The 89th Congress authorized increased appropriations to $5 million annually by 1967 for further pesticide-wildlife investigations.

In a later chapter of the Yearbook an extensive monitoring program for persistent pesticides in the environment is discussed. Information from this study will be most useful in judging what protection must be provided for wildlife.

While most tissue residues are expected to be quite low—measured in parts per billion or less—it is known that certain living organisms accumulate and magnify the effect. In 10 days oysters can accumulate tissue residues of DDT 15,000 times the environment level of some 10 parts per billion.

RESPONSIBILITY for fish and wildlife resources rests with the Interior Department and the State governments.

The regular Federal budget of the Fish and Wildlife Service was approximately $60 million in 1965. Additional Fish and Wildlife funds are provided from Federal taxes on sporting guns and ammunition, or Pittman-Robertson Funds, and Federal taxes on fishing equipment, or Dingell-Johnson Funds.

The two special funds, which amounted to $23.8 million in the 1965 fiscal year ending June 30, 1965, are apportioned to the States in relation to the number of hunting and fishing licenses sold and total land area. No State may receive more than 75 percent of its operating fund from this source.

Specifically these funds are "Apportioned to the States for fish and wildlife restoration projects involving purchase of land, improvement of areas of lands and waters for fish and wildlife, and to conduct research for restoration and perpetuation of these resources." The States in turn collected in the fiscal year 1964 some $72 million in hunting license fees, and $60 million in fishing license fees.

PROTECTION OF fish and wildlife is so complex and difficult that it is rather astonishing to find how much it contributes to the food supply.

In the United States the use of fishery products in 1964 amounted to 12 billion pounds. This does not include the catch of sport fishermen who spent something like 465 million days at this recreational pursuit—no one knows how many fish they caught.

The U.S. Trout Farmers Association annually supplies about 5.5 million pounds of fresh and fresh-frozen trout to the market.

Big game hunters enjoyed approximately 200 million days of recreation and as a bonus in 1964 returned with over 2 million head of game ranging from wild boar in Hawaii, elk in Colorado, to caribou in Alaska. This game dressed-out in excess of 223 million pounds.

Duck hunters shot and retrieved over 8 million wild ducks and geese in 1964. In the same year some 91,000 wild turkeys were harvested.

We can only guess at the contribution of the small game hunters, who in 1960 were in the field a total of 138 million days looking for pheasants, grouse, quail, doves, rabbits, and squirrels.

Now, sir, if you will pass me my shotgun. . . .

LIVESTOCK HEALTH

F. J. MULHERN

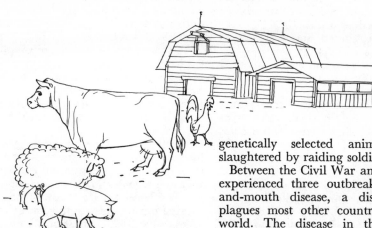

genetically selected animals were slaughtered by raiding soldiers.

Between the Civil War and 1900 we experienced three outbreaks of foot-and-mouth disease, a disease that plagues most other countries of the world. The disease in the United States was either in a mild form, or the lack of movement of animals assisted in its eradication before it became very widespread.

During the Civil War, land-grant colleges came into being. They provided education for many farm-reared persons who previously had not even considered the possibility of education to assist them in their farming or ranching practices. The land-grant colleges also ultimately produced people who took the newer knowledge to the grass-roots within each county and tried to stimulate farmers to adopt new ideas on farming and livestock raising and recognize the need for prevention, control, and eradication of diseases.

Veterinary education—or formalized study of it—first began in this country on October 2, 1884, at the University of Pennsylvania. Land-grant colleges opened other schools of veterinary medicine, and private schools were started. These schools became the nucleus for developing a professional group that provided the scientific know-how to protect our livestock from disease.

"OUR people together with the Indians had the last winter destroyed and kild up all our hoggs insomuch as of five or six hundred (as it is supposed) there was not above one sow that we can heare of left alive; not a henn nor a chick in the fort (and our horses and mares they had eaten with the first)."

This was a report made by Lord Delaware upon his arrival at the Virginia Colony in 1601. Fiske, the historian, reports that after the last basket of corn had been devoured, people lived for a while on roots and herbs and then turned to cannibalism.

GUARDING THE HEALTH of livestock in the early days was generally protecting against exposure and trying to give livestock an adequate diet. Knowledge about disease was so scant even in the human field that most treatments or prevention were rooted in quackery.

After repeated attempts to import and raise livestock, some basic species became established. Isolation helped prevent the spread of disease, and livestock continued to increase until the Civil War when some of the better

* * *

F. J. Mulhern is *Director*, Animal Health Division, Agricultural Research Service.

SHORTLY AFTER ESTABLISHMENT of the U.S. Department of Agriculture in 1862, the Department launched a national program to eradicate contagious pleuropneumonia. It did so because European countries had barred our animals because of the disease's existence in the United States. The program was successful. It was the first time a disease agent was eliminated from our country, truly a major accomplishment.

Vocational agriculture teachers came into being and gradually they succeeded in enrolling students from farms in their courses. Included in the courses were measures to protect livestock health.

Realizing that education must be applied to be of any use, the Extension Service was established to place educated men in each county with information on all phases of agriculture.

Down through the years vo-ag teachers and county agents increased, and they improved their contribution to the livestock industry and farming generally.

AFTER THE SUCCESS of the first eradication program, the Agriculture Department launched two major programs in the early 1900's.

First, Department researchers discovered that cattle tick fever (bovine piroplasmosis) was spread by a tick (*Boophilus annulatus*). This was the first confirmed knowledge of how a disease could be spread in this manner and it later led to unraveling the mystery of how yellow fever and malaria were spread.

An eradication program eliminated the tick from the South. Until that time, all attempts to improve breeds of southern cattle by imports from outside were unsuccessful because they died shortly after arrival from disease spread by ticks. The tick was eliminated from the United States in 1940. Occasional introductions have been promptly eliminated.

The second program was against sheep scabies that in advanced cases was reducing the production of wool

by 75 percent. The disease was becoming well established throughout our major sheep-producing areas and causing great havoc.

Foot-and-mouth disease struck the country six times after 1900. The 1914 outbreak spread to 22 States and the District of Columbia.

All these outbreaks were successfully eradicated.

These successful campaigns inspired State and Federal Governments to tackle other disease problems considered insurmountable at the time they occurred.

Another major step in protecting our food supply was establishment of a meat inspection system designed primarily to assure wholesome meat for consumers. Besides eliminating unwholesome meats from the food supply, meat inspectors assisted campaigns against communicable diseases of livestock. Inspectors were able to detect indications of infection at the time of slaughter, and to advise disease control officials who could investigate promptly and quarantine premises where needed.

Based on condemnation rates, the major disease in our cattle in 1917 was tuberculosis, with 200,000 carcasses withheld from markets each year because of it.

This disease was largely responsible for the human hunchbacks that existed at that time since the disease agent itself had an affinity for the human spine. Tuberculosis, or TB, could be transmitted through milk and from handlers of live or slaughtered animals, and was a major disease problem. In some counties more than 85 percent of cattle were infected.

Due to the successful efforts to eradicate diseases like contagious pleuropneumonia and foot-and-mouth disease, and the dramatic reduction in cattle tick fever, the Agriculture Department embarked in 1917 on a cattle tuberculosis eradication program. This program had great success, particularly in the early stages, and the incidence or number of cases found annually was reduced dramatically.

Besides the TB eradication program

for cattle, milk pasteurization was being initiated rapidly in a number of States. Pasteurization was eliminating spread of TB and many other diseases through contaminated milk.

WHEN THE GREAT DEPRESSION hit during the 1930's, the loss in individual income reduced demand for animal byproducts. Consequently, milk and dairy products in some cases were in oversupply, causing strong fluctuations in product prices and very low prices at livestock sales.

At the same time it was recognized that with the reduction of TB in our cattle, brucellosis or "Bang's disease" was the number one cattle disease problem in this country. Losses were estimated at $100 million a year. This figure was based on the number of animals that had to be replaced because of sterility as a result of the disease, the reduced number of calves produced due to brucellosis-caused abortion, and the reduction of milk supply in animals affected with brucellosis. In addition, brucellosis was the cause of undulant fever in the human population.

Congressional interest in the total picture was responsible for developing a national eradication program. Congress felt the program would eradicate a major disease, in so doing eliminate some of the unsatisfactory dairy type cattle, and at the same time help provide a more satisfactory price for dairy cattle.

Because of the low price of dairy cattle and milk, many producers were leaving farms feeling that dairy income would continue to be substantially reduced.

A brucellosis eradication program was initiated in 1937. By the end of 1964 the losses had been reduced 75 percent a year below what they were before the program started. Incidence of the disease in humans has decreased accordingly.

FOOT-AND-MOUTH DISEASE (FMD) was introduced into Mexico in the late 1940's. Because of the threat of FMD

entering our own country, the United States decided to participate in an international cooperative effort to eliminate the disease in Mexico. It was believed that if the disease entered our country, it would cost at least $100 million a year for vaccination alone to prevent epidemics. The disease was successfully eradicated in Mexico.

In 1952 vesicular exanthema (VE) broke out of California and spread to 41 other States before it was brought under control. Even though we previously had outbreaks of foot-and-mouth disease and trichinosis as a result of feeding uncooked garbage to swine, State and Federal Governments were not able to enforce a ban on uncooked feeding until this VE epidemic occurred.

As a result of the epidemic, laws were passed in all States requiring that garbage fed to hogs must be cooked first. This was a vital protective step against the introduction and spread of many diseases through garbage feeding. Since the incidence of trichinosis was much higher in swine fed raw garbage, cooking garbage before feeding it to swine helped protect our human population against this disease.

The outbreak in Mexico of foot-and-mouth disease and the spread of VE in the United States indicated the need for a well-established, well-understood animal disease defense organization. Such an organization has been established within each State. Periodic practice alerts keep the organization active and modifying its plan to changing times.

TODAY WE FIND a direct contrast between the circumstances that existed decades ago when isolation and restricted movements to markets provided a degree of protection to the livestock population from epidemics of disease. Now we find a multimillion livestock population in every species and daily movements of hundreds of thousands of livestock throughout the country in normal marketing practices.

Specially trained veterinary diagnosticians are strategically located to investigate any suspicion of a foreign disease being introduced. They and their laboratory support work around the clock when an investigation is underway. For each working day last year, two investigations on the average were being made somewhere in this country.

IN RECENT YEARS some disease programs established originally as eradication programs were not really out to accomplish complete eradication. They were designed rather to reduce the disease to an insignificant level. When today's low incidence of some of these diseases is compared with the original incidence, the programs have certainly been worth while. However, the low incidence allows a source of infection that threatens the entire population. Besides it requires a continuous, costly expenditure to deal with the disease even at these low levels.

In the old days chronic diseases like brucellosis and tuberculosis were primarily dealt with on a premises-to-premises basis. Today we must investigate the complete epidemiology of the outbreak on the premises, the potential spread to other premises, and the contamination of facilities used, and why some diseases persist under certain circumstances.

In recent years specialists have been assigned to premises where the last remnants of a disease exist so it can be entirely eradicated.

These specialists identify areas blocking eradication. Research is then launched to find a solution.

It takes great skill to examine all the factors that may be responsible for perpetuating a disease and to identify the factors responsible. Yet this is being done more frequently as our proficiency in this area develops.

THE RECORD of livestock and poultry disease eradication in this country indicates the great effort underway.

Incidence of brucellosis has been reduced to less than 1 percent in the 107 million cattle population in over 87 percent of the counties in our coun-

try. We expect to reduce it to less than 1 percent of the cattle in all counties of the United States by 1968.

The United States is expected to be free of cattle brucellosis by 1972, and to be rid of swine brucellosis by 1975. Since these species are the primary sources of brucellosis—or undulant fever—in people in the United States, the sources of infection for the human population will be eliminated. More than 44 million cattle are being screened or tested for brucellosis annually.

Cattle tuberculosis has been reduced to 0.08 of 1 percent. This is an extremely complex and chronic disease. At the present rate we will eliminate evidence of TB at the time of slaughter in our cattle population by 1994. Our efforts are directed at eliminating it even sooner. This requires tracing the origin of all outbreaks and the screening or testing of 9 million cattle annually.

To free cattle of the devastating effects of the screw-worm fly, this country has produced and sterilized over 19½ billion flies. The result is eradication of the fly in the Southeast and most of the Southwest. It is an outstanding example of a peaceful use of atomic energy, and eradication of a pest without using pesticides.

Incidence of hog cholera has been reduced since the State-Federal eradication program began in February 1962, and it is expected that this disease will be eliminated by 1972.

SCABIES IN SHEEP is expected to be eradicated by 1968. Efforts are being made to inspect sheep throughout the country, concentrating on heavy infection areas in the Midwest. In the eradication campaign, over 21 million sheep are inspected annually, and more than 100,000 were dipped during the 1965 fiscal year.

Scrapie in sheep, which has an unusually long incubation period of 42 months, presents a different type of disease with more challenging aspects in its eradication. The objective is to prevent its spread within three breeds

58

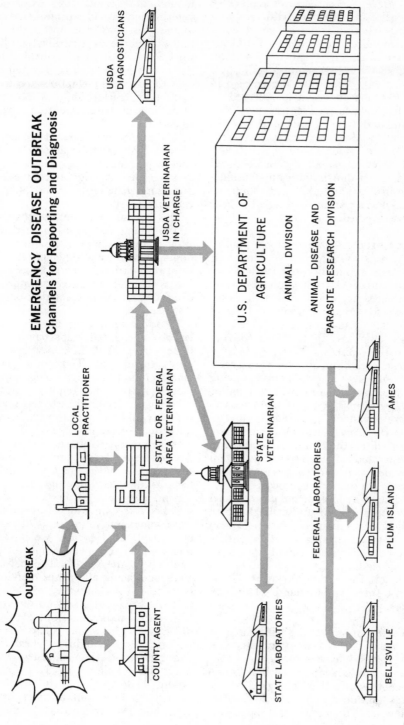

EMERGENCY DISEASE OUTBREAK
Channels for Reporting and Diagnosis

OUTBREAK

COUNTY AGENT

LOCAL PRACTITIONER

STATE OR FEDERAL AREA VETERINARIAN

STATE VETERINARIAN

USDA VETERINARIAN IN CHARGE

USDA DIAGNOSTICIANS

U.S. DEPARTMENT OF AGRICULTURE

ANIMAL DIVISION

ANIMAL DISEASE AND PARASITE RESEARCH DIVISION

STATE LABORATORIES

FEDERAL LABORATORIES

AMES

PLUM ISLAND

BELTSVILLE

59

of sheep in which it is known to exist, and prevent its spread to the other 18 breeds of sheep and the different goat breeds where it is not known to exist. This requires surveillance of 300,000 to a million sheep annually, and an extensive investigation covering all movements for the preceding 42 months once a lesion is observed.

All known cases of scrapie have been eliminated as they were found. Investigations to find new cases, research, and field studies are carried out simultaneously as we proceed to eradicate a disease with an unusually long incubation period and where the genes plus a transmissible agent appear to be involved.

PILOT STUDIES conducted on poultry diseases may provide a basis for dramatic elimination of these diseases in the future. Current studies are being conducted on air sacculitis, leukosis, causes for condemnations at time of slaughter, and a special project to raise chickens free of six highly contagious diseases.

Over 53 million animals are inspected annually at stockyards having Federal inspection in order to monitor the health on the 2.5 million premises where livestock are raised in this country. Any suspicious cases are reported to the State of origin and investigated. This inspection system provides a method of disease control during the marketing process.

Agriculture Department personnel have been sent to study the effects of radioactive fallout. These personnel are stationed throughout the country and have the responsibility of monitoring fallout that may occur on livestock from time to time. They provide an arm to our civil defense effort.

A SAYING GOES that if during the next 10 years the veterinary graduate of today doesn't have some means of continuing his education, he will be 50 percent as effective as a graduate of today that does. The practitioner of today and tomorrow will be advocating preventive medicine and eradication of diseases that exist. The veterinarian provides professional skill at the grassroots level and is the first line of defense in guarding our livestock food supply. He has behind him the newer knowledge concerning disease and surgical techniques and treatment that develop daily as the result of millions of dollars spent on medical research.

Advances in treating and preventing diseases that affect our animal population would not exist without a progressive, energetic, highly competitive, and competent biologic and pharmaceutical industry.

This industry has met the challenge of producing the products needed to protect our animal populations. Its desire to produce a better product has been responsible for continuously giving us the most advanced or improved drugs or vaccines to combat or prevent disease.

As newer knowledge develops, professionals in allied fields have joined forces to pool this knowledge and apply techniques. Today the physician, veterinarian, entomologist, radiologist, statistician, chemist, virologist, pathologist, bacteriologist, and serologist may all be engaged in eradicating a livestock or poultry disease.

In summary, we have reviewed the development of our efforts to guard the health of our livestock and poultry from its humble beginnings. Today we can proudly say that this is one of the safest countries in which to raise livestock and poultry, so far as disease is concerned. And besides we have the most wholesome meat supply of any country in the world. The constant challenge facing all groups mentioned is to "Keep it that way."

If the President made an inventory of livestock today, as Lord Delaware did in 1601, he would report the following: A cattle industry worth over $12 billion, a swine industry worth over $1.5 billion, a $3.4 billion poultry industry, a $4 billion horse industry, a $425 million sheep industry, and a $28 million goat industry.

SAFEGUARDING OUR MILK

MARVIN L. SPECK

MILK is produced and distributed with outstanding protection of its wholesomeness. When a high quality food is offered the consumer it must be prepared from a raw product of high quality. For this reason, great care has been given the way milk is obtained from the cow on the producing farm. Many years of experience and research underpin the farm base on which our modern dairy industry is founded.

Milk is defined as the "lacteal secretion, practically free from colostrum, obtained by the complete milking of one or more healthy cows, which contains not less than 8¼ percent milk solids-not-fat and not less than 3¼ percent milk fat" (U.S. Public Health Service). Colostrum is eliminated from milk for human consumption since it is needed for the health of the newborn calf and does not have a desirable flavor.

By this definition, marketable milk can be derived only from healthy animals. And the definition implies that milk must not be taken from cows too early, or too late, in the lactation period.

Milk contains an average of 13 percent solids, consisting of 3.9 percent fat, 4.9 percent lactose, 3.5 percent protein, and 0.7 percent minerals. (Minimum legal State requirements range from 11.0 to 12.3 percent total solids and from 3.0 to 3.8 percent fat.) These components and their balance have led to a description of milk as the most nearly perfect human food produced naturally. There are also a number of minor constituents in milk that contribute to man's nutritional needs. They include trace elements and vitamins.

Factors that cause a normal variation in milk constituents include the cow's age, unusual or extreme feeding, weather and season, lactation and gestation, and the breed of cow. Milk offered for human consumption is blended from so many different cows that these variations are kept at a remarkably low level.

Components of milk that contribute to its outstanding nutritional quality for humans also make milk a desirable food for other living organisms. As man attempts to obtain bovine milk for his use he must be constantly aware of competition by a number of these competitors. Chief among them are micro-organisms, and especially bacteria.

*   *   *

Marvin L. Speck is *Professor of Food Microbiology*, North Carolina State University, Raleigh. Before his present post he was assistant chief bacteriologist at the National Dairy Research Laboratories.

Bacteria may quickly make milk unpalatable for human use unless many safeguards are taken to prevent or minimize their entry and growth.

Repeated studies have shown that when desirable methods are used, relatively few bacteria are added to milk from air, or from equipment used in milk handling. And storage of milk at recommended refrigeration temperatures allows only minor growth of bacteria present.

THE MILK-PRODUCING COW is subject to infection by a number of microorganisms and some of them may cause illness in humans.

Bovine tuberculosis formerly occurred with alarming frequency. Within the past several decades a tuberculosis eradication program has been in effect which involves use of the tuberculin test. This has enabled dairy farmers to eliminate infected animals from the producing herd. Exposure of humans to infection has been essentially ended by having market milk originate from areas accredited as free from bovine tuberculosis.

Brucellosis is a disease that causes abortion in cattle. If the causative bacterium infects humans the disease is termed undulant fever. The rate of occurrence of brucellosis has been reduced greatly by quarantine of newly purchased animals, calfhood vaccination, and disposal of infected animals. The more recently developed brucella ring test also has been used successfully in detecting the disease and locating infected herds. Prompt isolation and treatment of infected cattle can then be accomplished. Through intensive attention to cattle health, grade A

Milking operation in a milking parlor.

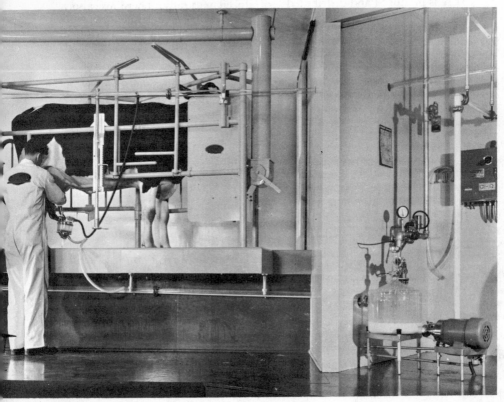

milk now is produced in brucellosis-free areas.

Bovine mastitis is one of the most costly diseases of milk-producing animals. This is an udder infection which frequently is caused by a bacterium not harmful to humans. However, a number of mastitis infections may be caused by staphylococci which are infectious for humans as well as animals. Many methods are used to detect mastitis. But once infection has occurred, irreparable damage may have been done to the udder. Therefore, dairy farmers are encouraged to use the best herd management practices available in order to prevent the onset of infection.

Control of this disease is best accomplished by preventing injury to the cow's udder. Proper use of correctly functioning milking machines eliminates one important cause of udder injury. Conditions that cause the cow to fall, or unclean bedding often lead to the onset of mastitis.

Veterinary treatment usually is necessary for an infected animal. During the infection, milk from the producing animal must be discarded. After the infection has been cured, one or more of the four sections of the udder may be unable to produce milk. Milk production by such a cow becomes too costly and it must be replaced in the herd at considerable financial loss.

Mastitis causes the greatest loss of revenue to the dairy farmer. For this reason, as well as concern for human health, a number of research projects are seeking ways to reduce the rate of occurrence of mastitis in cattle. Personnel involved in caring for cows and milking them must also be free from any disease in a communicable form. This includes carriers of infections who might otherwise appear completely healthy. In fact, a milk producer is obligated to inform the responsible health authority when a disease occurs, or is even suspected, among personnel on the dairy farm. Milk is thus prevented from becoming a means for transfer of disease-producing bacteria to consumers. Also, infection of cattle by certain human infectious agents is prevented.

Hand milking has generally disappeared as milk-producing herds have become larger. And since available farm labor has decreased, mechanical milkers have to be used for economy. Cattle should be fed adequate and proper nutrients so they can maintain health and produce desired quantities of milk. Milk quality also depends on the feed. Although most milk-producing animals require supplementary grain feeding, many successful dairy operations rely mainly on roughages like pasture hay and silage. Pastures should be properly drained of water that could form stagnant ponds and be a source of undesirable bacteria on the cow's coat. Fresh water must be available for the cow to drink.

Pasture should consist of proper grasses and be free from weeds that contribute undesirable flavors to milk—weeds like wild onion or garlic, bitterweed, and swine cress. When cattle eat these weeds unsavory tastes are usually present in the milk, although its nutritional qualities are unaffected. Use of modern weed control chemicals has helped free pasture from many unwanted weeds that lower pasture quality, and milk quality.

CHEMICAL COMPOUNDS have been synthesized that enable the farmer to combat insects and pests effectively. Without these chemicals the quality, as well as quantity, of many feed crops would be lowered markedly. Like many agents used to control undesirable agents, insecticides and pesticides must be used judiciously. Otherwise, they may be transmitted to milk.

Cows are not sprayed with insecticides containing chlorinated hydrocarbons since these chemicals can accumulate in fatty tissues and later appear in milk. Similarly, these insecticides must not be used to control flies around the milking area, where airborne droplets could possibly get into milk.

Contamination of forage crops with chlorinated hydrocarbon pesticides may occur when crops in adjacent fields are treated. To avoid this, spraying is done when air currents will not cause drift.

Efforts have been intensified to control pests by removing breeding places and by better sanitation. Less use of pesticides is needed then, and there is less chance for unwanted chemicals to get into foods.

MACHINES enable milk to be taken from the cow, weighed, and piped to a storage tank without exposure to contamination by dust and insects—formerly serious sanitation problems.

The dairy farmer must use extreme care in cleaning the equipment through which milk passes as it leaves the cow and is taken to storage. Equipment now can be cleaned mechanically without disassembly and reassembly after every milking. That is, equipment is cleaned and sanitized in place (or CIP).

Mechanizing sanitization usually enables equipment to be kept in a more sanitary condition than by hand cleaning. The success of CIP procedures has been made possible by development of many new products. Among them are new detergents, improved chemical sterilizing compounds, highly polished and hard surfaces on metal and glass equipment, and electrical power equipment.

Milk must be stored on the farm until enough is available for economical transportation to the pasteurizing or processing plant. During this period the growth of any contained bacteria must be prevented. Chemicals are not added as preservatives since they may unfavorably alter the milk's nutritive value.

The only practical means for raw milk storage is the use of very low temperatures. After milk is taken from the cow it should be cooled quickly to a temperature of about 38° F. This can be done with refrigerated storage tanks that cool milk quickly and maintain it at low temperature. The tanks are much more effective and sanitary than milk cans.

THE FARM STORAGE TANK has had a notable role in improving milk quality. Until its development and adoption by most market milk-producing areas, milk was stored in cans. The cans were immersed in refrigerated water. It required a long time to remove heat from the milk, and especially in the center of the can. During the extended period the milk was at temperatures above 50° F., bacteria which were present could grow. And it was nearly impossible to cool milk enough to prevent the growth of many bacteria during the storage period.

Since bacteria grow and multiply geometrically—that is, one cell forms two new cells, two form four, four form eight, and so on—uncontrolled bacteria growth can develop a large population in a relatively short period, particularly in a food like milk. Products formed as a result of this growth can cause off-flavors or spoilage.

When milk is kept at a temperature of 38° F. or less, there is little if any multiplication of bacteria during the periods milk is stored on the farm. And difficulties met in keeping cans in a desirable state of cleanliness are avoided—the tank can be cleaned and sanitized easily.

Raw milk is now usually delivered from the farm containing very low numbers of bacteria, and problems of flavor deterioration from bacterial growth have been nearly eliminated.

Milk usually is collected from the producing farm every other day. It is pumped from the farm tank into a tank truck. The driver removes a sample of the milk from the farm tank and takes it in a refrigerated container to the laboratory for analysis. He also inspects the milk to be sure no off odors are present.

During the time milk is in the refrigerated truck it is maintained at a low temperature until delivery to the pasteurizing or processing plant.

ONE OF THE MOST troublesome problems milk producers face is maintaining equipment in a sanitary condition.

If milk residues remain on equipment between milkings, the bacterial count of milk produced subsequently is increased. The residues provide nutrients for growth of bacteria that may survive the cleaning procedure, or that may be deposited on equipment from the air. Dairy fieldmen or sanitarians charged with quality control will not tolerate such a situation.

Cleaning equipment is much easier when surfaces in contact with the milk are smooth and highly polished. Materials most commonly used are stainless steel and resistant glass. Rubber or plastic tubing provide flexibility where needed. For any of the materials the smoothness of milk contact surfaces is essential. No cracks or open seams can be permitted. Care must be taken against scratches, pitting, and denting. During manufacture, sharp corners are avoided and welded joints and seams highly polished. All these precautions facilitate removal of milk solids during cleaning.

DETERGENTS have been formulated that will remove milk solids from equipment with a minimum of physical effort. These detergents cope with the unusual components present in milk solids. Surface active compounds are used to increase contact of the cleaning solution with all surfaces and solids on the equipment.

Chelating compounds suspend metallic ions and prevent their reaction to form salts that would precipitate on the equipment. Compounds for dissolving milk proteins and others for emulsifying milk fat are also incorporated. A desirable dairy detergent contains compounds to perform all these functions.

Some detergents contain a chemical sanitizer that causes bacterial destruction while cleaning. Residues of the detergent-sanitizer on the equipment during storage are toxic to any bacteria that might gain entrance.

Before the next use, equipment is rinsed with a sanitizing solution consisting of a chlorine, iodine, or quaternary ammonium chloride compound.

USE OF MILK as a food for people of all ages has led to the need for strict regulation of the composition and sanitation of milk from the time it is produced until it is consumed.

The need for sanitary regulations was brought out vividly at the beginning of this century when public health investigations linked insanitary milk with infant mortality. At that time much fluid milk was consumed raw. Lack of mechanical refrigeration, and of a workable concept of sanitation, made milk an easy prey to deterioration by bacteria. Furthermore, any contamination of milk by disease-producing bacteria from cows or humans was easily transmitted to the consumer.

Fortunately, public health authorities motivated the development of standards for milk composition and sanitation. Enforcement of these standards has stopped the spread of disease through milk.

The Federal Government has developed a specific interest in the sanitary quality of milk through functions of the Public Health Service (PHS). One of the most valuable contributions from PHS has been development of the recommended Grade "A" Pasteurized Milk Ordinance. This is a guide for milk production, transportation, processing, and delivery. Most agencies involved with milk control have found the recommended ordinance a valuable guide for production of high quality milk, and often adopt it with very few changes.

The U.S. Department of Agriculture also is involved with health-related aspects of the dairy industry through its Division that deals with animal health. This part of the Agricultural Research Service regulates interstate shipments of dairy cattle in an effort to eliminate contagious cattle diseases. Dairy research laboratories of the Department have also contributed information which has led to standards dealing with milk production, processing, and distribution.

The Food and Drug Administration is charged with formulating definitions

65

A mobile milk testing laboratory equipped for bacteriological and chemical examination of milk.

for dairy products, and is involved in surveillance of interstate milk shipments to insure that milk has not been adulterated. = PASTEURIZED

AT THE STATE LEVEL, milk quality control is usually a function of the State department of health or State department of agriculture. The agency collaborates with local governments in initiating and enforcing milk control programs, and may be the main liaison between local governments when problems arise on interstate milk shipments.

State agencies usually develop minimum standards, and local ordinances are somewhat more strict. When a milk supply is not governed by local ordinance the State agency can assume control.

'66! Generally, municipalities or counties have the last say in control of milk supplies.

THERE IS a growing tendency for municipalities to share control of milk supplies used commonly. Thus, inspection of farms and enforcement of regulations may be conducted by the local agency nearest the source of supply, and the more distant government accepts the results of jurisdiction by the other. This has involved close cooperation between governments in developing uniform standards and ordinances. Adoption of the Public Health Service's Milk Ordinance makes uniformity possible.

Local government units are responsible for milk supplies since they can have close surveillance of milk at all stages of its production. And they can quickly correct any malpractices.

Some regulatory agencies have mobile laboratories that go to remote areas to make chemical and microbiological tests of milk. Milk can be tested quickly after it is produced, especially if production methods are of questionable quality. This stimulates producers to do a good job.

MANY FACTORS affect milk quality on the producing farm. Every farm milking operation can't be identical. Personnel and working habits vary greatly.

To attain a more uniform sanitary quality of milk, ordinances specify many details to be followed during production. Sanitarians must file an inspection report to assure the health officer procedures are followed that should result in high quality milk. Following is a brief description of some factors conducive to sanitary milk production.

First of all, the milking barn, stable, or parlor should be planned with easy to clean floors and walls. It should be adequate for the size of herd to be milked. Ventilation minimizes condensates that foul walls and equipment. Since many operations are in hours of darkness, lighting helps maintain cleanliness. The milkroom should be separated from where the milking is done. Here milk is stored in refrigerated tanks, and equipment cleaned. The milkroom must also have hot and cold water and sinks for cleaning utensils.

MILKING IS DONE gently and carefully to protect the milk and the cow's udder, and avoid injury that could lead to mastitis. The udder must be cleaned of dirt first. Cleaning is usually by a sanitization treatment to minimize opportunities for bacteria to enter milk from the exterior of the teats and udder. As the udder is massaged during cleaning and sanitizing, a hormone is activated that causes milk to be "let down" into the cistern and it is obtained more easily from the udder.

A sanitary water supply is needed on the farm to assure proper milking facilities. Waste disposal, which can be a serious problem in rural areas, must not endanger water supplies. Water should be tested periodically for undesirable bacteria.

Regulatory agencies insist on proper cleaning and sanitizing of milking equipment after each use. While a variety of detergents may be used for cleaning, much attention is directed to the sanitizers that are allowed. Since it is difficult to sanitize by heat on the farm, and difficult to monitor, chemical sanitizers are the agents of choice. But of the many chemicals available, relatively few are permitted. The ones chosen must kill bacteria, yet be harmless to humans in residual amounts that might enter milk supplies. These compounds are halogens (chlorine and iodine) and quaternary ammonium compounds.

ATTAINMENT OF QUALITY cannot be relied upon by the sole use of police powers in enforcing regulations. The dairy industry has long recognized the need of educational programs for employees. Courses designed to teach the techniques of different jobs are offered by the industry, and in many States by the State college of agriculture. These short periods of intensive study have been extremely valuable in informing workers of reasons for the numerous regulations required in milk production and handling.

A further service to the dairy farmer is offered by the milk processing plant that employs dairy fieldmen. These men help the milk producer to obtain good milk-producing cows, and assist in pasture and feeding problems, and in many other facets of dairying. Often the fieldmen can prevent continuance of a malpractice that otherwise would lead to loss of cattle or rejection of milk by the processing plant.

MILK SAMPLE testing usually is conducted more frequently by industry laboratories—particularly in the case of larger companies—than by a regulatory agency laboratory. In many areas, dairy farmers have formed cooperatives that pool raw milk from member farms for sale to processing plants. These associations employ their own fieldmen and have laboratories for testing and maintaining the quality of their raw milk supplies.

Usually industry sanitation programs are more stringent than those of the regulatory agency. This is to assure compliance with the strictest regulations, and to use all available measures to maintain milk flavor during production, processing, and delivery.

METHODS USED in laboratory testing of milk are carefully developed, evaluated, and standardized. They are described in minute detail for the analyst. And after adoption by the American Public Health Association, they are compiled in a manual entitled *Standard Methods for the Examination of Dairy Products*. The manual is revised frequently to keep it up to date.

Uniformity of analytical procedures

has done much to develop confidence in the data obtained on milk supplies by different laboratories and personnel. To insure adherence to standard methodology, control laboratories must be approved by Federal and State agencies before they may conduct official testing. For analyses on milk to be upheld in cases involving legal arbitration, samples must be obtained and analyzed in ways stipulated by the *Standard Methods* manual.

VERY LITTLE MILK is sold in a raw state on regular markets; nearly all retail milk is pasteurized. Pasteurization may be accomplished by any one of several legalized heat treatments. They are: 145° F. for 30 minutes; 161° F. for 15 seconds; or any other procedure shown to be as effective as these treatments.

Pasteurization's primary purpose is to destroy any disease-producing organism that might be in the milk. Another purpose is the destruction of bacteria that are able to grow during refrigerated storage. To perform pasteurization properly, special processing plants are constructed for handling milk from many producing farms.

A TREATMENT associated with pasteurization is the homogenization of milk to reduce the size of fat globules. Vitamin D, which humans require, also is added to compensate for deficiency of this vitamin in milk. Currently much milk also is subjected to a vacuum treatment before pasteurization whereby unsavory volatile flavors—originating from grasses, wild onions, and silage eaten by the cow—are removed.

After the milk undergoes these processing treatments, it is packaged and kept refrigerated until delivery to the consumer or purchase from the retail store.

Processing operations are under surveillance by the same regulatory agencies involved in supervising milk production on the farm. As a result of precautions by industry and regulatory agencies, milk on the American market is now practically never involved as the cause of illness. And milk now keeps well during refrigerated storage due to sanitary procedures in production and processing.

While milk in the fluid state is by far the most commonly used by Americans, an increasing volume of milk is being dried.

The dried form can be stored easier and for longer periods when milk fat is removed; milk containing the fat develops flavor problems during storage. Therefore, whole dried milk is not currently available in any volume for consumers who prefer to reconstitute dry milk for use as a beverage.

A NEWER development in processing is the sterilization of milk, so that no refrigeration is needed during distribution and storage. Some objectionable features of sterile milk had to be overcome before the product could be marketed. These were a slightly cooked flavor and formation of a gel structure as a result of the high heat treatment.

Developments in technology and engineering advances have made it possible to sterilize milk—heating at about 280° to 300° F. for about 3 to 4 seconds—without these objectionable characteristics. Appearance of sterile milk on the market will now probably be governed mainly by economic factors.

For further reading:

American Public Health Association, Inc., *Standard Methods for the Examination of Dairy Products,* 11th edition. New York, 1960.

Association of Official Agricultural Chemists, *Official Methods of Analysis of the Association of Official Agricultural Chemists, 10th edition.* Washington, D.C., 1965.

Dahlberg, A. C., Adams, A. S., and Reid, M. E., *Sanitary Milk Control and Its Relation to the Sanitary, Nutritive, and Other Qualities of Milk.* Publication 250, National Academy of Sciences-National Research Council, Washington, D.C., 1953.

Foster, E. M., and others, *Dairy Microbiology.* Prentice-Hall, Inc., Englewood Cliffs, N.J., 1957.

U.S. Department of Health, Education, and Welfare, *Grade "A" Pasteurized Milk Ordinance.* Public Health Service Pub. 229, U.S. Government Printing Office, Washington, D.C., 1965.

DAMAGE BY RODENTS AND OTHER WILDLIFE

WALTER W. DYKSTRA

COMPETITION between man and the animals that share his environment is becoming more intense. It continues to grow as more and more land areas of the country are used for human needs.

Advances in industrial and agricultural technology have brought about changes in land use practices that affect the lives of many kinds of wild creatures, causing some of them to increase in numbers and others to decline.

These wild creatures include approximately 2,500 different native species of vertebrate animals. Their behavior patterns vary greatly, so that selective management practices often can reduce damage by one species without harming other members of animal communities.

Some birds and mammals cause damage to the interests of a few persons or special groups but the damage is often balanced by their positive values to society as a whole.

Many are migratory and spend only a little time at locations where their presence is objectionable. A number are furbearing or game species and others are admired for esthetic reasons.

Because of these beneficial qualities, procedures for combating damage by vertebrate animals must be based on different criteria than control of insects and other pests.

For example, deer browse upon fruit trees and are thus objectionable to orchardists, but their presence in a community is desired by many citizens. Priority is accordingly given nonlethal means for preventing or reducing damage. These include fencing, repellents, and scare devices.

RODENTS CAUSE GREATER economic losses than all other wildlife. They are our most abundant animals and their long incisor teeth are adapted for gnawing on food and fiber. Among the rodents, Norway rats still reign as public enemy number one.

Widely used anticoagulant rodenticides like warfarin are effective for rat

* * *

Walter W. Dykstra is *Research Staff Specialist* for pesticides and control methods, Fish and Wildlife Service, Department of the Interior.

69

control, and damage by rats is less than it was 20 years ago. It could be reduced much more if farmers adopt the practice of placing permanent protected bait stations at strategic locations around farm buildings like granaries and poultry houses.

Periodic placement of anticoagulant treated baits will prevent infestations from developing to serious proportions.

The rats die from internal bleeding after feeding on these baits over a period of several days.

Control is most effective if undertaken before granaries are filled and again just prior to winter weather when many of the rats and mice move indoors.

HOUSE MICE RANK SECOND only to rats in rodent destructiveness. They consume about 10 percent of their weight in food each day. Few creatures are more adept in adjusting to living in close proximity with man, whether on the farm or in an urban home. In stacks of stored food these mice can spend their entire life cycle of a year or more within a 10- or 15-foot radius. They may go for weeks without a drink of water if the food they eat contains a small amount of moisture.

Mice are difficult to control and their annual damage costs the Nation many millions of dollars. While the family cat may catch a few mice, more effective control is achieved through use of anticoagulant bait stations.

ORCHARDISTS can testify that meadow and pine mice have a great fondness for apple trees.

The best defense against these mice is a combination of control methods: Protection of natural predators, close mowing of grass, and the fall application of lethal baits.

Foresters similarly look upon the white-footed deer mouse as a destroyer of tree seeds. Development of effective rodent repellent seed coatings has made it possible to aerially reseed logged and burned-over forest lands

70

without significant loss due to these creatures.

This success story is marred only by the absence of equally effective methods for coping with other damage to forest regeneration by rabbits, porcupines, and larger mammals.

ADAPTABILITY OF WILDLIFE to changes in land use practices is illustrated in Western States where populations of pocket gophers increase tremendously following the introduction of irrigated crops. These burrowing rodents are particularly destructive to alfalfa, root crops, and water retaining structures like irrigation canals.

Development of a mechanical trail builder has greatly aided gopher control. This machine constructs artificial tunnels which are utilized by the gophers, and control is facilitated by an automatic bait-dispensing attachment. Its effectiveness is further enhanced by discovery of a highly lethal and well accepted chemical, DRC 714, for use in bait formulations.

INTRODUCED from South America as a fur mammal, the coypu, or nutria, has become established in aquatic habitats of the Gulf States and a few other localities in this country. In the South the nutria seems to have done as well or better than in its native habitat, and has become a nuisance in sugarcane, rice, and vegetables.

Development of harmful habits often seems to follow successful introduction of exotic animals. The nutria stands as a warning that nonnative species should be allowed into our country only after careful biological studies. Research on control of nutria is underway, and a promising control method is based on its behavior pattern of feeding and resting on objects that extend above the water. Carrot baits fastened on small rafts are readily found by the nutria.

PREDATOR CONTROL in North America dates back to the early settlers who used steel traps and strychnine to destroy wolves that preyed upon their livestock and to capture furbearers. Wolves, mountain lions, and bears were exterminated throughout major portions of their ranges.

SMALLER PREDATORS, including coyotes, foxes, skunks, and bobcats, have adjusted to changes in land use. While rodents, rabbits, birds, and other wildlife still comprise the major portion of their diets, some have acquired a taste for livestock and domestic fowl. Selective control is at times necessary.

In many parts of the country these smaller predators are probably as numerous as a hundred years ago, or more numerous. Their conflict with the interest of man is not limited to predation alone, since they may also spread rabies.

Foxes and skunks have been implicated in a rising number of epidemics in several parts of the country, including Northern States where this dread disease has seldom occurred. Biologists are particularly concerned over the part that may be played by bats in the spread of rabies to predators and through them to domestic animals and to man himself.

THE NEED FOR more selective methods of predator control has long been recognized, and new ways to limit their populations are being sought.

Prospects are good for using stilbestrol and other chemosterilants to inhibit reproduction of coyotes. Chemosterilants are mixed in tallow baits and placed along trails used by coyotes in late winter, just before the breeding season.

This birth-control technique, which has no other side effects on the coyote, does not pose a serious hazard to domestic dogs as the effects are temporary and dogs have two breeding cycles a year whereas coyotes have only one. Also, coyotes usually breed earlier in the year than most wild meat-eating animals. The perishable baits placed for coyotes deteriorate before the spring breeding season of other species and before bird migrations.

Many conservationists are opposed to use of steel traps for capturing predatory animals. A tranquilizer trap-tab has helped to reduce injuries to animals caught in traps and to prevent their escape. The tab consists of a cloth tablet wired to the trap jaw and containing the drug diazepam. Upon capture, the animals usually chew the tab and ingest the drug. They become tranquil in 10 to 30 minutes, and struggling is reduced. The effects may last 1 or 2 days.

STARLINGS ARE ONE of our least loved birds. They were introduced into New York City from Europe about 75 years ago and are now found in practically all parts of the country.

Their damage to cherries causes serious concern to many amateur gardeners and fruitgrowers. Year-round resident populations of starlings are increasing in California, where the birds are a new threat to that State's multimillion-dollar grape crop. During winter months thousands of starlings invade livestock feedlots in many Western and Midwest States, where they consume and contaminate large amounts of feed.

Starlings are being successfully controlled in some localities with decoy traps placed near fruit orchards. These small wire enclosures contain openings at the top that permit the birds to hop in but are too narrow for them to fly out. Food, water, and decoy birds serve as the attractants. If properly placed and operated, the traps can be used to capture many of the summer residents and their young before the damage period.

NUMEROUS STARLINGS were destroyed at western livestock feedlots during the winter of 1964–1965 by the experimental use of a new lethal agent. The chemical, DRC 1339, is highly toxic to starlings, blackbirds, and most other bird species, but has relatively low toxicity to mammals.

Since most songbirds migrate south during winter months, they are not endangered by control operations carried out in Northern States at that time of the year.

Further selectivity is achieved in these operations through the employment of scare devices such as carbide exploders to repel waterfowl from the treatment sites during their nighttime feeding periods.

BLACKBIRDS CAUSE heavy damage to corn and other grain crops. They are an especially acute problem in the Arkansas - Louisiana - Mississippi rice-growing region, where many of the birds gather during the autumn and winter months.

Although farmers have at times killed thousands of blackbirds in these wintering concentrations, legbands indicated few of the killed were responsible for summertime depredations to the rice crop—most were migrants from Northern States and Canadian Provinces.

THESE FINDINGS illustrate the importance of identifying segments of the continental blackbird population that cause damage before instituting control measures.

A decoy trap for blackbirds gives some relief from crop depredations. Scare devices, including carbide exploders, shell crackers, and amplified recordings of distress cries of these birds, likewise help.

While lethal baits are often ineffective and hazardous to desirable wildlife, there are indications that sublethal amounts of some chemicals such as Avitrol 200 can be used to create stress symptoms.

Affected blackbirds lose their muscular coordination and emit distress cries. These actions have a pronounced effect in frightening other birds in the flock away from the treated area.

RESEARCHERS ARE SEEKING substances to limit reproduction of birds as well as mammals.

Since practical use of the substances depends on getting them to the target species without exposure to other wildlife, research must be broadened to include a search for lures and baits. These include synthetic sex attractants or recorded mating calls.

Their discovery will stem in turn from findings in basic research on animal behavior, including animal communication systems and physiological peculiarities.

This research seeks points of vulnerability so measures can be aimed selectively at the target species.

AVOIDING BIRD PROBLEMS is often easier than repelling birds. Methods used include changing planting and harvesting dates, selecting bird-resistant varieties of crops like corn, and growing bird-sensitive crops like milo on land furthest removed from marshlands which are the favorite nesting sites for blackbirds.

Depredations upon small fruits by robins and other songbirds may be lessened by selecting plots away from tree plantings used as nest sites. Screening windows and other openings in farm buildings and using covered feed troughs are helpful in discouraging sparrows, pigeons, and starlings.

Since predation is one of nature's ways for limiting animal populations, the protection of hawks, owls, foxes, skunks, and snakes also indirectly serves to limit the overall numbers of objectionable rodents and birds.

FARM PONDS have become part of our rural landscape. Properly managed, they can produce several hundred pounds of game fish per acre each year. This type of farming is one of the most promising sources of high-protein foods for many of the underdeveloped nations.

Fishery biologists often meet three problems in management of farm ponds. They are excessive aquatic weeds, an overabundance of small fish, and unwanted species of fish.

Weeds can be destroyed with herbicides like dalapon which have a good margin of safety for most aquatic life. In the past, fish control has usually been accomplished through use of rotenone formulations. Now an antibiotic product of Streptomyces is being developed that is highly toxic to fish at levels of a few parts per billion, nontoxic to most food organisms, and readily broken down so it is harmless within a few hours after application.

EFFECTS OF A pesticidal treatment may extend beyond the pest species and harm many additional kinds of animal life in the environment. This is most likely to occur with several of the widely used broad-spectrum persistent pesticidal chemicals, like aldrin, endrin, DDT, dieldrin, and heptachlor.

Residues of several chlorinated hydrocarbon insecticides, including DDT, are found in virtually all animals analyzed by the Fish and Wildlife Service during recent years. Among these are specimens from remote areas—penguins and seals collected in the Antarctic, and vegetation, duck eggs, and ducklings from near the Arctic Circle. The presence of these residues in areas far removed from known treatment sites suggests that they may be transported in many ways, including particles of dust carried by air currents and through soil erosion.

SOME SPECIES OF FISH and wildlife are highly sensitive to pesticides. For example, 0.5 of one part DDT per billion parts of water proved toxic to shrimp after 72 hours. As a general rule, crustaceans, mollusks, and fish are the most sensitive, followed in the order of decreasing sensitivity by amphibians, reptiles, birds, and mammals.

Pesticide residue levels not considered dangerous to man may be well above the levels tolerated by sensitive species of fish and wildlife. Some may concentrate as they pass through organisms in food chains to lethal amounts at the end of the food chain, in animals like fish-eating birds.

In other situations, levels of only a few parts per million may adversely affect reproduction of fish and birds. If the residues of these pesticides

increase in the environment, they may deplete or exterminate some of the more sensitive species of animal life. Recognition of the danger from environmental contamination by persistent pesticides has led Federal agencies to reduce use of these chemicals in pest control programs and to expand the search for better control methods.

About 95 percent of all pesticides are applied by private, non-Federal users on farms and in forests, gardens, and homes. Users of these materials are urged to:

• Turn to chemicals for pest control only after carefully considering their use in terms of the need, anticipated results, and possible harmful effects;
• Use only chemicals registered for a particular pest and carefully follow instructions on the label;
• Make safety rather than cost the primary consideration in selecting materials and methods;
• Limit pesticide treatments to target areas and avoid contaminating lakes, streams, ponds, and other fish and wildlife habitats;
• Use the most selective chemicals at minimum dosage rates; and
• Avoid large-scale use of persistent pesticides known to concentrate in living organisms.

For further reading:
President's Science Advisory Committee, *Use of Pesticides*. U.S. Government Printing Office, Washington, D.C., 1963.
U.S. Department of Agriculture, *Warm Water Ponds for Fishing*. Farmers' Bulletin 2210, 1965.
U.S. Department of the Interior, *Anticoagulant Rodenticides for Control of Rats and Mice*. Wildlife Leaflet 402, 1959.
——— *Bird Control Devices—Sources of Supply*. Wildlife Leaflet 409, 1964.
——— *Characteristics of Common Rodenticides*. Wildlife Leaflet 337, 1959.
——— *The Decoy Trap for Blackbirds and Starlings*. 1964.
——— *The Effects of Pesticides on Fish and Wildlife: 1964 Research Findings of the Fish and Wildlife Service*. Circular 226, 1965.
——— *Manufacturers of Chemical Animal Repellents*. Wildlife Leaflet 464, 1964.
——— *Manufacturers or Importers of Rodenticides and Accessories*. Wildlife Leaflet 465, 1964.
——— *Rats—Let's Get Rid of Them*. Circular 22, 1953.

C. G. McWHORTER and J. T. HOLSTUN, Jr.

SCIENCE

AGAINST

WEEDS

C. G. McWhorter conducts weed science research for the U.S. Department of Agriculture, in cooperation with the Mississippi Agricultural Experiment Station, at Stoneville, Miss.

J. T. Holstun, Jr., is *Investigations Leader*, Weed Investigations—Agronomic Crops, Agricultural Research Service, Beltsville, Md.

WEEDS are as old as agriculture itself. From his earliest existence man has had to contend with these undesirable plants.

They are one of the most serious threats to our food supplies.

Weeds are persistent, unwanted, and often prolific. They reduce yields, increase cost and labor, and generally interfere with agricultural operations.

Yet man has trouble even defining weeds. Emerson's definition of a weed, "a plant, the virtues of which have not yet been discovered," falls short. For example, we know the virtues of bermudagrass as a forage crop in pastures, but it is also an obnoxious weed in many row crops. The Cherokee rose, despite its beauty, is a serious pasture weed. Volunteer barley plants are weeds in spring wheat.

Perhaps the best definition of a weed is, "a plant growing where it is not wanted."

NO PART OF man's food supply is immune to the adverse effects of weeds. Production of food from marine life, wild animals, domestic animals, field crops, vegetable crops, wild plants, and all other sources is significantly affected at one or more points by weeds.

In the United States more than $2.5 billion is spent annually to hold down losses from weeds.

Populations of the United States and the world are increasing rapidly. Much of our best agricultural land and water resources are being diverted to other purposes than food production. At the same time the proportion of food producers to the population is diminishing.

Consequently, food for more people must be provided by fewer producers from less land.

So it becomes increasingly necessary to minimize the interfering effects of weeds and other factors that limit crop production.

Weeds can adversely affect our food supply in many ways. These hazards are not of equal importance, however, and two facets are economically more important than all of the others combined. These primary hazards are:

• Competition between weeds and crops for minerals, water, light, and essential gases. Weeds, through competition, decrease yields and lower the quality of food from crop plants. They are poor substitutes for good forage plants in pastures and ranges. Fertilizer and irrigation water applied to feed crop plants is stolen by the weeds, thus increasing costs. Labor used to control weeds increases production costs. .Losses through this competition can be prevented only by early removal of weeds.

• Interference of weeds with crop harvesting. Harvesting machinery may be broken or damaged by large tough weeds. Bulky weed growth often increases crop losses during harvesting. Presence of weed trash in the harvested crop lowers the quality of the product as food. Its removal increases harvesting costs.

SOLUTION OF these primary problems would also solve many secondary problems. The minor or secondary problems, while not as extensive as the major problems, may be even more serious when they do occur.

Among the secondary problems are poisonous weeds that contaminate food supplies when intermixed with crops. For instance, flour made of wheat containing cockle is poisonous to man. This threat is not directly serious since poisonous plants are removed from human food during processing. Poisonous plants like halogeton, tall larkspur, poison darnel, pokeweed, and many others cause significant losses of meat animals and poultry, however.

Many weeds harbor disease organisms and insects that attack desirable crop plants. Onion thrips often live in ragweed and mustards before attacking an onion crop.

Curly top disease may be transmitted to sugarbeets by insects that live on weeds in grazing and wastelands. Cabbage maggots and aphids may live in wild mustards and later attack turnip, radish, cauliflower, and cabbage crops. Wild carrots often provide a habitat for the carrot weevil and carrot rust fly before these insects attack cultivated carrots. Many insects survive the winter months in weedy areas.

Large volumes of weeds interfere with fungicide and insecticide applications and may increase pesticide requirements.

AQUATIC WEEDS threaten our food supplies more seriously than is often recognized.

Weeds in irrigation canals seriously impede waterflow. In reservoirs they increase water loss through transpiration. Sudden blooming of some species of algae often kill fish by creating imbalances of dissolved gases in the water, or by producing substances toxic to fish, livestock, and humans.

Aquatic weeds seriously reduce the growth of more desirable plant species that provide food for fish. Weed growth in the ocean, streams, and lakes has prevented harvesting of marine food in some localities.

Weeds are even detrimental to our food supply from wildlife at times. Often natural vegetation or revegetation of cleared areas provides poor protection and food for wild animals and birds.

Substitution of selected plants like seed-producing grasses, lespedeza, berries, and others for natural weeds in open noncrop areas and along rights-of-way often increases both food and cover for wildlife.

PLANTS INTRODUCED by man are some of the worst pests in this country. Many continents have contributed to the weeds in the United States. Since their introduction was determined primarily by movement of people, Europe's contribution to our weeds is proportional to Europe's great contribution to our human population. .

As Americans moved westward, they carried along undesirable alien weeds. Common plantain, a weed introduced from Europe, was called "white man's foot" by the American Indian, since it closely followed the advance of civilization.

Writings of John Josselyn in 1672 record no less than 40 European weeds that had "sprung up since the English planted and kept cattle in New England." Of 200 important weeds listed in the U.S. Department of Agriculture Yearbook of 1895, a total of 108 were of foreign origin. A report in 1940 showed 526 alien weeds in California. Of these, 72 percent were from Europe and western Asia; 10 percent from eastern Asia, South Africa, and Australia; 10 percent from South America; and only 8 percent from States east of California.

WHEN OUR EARLIER pioneers settled in new homes and commenced crop production to supply food and fiber, the essential element in the battle against weeds was brute force. With civilization's advance in America, fingers and sharpened sticks were replaced with a hoe. In some row crops, the hoe was supplemented with the cultivator and plow. These are still essential

Scuba diving and underwater photography are used in research at Davis, Calif., on control of aquatic weeds in irrigation canals and farm ponds.

elements in production of many crops.

Other early control methods were mowing, flooding, cropping, smothering, pasturing, and burning.

Crop rotation was recognized more than a half century ago as a valuable supplement to plowing for control of weeds. It is still important.

WORK HAS BEEN conducted for several decades on biological control of weeds with insects and plant diseases. Complete eradication by the biological method is practically impossible, but an equilibrium may be reached in which the weed is no longer an economic pest.

The most outstanding example of biological control is cactus or prickly pear in Australia. Scientists were fortunate to find insects that attack only prickly pear.

The moth borer was most effective because it tunneled through practically all portions of the plant. Within a few years after the release of these insects, prickly pear was practically destroyed.

Other weeds that are effectively controlled biologically are thorny shrub and St. Johnswort.

Thorny shrub in the Hawaiian Islands is controlled by several types of moths and by a fly.

St. Johnswort in the Western United States is being controlled by leaf-eating beetles and a gall fly. Whole valleys of infested land in California have been returned to economic production. Within a few years, this weed will be greatly reduced in many other areas.

EVEN WITH THE MANY cultural, mechanical, and biological control measures at his disposal, man continued to suffer serious economic losses because of weeds. The need for better protection became urgent. Because of this, the use of chemicals for weed control has developed rapidly since 1944. Weedkilling chemicals are called herbicides.

The use of chemicals to control

weeds has a long history, but more has been learned about this science in the last two decades than in the entire previous history of mankind. Herbicides have had a tremendous impact on crop production, and have revolutionized not only weed control, but many cultural and mechanical operations as well.

Common salt was used as a herbicide centuries ago. At the beginning of the 20th century, investigators in Europe and the United States were studying sulfuric acid, carbolic acid, iron sulfate, copper sulfate, and other salts for the control of weeds.

In the 1930's, French workers discovered the selective herbicidal properties of yellow dye compounds of the dinitro cresol group.

That important discovery demonstrated the feasibility of chemically removing certain weeds without causing serious damage to crop plants. We call this selective action.

CHEMICAL CONTROL METHODS were not generally accepted until the late 1940's. Groundwork for this acceptance was laid by a number of researchers in the United States and England.

Following a report on 2,4-dichlorophenoxyacetic acid (2,4-D) synthesis by R. Pokorny in 1941, P. W. Zimmerman and A. E. Hitchcock found 2,4-D to be a growth substance. Paul C. Marth and J. W. Mitchell established the selectivity of 2,4-D by removing plantain, dandelion, and other broadleaf weeds from bluegrass lawns. This work in 1944 was followed closely by work of C. L. Hamner and H. B. Tukey who successfully used 2,4-D to control weeds in field crops.

During the same period English workers concentrated similar efforts on 2-methyl-4-chlorophenoxyacetic acid (MCPA).

THESE COMBINED discoveries had far-reaching effects in weed control. By 1949, producers used 2,4-D to control weeds on more than 20 million acres of small grains and corn in the United States. Rapid utilization of the selec-

tive weed control principle provided impetus for chemical industries throughout the world to synthesize and evaluate thousands of chemicals for weedkilling properties.

GROWTH OF THE HERBICIDE industry has been very rapid.

Commercial production of over 100 organic herbicides in the United States in 1964 totaled more than 260 million pounds. More than 36 million pounds of herbicides were exported from the United States in 1964. Most of this industrial development has occurred since 1945.

From 1959 to 1964, the value of herbicide exports from the United States increased from slightly over $6 million to more than $25 million. In 1964 herbicides comprised a little more than 29 percent of the total organic pesticide production in the United States. In all probability the use of herbicides will continue to increase in the future.

Herbicide usage in the United States is increasing rapidly. Herbicides were applied to an estimated 53 million acres of the Nation's croplands in 1959. In 1962, over 70 million acres were treated.

More than 70 percent of the summer grain crop in West Germany and nearly all the grain crops in the United Kingdom are treated with herbicides annually.

DISCOVERY AND DEVELOPMENT of new herbicides is expensive, and often frustrating. Development of a new herbicide may follow many pathways, but this process is started by a proven need to control a specific weed or weeds in a specific crop situation. This is known as market analysis.

Industry starts by synthesizing minute quantities of hundreds or possibly thousands of compounds. These are evaluated to determine their biological activity, including weedkilling properties.

A few score of the more promising compounds are synthesized in larger amounts and subjected to a more thorough secondary biological evaluation that may show the potential selective nature of the herbicides.

An essential part of biological evaluation of active herbicides is determination of degree of toxicity to animals and humans.

Compounds showing necessary margins of plant selectivity are studied further and preliminary studies conducted on potential consumer cost.

Of the original thousands of compounds, three or four are selected for further research.

Large samples are then synthesized, possibly up to a hundred pounds, for extensive field evaluation.

UNTIL THIS TIME, all research has probably been conducted only by researchers employed by the commercial organizations. Now experimental herbicide samples are supplied to interested U.S. Department of Agriculture and State agricultural scientists throughout the country.

During this period of intensive testing, considerable data are accumulated to assure proper use for weed control and to protect the public in the event the product will be sold commercially.

Treated plants grown under a variety of environmental conditions are thoroughly examined for herbicide residues. After critical examination of data, one or two of the original chemicals may be registered for experimental sales.

The first-year sales are often to the farmer on an experimental basis under a USDA-approved experimental label. The experimental label requires that use of the product be restricted to crops not grown for food or feed unless the data show that such a restriction is not necessary. Commercial, State, and Federal scientists intensify analytical studies looking for herbicide residues left on plants, in plant products, and in the soil. Studies on toxicity are continued.

If the herbicide passes short-term toxicity tests, more exacting studies are started. These determine longtime effects and usually last for a minimum of 90 days. A full series of tests may run continuously for several years during which the material is placed in the test animals' eyes, beneath the skin, on the surface of the skin, and is fed daily to the animals.

If the herbicide passes these exacting tests and residues in feed or food exist, the Food and Drug Administration (FDA) is petitioned for chemical residue tolerances.

If the use of a herbicide does not result in any residue, it may be registered on a "no-residue" basis. This means that no amount of the herbicide in food or feed products is permissible.

Tolerance is the amount of chemical allowable in a crop product. All chemicals to be applied to food and feed crops must be approved by the Agriculture Department, and tolerances are used in preparing the specific instructions for use on the label of the herbicide.

The legal residue tolerances established by FDA cannot be exceeded. Food containing the herbicides in excess of the maximum tolerance may be removed from the public market and condemned.

The Agriculture Department is petitioned for registration of a pesticide label.

If the label is obtained, the company is ready to manufacture and offer the product to the public. This involves constructing full-scale manufacturing facilities, selecting packaging and labeling practices, and determining wholesale and retail price structures.

Usage recommendations, sales literature, and other forms of advertising are prepared and market studies are undertaken.

Market studies and consumer analyses continue on a yearly basis.

HERBICIDES are placed on the market only after much research to insure that the product will be effective for the intended purpose, and that the use will cause no harm to man, desirable plants, or animals. Some idea of the extent of this research can be obtained from looking at the costs for developing a typical herbicide for use on a food crop.

Estimates of this cost are:

Item	Cost
Synthesis and initial evaluation	$100,000
Patent	10,000
Field evaluation	500,000
Pilot plant production	75,000
Analytical techniques	150,000
Residue studies	800,000
Toxicological studies	100,000
Formulation and packaging studies	150,000
Registration, miscellaneous	150,000
Total cost	$2,035,000

THE TOTAL does not include the cost incurred by State and Federal extension, research, and regulatory agencies. This additional cost by public service agencies varies between $250,000 and $500,000.

A herbicide often costs over $2 million before the first package is sold. In determining the overall cost, the manufacturer must consider the developmental cost, continuing manufacturing cost, packaging, shipping, and advertising. Cost of herbicide development varies, but this will be less than $1 million only if no stumbling blocks are encountered. Development of some pesticides has cost more than $3 million including contributions of industrial, State, and Federal scientists. In the end these costs are paid by people who buy and use pesticides, people who buy products produced through the use of pesticides, and by people who pay taxes.

The most costly single item in herbicide development is residue studies.

All herbicides eventually reach the soil even if not applied directly to soil.

When a chemical is applied to weeds, rainfall washes it from plant surfaces onto the soil or else treated leaves fall to the soil. This herbicide may affect the purity of soil or water, so herbicide residue studies are carried on continuously by State, Federal, and private research organizations. This research begins well before the first experimental label is granted and usually continues so long as the herbicide itself continues to be used.

Soils vary greatly in composition and reactivity. Complex and ever-changing processes occur continuously. This is to be expected since soils are composed of mineral matter, living and dead organic matter, water, and air. This mixture has pore spaces of many sizes. These are filled with water and air which contain living microorganisms. The complexity and variation of the soil system makes the study of herbicide residue complicated, expensive, and time consuming.

Weed scientists are vitally interested in the following problems associated with soil residues: Movement by leaching or volatilization; retention of active or inactive forms; chemical reaction between herbicides and different soil components; and the rate and nature of herbicidal breakdown, whether chemical, biological, or physical.

Considerable progress has been made on residues, but much more information is needed.

Weed researchers want to know more about persistence or carryover of herbicides under different environmental conditions so they can establish safe rotational practices. They especially want information on components of the soil affecting activity so dosage requirements of soil-applied herbicides can be more accurately predicted. This is needed in order that herbicides may be recommended at the lowest possible rate.

Eventually, the method and rate of herbicide application may be based on weather forecasts and chemical analysis of soil samples from farmers' fields.

PARALLEL TO RESIDUE WORK, research is often conducted on the metabolism of herbicides in plants.

Metabolism studies cover changes in herbicides and the effect of these on plant growth and development. The studies help scientists better understand selective action and insure safety to man and animals. This additional knowledge leads to methods by which selectivity may be increased, resulting in increased weed control and reduced injury to crops.

It is important to know what new chemicals are created when a herbicide is applied to plants, and to determine the cause and significance of selectivity. Chemical control of weeds hinges on the property of the given herbicide to affect only a given weed or group of weeds.

Selectivity—the basis where a chemical formulation leaves the crop unharmed but kills weeds—is often accomplished through the way the herbicide is metabolized.

AN EXAMPLE OF A SELECTIVE herbicide is 4-(2,4-dichlorophenoxy) butyric acid (2,4-DB) which is effective in controlling cocklebur and some other annual broadleaf weeds in certain legumes. Spray applications of 2,4-DB applied to these legumes infested with broadleaf weeds will provide effective weed control with little crop injury. Weeds effectively convert herbicidally inactive 2,4-DB to active 2,4-D, but legumes are relatively inefficient in this conversion.

Another highly selective herbicide is 3',4'-dichloropropionanilide (propanil) which is effective against annual grasses in ricefields. This chemical does not injure rice, but is highly effective in killing weeds after they have emerged. One application of propanil has increased yields in nontilled rice to over 5,000 pounds of rough rice an acre. The average gain from one propanil treatment approximates 1,800 pounds an acre.

FOLIAGE-APPLIED HERBICIDES like 2,2-dichloropropionic acid (dalapon) and 2,4-D enter the plant through the leaf surface. This entry is a complicated process, and is currently under intensive investigation.

After entry, many herbicides move to other parts of the plant. Translocation of a chemical throughout the entire plant may occur within 1 hour.

This is most rapid under conditions favoring fast growth. Cold or dry weather along with other unfavorable growing conditions decrease herbicide translocation.

Translocation distributes a herbicide throughout many portions of a weed, but usually concentrates the chemical in the most actively growing parts. In these areas, the chemical may disrupt weed growth.

Dalapon interferes with the formation of pantothenic acid, one of the B vitamins essential for plant development. Some herbicides interfere with the formation of the amino acids which are the building blocks of proteins. Others prevent weeds from producing or using glucose, sucrose, or more complicated carbohydrates.

Herbicidal effectiveness depends upon proper application. Low rates of herbicides are generally used, so special equipment is needed to provide uniform coverage. This is not always easy because of the wide diversity of herbicide formulations.

Herbicides are formulated as wettable powders, granular materials, emulsions, and solutions. Any of these may be applied as a spot treatment, broadcast, in bands, or directed to a specific part of the plant.

Water or oil is used when herbicides are formulated as solutions, wettable powders, or emulsions.

Granular materials are applied with special mechanical spreaders like those used for broadcasting crop seed at planting. Sometimes these materials are spread by hand.

Spraying is the most common method of herbicide application. Extremely small amounts can be applied uniformly in a spray since dilution can be sufficient to provide uniform coverage.

Sprays can be accurately directed underneath growing crop plants. This keeps most of the herbicide off the plant. Calibration and rate control is considerably easier with spray machines than with granular applicators.

Farmers spend millions of dollars annually for hose, nozzles, nozzle tips, tanks, pressure gages and regulators, valves, and pumps.

Granular formulations have distinct advantages for some purposes, and their use has increased in recent years. Water is not needed, and this is an advantage in some operations.

Granules being applied to the soil tend to fall through the leaves of crops before they are absorbed by the plant. This, of course, minimizes injury to the crop.

Processing a herbicide and having the means to apply it meet only partially the requirements of efficient usage in modern farm production. Actual use must be worked into an overall farm program. The optimum date and rate of herbicide application depends on the crop stage, the stage of the weed, weather conditions, and on other factors.

Often a number of herbicides are used during a single crop season.

Sensible use of herbicides in farm production reduces the amount of hand labor and lowers the cost of production. This results in a more economical product for the consumer. The use of herbicides in cotton reduces the cost of weed control $10 to $15 an acre. It may reduce labor requirements for weed control up to 60 percent.

Controlling weeds chemically in oats, barley, wheat, and rangelands has increased productivity approximately 20 percent. Quality may also increase proportionally to higher productivity.

Eradication of brush and poisonous weeds in pastures and grazing lands increases productivity through increases in yield and improved quality in milk and meat.

Controlling weeds in horticultural crops like strawberries often reduces hand weeding costs more than $100 an acre. Hand labor for removing weeds from many vegetable crops, sugarcane, sugarbeets, soybeans, and corn is no longer available at costs farmers can afford. In these situations herbicides are irreplaceable.

Herbicides, as currently used, protect rather than endanger our food sup-

A spoonful of 25 percent fenuron pellets, thrown from horseback, will kill a medium sized mesquite bush. This demonstration was at Las Cruces, N. Mex.

plies. Effective protection of food supplies against weeds would be of little value if the herbicidal treatments adversely affected food quality and purity. This point is well recognized and jointly supported by public service research agencies, the herbicide-producing industries, and the State and Federal regulatory agencies. Their safety record in the use of herbicides is good.

Herbicides, when used according to instructions on the label, have never caused a reported injury or death of any person through contamination of food (as of July 1, 1965). No safety system, however, is infallible. For this reason, research on herbicides and monitoring of residues continues. Registered uses have been and will continue to be canceled or modified whenever

81

additional data indicate that such action is required. Also, registrations can be canceled if the original purpose for the registration ceases to be of importance.

Safety of herbicides to wildlife, livestock, and fish has been almost equally impressive. A few occurrences of injury and death of animals, birds, and fish have been reported. Even these, for the most part, resulted from accidental deviations from label instructions, negligence in safeguarding stored herbicides, improper disposal of unused herbicides, or purely unavoidable accidents. In all probability more valuable animals have been killed by a single species of poisonous weeds than have died as a result of all mishaps with herbicides.

Our greatest difficulty with herbicides has been occasional injury to crop plants. Injury to nontreated crops has resulted from residues in the soil, and from drift. Direct treatments to control weeds in specific crops have also injured crop plants. Continuing research to avoid these injuries is absolutely essential.

THIS RECORD OF SAFETY is in part the result of the extensive research conducted by Federal, State, and industrial agencies before the herbicides were approved by the U.S. Department of Agriculture for use.

Every label has been carefully worded to insure safe and effective use of herbicides. The label is reviewed in detail by the Agriculture Department, the Interior Department, and the Department of Health, Education, and Welfare.

Herbicide users are constantly urged to read and abide by regulations on the label down to the last exacting detail. Not only should directions be followed closely, but particular attention should be paid all special warnings and cautions.

When directions say, "Use one pound/acre," use one pound—not more or less! Likewise, if the label says, "Do not apply after seedhead formation," it means exactly that!

SINCE THE EARLY DAYS of the agricultural chemical industry, the Federal Government has considerably broadened the scope of legal requirements regarding residues. In addition, most States have enacted legislation on the use of pesticides.

The Federal Insecticide, Fungicide and Rodenticide Act of 1947 (expanded in 1959) is the basic pesticide law.

This protects the public from mislabeling and also protects users from personal injury or economic loss by prohibiting adulteration.

INITIALLY, consumer protection against pesticides in food supplies was provided for in the Federal Food, Drug, and Cosmetic Act of 1938. Under this act, tolerances were granted only to chemicals essential to production and storage of crops, and the Federal Government was required to prove that material in the food was poisonous before it restricted continued use of the material.

The consumer was provided with additional protection in 1954 by the Miller amendment to the Food, Drug, and Cosmetic Act.

This amendment transferred the burden of providing research to establish tolerances from the Federal Government to the pesticide producer. In addition, pesticide manufacturers must now develop analytical methods for determining residues on specific crops.

CULTURAL, biological, and chemical control of weeds is essential to continued abundant food supplies. Development of weed control practices requires cooperative efforts of many research disciplines. Major efforts are required from the fields of organic chemistry, biochemistry, plant physiology, agronomy, horticulture, aquatic biology, ecology, agricultural engineering, analytical chemistry, microbiology, soil science, biometrics, and animal physiology. And efforts in most of these disciplines are necessary for the development of each new weed control measure.

WEATHER

AND FOOD

LAWRENCE C. RANIERE

Lawrence C. Raniere is *Agricultural Weather Services Coordinator*, Office of User Affairs, Environmental Science Services Administration (ESSA), Department of Commerce. The Weather Bureau is now a part of ESSA.

A GRICULTURAL technology has contributed significantly to improving our Nation's food production, but climate limits the agricultural capacity of any country. Nearly every element in planning, producing, shipping, and marketing food products is directly or indirectly linked to the vagaries of weather.

Although American agriculture is blessed with a normally favorable climate, the proper use of meteorological information in all phases of the food industry results in great savings. These savings initially benefit the food producer but ultimately they mean lower or more stable food prices to the consumer, as well as better quality food.

WEATHER'S IMPORTANCE in food production hinges upon the dependency of all life on its surrounding environment. The very survival of life on earth is closely governed by the state of the atmosphere or "ocean of air" in which we live. Plants and animals must continually adjust to climatic changes or perish. A vast variety of plant and animal species have evolved and perished since life began.

In history there are innumerable accounts of the rise and fall of civilizations, and of mass migrations, influenced by climatic change or catastrophic weather. In many cases these influences resulted from the effects of weather on agriculture.

An example is the mass migration of Irish to the United States during the middle of the 19th century. This resulted from a weather-induced potato fungus disease epidemic which created a famine in Ireland. More recently, adverse or limiting weather conditions

83

contributed to grain shortages in Russia and China which could have important political effects.

IN ADDITION to natural species variation and climatic change through the ages, there have been continual man-made alterations resulting in the domestication of plants and animals and the modification of local environments.

Man's endeavor to domesticate or "train" plants and animals for his own advantage has progressed steadily. One of the major objectives in developing new commercial varieties or strains of plants and animals is breeding for weather resistance.

Through natural selection, screening, and other breeding techniques, scientists have developed frost resistant strawberries, winter hardy wheat, drought resistant corn, low chill requirement peaches, heat tolerant livestock, and many more weather resistant food products. Today, a challenge to plant breeders is the quest for crop varieties resistant to air pollution.

These applied genetic advances and comparable ones in all phases of agricultural research have contributed significantly to improving food products and increasing total yields in recent years. But tremendous food losses still are brought about by hail, wind, rain, drought, and freeze. Other losses from erosion, insects, and diseases are also highly influenced by the weather.

PRECIPITATION IS the most common and far-reaching weather element that affects our food production. A good supply of soil moisture from adequate winter snow and rainfall, combined with well-distributed rains throughout the growing season, generally results in higher U.S. crop yields. Prolonged snowmelt in the mountainous regions of the West, where normal rainfall is low, helps supply water to the western cattle and livestock industry during the warm months.

Poor distribution of rainfall or complete absence of rain over a considerable period results in drought.

Prolonged droughts in the West may cause complete loss of crops or forced sale of livestock as a result of drastically reduced water tables. Similar losses sometimes occur east of the Mississippi. But more common results of unusually dry weather in the normally moist Eastern States are sharp reductions in yield, or increased costs as a result of having to irrigate.

Excessive precipitation or rapid snowmelt results in erosion and flooding which often cause great food losses in the spring and early summer throughout the country. Locally heavy showers which are common during the summer, and later hurricane rains threatening the Eastern States, may aid food producers by furnishing necessary soil moisture. On the other hand they commonly are the cause of serious crop damage, particularly during the harvesting season.

ONE OF THE MOST dreaded agricultural weather hazards is hail.

Extreme southern areas of Texas, Florida, and the entire west coast are the only regions of the United States which ordinarily do not experience hail. The rest of the country may have hail 1 to 8 days a year, depending on location.

The greatest frequency is in the central Great Plains and Intermountain region of the West, where many areas average 4 or more days with hail a year. Most of the Eastern States have hail less than 2 days annually.

Serious hail losses in the food industry may occur any time during the growing season, but the most critical and vulnerable period for damage is just before and during harvest.

TEMPERATURE RUNS a close second to precipitation as the most important weather variable affecting our food production. Abnormal temperature readings are "normal" throughout most of the United States, particularly in the Midwest and Great Plains where frequent and sharp air mass changes commonly occur.

Unusually low temperatures may

84

cause crop and livestock losses. Freeze injury or losses caused by rapid cooling of the earth immediately surrounding growing crops commonly occurs during the spring and fall. In extreme southern areas like Florida, California, and the Lower Rio Grande Valley of Texas, citrus and other crops are vulnerable to these radiational freezes called "winter frosts."

In contrast to radiation freeze, advective or transported freezes are caused by subfreezing weather associated with the southward movement of cold polar air masses. Severe cold outbreaks, in combination with blizzard producing high winds and snow, wreak havoc on the livestock industry and on fruit crops in many sections. Most freezes are a combination of radiation and advective cooling.

Susceptibility of food products to freeze losses depends on location, type and variety of produce, and stage of growth or development. Striking contrasts in losses occur in local areas where susceptibility factors differ. This has led to the elimination of the "killing frost" terminology in the Weather Bureau's statistics.

SOME COMMODITIES are sensitive to chilling temperatures that are above freezing, at certain stages of development and after harvest. Beginning with seed germination and seedling development, normal growth of many annual and perennial food plants fails if low temperatures prevail for extended periods.

Corn, for instance, cannot be grown in areas where the mean summer temperature is less than 66° F. Several warm climate fruits and vegetables like bananas, tomatoes, and peppers will not tolerate long exposure to low temperature, particularly after harvest.

Yet chilling is a vital requirement for normal growth and preservation of a number of crops. Several cereal crops must be planted before the end of winter in order to develop successfully within a year of the time of sowing.

Some fruit crops have similar requirements. Peach trees will not break dormancy normally unless exposed to minimum chilling conditions. Some commercial apple varieties must spend a minimum number of hours below certain critical temperatures if they are to remain free of a postharvest rot known as "scald."

Besides these "direct" chilling sensitivities, a number of food plants have a variable requirement for rhythmic fluctuations in temperature known as thermoperiodicity. Tomato plants will not set fruit abundantly unless warm days are accompanied by relatively cool nights during blossoming.

HIGH TEMPERATURE may limit plant and animal food production as well as storage.

The direct effects of high temperatures on food plants include stem lesions, heat cankers, and sunscald damage. Sunscald in fruit trees commonly occurs during the winter or early spring months when a temperature differential up to 50° F. may exist between shaded and unshaded sides of tree trunks.

Excessively high temperature may kill or debilitate some vegetables as a result of direct burning, water-loss stresses, or excessive respiration primarily after harvest.

Milk and egg production are curtailed by high summer temperatures, particularly in Southern States. Special facilities for ventilating chicken coops and barns are necessary on farms in most regions of the country if maximum production is to be realized. This is true also with swine; shade, overhead sprinklers, or air-conditioned quarters are commonly provided.

WIND CAN HAVE an adverse effect on food production. Direct damage due to high winds occurs frequently. The most common losses are from severe local storms. Vulnerable field crops like corn, wheat, and tobacco may be flattened, or developing tree fruits blown to the ground by strong winds which are a product of thunderstorms in the warm months throughout most of the country.

85

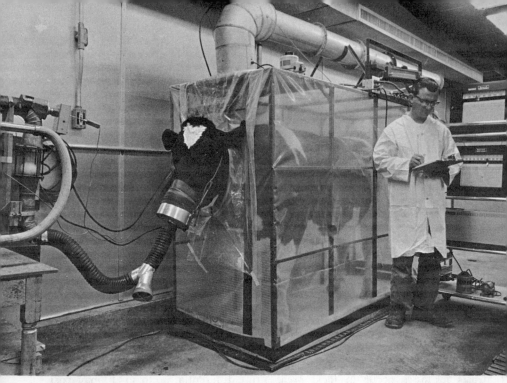

A Holstein cow in a "sweat tent" at Beltsville, Md., as part of a study to find how to produce milk more efficiently in hot climates. Physiologist Albert J. Guidry checks the composition of air breathed by the cow and surrounding her body when she sweats. Researchers are studying panting and sweating, two ways a cow beats the heat.

During spring and summer, less common but far more destructive winds accompany tornadoes that develop primarily in the Midwest but also in Southern and North Central States. Tornadoes may uproot trees, overturn vehicles, and completely destroy farm structures.

Occasional losses occur from winds due to changing air masses in the spring. Although direct food losses from these seasonal winds are generally minor, some spring crops like asparagus are particularly sensitive to blowing soil. Irregular, twisted spear growth from "sandblasting" seriously reduces the quality of marketable asparagus.

Tropical storms which may reach hurricane proportions commonly affect the Southern and Eastern States during the late summer and fall. High wind and driving rain over widespread areas in the path of a tropical storm cause considerable losses to many fruit and vegetable crops that are approaching harvest.

DURING WINTER, cold temperatures are often accentuated by high winds which introduce a chill factor.

Much of the livestock losses that are associated with winter cold waves would be avoided if the animals were not exposed to strong winds in combination with low temperature and precipitation.

Water loss in growing crops is intensified by high wind. Therefore, prolonged windiness with little or no precipitation during critical periods of the growing season may reduce the yield of food crops.

Some wind, however, is believed favorable to crop production by allowing more light to penetrate the foliage and increasing the carbon dioxide content of the air needed for photosynthesis.

THE MOST IMPORTANT prerequisite for all life on earth and the driving mechanism of our weather is solar energy, and yet the sun is the environmental factor taken most for granted by man.

There is good reason for this paradox. Although plants and animals are sensitive in many ways to the duration, intensity, and quality of sunlight, seasonal fluctuations of this vital environmental ingredient are so reliable that life has adapted to seasonally recurring changes.

Short-term erratic variability in sunlight which is caused by weather conditions has only a limited effect on normal life activities at any given location. Very small fluctuations in sun energy reaching the earth due to sunspots are not known to have any effect. It is only when man attempts to alter seasonal biological events that light becomes an important limiting factor in food production.

Culture of food plants in greenhouses often requires supplemental lighting with incandescent and fluorescent lamps. This lighting augments the total hours or intensity of natural sunlight for economical production of greenhouse vegetable crops like tomatoes and peppers during the late fall and the winter.

THE FACTORS ALREADY discussed are the most common and significant atmospheric elements that affect our food industry. But a number of other adverse effects also are due to weather conditions.

Lightning damage, though localized and of minor importance, is more common than suspected by many producers. Individual fruit and nut trees may be extensively damaged by lightning. Vegetable and field crops may show characteristic dying (necrosis) in small radiating field patterns.

Recent work by agricultural scientists has revealed evidence that shortened supplies of carbon dioxide, vital in photosynthesis, commonly occur in rapidly developing corn plantings. When major growth factors are otherwise favorable and air movement through a developing crop is very small, reduced amounts of carbon dioxide from poor circulation may become a growth-limiting factor.

POPULATION, INDUSTRIAL, and transportation growth in the United States has brought into sharp focus the problem of air pollution. Smog-producing dust particles and gases that are byproducts of our society are being released continually into the air where they are dispersed by wind and atmospheric turbulence. Fortunately, our atmosphere efficiently dilutes them over most of the country most of the time.

During isolated episodes of atmospheric stability, however, the health and welfare of the general public and the animal industry may be threatened by high levels of air pollutants. The typical weather pattern involves stable, stagnant, high pressure air masses. They occur most commonly in the fall over many Midwestern and Eastern States, and throughout much of the year in southern California where topographical features and population density accentuate the problem.

Plant life is generally vulnerable to much lower levels and greater varieties of air pollutants than animals or humans. Some plant species can't survive in industrial metropolitan areas. As a result of extreme sensitivity, a number of food plants develop symptoms of leaf stippling, silvering, banding, flecking, or general decline when exposed to low levels—a few parts per billion—of certain air contaminants. Alfalfa, oats, table beets, spinach, endive, celery, and Swiss chard are among the most seriously affected food crops.

SULFUR DIOXIDE, ozone, carbon monoxide, oxides of nitrogen, hydrocarbons, aldehydes, and organic acids are generally the most common and widespread injurious air contaminants. Automotive combustion produces a good share of these pollutants.

Gaseous chlorides, fluorides, bromides, and other industrial byproducts may cause damage within localized areas but they account for only a small percentage of the plant losses from air pollution.

SINCE THE ATOMIC AGE began in the mid-1940's there has been concern over the effects of radioactivity on life. The immediate impact of a nuclear explosion on adjacent life has been well documented. But controlled testing from time to time raises many pressing questions over the long-term effect of radioactive fallout.

Air, plant, animal, and soil surveys conducted in the United States have shown perceptible increases in radioactivity following nuclear testing in other regions of the Northern Hemisphere.

High level wind and seasonal precipitation patterns combine to produce significant increases in radioactive fallout during the spring season in the midlatitudes. Until now, however, it has not been possible to detect even minor effects of radioactivity on our overall food production.

COMMERCIAL PESTICIDES are another source of air pollution of great concern in recent years. Although they are generally more localized than radioactive fallout in their effect, a wide variety of noxious chemicals from pesticide use has been detected in various food products.

Modern farming practices require extensive use of chemicals to promote growth and protect produce from insects, diseases, nematodes, and weeds. Pesticide application immediately before harvest and aerial "drift" of pesticides to other crops in neighboring fields may lead to chemical residue problems.

Livestock occasionally ingest and store quantities of pesticides as a result of eating contaminated feed.

Runoff-producing rains may compound the problem by contaminating water supplies.

Along with proper timing and recommended dosages, an assessment of weather conditions during pesticide application helps greatly to minimize harmful side effects of these chemicals.

Atmospheric factors influencing our food industry have been discussed, thus far, in terms of their specific, direct effects. But combinations of two or more factors may occur simultaneously or in sequence. Complex multiple effects, difficult to assess, often result.

Long-term, chronic declines of plants and animals, for example, are sometimes due to a complex of conditions.

PLANTS AND ANIMALS grown for food do not exist in a vacuum. They live in interrelated biologic communities, or ecosystems, encompassing many life forms. Under natural conditions plants and animals living together constitute the so-called "balance of nature." A third and essential element in this relationship is the physical environment.

Weather and atmospheric conditions affect individual plants or animals within biologic communities in different ways. Pernicious insects, diseases, nematodes, and weeds may be favored by environmental conditions at the expense of crops or livestock. Weather in this manner exerts an indirect but significant effect on food production.

Rainfall and atmospheric humidity favor the development of most fungus diseases, as well as the growth of weeds. Temperature governs the survival of nearly all food pests and is often a good predictor of insect emergence, nematode activity, and disease development. Wind and rain commonly serve as vehicles for the spread of insects, fungus spores, bacteria, and weed seed.

AGRIBUSINESS DECISIONS and operations are most sensitive to atmospheric conditions during the planning and producing phases. Temperature, humidity, and other environmental factors can be controlled in shipping and marketing, although serious losses related to these factors continually occur during food storage and transit.

Food producers every year are faced with planning decisions concerning what to produce, when and where to begin production, when to harvest, and where to market. For agribusiness planning more than a month in advance, climatological records based on 30 or more years of past weather conditions are an indispensable tool for decisionmaking.

Standard tables of local normals, extremes, and risk probabilities for key weather elements are readily available from the Weather Bureau. Extensive food losses can be avoided every year if production and related operations are properly planned and geared to local climatic conditions.

Studies based on climatological information have shown that plant growth is approximately proportional to the amount of heat or temperature accumulated above some threshold temperature, such as 43° F., which roughly corresponds to the minimum temperature for growth. Such heat sums are called "growing degree days" or "growth units."

THE TOTAL NUMBER of growing degree days required for maturity varies with crop variety as well as with the species of plant. Climatological studies have established that the various pea varieties, for example, require a range from about 1,200 to 1,800 growing degree days. This method of reckoning the time of maturity has been applied by the canning industry, since the planting dates of peas and other field crops can be scheduled to maintain an orderly supply for processing.

This heat unit system is helpful in selecting crop varieties appropriate to different farming areas. It also has been used in scheduling spraying and harvesting work in fruit orchards. Since insect emergence and development likewise respond to temperature, heat sums have been used to predict epidemic outbreaks of insects.

AFTER CAREFULLY PLANNING the what, when, and where of production with the aid of climatology, a food producer makes use of various techniques for manipulating or modifying the local environment, or microclimate, to minimize weather stresses which often cause reduced quality and yields.

A farmer actually begins to alter the microclimate that will surround his crops when he first prepares a seeding or planting bed in the soil.

Periodic cultivation during crop development may favorably modify the atmospheric conditions immediately surrounding growing plants. On the other hand, crop cultivation often intensifies the adverse effects of drought or of frost.

Irrigation to increase crop yields is a major means of modifying local moisture and temperature effects. Besides supplementing natural precipitation, overhead sprinklers have been used successfully for frost control.

WIND OR AIR MOVEMENT near the ground is often modified.

Wind machines are used in some regions under temperature inversion conditions to mix the cold surface air in fruit and vegetable crops with warmer air aloft to prevent local freeze damage. Citrus fruit producers in Florida and California are the most frequent users of wind generators, although these devices are becoming more popular on other crops throughout the country.

To reduce high winds, barriers of tree rows, high growing hedges or even strips of grain crops are commonly used, particularly in the Midwest and Great Plains. Windbreaks serve effectively to reduce evaporation, curtail soil erosion, and shelter livestock.

The microclimate can also be modified with fogging and heating devices like smudge pots to suppress frost; shielding and shading materials to reduce sunlight and also to prevent cooling and freeze injury; and plastic covers, mulches, and inert powders to conserve soil moisture or warmth.

Lake and ground water evaporation is effectively suppressed by certain alcohols. But since the surface films produced by those materials are readily dissipated by wind, their use is often too costly.

IN RECENT YEARS attempts have been made to modify weather on a more grandiose scale.

Cloud seeding with salt or silver iodide crystals has had some limited, localized success under atmospheric conditions highly conducive to natural rainfall. Practical problems and limitations make this practice of questionable value for anything but research.

Similar results have been obtained in cloud-seeding efforts to suppress hail and, on a larger scale, to alter the course and intensity of tropical storms. These efforts show some promise for the future, but the legal and ethical problems of widespread weather modification are staggering, even on a purely local scale.

HOW MUCH WEATHER information can be profitably applied to protection of our food supply depends largely on four interrelated things:

• The extent of crop or livestock response to weather factors and knowledge of these bioclimatic relations.

• Climatic probability of occurrence of influential weather elements, and the ability of the meteorologist to predict their occurrence.

• Existence of two-way communications facilities by which specific weather forecasts and allied information can be requested and effectively distributed to food producers and to related business interests.

• The producer's capability to act upon alternative decisions, based on available weather information, which result in economic gain.

IN COOPERATION with the U.S. Department of Agriculture and universities throughout the country, the Weather Bureau has increased its service to agriculture to better meet the food producer's needs for meteorological information.

The Weekly Weather and Crop Bulletin and other climatological services are provided. Agricultural Service Offices have been established in several States, usually in cooperation with the principal agricultural research experiment station in the area. Specially trained agricultural meteorologists work closely with agricultural research personnel in determining plant-weather relationships.

Knowledge of these relationships leads to improved agricultural practices. These in turn increase production and may lower costs.

THIS JOINT research effort sometimes involves existing data or sophisticated instrumentation for small-scale weather studies in the crop environment. If required, other observation stations may be established in agricultural areas to supplement existing Weather Bureau networks.

The Weather Bureau works closely with the State-Federal Extension Service and research personnel. This work involves issuance of advisories for farming operations based on extended forecasts and the climatology of the area, and the feedback from farmers of needed weather data.

THE AGRICULTURAL weather forecast is usually obtained from the local Weather Bureau office. Forecasters with agricultural training or background issue the day-to-day forecasts and advisories which give warning about severe weather conditions.

Weather information must be delivered to the users with an absolute minimum of delay.

A teletypewriter system provides high-speed, instantaneous delivery of forecasts to mass news disseminators like radio, television, and newspapers. This fast-working cooperation with news media is an integral part of any specialized weather service program.

THE FOOD PRODUCER plans his activities to take advantage of favorable weather periods and to minimize the results of unfavorable weather. The agricultural weather forecast aids in this planning by giving a reasonable estimate of specific weather factors anticipated during the following 36 to 48 hours.

Weather outlooks for more extended

periods, perhaps utilizing more climatology than standard forecast procedures, help farmers in their long-term decisions.

The specialized agricultural forecasts emphasize the probable occurrence of weather elements that crops of the area are most sensitive to. They are devised to help in solving operational problems.

Sometimes food producers need more highly personalized weather services that apply only to a specific location or commodity. These special requirements are met by private weather forecast firms.

SPECIALIZED METEOROLOGICAL services provided by the Weather Bureau for food producers include forecasts and warnings of frost and freeze threats, planting and harvesting dates, insect and disease problems, crop spraying conditions, livestock weather, shipping conditions, and irrigation advisories.

In most cases these forecasts must be tailored to particular crops. At present it is possible to forecast asparagus, pea, corn, and peach harvest dates with sufficient accuracy and leadtime to permit producers to schedule their work crews and control labor costs more closely.

Procedures based in part on past and current weather can estimate the relative population and emergence dates of the Japanese beetle, hessian fly, corn flea beetle, and cotton boll weevil.

Needless spraying to control weather-sensitive plant diseases—like potato and tomato late blight, lima bean downy mildew, Cercospora leaf spot of peanut, and apple scab—can be avoided through use of disease outbreak forecasts which are issued jointly by meteorologists and by agricultural extension specialists.

Crop irrigation advisories are based on soil moisture forecasts.

As FURTHER KNOWLEDGE is obtained on crop and livestock weather relations through joint research efforts between meteorologists and agricultural scientists, many more practical applications

of basic facts in the form of operational forecasts will be possible.

Work is continually in progress to improve basic meteorological services that will bolster several specialized weather service programs including agriculture.

Weather Bureau researchers in extended forecasting are striving toward acceptable 2-week forecasts and seasonal outlooks in the future. Short-range forecasts are being greatly improved by better interpretation and application of radar observations.

Expansion of existing observational and rain gage networks will permit more accurate presentations of local weather conditions and forecasts. Development of air pollution forecasts for food production purposes may be necessary in some areas.

Most meteorologists believe the current limitations in weather services are due mainly to gaps in communication and in user interpretation of available weather information. By improving rapid communication capabilities and by stepping up user education efforts, existing forecast services can become immeasurably more useful to the food industry of the nation.

GREAT STRIDES have been made over recent years in agricultural science technology, resulting in phenomenal increases in production and improved quality of food products. Yet weather, with complex environment-technology interactions, remains an important limiting factor in any agribusiness enterprise.

The Weather Bureau is continually strengthening its support services to the American food industry, drawing on all the resources of modern science.

For further reading:
Smith, L. P., *Weather and Food*. Freedom from Hunger Campaign, Basic Study No. 1, World Meteorological Organization, Geneva, Switzerland, 1962.
U.S. Department of Commerce, *A Nationwide Agricultural Weather Service*. 1965.
Waggoner, P. E., "Agricultural Meteorology." *Meteorological Monographs*, Vol. 6, No. 28, American Meteorological Society, Boston, 1965.

KETCHUP FOR A SMALL BOY:

THE MARKETING MARVEL

KERMIT BIRD

OUR tale ends with a small boy pouring ketchup on his hotdog. It begins with a group of farmers in various parts of the country. In the main it's a story greater than our space program. It's our far-flung food marketing system in operation.

Like ketchup itself, there are many ingredients. But let's start at the beginning. . . .

A TRUCK FARMER in California opens the floodgate that diverts water into his field of ripening tomatoes. This is the final watering of his crop and, as he waits, he looks over the vine-covered field. He estimates his yield this year will be 18 to 20 tons per acre.

In another western valley a second farmer cultivates his garlic.

Across the country a Michigan farmer threads his tractor between trees in his apple orchard. He looks back over his shoulder and watches the fine mist rising from his sprayer. Will he be able to prevent insect damage that may lower the grade of his apples?

Also, in the Midwest, an Ohio farmer distributes baskets between the rows in his tomato field. He has hired a crew of migrant workers, and they will start picking tomatoes in the morning. He makes a mental note to tell his wife to make five gallons of iced tea for the crew. He knows tomato picking is hot work, and the workers certainly will appreciate a cool drink.

A farmer in southern Louisiana prepares his field of sugarcane for harvest. Rainfall has been plentiful and the cane grew tall. As he chews on a succulent piece of stalk, savoring its sweetness, he wonders who·will use the sugar from his crop. . . .

AN ONION FARMER in California receives payment for his onion crop. As he walks down the street to settle his fertilizer account, his thoughts take him back to the planting of the onion seed 4 months earlier. Other California farmers are busy raising red peppers and paprika.

A West Virginian drives his farm

*   *   *

Kermit Bird is an *Agricultural Economist* in the Marketing Economics Division, Economic Research Service.

truck onto the scale of the local paper-mill. He has been using his slack season time to cut pulpwood from the farm woodlot. As he gets a nod from the weighmaster, he wonders about the end use of the paper from this load of wood.

Another pulpmill, this one in Georgia, has just finished making huge rolls of heavy brown paper. They now are on their way to a nearby boxmaking factory.

All of these events took place during the summer.

Earlier in the year, other farmers around the world were growing products that will end up as ingredients in an American food.

Black pepper from southeast Asia and spices from equally distant parts of the world now are on ships heading across the seas toward U.S. ports.

NONFARM INGREDIENTS, too, are part of our story.

Crystal white salt comes from a deep mine in Texas.

A bottle manufacturer in New York renews his contract for sand. This day he is pleased because he just got word a ketchup company accepted his bid for several million bottles.

A tin plate rolling mill in Pennsylvania ships rolls of thin steel sheet to New Jersey. There, a metal product fabricating company will use the sheets to make bottle caps.

An Indiana company manufactures glue from the byproducts of a nearby livestock slaughter plant.

OTHER ACTIVITIES play important roles in our story.

Railroad crews ready their cars and tracks. Truck company mechanics repair equipment and order replacement parts. A Mississippi barge fleet operator cleans his barges for hauling sugar.

Telephone and telegraph companies put up new lines and maintain present ones. Some companies install short-wave radio equipment.

Many firms order coal, fuel oil, and gas.

A company in Michigan orders lumber for pallets and bulk boxes.

Maintenance men in an Ohio ketchup plant scour shiny kettles, test boilers, clean out storage areas, and do many other routine chores.

Sanitation engineers of the plant inspect every piece of ketchup equipment and fill out their reports on cleanliness.

Officials of the ketchup company study their charts and estimate next year's demand for ketchup. They coordinate the forthcoming operation.

Several months later the tomatoes harvested in Ohio, the tomato paste and onions from California, vinegar from Michigan apples, sugar from Louisiana, garlic from the West, paper labels from West Virginia, shipping cartons from Georgia, salt from Texas, pepper and spices from the Orient, bottles from New York, caps from New Jersey, and glue from Indiana merge in the Ohio food processing plant.

All these food ingredients, containers, and supplies will be used to create a bottle of ketchup.

THE FOLLOWING SPRING a small boy in the city pours ketchup on his hotdog. He finds nothing unusual about this. Like most small boys, he knows little about farmers, food marketing, or processing.

His only interest at the moment is enjoying what he eats.

He assumes it his natural right to have all the ketchup he wants, and when he wants it.

He would feel mistreated if the bottle became empty before he had liberally sprinkled his french fries.

He has never heard of fork-trucks, pallets, flame-peelers, or sugar barges. He could care less about tie-in promotions, fermentation, or refrigerated railroad cars—common trade terms in processing and marketing the thing of the moment he does care about, the ketchup itself.

FARMERS, PROCESSORS, and marketing people who take part in supplying ketchup ingredients, containers, and associated services have little in common with the small boy. Yet many of them are interested in him. He and the other ketchup consumers are the source of their income.

Let's follow the various farm products going into ketchup—from the time they leave their fields until they arrive at the ketchup plant.

Then, let's trace one fictional bottle of ketchup on its travels to the small boy's hotdog and french fries. By trailing this bottle we gain a clearer idea of how our food marketing system works.

BUT FIRST OF ALL, let's take an overall look at the agricultural marketing system itself.

Ketchup is only one of about 33,000 different grocery products manufactured and sold in the United States.

The average supermarket handles some 7,000 to 8,000 items. The foods we buy there are safe and nutritious. And like the small boy with his ketchup, Americans take their wholesomeness for granted.

OUR 200 MILLION Americans buy their food regularly. So few breakdowns occur in the marketing system that no person ever goes long without food—if he has money to pay for it.

We have an abundance of foods available, and a wide variety as well. A wondrous assortment of quality, size, brand, and type of package is ours to command. Every day of the year each of us can have well-balanced, delicious meals from a variety of foods.

FOOD MARKETING is a large industry. In the United States almost 5 million people handle and process about a billion pounds of food daily.

The bill for marketing our farm foods is around $48 billion a year. Although not exactly the same figure, it may be compared with the "national income" of $25 billion originating in the construction industry, and the $12 billion from motor vehicle manufacturing.

Our foods weave their way through the marketing system almost as if by magic. Yet they are not handed to us

ready made. Nor, as we shall see, is there anything magical about the planning, the risks, and the hard work that make our system operate so smoothly. Produced in different areas of the country, each food comes to market in the approximate quantity which is needed.

THE LOGISTICS of farm marketing challenge the imagination.

For comparison, during World War II a maximum of 12.3 million persons were in our armed services. That they were adequately fed is regarded as a great achievement. This "marketing" was done in a rigidly controlled system, with lots of effort to see that the right foods, in the right amounts, went to the right place, at the right time.

But metropolitan New York City alone contains a similar size group— about 11.5 million persons. No single organization orders and distributes these foods. Yet, every day, year after year, New Yorkers have their food needs met.

Commodities arrive on schedule, and move through repackers and wholesalers to thousands of retail stores, restaurants, and other away-from-home eating places.

FOODS TRAVEL long distances in a steady flow. Oranges and other citrus products come from Florida and California. Maine and Idaho supply whole trainloads of potatoes. Refrigerator cars and trucks loaded with sides of beef arrive from Kansas and Nebraska. Iowa ships pork. Milk rolls in from upstate New York.

Cheese comes from Wisconsin, and Minnesota sends butter. Virginia provides peanut butter, and North Carolina, sweetpotatoes. Washington ships apples, and Massachusetts, cranberries. Wheat for bread comes from an Oklahoma elevator. Carloads of soup come from New Jersey.

ALTHOUGH MANY of these foods are fresh, steps have been taken to maintain their quality or even improve them. Most have been washed or cleaned. Almost all were inspected, sized, and graded. Quality is continuously checked.

Foods not arriving in fresh form have been processed in many ways. As with fresh foods, workers check the quality many times.

Both fresh and processed foods become more valuable as the many services are added to them on their way from farm to home.

Now let's return to the farmers who supply ingredients for the bottle of ketchup.

Let's follow the products of their farms as they move through the marketing system network.

When the tomatoes ripened in the California sunshine, the farmer rented a recently developed tomato-picking machine. An intricate, expensive piece of equipment, it replaces many itiner-ant laborers who formerly performed this backbreaking work. After the machine picks the tomatoes, the farmer loads them and hauls them to a weigh station.

The previous winter the farmer and the tomato processing company signed a contract for the tomatoes. They agreed to a certain price per ton for U.S. No. 1 tomatoes, a lower price for No. 2's, and nothing for culls.

A TRAINED INSPECTOR, jointly employed by the Federal-State Inspection Service, samples each load and grades the tomatoes by their size, color, and quality. After weighing, the tomatoes go on to the processing plant. In this plant the tomatoes are made into a paste that becomes one ingredient in the ketchup.

At the plant unloading dock, workers

After washing, tomatoes at factory are given close inspection. This is the first of several preparatory stages in tomato ketchup processing.

unload the tomatoes onto endless conveyor belts that take them into the plant.

All the tomatoes are processed except the poor ones that should not have been picked.

Sprayers wash them. Electric-eye machines sort out the defective ones. Trained workers inspect the rest and eliminate the poor ones the electric eyes missed.

One machine chops them into a pulp. Workers cook the pulp and strain out the skins and seeds.

They extract some of the water so the moisture content drops from 94 to 74 percent. Removal of water lowers transportation costs of the tomatoes and puts them in a less perishable form and easier to handle.

WORKERS STORE the paste in 10,000-gallon tanks. When a tank becomes full, nitrogen gas is pumped into the tank and its pressure pushes the tomato paste out into an especially designed tank car. Nitrogen is used because it does not oxidize the tomato paste and affect its quality, as air would.

When filled, the tank car starts on its 5-day trip to Ohio. During transit, rail inspectors maintain the paste temperature within the car to keep its quality at a high level.

At the ketchup plant, pumps unload the tank car and the paste is held for the ketchup making process.

Our other tomatoes—those grown in Ohio—are picked in ⅝-bushel baskets. These tomatoes are inspected, as were the western ones, but they are shipped in fresh form to the nearby ketchup factory. Here they are washed, inspected, and the poor ones removed. After being chopped into fine pieces, their skins and seeds are removed. All through the process the tomatoes are handled carefully to retain the bright red color, the ripe tomato flavor, and the vitamins. They, too, are used for ketchup and are the most important ingredient. The whole ketchup making process is geared to their ripening.

OUR LOUISIANA SUGARCANE, harvested by huge machines, is field-loaded onto large hauling vehicles. Giant tires keep the machines from sinking into the soft soil. A steady stream of the haulers

Harvesting sugarcane on the Warren Harang farm in Thibodaux, La.

After harvesting, cane is left in windrows. Later the trash is burned, and the stalks loaded on a wagon as in this Louisiana scene. The stalks are then hauled to the mill.

makes quick work of the harvesting operation.

At the sugar mill, machines wash the cane and press out the juice. Raw sugar is the end product of this mill and in this brown sticky form it goes to the sugar processing plant in the city. At the refinery the raw sugar goes through many steps and ends up as sparkling white crystals. A pneumatic tube funnels the free-flowing sugar into 100-pound multiwall paper bags. These are then stored.

Later, when the order comes in from the ketchup company, conveyors carry the sugar sacks onto barges waiting on the refinery bayou.

Each of the barges holds hundreds of tons of sugar.

A SMALL TUG pushes these leviathans of the inland waterways out to an assembly point on the river. There, the sugar-loaded barges join other barges loaded with coal, oil, sulfur, and cotton.

A giant tug pushes a tow of these barges up the Mississippi on the 1,000-mile trip to Ohio. During the trip the sugar needs no heat or refrigeration since it is relatively nonperishable.

Two weeks later, at the tomato processing plant on the upper reaches of the Ohio, conveyors unload the sugar, and it is trucked to the ketchup processing plant.

There, the sugar is stored clean and wholesome until it is needed for making ketchup.

THE WESTERN FARMER who produces garlic for our ketchup also harvests his crop by machine. A digger lifts the pungent bulbs out of the soil and loads them onto a rubber-tired farm wagon.

At the garlic drying plant, a Federal-State inspector grades and inspects the bulbs. Garlic bulbs are separated into garlic cloves. Workers peel and inspect them for quality. Then they are sliced and dehydrated. Part of the dried garlic is ground into powder. After passing another quality control inspection, the dehydrated garlic is packed into 55-gallon containers that are air and moisture tight.

97

LOADED ON CARS, the drums of garlic powder start their trek east to market. In Ohio, quality control men draw samples of the garlic and examine them for purity and pungency.

Garlic grows in but few areas of the United States and farmers produce only about 40 million pounds annually. Powdered garlic is a minor but important flavoring ingredient in many prepared and processed foods.

OUR MICHIGAN FARMER uses local labor to pick his apples. The pickers put the apples in pockets of aprons tied around their waists, and then dump the fruit into large boxes. The farmer hauls them from his orchard to the processing plant.

These boxes, holding about 1,500 pounds each, were made in a Michigan lumber mill. A machine dumps the apples into a water flume without damaging them.

At the processing plant, machines wash, size, and sort the apples.

Some go through another machine that peels, cores, and cooks them. Some go to an applesauce line and are canned. Others are sliced for pies and frozen or canned. Those going to a cooker may end up as apple butter.

OUR APPLES are the peels, cores, and offgrades. Some are undersized, nicked, damaged by hail, or offcolor.

After they're pulped, the juice is pressed from them. The resulting amber-colored apple juice then is fermented twice.

Sugar in the juice is first changed to alcohol. Then, the alcohol goes through generators that convert it to acetic acid. This acid is the basic ingredient of vinegar and is responsible for the distinctive flavor. At the end of the process the vinegar is pasteurized to stop fermentation. Automatic sensors control the vinegar temperature and acidity.

WHEN the ketchup manufacturer placed his order for cider vinegar, the apple processor called the railroad and asked to have a rail tank car on the company siding so he could pump vinegar into it. In the morning of the following day, the car arrived at the Ohio ketchup plant.

WE LEFT our onion farmer on his way to cash his onion crop check. His field had yielded 23 tons per acre, which is better than average for the area.

Now the farmer can pay some of his bills for seed, fertilizer, insecticides, and for equipment.

But what happened to the onions? He harvested them a week earlier with a machine that dug, topped, and loaded them onto bulk-bed trucks.

Hydraulic lifts unloaded the onions at the dehydration plant where they were inspected, graded, and sized. After being stored and cured for a few days, they are again sized and graded with the culls discarded. Onions under 2 inches in diameter are sold on the fresh market and the rest are processed.

OUR ONIONS must be dehydrated. First they are peeled by a flame-peeler which is in reality a furnace fired to 2,000° F. It burns off the paper shell and hair roots.

After the charred skins are removed by high pressure washing, workers reinspect the onions.

Whirling high-speed knives cut ⅛-inch slices that are spread on a continuous, stainless steel belt.

Hot air, blown through this moving perforated belt, dries the onion slices to 4-percent moisture.

The dried onions are stored in 55-gallon fiberboard drums that have foil-laminated linings designed to keep out moisture and to assure cleanliness.

THE KETCHUP COMPANY specified the type, size, and pungency of the dried onions wanted. When the onion powder arrived at the Ohio plant, it was stored in a low-humidity, temperature-controlled room. Although onions are only about 2 percent of the weight of the final ketchup product, they are responsible for much of the characteristic ketchup flavor.

Farmers producing the paprika and red peppers had similar tasks harvesting their crops. Handling, drying, and transportation was like that for the garlic and onions.

Our West Virginia farmer's logs were made into pulp. By chemical treatment the company derived a high grade of paper.

It ships this paper to another company that prints labels—which later are used on ketchup bottles.

A Georgia pulp plant made heavy, durable, brown paper. Rolls of this paper were then sent to a nearby box-making factory. There, three layers of brown paper are glued together to form endless ribbons of corrugated fiberboard.

The fiberboard moves on to another machine that cuts off sheets of this board—just the right size for cartons. Dividers, made of the same material, will separate the bottles within the ketchup case.

Huge stacks of the unassembled cartons and the divider sheets are bound by thin steel straps into large bundles and shipped to a bottle plant in New York.

Weeks later, the New York bottle company workers assemble the cartons—using Indiana glue to seal the bottoms. A machine fills the cartons with the empty ketchup bottles to be shipped to Ohio.

Thus, these cartons are used for shipping empty bottles to the ketchup plant, and then for shipping the filled bottles. They may even get a third use in the retail stores if the checkout boys use them for packing groceries for the customers.

As the last carload of empty bottles leaves his plant, the manager muses about the various foods packed in glass. He has read in a trade magazine that glass containers are used for over 400 million cases of foods annually.

Ketchup, chili sauce, fruit juices, vegetable oils, and vinegar are of particular interest to him, for his factory specializes in making bottles for these foods.

Now let's visit the ketchup plant. During the harvest season this one tomato processing plant packs 100,000 bottles of ketchup daily. Even with this output it serves only a part of the

Onions are unloaded at the plant.

Nation's ketchup needs—the Eastern Seaboard.

The company has several plants which produce ketchup elsewhere in the country.

Other companies have similar processing operations, and 200 or more factories supply the Nation's ketchup needs.

In total, these companies produce about 40 million cases of ketchup annually.

After a year of getting ready, complete supplies are now either assembled and ready for making ketchup, or they are on their way to the plant.

Ketchup preparation, mixing, and cooking is done in batches in large kettles.

As the recipe takes form, chefs measure each ingredient.

Too much or too little of any of the various items would change the taste, color, texture, thickness, or keeping quality.

The chefs carefully guard their special recipe.

Stainless steel pipes carry the tomato paste to the ketchup kettles. Fresh pulp from ground-up tomatoes are brought in by other pipes.

Still other pipelines bring in cider vinegar. Dried onions are stirred into the mixture.

The sparkling sugar from Louisiana and the white salt from Texas become a part of the now steaming mixture.

WORKERS bring in carefully measured amounts of the garlic, paprika, red pepper, and black pepper from the spice rooms.

During ketchup cooking, quality control technicians keep sampling and testing the product for color, purity, taste, acidity, and consistency.

White-frocked college girls perform some of the tests. These girls major in chemistry during the winter, and spend their summers in laboratories learning how to use their knowledge in a practical way.

THE FINISHED KETCHUP flows to filling machines.

Not all ketchup is bottled. Some is put in No. 10 cans that are used by restaurants and institutions.

Our ketchup goes to a bottle-filling machine that coordinates the flow of ketchup bottles, labels, and caps. Both bottles and caps have been carefully cleaned.

Row after row of these busy machines fill the thousands of incoming empty bottles.

When filled and capped, the bottles move on belts like red, white-hatted penguins to where they are cooled and labeled. Conveyors move them to the case-filling operation. Here, other machines place them in cases and close and seal the tops.

Conveyors move some of the cases to rail cars or trucks. Other cases go into storage.

Our particular case goes to a large storage room in a nearby building. The following spring it is loaded on a van truck.

We follow that case as it goes through the marketing system.

THE TRACTOR-TRAILER carrying our case is on the Pennsylvania Turnpike on its way to New York City.

Loaded with 800 cases of ketchup, this truck has a payload of 10 tons.

In New York the truck arrives at a warehouse owned by one of the local chains.

Fork-trucks make short work of unloading the palleted cases. A pallet is a wooden frame about 4 feet square. Loaded with packages, the whole unit may be lifted and moved about by fork-trucks.

This warehouse serves all the chain's retail stores with their dry groceries. Other warehouses of the chain stock and distribute perishable foods.

AFTER SEVERAL WEEKS of storage, a fork-truck transfers our pallet of ketchup cases onto a truck owned by the grocery chain.

This truck, loaded with dry groceries only, has a twice-weekly route to each store it services. It leaves the warehouse at 1 a.m.

100

Next to our pallet of ketchup there are cases of canned meat and behind it, evaporated milk. On the one side, there is gelatin dessert and on the other side, cake mix.

On this chilly spring morning the truck is partially unloaded at a neighborhood supermarket. There, in a backroom of the store, our case of ketchup is again stored.

THE STORE MANAGER prides himself on his store's high volume record—over $3 million.

Last year his store was in the "top five" in the contest his company has for its 213 stores. He earned a trip to Bermuda for himself and his wife.

He is knowledgeable and knows, for example, that grocery stores in the United States have sales of over $53 billion annually.

A "PROFILE" showed that about half of his customers are under 35 years of age.

Forty-four percent of the housewives shop for families of four or more persons.

He knows his customers are economical shoppers and like price specials. So now he plans this week's special around hotdogs, rolls, and ketchup.

Clerks make final preparation for the forthcoming sales promotion.

Our pallet of ketchup cases is towed to the front of the store on a dolly-jack.

There, in the middle of an aisle, the half-opened cases of red ketchup bottles are stacked.

Wrapped around this pile are banners proclaiming national hotdog week. An eye-catching display extolls their virtues: "Food for red-blooded boys," "Nutritious," and "Low-Priced."

Special prices make combined purchases of hotdogs, rolls, and ketchup appealing.

ON THURSDAY, a young housewife alert to good buys places our bottle of ketchup in her shopping cart. When she completes her shopping, she transfers the groceries to the basket which her husband had fastened to the baby's stroller.

As she walks the five blocks to her apartment building, she reviews her supper menu.

For herself and her husband, there are lamb chops. Her three school age boys will enjoy their hotdogs and buns. The 2-year-old girl will have a hotdog cut up into pieces which she can eat with her fingers.

As a green vegetable, the housewife has bought fresh asparagus to serve with a cheese sauce. Instant mashed potatoes will go well with this meal. No, instead she will serve frozen french fried potatoes!

Dessert is a frozen blueberry pie she will bake while the rest of the meal is cooking. All four children drink milk. She will brew tea for herself and her husband.

And oh yes, she won't forget to include the ketchup with the hotdogs and french fries—her boys would remind her anyway, she knows.

AT SUPPER, the hungry little ones race into the home with a hasty greeting. After a quick wash of dirty hands, they sit down at the table, say grace, and help themselves to the food.

The mother smiles as she thinks of the lamb chops still inside the refrigerator. She didn't have time to cook them, so she and her husband are also eating wieners.

The small boy at the end notices the new bottle of ketchup.

He struggles with the cap, finally gets his Dad to open it, and then pours a walloping portion of the spicy liquid on his hotdog sandwich. As he swallows the first bite, a glow comes over his face.

"Gee great," he mumbles through a mouthful.

He pauses long enough to wipe his red-smeared lips and serve himself some french fries. He smothers them with ketchup too, and digs in.

He smiles and turns to his mother, "What's new, mom?"

Our small consumer is satisfied. And our farm-to-table story is ended.

PACKAGING AND PROTECTION

ROBERT E. HARDENBURG

PACKAGING is tremendously use-ful for protecting food during marketing—not just a necessary evil increasing food costs. Consumers now receive products in fresher condition, with more potential shelf life, and greater appeal and convenience be-cause of packaging advances.

Packaging is a multibillion-dollar business and food packaging, with its thousands of consumer-packaged items, is the largest segment of the industry. New packages and great numbers of new or improved packaging materials are in continuous development. They provide better protection for our food than ever before in history.

WORLD POPULATION is increasing at a rate of about 144,000 every day. So the task of producing enough food, and processing, storing, marketing, and continuously protecting it, will become increasingly important.

For many centuries inadequate transportation and refrigeration pro-hibited wide distribution of perishable foods. These foods had to be consumed locally in season. Less perishable foods received only crude bulk packaging with little concern for sanitation or for quality maintenance.

Beginning about 1800 and continu-ing till today man has made giant technological advances in many fields of science. He developed sources of power to run machinery; transporta-tion improved. During this same time-span, he developed the science of food technology and gradually learned new ways to process and package foods.

Progress in canning has been con-tinuous since about 1809.

Today's canning plants are highly efficient operations where a single processing line may produce more than 600 containers of wholesome food every minute.

We are all familiar with the sight of thousands of cans and glass jars in our supermarkets. Some are transported great distances, as sardines from Nor-way and pineapple from Hawaii.

We see the great supermarket array of packaged frozen foods now com-monplace and we accept vacuum-packed foods, gas-packed foods, dried foods, chemically preserved foods, and packaged fresh produce.

Materials used for food packaging include wood, wood veneer, fiber-board, paperboard, paper, cotton, burlap, packaging films, aluminum foil, steel, aluminum, and glass.

Packages made from these materials may be rigid or flexible, large or small,

*   *   *

Robert E. Hardenburg is a *Research Horti-culturist* with the Market Quality Research Division, Agricultural Research Service.

and produced in hundreds of combinations and variations with and without coatings or liners to achieve desired protective characteristics.

THE TYPES of food packages in use today seem endless. Most provide product protection, some do another job.

There are egg cartons, window-boxed pies, canned juice, variety cereal packs, shrink-wrapped ham, cellophane-packed spinach, frozen dinners, 20-bushel bulk boxes for handling and storing apples, fiberboard cartons for shipping 24 heads of lettuce, and individual serving packs of crackers and jelly.

We have take-home cartons, disposable bottles, reuse containers, multiple packs, combination food packs, vacuum packs, see-through packs, reclosable packs, and packages within a package. Some packages may be frozen, some may be baked, and some may be boiled. Other packages pour, have easy-open features, may be squeezed, or operate with a pushbutton.

PRODUCT PROTECTION to maintain quality for an adequate marketing period is the major function of food packaging.

But it no longer is enough just to design a package that protects the product. The package must be economical to use and must promote sales. It may provide convenience, save time in shopping, save shelf space, prevent pilfering, make handling easier by unitizing, or provide a host of other services.

Protective packaging should retard deterioration from all sources that lower product quality from point of production to the consumer's table. With many highly perishable foods, this is still difficult, and shelf life is short even with today's protective packaging plus refrigeration.

Causes of deterioration must be known and understood for each product, along with the product's special needs, and its physical and chemical properties. For example, how deep can ripening fresh tomatoes be packed if pressure bruising is to be avoided?

MAJOR PROTECTIVE packaging requirements are as follows:

• Physical protection is needed to prevent product crushing or bruising and to provide stacking strength for normal handling—wood boxes, fiberboard cartons, cans, and glass jars provide this protection.

• Moisture loss or moisture gain must be minimized. Product shriveling and underweight packages result when moisture loss is excessive. Dried foods lose crispness or they mold when moisture content increases above specified levels.

• Sanitary protective barriers are required to prevent contamination from dust, and entry and destruction by micro-organisms and insects.

• Gain or loss of gases such as oxygen, carbon dioxide, and nitrogen from packages is critical for many products and must be minimized. Excess contact with atmospheric oxygen hastens quality deterioration of many processed products.

• Odor loss or pickup often must be avoided. Product aroma may pass rapidly out of some packages, resulting in quality deterioration. A better barrier film or container is needed in these cases.

• Flavor loss should be minimized.

• Grease or fat loss must be minimized in some products.

• Color changes have to be avoided. Often this involves partial or complete exclusion of light.

The importance of these packaging requirements is associated with length of shelf life desired. A container like a glass jar, metal can, or foil-film laminated pouch may be needed when long shelf life is desired. Less expensive packaging, providing less protection, may be adequate if there is a rapid product turnover.

MORE AND MORE FOOD companies now realize the importance of packaging and have established packaging departments. Others use packaging consultants.

Much testing of proposed new packages goes on under simulated marketing conditions before commercial acceptance. Continual research and evaluation of existing packages is essential to escape loss of business to competitors.

Michigan State University offers a 4-year course in packaging. Many other universities also teach courses in packaging.

The Packaging Institute, the Produce Packaging Association, and many other trade associations provide adult education in packaging. Trade journals like Modern Packaging, Package Engineering, Food Engineering, and Food Technology publicize the results of packaging research.

FRESH FRUITS AND VEGETABLES of many kinds are highly perishable and deteriorate rapidly, if not handled carefully and refrigerated.

Packaging of produce is particularly important to prevent damage during handling that can cause bruising and thus reduce salability or open the surface to infection and spoilage by micro-organisms.

A primary function of produce packaging is to retard moisture loss and prevent deterioration like shriveling of peppers, berries, and root crops, or wilting of vitamin-rich leafy green vegetables.

Sanitation is another reason for modern produce packaging. Products like fresh spinach and tossed salad mixes which may be eaten raw need to be properly packaged to reduce the chance of contamination. Fruits often attract gnats or fruit flies while on display in stores. Packaging fruits in transparent bags helps keep them more sanitary.

FRESH PRODUCE GIVES the packaging researcher a special problem.

Tissues are still alive after harvest and after packaging and must be kept alive if produce is to be marketed in fresh form. Respiration continues. Oxygen must be supplied for respiration, and carbon dioxide and heat are given off. Thus, usually there must be some provision for gas exchange.

In this respect, the problems of fresh produce packaging are different from those in canning or freezing, which kill the tissues. An airtight container normally cannot be used for fresh produce.

In a film package with low oxygen permeability, all the free oxygen is used by the produce in a short time at room temperature, and respiration becomes anaerobic. In anaerobic respiration—respiration in the absence of free oxygen—alcohol and carbon dioxide are produced. This type of respiration is sometimes referred to as fermentation or suboxidation.

Free oxygen is no longer being used, but carbon dioxide is still being produced, so the total volume of gas in the package increases and the package swells. This can be demonstrated easily by sealing sweet corn or other items with a high respiration rate in a non-ventilated film bag.

Carbon dioxide concentrations of 20 to 40 percent may develop in airtight packages in a day or two at warm temperatures.

As a result of the absence of oxygen and the accumulation of carbon dioxide, alcohol, and other products of anaerobic respiration, the cells may be killed and the product becomes unsalable. Even before this occurs, fruits and vegetables may develop winey or other undesirable odors and flavors under such conditions.

FILM VENTILATION is a means of allowing more gas exchange through produce films which have inadequate oxygen and carbon dioxide permeability.

Some of the more permeable films allow sufficient oxygen passage to supply a certain fruit or vegetable held at 40° F. without any added ventilation. But the packer cannot guarantee temperatures during marketing or in consumers' homes. These films would have to be many times more permeable to oxygen than they are at low temperature to supply the much higher respiration needs for oxygen at 70°, 80°, or even 90° F. existing in some stores or homes.

Thus perforated film packages for

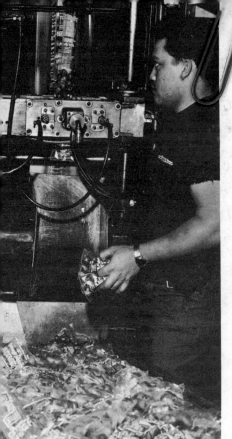

Automatic packaging machine at a Boston plant simultaneously forms the film bags and fills them with a predetermined amount of radishes.

rom production areas to market in heavy crates with snow ice between layers of carrots to maintain freshness.

Green tops were thought to be essential to convince housewives they were getting fresh carrots, not storage carrots. But it was not easy to keep them fresh during retailing. Flabby carrots with wilted tops were a common sight before 1950.

Research by horticulturists of the U.S. Department of Agriculture showed that the carrot tops draw moisture from the roots and hasten shriveling. *NB* Removing the tops doubles the shelf life. Removing tops and packaging in 1-pound moistureproof film bags further reduces moisture loss and markedly increases the shelf life.

Bunched carrots displayed 6 days at 70° F. with 50 percent relative humidity lost 48 percent in weight, with tops removed 29 percent, and in a perforated polyethylene bag 4 percent. Under refrigeration polyethylene packaged carrots have a shelf life of at least 2 to 3 weeks and moisture loss is usually less than 1 percent.

RETAILING STUDIES by R. L. Hawes and D. R. Stokes of the Agriculture Department showed that waste and spoilage losses of prepackaged carrots were much less than for bunched carrots—less than 1 percent compared with more than 8 percent—principally because there was less breakage of the packaged roots in consumer handling and no loss of salability from deterioration of the tops.

Consumer packaging of carrots is now done in producing areas. Not shipping the inedible tops—they make up 15 to 30 percent of the weight of a bunch—allows more carrots to be shipped per rail car. Use of less expensive shipping containers like veneer wirebound crates, multiwall-kraft bags, or heavy-duty polyethylene bags each holding twenty-four or forty-eight 1-pound polyethylene bags was also possible with the switch to consumer packaging.

A scant 1 percent of fresh carrots marketed in 1951 were prepackaged in

produce are a common sight in supermarkets. Experiments by the author showed that the oxygen concentration in small film packages perforated with two ¼-inch holes or four ⅛-inch holes will stay close to that in normal air, which contains 21 percent oxygen. This amount of ventilation has a negligible effect on weight loss.

More perforations may be needed when it is desired to allow more water vapor to escape and provide some control of relative humidity. This is discussed later in the chapter.

LET'S LOOK at the development of carrot packing. Most readers will remember the days of bunched carrots. They were shipped long distances

105

Lettuce is harvested, packaged, and boxed in one continuous operation in the field, at Salinas, Calif. At top, lettuce is picked and put on conveyors that take it inside packing van. At right, lettuce head is placed on sheet of plastic film and pushed through hole. Lettuce comes out on other side of hole (left) where a worker passes film-wrapped head over hotplate, which seals film around head. Lettuce is then boxed and dropped off for another truck to pick up.

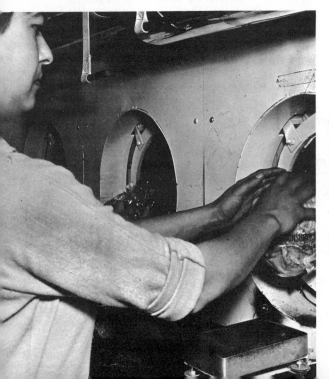

film bags. Most of them are in 1966 and with less spoilage, a longer shelf life, and better salability. Prevention of moisture loss is equally important for radishes, parsnips, and some other root crops, and a similar switch to moisture-proof polyethylene bags has occurred.

INCREASED USAGE of moistureproof film bags for marketing potatoes, onions, and citrus has developed since 1953. This occurred under the pressure of attempts to make produce departments self-service.

Mesh or paper bags were used to unitize loose produce. They did not restrict moisture loss.

Tests showed that either polyethylene or rubber hydrochloride film bags could be used for packaging potatoes, onions, and oranges. Moisture loss during marketing was minimized. However, further testing by the author and others in the Agriculture Department determined that the films were more moistureproof than desired for these particular produce items.

This problem has called for more research on use of the films.

MOST FRESH FRUITS and vegetables keep best under high relative humidity of 85 to 95 percent to retard moisture loss. However, moistureproof films like polyethylene when used for produce maintain even higher relative humidities, approaching or reaching 100 percent.

Humidity approaching saturation is detrimental to good keeping of onions, sweetpotatoes, potatoes, and oranges. Decay, surface mold, and rooting may be stimulated by the high humidity, particularly at warm temperatures.

The author and other researchers found that ventilation of film bags with punched holes was a way of providing some regulation of package humidity. To illustrate, the humidity as measured with an electric hygrometer averaged 98 percent in 3-pound polyethylene bags of onions without perforations. In 2 weeks at 75° F., 71 percent of the onions were rooted. Rooting is undesirable in onions as the bulbs soften.

Relative humidity was much lower in bags perforated with thirty-two ¼-inch holes and only 4 percent of the onions developed roots. This amount of film ventilation increased weight loss but did not cancel the desirable moisture-retentive property of polyethylene bags. Moisture losses are still less than would occur in mesh or kraft paper bags.

Potatoes packed in nonperforated polyethylene or in polyethylene bags with only a few holes developed surface mold and in some lots decay was high. Keeping quality was much better in these 10-pound film bags when they were ventilated with 48 or 64 of the ¼-inch holes, as this allowed some moisture vapor to escape.

Early experiments in shipping Florida oranges in polyethylene bags showed decay in them was higher than in open-mesh bags. The high humidity maintained in the film bags favored mold growth. Perforating the bags reduced the amount of decay.

Currently 5-pound polyethylene bags are still used for oranges but they are ventilated with as many as 64 to 80 of the ¼-inch holes. In addition, fruit is often hydrocooled and treated with fungicides before packaging to inhibit spoilage.

Shrink-film packaging is one of the newer packaging developments. It was first used in France about 1936 for the packaging of meat.

Some lettuce is now trimmed and overwrapped with heat-shrinkable films in production areas. Sometimes giant machines that move through the fields do the job. Quality maintenance is good when lettuce is precooled before shipment and adequately refrigerated in transit.

Pulpboard or chipboard trays of fruit or loose vegetables are sleeve wrapped or fully overwrapped with shrinkable film and then passed through a heat tunnel to shrink the film and immobilize the contents. Apples develop fewer bruises during retail handling in shrink-wrapped packages than in the widely used polyethylene bags.

With either of these consumer packs, good shipping containers with dividers between units are needed to prevent handling damage during shipment.

Other successful uses of shrink packaging are with fresh, smoked, and cured meats; fresh and frozen poultry; and with cheese.

PACKAGING FILMS shrink up to a maximum of about 80 percent when exposed to heat in hot water or in hot-air tunnels.

For many shrink-packaging jobs involving a final shrink to tighten a loosely wrapped package, only a small 5 to 10 percent shrink is needed. However, for a contour wrap of a frozen turkey or an odd-shaped tray of produce, film shrinkage of 50 percent or more may be desirable.

Balanced shrink in both the longitudinal and transverse directions is usually needed.

HEAT-SHRINK characteristics are built into films during manufacture by stretching under controlled temperatures and tensions to create molecular orientation, and then locking the film in this stretched condition by cooling.

One outstanding feature of shrink films is their ability to make a skin-tight package over irregular shaped objects. Products are immobilized so damage during normal handling may be reduced.

Major types of shrinkable films are polyethylene, polypropylene, polystyrene, polyester, polyvinyl chloride, polyvinylidene chloride copolymer, and rubber hydrochloride. They provide a broad variety of desirable characteristics.

SHIPPING CONTAINERS made from wood, metal, corrugated board, solid fiberboard, and multiwall paper deserve tremendous credit for protecting our food supply, yet often are not seen by consumers.

Throughout distribution, packaged products are handled and rehandled many times, loaded, unloaded, and stacked in storage several layers

deep. Each shipping container must withstand high vertical pressures to which it may be subjected, and the impacts of sudden stops and starts of trains and trucks.

Growth in use of corrugated shipping containers continues to expand. They are light in weight, free from rough surfaces inside and out, and usually low in cost compared with wood containers.

Lettuce, citrus, apples, and many other kinds of produce which formerly were shipped in wood containers now move to market in corrugated fiberboard boxes.

THESE CONTAINERS continue to be modified to improve stacking strength and resistance to moisture. More protective cushioning materials are used with corrugated boxes.

Apples are commonly packed in full-telescope-type corrugated boxes with molded-pulp trays for each layer of fruit. High quality Golden Delicious and McIntosh apples, which are easily bruised, are often packed in cell-type corrugated boxes with each apple partitioned in its own cell. Bruising damage is less than in older place-packing methods faced with a bulge before lidding.

Corrugated boxes of 50-pound capacity are now used increasingly for potatoes and sweetpotatoes.

Sweetpotatoes shipped in corrugated boxes developed less decay than comparable roots shipped in bushel baskets in tests conducted by the Agriculture Department. Decay in baskets was reduced about 50 percent by using an excelsior cushion between the cover and the roots.

With California potatoes, shipping in corrugated cartons reduced bruising, skinning, and skin discoloration compared to potatoes packed in 100-pound burlap bags.

Corrugated boxes cost more than burlap bags, but this is partially offset by reduction in waste.

A new 38-pound capacity veneer-fiberboard box is used increasingly for shipping eastern peaches, as it has good strength and provides added protection. Peaches shipped in these boxes reportedly had only a third to a half as many cuts and bruises as peaches which were shipped in veneer baskets with crown covers.

THE CHANGEOVER to fiberboard boxes from wood boxes for apples, citrus, and other perishables has increased the problems of cooling.

Produce in bulge-packed wood containers cooled readily because the bulge kept containers separated and exposed to circulating cold air.

Packed fiberboard boxes usually have no bulge. Consequently, boxes may be stacked tightly against each other in rows or on pallets unless care is taken to space them for desired circulation. If fiberboard boxes are tightly stacked, cooling is slow.

This problem is solved, allowing good keeping quality, if fruit is precooled before packing. For nonprecooled fruit in fiberboard boxes, spacing between rows of containers for air circulation is essential.

The cooling rate is increased further by venting the boxes with holes or slits, providing that the vents are in positions where they are exposed to moving air.

POLYETHYLENE BOX LINERS are used extensively to lengthen storage life of pears, sweet cherries, and Golden Delicious apples.

Pears are stored at 30° F. in regular boxes with thin gage (0.0015 inch) polyethylene film liners. Fruit respiration builds up a beneficial modified atmosphere within the tightly sealed liners, which is usually about 2 to 4 percent carbon dioxide, 10 percent oxygen, and the balance nitrogen. This allows a storage period 6 to 8 weeks longer than without liners.

Pears packed and stored in sealed liners are firmer, greener in color, have less scald on removal from storage, and have a better shelf life than pears stored without liners.

A 1965 innovation was to enclose a waxed kraft paper pad or envelope containing 1 pound of hydrated lime in each film-lined box. The lime absorbs carbon dioxide, keeping it at about 2 percent. Allowing carbon dioxide to accumulate to a concentration of 4 or 5 percent may cause brown core, which is an internal disorder of pears.

Golden Delicious apples benefit from film liners chiefly through reduction of moisture loss and shriveling. Consequently the liners need not be sealed but are usually just overlapped. A storage life of 5 to 7 months at 31° to 32° F. is possible with the liners, and moisture loss can be kept at 1 percent or less.

SWEET CHERRIES are protected in sealed polyethylene liners for as much as 2 to 3 weeks at 31° F. following harvest, and then may be shipped long distances to market. Here again a beneficial modified atmosphere of about 6 to 9 percent carbon dioxide and 3 to 10 percent oxygen and high humidity develops.

This atmosphere reduces decay during storage and transit, minimizes moisture loss, and preserves the green color of the stems and bright color of the cherries for longer periods than without liners.

Use of bulk boxes or pallet boxes holding 14 to 24 bushels of produce is expanding because of handling economies possible with modern forklift trucks. These giant containers originated in New Zealand in 1953.

Sometimes harvesting is directly into these containers followed by movement to processing plants or storage. Depending on the dimensions of pallet boxes, about 20 percent more produce can be stored in the same storage space compared with individual bushel boxes handled on pallets.

Bruising and mechanical damage in these bulk boxes is usually no worse and often is slightly less than in regular wooden field crates. A possible reason is that when bulk boxes are full of apples or other produce, they are too heavy to be lifted manually and dropped or carelessly handled by workers. Also, a smaller percentage of the fruit is in contact with surfaces of the container.

INSECT INFESTATION of packaged foods is a cause of tremendous losses in the United States each year.

Food processors have to adopt good insect-control programs which insure that their product is insect-free when it leaves the plant. They must also protect their commodity against insect infestation throughout marketing and until opened by consumers. Here the only suitable means is to use insect-resistant containers.

Research at the Stored-Product Insects Laboratory of the Agriculture Department in Savannah, Ga., showed that improved packaging methods now will provide protection against insect infestation.

Packaging materials, container construction, and tightness of closures are important. However, certain borers and beetles can enter food packages made of cloth, paper, film, foil, or combinations of these materials regardless of how well they are constructed. So chemical treatment to prevent penetration is essential.

Pyrethrum in combination with piperonyl butoxide applied as a coating to the outer ply of properly constructed multiwall paper bags is effective as a repellent in preventing insect infestation of flour for many months.

MEAT AND SEAFOOD packaging for the self-service supermarket has expanded tremendously. An ever-increasing number of consumer-size items are protectively packaged, using a full range of container types including metal cans, aluminum foil, films, paper, paperboard, and combinations of these different materials.

Packaging problems and requirements are complex. There is a great variety of products—red meats, poultry, fish, and other seafoods—and they come in fresh, frozen, cured, and heat processed forms. Adequate packaging of these perishable products is a challenge to the industry.

COLOR PROBABLY IS the most important single factor for consumer acceptance of packaged meats. Control of moisture loss to prevent product drying or desiccation is also important. Fresh meat will turn dark red if permitted to dehydrate in the open air.

Flavor and odor loss or pickup must be avoided. Undesirable odors and flavors may be due to contamination before packaging, absorption during storage, or from foreign matter in containers or packaging materials.

DESIRABLE TEXTURE and juiciness should be preserved. Greaseproof packaging materials must be used because of the fat content of meats.

Associated with the fat content and storage of meats is the rancidity problem. Oxidative rancidity can be minimized in frozen meat products if packaging materials exclude oxygen. Since fresh meats are generally marketed rapidly, they do not encounter the problems of rancidity.

Microbial contamination and spoilage must be avoided. Meat is an excellent medium for growth of many types of micro-organisms, particularly bacteria.

FRESH MEATS ARE usually packaged in supermarkets because of their high perishability even after packaging.

A moistureproof cellophane, coated on one side with nitrocellulose, is most widely used to overwrap trays of fresh meat.

The coating on the cellophane, placed away from the meat, is permeable to oxygen but quite impermeable to moisture vapor. Thus some oxygen can enter, which is desired, but moisture loss from the package is restricted.

Freshly cut beef has a purple-red color that has little display value or consumer appeal. This color is attributed to the presence of the complex protein myoglobin. After a few minutes' exposure to the air, a bright red color develops that is very desirable. The oxygen of the air converts the purplish-red myoglobin to bright red oxymyoglobin; this is accomplished in only a few minutes.

110

A desirable packaging film must continue to supply enough oxygen to keep the bright red color as long as possible.

Prolonged exposure to oxygen changes the red color to brown, as oxymyoglobin is converted to metmyoglobin. This may occur in 24 to 48 hours or less, even under good refrigeration and sanitary handling procedures.

Surface drying, elevated temperatures, and bacterial contamination will speed discoloration.

FRESH MEATS can be packaged in flexible films which are impermeable to both moisture vapor and oxygen, and shelf life is much longer. Exclusion of oxygen keeps the meat purplish-red, which is less appealing to consumers. But even after extended storage, the meat will still develop good red color when it is opened and exposed to the air.

This use of impermeable films, sometimes called anaerobic packaging or vacuum packaging, will allow fresh meat packaging at a centralized warehouse rather than in supermarkets.

Experiments by Z. J. Ordal of the University of Illinois showed that ground beef packaged in saran film with low oxygen permeability still had good flavor after 10 days at 30° F. The use of saran, which excluded oxygen, provided a means for controlling psychrophilic bacteria. These are the bacteria that grow well under refrigeration and are commonly associated with fresh-meat spoilage.

Ground beef packaged in opaque oxygen-barrier films in vacuum packs is now seen increasingly in today's supermarkets.

CURED MEATS, in contrast to fresh meats, retain their bright pink and red colors better in an oxygen impermeable package than in one that is oxygen permeable.

Therefore, cured meats can be vacuum packed in impermeable transparent films to provide better protection from discoloration.

The cardinal principle for packaging cured, smoked, and table-ready meats for retailing is to exclude both oxygen and light, since both accelerate color deterioration.

Lighting in a refrigerated display case readily fades the color of sliced cured, smoked, and table-ready meats—ham, bacon, bologna, and luncheon meats—when they are packaged in semimoistureproof cellophane, an air-permeable film. Exposure to light for as short a time as 4 hours may cause objectionable fading.

Opaque labels are essential, therefore, on the side of cured meat packages exposed to light, if the films are air permeable.

Remarkable progress has been made recently in developing combination packages of three or more materials laminated together—useful for vacuum and nitrogen backfilled packages. Four-ounce flexible packages of dried beef are often this type, which may be a combination of cellophane, aluminum foil, and polyethylene.

After the package is filled, air is evacuated and then the package is backfilled with nitrogen to retain looseness of the slices and to protect the product from oxidation. This package protects both color and flavor better than cellophane-overwrapped window cartons.

HOTDOG PRODUCERS use many types of films and film laminates, providing different amounts of protection. A billion and a half 1-pound packages of hotdogs or frankfurters are produced yearly—big business indeed. The amount of film required, 11 inches wide, would reach around the world 11 times.

For best protection, hotdogs are packed using barrier films like saran, polyester, or nylon which exclude oxygen.

Skintight vacuum packs for bacon now provide better protection than previous window cartons. Good color is retained, and rancidity is retarded, allowing up to 8 weeks of refrigerated shelf life. One such package uses a laminate film of 1-mil (0.001 inch) nylon

111

and 2-mil polyethylene coated with 0.1 mil of saran and a polyethylene-coated backing board to support the bacon.

Great quantities of fresh poultry are packaged and distributed through supermarkets. Much of this fresh product is shipped from processing plants to stores in wirebound crates lined with waxed kraft paper and with ice mixed with the poultry.

A NEW DEVELOPMENT is to ship prechilled fresh poultry in corrugated boxes without ice—commonly known as a dry pack. Fluids from the chilling process are absorbed by special paper toweling liners.

Poultry shipped in these boxes reportedly maintains a fresher appearance because the product is not subjected to skin bleaching by melting ice.

Fresh poultry usually is prepackaged after it reaches the supermarket. Here semimoistureproof films are desired which have fairly high gas permeability. If films are too moistureproof, slime formation is increased. If they are too impermeable to gases, odors that develop within the package may accumulate and become objectionable. These off odors are due to slowly developing bacteria on poultry surfaces, which grow even under refrigeration.

The film also helps maintain the fresh bloom and protects against shrinkage and dehydration. Dehydration results in darkening of the meat.

Cut-up poultry has the same film requirements, but pulpboard trays are added to aid in unitizing and to absorb the moisture "drip" that exudes from cut meat.

FROZEN POULTRY is shipped in corrugated boxes which must be rigid enough to withstand abuse and protect the product. It has, of course, a much longer shelf life than fresh poultry when adequately packaged and kept frozen.

The primary problem in frozen meat and poultry is preventing freezerburn, a type of deterioration caused by dehydration which leaves white or bleached areas. Packages should be moistureproof and skintight to avoid freezerburn; heat-shrinkable films may be used to advantage.

Polyvinylidene chloride and irradiated polyethylene films both allow high shrink and make good contour packages. Removing the air from film packages after the birds are inserted assists in retarding oxidation, which is the cause of rancidity during prolonged freezer storage.

Edible coatings of acetylated monoglycerides have been approved for use on food.

Meat, poultry, and even nut meats which are dipped in these materials lose their moisture slowly.

It is likely that such edible coatings will find commercial use in the future. However, they do not provide as much protection as moistureproof films so they probably will be used in conjunction with other packaging.

OVER A BILLION POUNDS of seafood is marketed annually in the United States either chilled or frozen. All of it is packaged in shipping containers or consumer packages at some time during marketing. Considerable research in this field is done at regional laboratories of the Bureau of Commercial Fisheries, Department of the Interior.

Fresh fish and shellfish spoil as a result of bacterial or enzymatic action. Low temperature is the most important single factor in retarding spoilage. If a temperature of 32° to 35° F. is maintained, fish may remain acceptable for as long as 9 days from the time when they are caught.

Packaging is the second most important factor in extending keeping quality of fresh fish. Bulk containers serve to hold the fish, and crushed ice maintains low temperatures. Metal and wood boxes are widely used.

Water-resistant fiberboard boxes are now employed to some extent because of their good insulating properties. Reportedly, fish can be kept at low temperatures in these boxes with considerably less ice than in conventional wood boxes.

FROZEN FISH NEED protective packaging that will prevent moisture loss and oxidation of fats.

The usual consumer package for frozen fish fillets is the waxed carton with a waxed-paper overwrap. To eliminate dehydration during frozen storage, however, packaging materials with very low moisture-vapor transmission rates must be used.

Some plastic wax coatings and plastic films—polyethylene, polyester, and polyvinylidene chloride—or combinations of these materials with paper have excellent moisture-barrier properties. They are finding increased use for packaging fish.

Fatty and moderately fatty fish must be protected against oxidation of the fats.

Rancidity develops as a result of the reaction of the fat with oxygen, which is in the package initially or which migrates through the packaging material. If this occurs, quality declines and consumers are dissatisfied.

VACUUM PACKAGING in shrinkable film bags that prevent transmission of oxygen is one solution. Air is removed from the package and the film shrunk tightly around the product.

Purging the package with nitrogen is another method of removing oxygen before sealing. This method is good where a loose-fitting package is desired.

Another method of protecting fishery products against rancidity consists of coating the unwrapped product with gels prepared from seaweed extract or solutions of corn-sirup solids. These materials provide coatings that resist the penetration of oxygen.

Antioxidants incorporated into packaging materials are also of some value in preventing oxidation, particularly where there is close contact between the package and the product.

The variety of frozen foods now available in supermarkets is immense; all are packaged for protection.

This variety continues to grow rapidly. It includes practically a full range of food types: Meats, fruits, vegetables, beverages, bakery products, dairy products, and desserts. Each comes in a variety of forms and with more and more built-in services to please consumers.

Many kinds of frozen dinners and combination foods are available.

Newer items include frozen packaged salads, and cranberry apple salad with walnuts.

Preservation is primarily through the freezing process with subsequent storage at o° F. or below. However, good packaging is a physical means of extending the storage life of frozen foods. With no protective packaging, most frozen foods would become unmarketable or unpalatable in a few weeks' time. Wood, metal, glass, paper, and plastic materials have been used successfully.

Packaging protects frozen food from dirt, insects, and micro-organisms before and during storage, as well as during thawing and preparation for cooking. For fruits packed in sirup, waterproof packaging is of prime importance; for obvious reasons leaky cartons must be avoided.

Protective packages are also designed to overcome the conditions of low-temperature storage which desiccate foods and cause freezerburn.

FREEZERBURN was mentioned earlier but deserves further emphasis because of its importance. It may irreversibly alter the color, texture, flavor, and nutritive value of frozen foods.

The snow or frost that accumulates on coils in a freezer comes from moisture vapor in the air condensing and freezing.

As moisture is removed from circulation, any moist product in the room will give up more water vapor.

Thus there may be a constant loss of water in the form of vapor (sublimation) from the unprotected materials in the storage area.

Moisture-vaporproof packaging materials must be placed around the food to eliminate or minimize yielding of moisture to the freezer coils. If much desiccation occurs, the food develops freezerburn. Visible frost may develop even within good packages if storage temperature is allowed to fluctuate.

ONE OF THE SIMPLEST protective coatings for frozen foods is to glaze or coat them with ice. Glazing has been widely used in the fishing industry.

More commonly, barrier films, aluminum foil, and special papers provide protection from desiccation.

These packaging materials must not impart any odor or flavor to the product. They should also prevent odors from other products stored in the same room from contaminating frozen food. Odors and flavors from fish and smoked meats may migrate into other foods, if not adequately packaged in impermeable materials.

Some new products like frozen chopped onions may lose their desirable aroma if the package is an inadequate barrier. Transparent pouches of saran-coated cellophane laminated to polyethylene make a gastight package which provides good aroma protection.

LIGHT CAN BE damaging to the color and flavor of frozen green vegetables like peas, particularly if storage is at temperatures higher than 0° F.

Peas held only a week at 20° F. in transparent packages in an illuminated display case may become slightly bleached or mottled, and flavor is damaged. Bleaching and flavor loss are severe after 3 or 4 weeks of exposure to light.

The peas absorb radiant energy from the light. This creates a temperature difference within the package, and moisture is lost to surrounding air-spaces and container walls.

Opaque packaging materials, therefore, are desirable. The popular 2-pound transparent polyethylene bags for loose-frozen free-flowing vegetables (pour and store) are satisfactory for retailing under lights if temperatures are maintained at 0° F. or below.

AN IMPORTANT PACKAGING innovation, now expanding rapidly, is heat-in-bag or boil-in-bag frozen foods—frozen

main dishes and frozen vegetables in sauces. Production was already over 300 million units a year in 1965.

Polyester film laminated to polyethylene is in wide use. This protects the food in both below zero temperatures and in boiling water. The see-through polyester bags of food are simply placed in boiling water, steamer, or electronic oven until cooked.

The consumer is assured of flavor and nutrients being sealed in the package. She need not concern herself with having to clean or scour pans.

COMBINATION PREPARED FOODS in boilable bags require the package to be an excellent barrier material against water, moisture vapor, gases like oxygen, and grease.

Restaurant owners, hotels, and drive-ins like boil-in-bag frozen foods because orders often can be filled 50 percent faster than by conventional methods and a variety of gourmet meals can be easily provided.

Dozens of frozen prepared foods can be heated simultaneously in the same cooking cauldron. These include broccoli au gratin, lima beans in butter, creole succotash, roast beef with gravy, and chicken a la king. The boilable bags are packed in opaque protective cartons picturing and describing the finished product.

Rigid aluminum foil containers are widely used as containers for frozen dinners, bakery products, and pizzas where baking is required. These foil containers have excellent heat conductivity for rapid baking. They are moisture- and vapor-proof, odorproof, and greaseproof. They may also be coated on the inside if protection from food acids is needed.

FOOD PRESERVATION by canning or heat processing leads all other methods and provides maximum storage life.

It changed the eating habits of modern man. Scurvy and pellagra, dread diseases caused by lack of certain vitamins, are almost unknown wherever canned fruits and vegetables are enjoyed. And canning has proved one of

114

the greatest laborsaving devices in the American home.

Canning dates back to 1795 when Nicolas Appert, a Frenchman, discovered that food heated in sealed containers was preserved if the container was not reopened and the seal didn't leak. Scientists in those days did not know the cause of food spoilage but the canning process worked.

METAL CANS, glass jars and bottles—these are the commonplace yet fabulous containers that protect our canned foods. Some flexible packages made from lamination of films or film and foil now withstand heat processing temperatures and will be entering the picture. Laminated materials are a combination of two or more materials bonded together by heat and pressure.

Metal cans and glass containers help insure good quality for thousands of different packaged foods. Today's supermarket shelves are lined with cans, bottles, and jars.

No container comes close to the metal can in total production. Over 48 billion metal cans were produced in 1964. Glass containers are in second place with production now over 27 billion containers annually.

The average American family uses about 600 food cans annually. Americans open about 131 million food cans every day.

Cans and glass containers are an indispensable part of our plentiful food supply. Both are strong and provide exceptional protection. Both withstand the high temperatures needed to sterilize foods and the pressures built up to provide an airtight vacuum container.

THE PURPOSE of heat processing is to destroy pathogenic and spoilage organisms that may be present in raw food materials. Sealing the container prevents reinfection of the food. Having a vacuum in containers is one way to remove oxygen.

A vacuum in canned foods helps protect color and flavor of products, assists in retaining vitamins, prevents rancidity due to oxidation, and helps retard corrosion of cans and corrosion of closures on glass containers.

Approximately 4 million tons of metal, mostly steel, go into the manufacture of cans each year and only about $\frac{5}{10}$ of 1 percent is tin. Thus, tin cans are a misnomer.

Thin tin coatings, applied efficiently by modern electrolytic methods, protect the steel from both external and internal corrosion.

In addition, other baked-on organic coatings or "can enamels" are used with the modern sanitary can, preventing interaction between metal and various foods. They aid in preserving the attractiveness of food and the appearance of the can, or may even replace the tin coating.

Products like rhubarb, tomato juice cocktail, and some fish products are noted for their detinning action on tinplate. Therefore, these foods are packed in enamel-lined cans. Highly colored fruits, like cherries and berries, fade when packed in plain cans. Can enamels formulated from oleoresins prevent this fading.

MANY VEGETABLES like peas and corn contain sulfur-bearing protein constituents. During processing these compounds break down, yielding sulfur residues that react with tin and iron of the container to produce dark-colored metal sulfides.

These deposits are similar to the tarnish found on silver spoons in contact with eggs. Like this tarnish, "sulfur black" in cans is harmless but nevertheless is objectionable because of its appearance.

Now sulfur-bearing foods are packed in containers with an oleoresinous coating with zinc oxide pigments, which trap the sulfur and prevent discoloration.

Beer and beverage containers have double coatings that prevent flavor changes. Meat cans may have special phenolic coatings with fatty acid amides to prevent the contents from sticking.

Aluminum cans are growing in popularity because of their light weight,

115

791–476 O–66—10

corrosion resistance, and compatibility with certain foods and beverages.

Current applications for aluminum cans include beer, soft drinks, frozen fruit juices, dairy products, and canned meats and fish—like sardines and tuna.

The aluminum pull-tab end, an important packaging innovation, has had much to do with increased usage of aluminum cans. The pull-tab end does not contribute to product protection, but it has sales appeal and convenience.

Fiber cans with a fiber body and metal ends and liquid-tight paper containers have a role in protective packaging of items like cocoa, salt, fruit juice, and milk.

The paper milk carton, which first reached the markets in 1934, has expanded to the point that 18 billion were produced in 1964. These are now mostly polyethylene-coated paper cartons, which have gradually replaced wax-coated cartons for both milk and chilled juice.

USE OF GLASS CONTAINERS for food and beverages continues to grow in constant competition with metal cans.

Glass jars are used for most processed baby foods. Glass bottles are excellent containers for milk, soft drinks, soluble coffee, and many other beverages. Glass containers predominate for home canning.

Glass has many characteristics that play a role in providing protection for food. Glass is chemically inert, so it does not react with foods to produce flavor changes. For foods like pickles, ketchup, and mayonnaise, glass containers are ideal.

Glass is almost 100 percent impermeable, nonporous, and odorless. It is transparent, allowing the contents to be inspected for quality. Glass containers are strong so they give good physical protection. And each year they are being made stronger, yet lighter and thinner. They are easy to open and to reseal to store unused portions of the contents.

As with cans, glass containers may have various surface treatments to improve performance. Colored glass can give protection against light rays where required. For example, a Wisconsin dairy showed that amber-colored glass protects milk from the flavor changes which are a result of exposure to the sun.

Returnable bottles for milk, soft drinks, and beer are among the lowest cost containers found in packaging—averaging less than half a cent per trip.

GLASS CONTAINERS are useful packages to food processors only if properly capped or sealed. Good seals are needed to prevent contamination and to prevent transfer of gases.

Currently, many closure types are made from metal, plastic, cork, rubber, and paper. They are continually being improved.

Some provide pilfer-proof seals. Some provide hermetic or airtight seals, and others are nonhermetic.

High utility closures are available with improved gaskets for vacuum-packed foods. These maintain the vacuum, protecting quality and increasing shelf life of the product.

Appreciable growth of aerosol packaging of food is expected, since numerous new propellent gases have been approved by the Food and Drug Administration.

Aerosol packaging until recently was limited to whipped cream and to other toppings. Soon there may be aerosol mayonnaise, honey, ketchup, and fruit purees.

This is more than just convenience packaging. Foods packaged in hermetically sealed containers with a propellent to eject the product are protected from evaporation, from contamination by micro-organisms, and from oxidation. One-way valves permit dispensing food but prevent entrance contamination.

Whipped cream is the most familiar aerosol product and is a food that benefits from aerosol packaging. Leftover hand-whipped cream often deteriorates or is discarded, while aerosol whipped cream may be dispensed in desired portions and the container put back in the refrigerator for future use.

116

BAKERY PRODUCTS are packaged to protect them both from drying out and from gaining moisture.

Protective packaging is particularly important in keeping the freshness and crispness of crackers and cookies. If the packaging material gives adequate protection against moisture vapor transmission, it can be expected to protect the product from dust, dirt, mold spores, and off odors.

Consumer packages and shipping containers for crackers and cookies also provide structural strength for protection from crushing during marketing. Fragile pastries are protected in overwrapped molded plastic trays, paperboard cartons, or window boxes.

Waxed glassine gives bakery products dependable protection from moisture vapor. Other materials that do the job include waxed paper, glassine, foil, cellophane, polyethylene, and polypropylene.

SUCCESSFUL PACKAGING of potato chips is not simple. Loss of crispness and rancidity are factors limiting shelf life.

Rancidity in potato chips results from the reaction of oil with oxygen in the presence of light or heat. A good oxygen barrier is especially needed to retard rancidity. Recent research shows that a saran-latex coating on glassine bags effectively excludes oxygen, preventing rancidity of chips.

Shelf life of shelled nuts is markedly extended with good packaging.

Nuts packed under vacuum in metal cans are protected for long periods from darkening and flavor changes caused by oxidation and exposure to light. Moisture loss or gain is prevented.

Transparent film bags or pouches also are widely used for packaging shelled nuts. They are less costly and lighter in weight than metal cans, but do not provide as much protection from oxygen, light, moisture, and insects. Consequently, shelf life is less in film bags than in vacuum cans.

Greater barrier properties have been built into films through coatings and laminations. An adequate shelf life for nut meats in film bags is now possible with these improved films. Replacement of the air in film packages with nitrogen markedly retards rancidity and darkening.

MANY IMPROVEMENTS in convenience packaging of food are seen in our supermarkets.

Convenience packaging involves shape and size of containers that allow easy pouring, serving, carrying, reclosing, and storage in refrigerators.

The trend toward individual servings of mustard, ketchup, cream, sugar, soluble coffee, jelly, salt, and pepper is increasing rapidly. Recent improvements in laminating polyethylene film to foil, cellophane, and other films, which make better barrier packages, open the possibility of marketing many other foods in portion packs.

Many unique films have been created to meet multiple needs of foods.

A new "3-ply" film for bread is made of a thin layer of polypropylene sandwiched between outer layers of polyethylene—yet the entire film is a thousandth of an inch thick.

A new "6-ply" film pouch is available for vacuum packaging foods like fresh shredded Cheddar cheese, dried beef, and soup mixes. This is a lamination of cellophane-polyethylene-cellophane-polyethylene- aluminum foil-polyethylene.

Individual strips of bacon in foil envelopes, which may be dropped in a toaster, may soon be marketed.

THESE ARE JUST a few of many tailor-made packaging developments.

We can be sure the food and container industries will continue to keep abreast of new developments in packaging materials and food processing, and create even better food packaging for the future. This will be done at an economic cost.

We know it's what's inside the package that counts. Packaging can't improve food quality. But with proper storage plus the right package to protect each food from deterioration, waste and spoilage are minimized.

JOHN E. CLAYTON

SHIPPING,

HANDLING,

AND 'TLC'

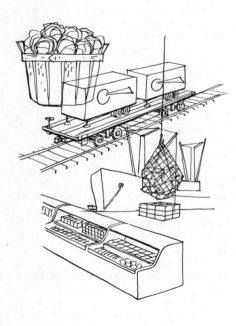

John E. Clayton is *Chief*, Transportation Research Branch, Transportation and Facilities Research Division, Agricultural Research Service.

118

I T takes lots of lettuce to make 2 billion sandwiches, or 2½ million salads. Yet poor handling can easily cause that much lettuce to be thrown away before it reaches our tables. And similar losses in other perishable foods are common from the lack of Tender Loving Care (TLC)—and know-how.

Mechanical damage causes the loss of two heads in each box of bulge-packed lettuce, industry people say. American farmers produced roughly 75 million boxes of lettuce in 1965, and most of it went to market bulge-packed in boxes.

Damaging two heads in each box would cause us to throw away close to 150 million heads simply because we put more lettuce in a box than it was built to hold.

This is enough lettuce to make almost 2 billion bacon, lettuce, and tomato sandwiches.

Transit temperatures above 60° F. in the center and lower layers of the load and freezing in the top layers caused 23 trailer loads of lettuce to be "abandoned to the carriers"—thrown away—in three Texas markets during 1 week in 1962.

This failure to maintain proper transport temperatures kept 2½ million lettuce salads from reaching American tables.

EXAMPLES OF PRODUCT losses can be given for a long list of farm products—poultry, meat, livestock, tomatoes, watermelons, celery, grapes, cantaloups, and potatoes.

We don't know exactly how big these losses are each year, but we do know that they are large.

One estimate puts the amount of perishable food lost between the farm and the kitchen at enough to feed millions of people annually. Another says the output of one in every 5 acres devoted to perishable food production is lost each year to spoilage and waste.

Analysis of inspection records for 7 years in the New York City market shows decay caused the loss of about 3,000 carloads of produce annually in that market alone.

AMERICAN RAILROADS for some years have paid loss and damage claims from $10 to $12 million a year just for fresh fruits and vegetables, with occasional jumps to $18 and $20 million. These claims probably are less than actual losses because not all damage results in a filed claim.

Fresh fruits and vegetables are not the only farm products that suffer losses in transport. The railroads paid $11,671,800 in grain loss and damage claims in 1964, and another $9 million in claims for grain mill products. In the same year they paid $695,300 in claims on frozen food and $12,085,500 for "food and kindred products."

WHY WORRY ABOUT IT when we have plenty of most foods, even after throwing away large quantities between the farm and the kitchen? Here are three good reasons:
• Losses in transit add to the cost of getting food through the marketing system and to the consumer, and raise the price for the food we eat.
• Damage in handling and transport lowers the nutritive value and tastiness of many of our foods.
• Food saved by reducing handling and transport damage and losses can help feed hungry people in parts of the world where food is less abundant than it is in the United States.

MANY FRESH fruits and vegetables, live poultry and other living, breathing, and breakable farm products are handled as if they were anything but easily damaged.

It is not unusual to see a workman press down with his knee on a reluctant lettuce box before stapling the top flaps together. Some growers even have a steel clamping device to press the bulge-filled boxes into a more rectangular shape before stapling the flaps.

The boxes of lettuce then are hauled to the cooler and carefully put on pallets for efficient handling at this point. But when the boxes are taken out of the cooler for loading in a transport vehicle, they are taken off the pallets and loaded into the truck or rail car by hand. The boxes are tossed into place as they are stacked in the transport vehicle.

Live chickens are driven, caught, put in coops, and handled in ways that bruise up to 35 percent of the birds in some flocks.

The bruised flesh must be trimmed off and discarded when the birds are prepared for the market.

MANY THINGS can cause damage and losses in handling and transporting farm products.

But the main culprits are rough handling, deficiencies in shipping containers and transport equipment, and improper use of transport equipment.

Shipping containers may not be strong enough to protect the products. They may absorb too much moisture and collapse from overhead weight. Or they may be the wrong size or shape for products to fit into them without bruising, crushing, or breaking.

TRANSPORT EQUIPMENT used to move products from farm to consumer often has not performed well in the past. Truck-trailers were found to leak too much air for effective refrigeration of perishable products, and refrigeration units were unable to supply the cooling capacity indicated by their output ratings. Both factors contributed to transit damage and loss for products that require refrigeration.

Some railroad boxcars have leaked grain through cracks, holes, and faulty grain doors.

Recent years have brought significant improvement, but the task of developing satisfactory equipment to protect farm products in transit is far from finished.

One improper use of transport equipment is selecting the wrong type for the job. Refrigerated vehicles designed especially for hauling frozen foods, for example, ordinarily don't do a good job of removing field and respiratory heat from the center of perishable nonfrozen loads. This is because air circulates around the load instead of through it.

119

"Fishyback" container is lifted from truck to ship at top. Below, containership steams off.

Researchers in the U.S. Department of Agriculture and the National Bureau of Standards, with the help of industry, have developed a rating method for refrigerated trailer bodies. Industry has developed a rating method for refrigeration units for truck-trailers.

These two methods together make it possible to measure with fair precision the refrigeration capacity needed for particular types of trailer bodies, and to make certain a unit is used that will do the job. Trailers can be built that come closer to doing a good job of keeping perishable products at proper transit temperatures.

The result has been a reduction in damage and losses from deficiencies in refrigerated transport equipment. A similar rating method for refrigerated delivery truck bodies soon will bring better performance and reduced losses in local food deliveries.

A cold-wall trailer does a better job of keeping frozen foods at proper temperatures in transport. This is another improvement. Cold air circulates around and under the load of frozen food, keeps more even product temperatures, and reduces the possibility of damage.

DOOR CURTAINS for refrigerated trucks and trailers have reduced the amount of warm air that enters when the vehicles are opened for loading and unloading.

Product temperatures are kept closer to desired levels, and damage to perishable products is reduced.

Air ducts that cause cold air to flow to the rear of a trailer, then down, under, and through a load of perishable products also have brought a better job of refrigeration.

Without these ducts, the cold air would turn downward soon after it leaves the refrigeration unit in the front of the trailer and return to the cooling coils without touching the products at the rear of the trailer. Products in the front of the trailer could suffer freezing damage while those in the rear were damaged by too high temperatures.

AIR SCOOPS have been developed to help bring more outside air into piggyback trailers. This results in a better job of cooling products that can be transported under ventilation instead of refrigeration.

An under-the-floor scoop that brought air up through a load of watermelons en route from Florida to northern markets helped keep the melons at lower temperatures and reduced the possibility of transit damage and losses.

RESEARCH also has brought a better transport environment for live hogs transported by truck. When transported in hot weather—above 80° F.—these animals become uncomfortable. They lose weight and some die.

A device that sprinkles water on hogs during their truck trip helped keep them cool and reduced weight losses and deaths. In 31 tests over long and medium distances, 18 deaths occurred in trucks without sprinklers and none occurred in trucks with them.

CONTAINERIZATION is another transport and handling technique that offers significant opportunity to trim damage and losses of farm products. Individual boxes—on pallets or case-by-case—are placed in large van containers or trailers, usually 20, 35, or 40 feet long, and moved from origin to destination as a single unit.

A containerized shipment of grapefruit from Florida to Switzerland had much lower spoilage losses than normally experienced by the break-bulk or case-by-case handling technique.

This reduction was brought about in part by reducing from about 10 to 2 the number of times individual boxes had to be handled. Also, the fruit was kept in the proper environment throughout the trip instead of being subjected to high temperatures when transferred from one transport vehicle to another.

BETTER LOADING PATTERNS have reduced damage for many products shipped in bags, boxes, and cartons by preventing damage to containers and

121

by making channels for air circulation to help keep the products at proper temperatures and humidities.

One such loading pattern for citrus fruit packed in ⅘-bushel corrugated fiberboard boxes enabled Florida shippers to use this container with little damage to the box or the product.

Early-crop potatoes can be kept cooler and drier on the way to market by stacking the bags of potatoes in an "airflow" loading pattern that permits air to move through the load. Patterns for 50- and 100-pound bags developed in truck test shipments from New Jersey to Florida markets helped reduce losses from spoilage in transit.

BETTER LOADING PATTERNS have reduced damage and losses in transport for apples, fresh peas, bagged onions, and for other products.

Stable loads and channels for air circulation can be applied to additional products so a greater proportion of our produce can reach markets in salable and edible condition.

Damage to long-type watermelons is considerably less when they are loaded crosswise in a rail car instead of lengthwise. Melons shipped from Florida, Georgia, and South Carolina to northern markets in 1953 and 1954 had 70.5 percent less damage loaded crosswise than similar melons which were loaded lengthwise.

EASTERN-GROWN PEACHES shipped in newly developed fiberboard and wirebound veneer-fiberboard boxes suffered less bruising than the same kind of peaches shipped in bushel baskets.

California long white potatoes had significantly less bruising, skinning, and skin discoloration when shipped in 50-pound fiberboard boxes than when shipped in 100-pound burlap bags. Twenty-one percent of potatoes in test shipments of 100-pound burlap bags were skinned or discolored. Only 11 percent of potatoes in test shipments of 50-pound fiberboard boxes suffered this kind of damage.

Shipping damage to frozen tom turkeys has been found least if they are shipped packed tightly in a structurally strong container. A space ¼-inch to 1-inch deep should be left between the top surface of the turkeys and the top of the box. Tests showed no product damage and little damage to film wrappers for turkeys shipped this way.

Preliminary studies indicate 60 to 70 percent of the bruising of live chickens occurs during driving, catching, and cooping. Twenty-five percent of this bruising could be avoided by removing feed troughs, water fountains, and similar obstructions before driving and catching. Limited trials suggested bruising could be reduced another 2 to 3 percent by using a new style plastic coop instead of the conventional coop made of wood.

Changing the way lettuce is trimmed in retail stores can reduce trimming loss from 12.2 pounds to 8.8 pounds for each 24-head box of lettuce. Research shows this reduction can be achieved by removing the outer leaves before trimming the butt.

PUTTING A NUMBER of individual boxes on pallets and handling them through the marketing system like a single unit is one way to reduce the number of times products are handled. And reducing the number of handlings cuts damage and losses.

With this technique, each box may be handled once as it is placed on a pallet and again as it is taken off the pallet for local distribution or sale.

Individual handlings of boxes can be cut to a fraction of those required by the "break-bulk" system, in which boxes are handled one at a time. If boxes are palletized in the origin and destination warehouses but handled individually into and out of transport vehicles, just extending palletization through transport can halve the number of individual handlings.

A large food distributor cut damage by 64 percent in shipments from its plants to distribution centers by palletizing instead of using case-by-case handling. Damage in shipments directly to customers was practically eliminated.

THE GIANT JOB OF REFRIGERATION

W. T. PENTZER

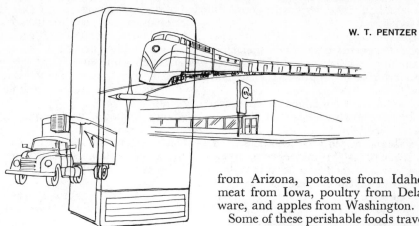

FOOD habits of Americans have changed greatly since the advent of refrigeration a little over 100 years ago. We eat more perishable foods the year round, in season and out of season.

We can purchase meat, fish, poultry, eggs, milk, ice cream, lettuce, strawberries, citrus fruits, bananas, and apples, to name only a few perishable foods, almost any day of the year. The variety of fresh and frozen foods available today is truly amazing.

Less than 100 years ago many persons in small cities and villages in America kept a milk cow as the only way to have fresh milk.

Meat came from cattle slaughtered locally, driven or shipped to where they were needed. In those days there were no refrigerated vehicles for shipping dressed carcasses. The mainstays in the diet then were bread and cured meats.

Development of railroads, waterways, and roads brought city and country closer together. Refrigeration made it possible for even perishable foods to be shipped long distances.

Today, a New York City housewife shopping for food may purchase citrus fruits that came from Florida or California, carrots from Texas, lettuce

from Arizona, potatoes from Idaho, meat from Iowa, poultry from Delaware, and apples from Washington.

Some of these perishable foods travel 2,000 to 3,000 miles to reach the New York market and are a week or more on their journey. This is time enough for the food to spoil from microbial action or become overripe and worthless. Here is where refrigeration plays its role, arresting the processes that can lead to deterioration.

ICE PROVIDED the only practical means of keeping large quantities of perishable foods cool in warm weather until approximately 1880.

Today ice is still used in great quantities by the food industry for cooling fish, poultry, dairy products, fruits and vegetables, and beverages.

The 1963 production of ice was 20 million tons according to the National Ice Association. Ice production has decreased since World War II, when the annual value was $427 million, compared with $210 million in 1963. The decline has come about because of the replacement of iceboxes in the home and elsewhere with mechanical refrigeration equipment.

The largest use of commercial ice production today is for icing railroad cars, trucks, and the fishing fleet. About 14.5 million tons were used for these

* * *

W. T. Pentzer is *Director* of the Market Quality Research Division, Agricultural Research Service.

123

purposes in 1963. The remaining 5.5 million tons produced were used as cubed or crushed ice by restaurants, hotels, and by other institutions.

FISH WAS ONE of the first perishable foods to benefit from refrigeration. The captain of a Gloucester, Mass., smack put ice on board to preserve a catch of halibut in 1838.

In 1858 iced containers of fish were shipped from New England ports to New York City.

Fish was frozen with ice and salt as early as 1861. This may have been the beginning of the frozen food industry. Special pans for freezing the fish were developed, and the tightly filled, covered pans were packed in a mixture of ice and salt.

After freezing, the fish was coated with ice by dipping it in water.

Fish frozen in this way was held at 20° F. for 8 to 10 months. The storage rooms were refrigerated with ice and salt, later by mechanical refrigeration.

PRESENT PRACTICES have been built on these early techniques.

Fish like haddock and cod, caught by trawl off the New England and Canadian Maritime Provinces coasts, are eviscerated, washed, and iced in pens in the vessel's hold. Other small fish, like ocean perch and whiting, are iced without eviscerating because of their small size.

Shrimp are harvested by trawl and beheaded, washed, and stored in ice in the holds.

Fish of the Pacific Northwest, like halibut and sable, are eviscerated, washed, and iced in the vessel's pens. Pacific salmon, caught by seines for use in canneries, have recently been stored whole aboard the vessel in hold tanks containing sea water refrigerated to about 30° F.

Tuna caught offshore are usually frozen at sea. Those caught inshore are often iced in the round (not eviscerated) on the vessel. Many of the small inshore tuna boats make use of refrigerated holding coils to reduce the ice losses during long trips.

ICE USED ON BOARD ship must be clean and of low bacterial count, which calls for sanitary practices in manufacture, handling, and storing.

Enough ice must be used to cool the fish to about 32° and keep it cool. Ice does something else. As it melts, it washes off slime and bacteria, and prevents undesirable microbiological conditions in fish stored in the hold of the vessel.

About 1 pound of ice is required for every 2 pounds of fish.

Depending on the species, fish can be kept in ice without spoiling from 2 days to as long as 28 days.

WHEN BROUGHT ON SHORE, fish are stored in ice in refrigerated rooms not warmer than 35°, until they can be processed or distributed as fresh fish. Some ice meltage is desired to keep the fish washed with ice water. Ice is used to keep the packages of fresh fish chilled until they are sold.

The fishing industry uses a great deal of refrigeration, and a lot of it is in the form of ice.

Heaviest usage is by Pacific coast fishers and for shrimp.

The annual catch of fish and shellfish by U.S. vessels off our coasts and on the high seas is about 5 billion pounds valued at almost $400 million to the fishermen.

About half the catch is used for food, and the balance principally for fish meal and oil.

If ice was used on board vessel at the ratio of 1 pound per 2 pounds of fish, the 2.6 billion pounds of food fish would have required 650,000 tons of ice.

LOSS OF ICE from melting on board the vessel before use, and other refrigeration required would increase the refrigeration to perhaps 1 million tons. Another 400,000 tons of ice would be needed during distribution.

The refrigeration for food fish would then total approximately 1.4 million tons of ice. (A ton of refrigeration represents the cooling obtained from melting a ton of ice and is equal to 288 thousand British thermal units.)

124

To freeze fish on board ship, as in the tuna fleet, about 44,500 tons of refrigeration would be needed. To supply refrigeration to the holds of the albacore fleet would require 1,500 tons.

To cool precooked tuna prior to cleaning and packing canned tuna would require more than 600,000 tons of refrigeration.

About 285 million pounds of fish, crab, and shrimp are frozen annually, requiring approximately 145,000 tons of refrigeration.

Without counting refrigeration required to store the frozen product, an estimate can be made that the fishing industry uses 2.2 million tons of refrigeration annually to protect fish from spoiling and convert it into a less perishable frozen or canned product.

THE MEAT INDUSTRY as we know it today could not have developed without refrigeration. Prior to the Civil War, meat slaughtering houses used little refrigeration. They were located in the centers of cities where the meat could be consumed.

As livestock production along the Atlantic seaboard proved inadequate for eastern cities, animals were driven on the hoof to markets. Cattle and sheep withstood this method of transport better than hogs.

When railroads were built, connecting the West with the East, a heavy traffic developed in freighting live animals in stock cars to the East.

Fresh meat could be shipped considerable distances in the winter, but summer temperatures were too high even for curing meat. Curing everywhere was a winter operation. Ice was being experimented with to permit summer curing, but refrigeration was not practiced until the early 1870's for this particular purpose.

THE PENNSYLVANIA RAILROAD in 1857 insulated 30 boxcars with sawdust and installed iceboxes in the doorways. These cars were later remodeled by suspending the iceboxes overhead at either end, and they were used for transporting meat.

The Davis Refrigerator Car was patented in 1868 and 1869. It was cooled by ice and salt in tanks which could be refilled from the roof. It became one of the most widely used cars of the early days. Successful shipment of fresh meats from Chicago to Boston in 1869 in the Davis car inaugurated the dressed beef industry.

The Michigan Central Railroad experimented in the early 1860's in transporting fresh meat from Chicago to the East, using boxcars with ice bins built above the floor at each end.

EXPERIMENTATION with refrigerator cars on a commercial basis was to a large extent by meatpackers and fruit shippers and receivers.

The meat business was growing fast, and Swift had moved his New England packing business to Chicago. Railroads were not anxious to build refrigerator cars for dressed meat. They were satisfied with the returns from transporting live animals in stock cars.

Meatpackers were forced to purchase their own cars, and even today they own a small fleet of refrigerator cars. Improvements were made to provide lower temperatures in the cars.

By 1881 the business of shipping dressed beef from Chicago to the East had become well established.

ICE REFRIGERATION was nowhere more important between 1860 and 1890 than in meatpacking.

Ice was used in transporting meat and to cool it as well as to preserve it in the packing plant.

Some meat was frozen using ice and salt mixtures.

The meatpacking industry, concentrated in Chicago, brought the cold storage warehousing industry there also. They developed together, making the transfer from ice refrigeration to mechanical refrigeration about 1890.

Today, the same requirements for the refrigeration of meat prevail as did 100 years ago.

Body temperature of a beef animal at slaughter is around 102° F. After slaughter and continuing for 30 hours

125

or more, changes occur that generate heat.

Temperature of the deep round part of the carcass is about 105° F. when the carcass enters the chiller. To prevent spoilage the carcass should be reduced to 35° F. as rapidly as possible. In practice, after 20 hours of cooling, surface of the carcass will be 35° to 45° F. and the deep round about 60° F. Cooling will be completed in the holding cooler.

Beef is chilled in rooms held at 32° to 34° F., at 90 to 95 percent relative humidity. About 25,000 British thermal units (B.t.u.'s) would be required to cool a beef carcass of 500 pounds from 102° to 35° F. (A ton of ice, in melting, produces a ton of refrigeration, absorbing 288,000 B.t.u.'s.) This calculation is based on the average specific heat—heat capacity compared with water as 1.0—of meat as 0.75.

With other sources of heat to be considered, like heat leakage and heat generated by fan motors, the refrigeration requirement could well be 20 percent greater or 30,000 B.t.u.'s. This would amount to about 60 B.t.u.'s per pound of meat cooled.

CHILLING OF HOG CARCASSES follows much the same pattern as beef. The specific heat of pork is somewhat less, 0.57 instead of 0.75, and the carcasses smaller, averaging 180 pounds compared with 560 for beef.

Present practices require chilling to an internal ham temperature of 37° to 39° F. overnight. Temperature at time of slaughter varies from 100° F. to considerably higher. The refrigeration requirement may not differ much from beef in view of possibly higher initial temperatures.

In cooling lamb carcasses, the objective is to reduce slaughter temperatures of 98° to 102° to 34° to 36° F. in 12 to 14 hours, and to hold the carcass at these temperatures until shipped. Approximately the same chilling procedures are followed for calf cooling.

Humidity and air circulation are controlled in meat cooling to avoid drying the carcass too much, and to

avoid forming moisture on the carcass, which promotes bacterial growth.

The packinghouse may provide refrigeration for holding the beef carcasses for aging or the hog carcasses for cutting.

Total slaughter of meat in 1964 as reported by *The National Provisioner* was 31.8 billion pounds.

The breakdown by species was cattle, 16.4 billion pounds; hogs, 14.1 billion; calves, 600 million; and sheep and lamb, 700 million.

Total dollar sales of meat was about $14.6 billion.

The 1963 census records 2,992 meat slaughtering and processing plants to handle the 31.8 billion pounds of meat.

IF A REFRIGERATION requirement of 60 B.t.u.'s per pound is assigned to cool and hold meat at the slaughtering plant, about 6.6 million tons of refrigeration would be required.

If meat freezing is done at the processing plant, the input of refrigeration for freezing 696 million pounds (estimates for 1964 from *Quick Frozen Food Magazine*) would amount to an additional 348,000 tons of refrigeration, using a rough figure of a ton of refrigeration for a ton of frozen product. This would bring the total refrigeration requirement for cooling, holding, and freezing to about 7 million tons. The meat industry obviously rates as a giant in food refrigeration.

WILLIAM TAYLOR in the 1900 Yearbook of Agriculture traces development of the fruit industry in this country and in other parts of the world with the coming of refrigerated transport.

In 1800 there was no important fruit industry in the world other than growing grapes in Europe for making wine. As late as 1871 there were only a half dozen fruiterers in London and all they offered for sale were lemons and oranges and local fruit in season.

The potential in climate and soil for fruitgrowing was the same as today. But rapid and regular transportation and refrigeration were lacking.

As steam was applied to ocean transport and railroads during the middle 1800's, orchards and vineyards expanded. Railroads penetrated the interior of North America and Australia and opened up new fertile regions. California became perhaps the most conspicuous example in history of the rapid growth of a fruit and vegetable industry.

One of the first cold storages built in this country was for fruit. It was constructed in 1856 by the Rev. Benjamin Nyce, preacher, teacher, and chemist of Decatur County, Ill.

ICE WAS PLACED overhead in an insulated bunker with a metal floor which made the ceiling of the room. Warm air rising from the product was cooled by the cold ceiling and became heavier, providing air circulation by gravity. Calcium chloride was placed in the room to lower the humidity.

A ventilating fan was installed to bring in outside air. It was powered by a windmill.

Later, Nyce abandoned the idea of ventilation and made the rooms as tight as he could, using metal lining and beveled, tight doors. He had the idea, then considered foolish, that a buildup of carbon dioxide given off by the fruit would make apples keep for a longer period.

Use of airtight storages for apples was not perfected until many years later, in England by Kidd and West in the 1920's and in this country in the 1940's. In fact, the bringing in of outside air to provide ventilation had a heavy following in the early 1900's, and several systems were developed to gain benefits credited to fresh air.

BY 1878 THERE WERE several commercial fruit storages. One in New York City and another in Chicago were chilled with ice.

The Western Cold Storage Co. of Chicago converted to a semimechanical system in 1866, using coils in the room through which ice-cooled brine was circulated. An ammonia compressor was installed in 1890 to cool the brine.

By 1901 there were 600 cold storage plants for fruits and other produce, using mechanical refrigeration and totaling 50 million cubic feet. All classes of cold storage space, including meat, amounted to 150 million cubic feet.

REFRIGERATION in transit was also developing fast in the late 1800's.

The first carlot shipments of fruit from California were made in 1869, consisting of 33 tons of pears, apples, grapes, and plums. The shipments were in nonrefrigerated, ventilated cars. These shipments were successful, thanks to carefully selected fruit from the foothill districts.

All shipments prior to 1888 were made in nonrefrigerated cars.

Refrigerator cars available in 1868 were intended for meat. They had about a 3,000-pound ice capacity. This was enough refrigeration for prechilled meat carcasses but not for warm loads of fruit. Early attempts to use these cars for peaches and berries failed because of decay development.

PARKER EARLE, by cooling strawberries before loading them into the car, was successful in shipping fruit from southern Illinois to Chicago, Detroit, and other northern cities in 1878.

Earle and Thomas in 1886 set up a business of fresh fruit transportation with 50 cars owned by the Detroit Refrigerator Car Co. operated over the Michigan Central Railroad.

The California Fruit Transportation Co. was subsequently organized to operate these cars. By 1891 they had about 600 cars operating in all parts of the United States.

The car was known as the Hutchins Refrigerator and was the first with ice bunkers holding 4 to 5 tons. Well constructed, the car had 4 inches of wool insulation, and was equipped with overhead ice tanks as well as end bunkers.

Other carlines were soon formed. Armour Packing Co., which had specialized in equipment for fresh beef, entered the fruit transportation field and became the dominant car owner.

127

THERE WAS NO construction standard for refrigerator cars at this time and many were poorly made and gave poor results. Georgia peachgrowers in desperation appealed to the U.S Department of Agriculture for assistance. G. Harold Powell was placed in charge of investigations on picking, packing, cooling, and temperatures in transit in 1903.

Out of these studies came recommendations for a standard refrigerator car. The recommendations were put into effect in 1918 while the carriers were under Government control. The standards were updated after World War II, as a result of joint studies by the Agriculture Department and the Association of American Railroads.

Early work conducted by Powell in California with citrus fruits showed that careful handling during harvest and packing plus good refrigeration would prevent excessive loss from decay.

Similar studies were made with Florida citrus and with peaches, apples, plums, pears, sweet cherries, and cantaloups as well as with other fruits and vegetables.

Intensive investigations also were made on precooling.

A precooling unit mounted on a railroad car that was owned by the Agriculture Department was sent into fruit districts to demonstrate how to prevent decay and overripeness by means of prompt cooling.

As a result of these studies and demonstrations, precooling plants were built by the fruit industry and the refrigerator car companies.

LATER, portable fans were developed for car precooling. Still more recently, cars equipped with fans were built to use for precooling and to insure air circulation in transit.

Research was conducted on cold

Two entire rail cars of freshly harvested vegetables can be cooled in this two-tube vacuum cooler at a cooling plant in Tolleson, Ariz.

storage to determine the best temperatures and humidities for storing each kind of fruit and vegetable.

DISEASES that cause serious losses in shipping and storing fruits and vegetables were studied. Market pathology laboratories were established in Chicago and in New York City to help the industry and the inspection agencies recognize the cause of losses.

Current research includes studies on controlling the proportion of oxygen and carbon dioxide in the storage atmosphere.

Today almost 1½ million carloads (30 million tons) of fresh fruits and vegetables are shipped each year by rail and truck in the United States. About 35 percent are shipped by rail and 65 percent by truck.

It is difficult to find a fruit or vegetable among the 85 kinds listed in the United Fresh Fruit and Vegetable Association's guide to monthly availability that would not be refrigerated at some time of the year or at some step in moving it from the farm to the consumer.

THE 20 MOST IMPORTANT fruits and vegetables are shown in an accompanying table. They differ in the temperature that is required for storing and shipping.

Bananas, lemons, unripe pineapples, tomatoes, sweetpotatoes, and winter squash suffer chilling injury if stored at temperatures below 56° F.

Avocados, some grapefruit, cucumbers, snap beans, and sweet peppers are injured by holding at temperatures which are below 45°.

CRANBERRIES, potatoes, watermelons, ripe cantaloups, and some varieties of apples and oranges keep best in the range of 36° to 40° F. At 32° they are injured by chilling.

Florida-grown grapefruit, tangerines, and tangelos are stored at 32° F. even though some chilling injury may occur as a result.

This injury is preferable to decay that will develop at higher temperatures. Symptoms of chilling injury are pitting, internal discoloration and softening, off-flavors, and susceptibility to the development of decay.

Fruits and vegetables listed in the table that are not marked as susceptible to chilling injury keep best at 32° F. or at slightly lower temperatures.

Annual Supply of Major Fresh Fruits and Vegetables

Million Pounds

Fruits

*Apples	3,875
*Bananas	3,824
*Oranges	3,478
Peaches	1,796
*Grapefruit	1,758
Grapes	699
*Lemons	548
Pears	529
Plums, prunes	265
Strawberries	265
*Tangerines	246
*Avocados	113
Nectarines	95
*Pineapples	93
*Tangelos	81
Cherries	76
Apricots	38
*Cranberries	38
Coconuts	35
Blueberries	31
Total	**17,883**

Vegetables

*Potatoes	15,970
*Watermelons	3,119
Lettuce	2,921
*Tomatoes	2,400
Onions, dry	2,211
Cabbage	1,928
*Cantaloups	1,607
Corn	1,550
Celery	1,470
Carrots	1,304
*Sweetpotatoes	1,210
*Cucumbers	529
*Snap beans	473
*Sweet peppers	454
Radishes	350
*Squash	310
Greens, miscellaneous	253
Turnips, Rutabagas	233
Cauliflower	227
Onions, green	187
Total	**38,706**

*Susceptible to chilling injury.

Source: Guide to Average Monthly Availability of Fresh Fruits and Vegetables, United Fresh Fruit and Vegetable Association, 1964.

129

REFRIGERATION practices used today by the fruit and vegetable industry are specialized to meet specific requirements of the commodity. Cold storage of apples, for example, is adapted to differences in varietal requirements.

Most of the apple crop, except early shipments, is placed in cold storage as soon as harvested and moves to market during fall, winter, and early spring. About 75 percent of the crop is marketed from November through August.

Usual storage temperatures are 30° to 32° F. However, varieties like Yellow Newtown from California and McIntosh and Rhode Island Greening from New York and New England require higher temperatures of 38° to 40° F. Controlled atmosphere storage is provided for these varieties to retard ripening that would slowly take place at 38° to 40° F.

Tight rooms are constructed and oxygen is partially depleted by respiration of the fruit, and carbon dioxide (CO_2) from respiration is allowed to accumulate to desirable levels. Excess carbon dioxide is removed by washing the air with water or exposing it to lime or some other absorbent. Oxygen concentrations are maintained by drawing in outside air.

McINTOSH APPLES are usually stored in atmospheres of 2 to 5 percent CO_2 and 2 to 3 percent oxygen and 38° F. The Yellow Newtown variety is stored in 5 to 8 percent CO_2 and 2 to 3 percent oxygen at 38° to 40° F.

There were 1,612 cold storage plants for apples in the United States in 1963 with a total capacity of 243 million cubic feet.

Controlled atmosphere storage rooms were available in 265 plants and represented about 12 percent of the total apple storage space.

The amount of refrigeration used to cool that portion of the apple crop stored, estimated as 59 million bushels, would be approximately 385,000 tons, assuming they were cooled 40° F. and using 45 pounds as the weight of a bushel of apples. A specific heat figure

of 0.87 was used for apples and an allowance of 20 percent for inefficiencies and losses. Storage and refrigerated transport of apples would require several hundred thousand tons of additional refrigeration.

REFRIGERATION plays a very important role in the marketing of bananas.

Almost 68 million bunches of bananas were imported into the United States in 1963, practically all from Central America. Bananas are harvested when green in color, brought to the ports, and loaded into refrigerated banana ships that hold approximately 50,000 to 80,000 bunches.

Bananas are usually 75° to 80° F. when loaded and must be cooled in 12 to 24 hours to the desired carrying temperature of about 55° F.

Refrigeration capacity of most banana ships is about 200 tons. The voyage to the United States requires 3 to 9 days.

After reaching port, bananas are sorted by grade and color, and transferred to rail cars or trucks for transport to the terminal market. They are then ripened in special rooms under controlled temperatures and humidities and distributed to the retail trade.

Just the refrigeration required to cool the annual supply of bananas to the desired temperature for transport, say from 80° to 60° F., would require about 265,000 tons of refrigeration. Refrigerated transport could well add 200,000 tons additional refrigeration.

ORANGES ARE PRODUCED almost the year round and are stored only to a limited extent to supply requirements in summer and fall until the new crop of oranges comes to market.

Shipments of oranges made in warm weather are precooled before shipment. Warehouse cooling is the most common practice. Some car-precooling is used in Florida and hydrocooling as well for fruit packed in consumer bags.

Peaches are subject to decay and softening unless well refrigerated. Hydrocooling is used in eastern districts and cooling by air in precooling rooms or refrigerator cars in western districts.

Grapes are precooled prior to shipment or as they are stored.

Lemons are usually harvested when green in color and stored at about 55° to 58° F. where they gradually become yellow and more juicy. Refrigeration is used to cool lemons to the desired storage temperature and to hold them at this temperature.

All the other fruits that are listed in the table require some refrigeration for storage and shipment.

The chief crop of potatoes is harvested in the fall and only the first shipments are refrigerated.

The potato crop in Maine, the Red River Valley of Minnesota, and North Dakota move into storages cooled by outside air. The early Southern and California crop is refrigerated to prevent decay.

Special attention is given to potatoes intended for processing. They may be damaged in cooking quality if they are stored or transported at temperatures any lower than 50° F.

LETTUCE, most of it originating in California and Arizona, is almost all vacuum cooled after packing into fiberboard cartons holding 4 to 5 dozen heads.

A typical cooling job would be the removal of 30° of field heat, cooling from 68° to 38° F. in about 30 minutes. Cooling is accomplished by evaporating the moisture from the heads of lettuce under a high vacuum at which water boils at 32° F.

The moisture released must be condensed if the vacuum is to be maintained. This is done with a mechanically refrigerated condenser, a second vacuum chamber filled with ice, or with a steam ejector system and a barometric condenser.

There are 45 to 50 vacuum cooling plants in the Arizona-California lettuce districts. It is estimated the refrigeration required to cool the lettuce crop before shipment would amount to about 300,000 tons.

Before vacuum cooling came into use, about 25 to 30 pounds of ice were placed in the package to do the cooling job. The load would also be covered with crushed ice. The amount of ice used to refrigerate a carload of lettuce would often weigh as much as the lettuce.

Consequently, ice would remain in the crates, on top of the load, and in the ice bunkers on arrival.

Today lettuce is not iced. Bunker ice in fan cars or mechanically refrigerated cars are used for transport.

TOMATOES, susceptible to chilling like bananas, are seldom precooled and are transported at temperatures of 55° to 65° F. depending on the degree of their ripeness. They are ripened after reaching market.

A crop like dry onions may be stored many months to lengthen the marketing season. A temperature of 32° F. and low humidity of 70 to 75 percent are recommended.

Cabbage is another long storage crop and it requires temperatures of 32° F. The spring crop is refrigerated while it is in transit.

Only a rough estimate can be made of the total refrigeration used in getting the fresh fruit and vegetable crop cool, ready to ship, and keeping it cool during storage and transport.

Eliminating some commodities that do not require cooling or transit refrigeration, like watermelons and most of the potato crop, the cooling load alone could amount to 2 million tons. Storage and in-transit refrigeration could well be an equal amount.

The commercial frozen pack of fruits during 1964 was approximately 702,000 tons, with citrus juices and strawberries the most important items. Frozen vegetables amounted to 1,320,000 tons. Potato products made up more than a third of the total. Peas, corn, broccoli, and spinach were other important items.

Over 2 million tons of refrigeration would be required to freeze 2,022,000 tons of frozen fruits and vegetables. A rough estimate then for cooling, storing, shipping, and freezing fruits and vegetables would be 6 million tons.

131

THE POULTRY INDUSTRY is another very large user of refrigeration.

The Agriculture Department carried on extensive investigations to improve practices of handling and storing poultry, beginning about 1910. Miss Mary Pennington was one of the pioneers in this early work. Methods of killing, dressing, and refrigeration were gradually worked out.

Cooling in air and nonevisceration, or "New York dressed," was favored. Later, evisceration under careful sanitation practices and cooling in ice water became the accepted practice.

BROILERS today are shipped thousands of miles from the large production areas of Georgia, Arkansas, Delaware, Maryland, Alabama, North Carolina, and Mississippi.

Poultry cooled quickly in special cooling equipment, packed in ice, and transported in refrigerated trucks and cars can be delivered in good condition more than a week after killing. The poultry will still have several days of shelf life if it is refrigerated in the retail store.

In the last 18 years the broiler business has shown a remarkable growth. Production in 1945 was 350 million birds and by 1964 it was 2.16 billion birds, amounting to about 7.5 billion pounds. Broilers are produced through-

out the year in this country. Over 90 percent are not frozen.

THE PRIMARY PROBLEM in refrigerating broilers is microbial deterioration. Lowering the meat temperature as near freezing as possible is the best protection against growth of microorganisms and chemical changes in the meat and the fat that affect color and flavor of the birds.

Internal temperature of the chicken after feather removal and evisceration is 70° to 90° F. The poultry should be chilled quickly to about 35° F.

Very few birds are chilled today in air. Cooling in a slush of ice and water under agitation is common, and several kinds of coolers are available to speed up the process. Water in the chill tanks and in the chillers must be kept clean.

Prolonged holding in chill tanks is avoided to keep the meat from absorbing large amounts of water.

The refrigeration requirement for poultry is about 0.7 to 1.5 pounds of ice per pound of poultry processed, with poultry chilling taking 0.4 to 1.0 pound, icing the shipping crates 0.25 to 0.35 pound, and icing trucks and trailers 0.05 to 0.15 pound.

A rough estimate of refrigeration used by the broiler industry to protect this perishable food would be about

Production line at a chicken processing plant near Salisbury, Md. Processed chickens are chilled in the carts in foreground.

7.5 billion pounds or 3.75 million tons of ice.

Most of the turkeys, ducks, and geese produced are marketed frozen and, of course, chickens are also frozen.

Freezing is the best method of preserving poultry meat for any long time, and excellent practices have been developed for fast freezing, packaging, storing, and distributing. Freezing in air at −30° F., or in brine or other liquid at −20°, and holding at 0° or below are recommended practices.

It is estimated that about 2.3 billion pounds of poultry are marketed frozen, with turkeys more than half the total. Frozen meals containing poultry are not included in this figure.

Using the rough estimate of a ton of refrigeration to freeze a ton of poultry meat, 1.15 million tons of refrigeration would be required for the frozen poultry business, not counting storage and transport requirements.

EGGS WERE PRESERVED—although not very well—in water glass (sodium silicate), limewater, or by some other chemical means before refrigeration was available. In the 1880's ice refrigerated rooms began to be used for the storage of eggs.

Quality of storage eggs was not very dependable, for most came from small flocks on the farm. The farmer sold them to grocers. Egg merchants bought them from the grocers, often several weeks later.

The egg business continued to grow despite lack of quality control. By 1917, cold storage of eggs amounted to 7 million cases of 30 dozen each.

The Agriculture Department in 1913 installed a refrigerated egg packing establishment on wheels and sent it on long trips to the Midwest where farmers and dealers were shown how to care for eggs. They were encouraged to produce infertile eggs of lower perishability. Shippers were urged to chill eggs to 50° F. before loading into refrigerator cars.

Eggs were frozen commercially, beginning about 1900. After 1930 when cold storage holdings were 11 million cases, storage of shell eggs declined because of year-round production by commercial flocks. Frozen eggs came into greater use because of the growth of commercial bakeries and less baking in the home.

Annual production of eggs today is about 5¼ billion dozen. About 85 percent or 149 million cases are consumed as shell eggs. Cold storage of eggs is no longer large, seldom exceeding several hundred thousand cases. About 15 million cases of the total production of 175 million cases are broken commercially for frozen and dried egg products. Six percent of the production is used for hatching purposes.

DETERIORATION in shell eggs results from decomposition by molds and bacteria, changes due to chemical reactions, and absorption of flavors and odors from the environment.

If eggs are fertile, serious chemical changes take place at temperatures above 85° F. Commercially produced market eggs are infertile. As the egg ages, the white thins and the yolk flattens. Many different kinds of mold attack eggs.

Oil coatings are often applied to eggs within 24 hours after laying, to entrap the natural carbon dioxide in the egg. This helps retard aging and the loss of moisture.

Prompt cooling at the farm to 29° to 30° F. would give maximum protection, but condensation and resultant mold then is a problem. Cooling to 50° to 60° F. in air of 70 to 80 percent relative humidity is recommended.

Cold storage at 29° to 30° F. and at humidities of 85 to 90 percent are recommended, using the lower humidity if the eggs have been oiled.

COOLING 149 MILLION CASES of eggs consumed as shell eggs would require approximately 484,000 tons of refrigeration, if all the eggs were cooled 20°, say from 80° to 60° F:

About 360 million pounds of liquid eggs are frozen annually. Using again a rough estimate of a ton of refrigeration to freeze a ton of product, 181,000

133

Stainless steel bulk milk tank.

tons of refrigeration would be required for this purpose.

The refrigeration required by the poultry industry is estimated as 3.75 million tons for cooling broilers, 1.15 million tons for freezing poultry, and approximately 700,000 tons for cooling and freezing eggs, making a total of about 5.5 million tons.

MILK PRODUCERS in colonial times knew milk would sour quickly in warm weather, but they did not know why.

Sultry weather and thunderstorms were directly associated with souring. Not much could be done to protect the milk except keep it in a cool place such as the well, cellar, or spring. About 1860 ice came into general use to prevent milk from souring.

As early as the 1840's milk was shipped from upstate New York by rail into the city. The Erie Railroad transported 3 million quarts of milk in 1842–1843.

Some farmers in 1849 were cooling milk in cans by stirring it with a tin tube filled with ice. In 1851 butter was shipped by rail in small iced containers. Ice refrigerated rooms were to be found in well equipped dairies in the Northern States in the 1880's.

Long distance shipment of butter and cheese to eastern markets from the Midwest began about the time refrigerator cars became available in the early 1880's.

ON-THE-FARM COOLING of milk, placing the cans in cold water or flowing the milk over cold metal surfaces, began to be practiced in the late 1800's and early 1900's as it became generally understood that low temperatures checked the multiplication of bacteria in the milk.

The Agriculture Department advised producers in the Northern States to harvest a crop of ice each winter for the summer cooling of milk.

Some cities prohibited entry of milk warmer than 60° F. Insulated jackets over milk cans helped prevent warming during the trip by wagon to the railroad receiving station. When milk reached the city for bottling, it was cooled to 45° to 50° F.

Butter churning moved from the farm to creameries where a more uniform, higher quality product could be made, largely through better sanitation and controlled temperature.

By 1915 mechanical refrigeration had replaced ice refrigeration in the large creameries. Butter storage became quite extensive.

During 1915, the first year for cold storage statistics, a total of 100 million pounds of butter were in storage by September 1, the peak of production.

COLD STORAGE WAREHOUSING stabilized the dairy industry.

Cheese manufacturers found controlled temperatures the answer to the problem of curing cheeses of various kinds that had specific temperature requirements.

The present era of the dairy industry has seen the once widely used milk can replaced by stainless steel tanks, at the farm and on trucks and rail cars, for the bulk handling of milk.

Total milk production in 1964 was 126.6 billion pounds. Factory products accounted for 64.1 billion pounds, with butter, cheese, and ice cream the most important. Consumption of fluid milk off the farm was 52.9 billion pounds. Farm consumption made up most of the rest of total production.

Present day practices call for cooling milk to 38° F. within an hour after it is produced. Milk is kept cool in refrigerated holding tanks or cans at the farm and during its transport to the milk plant.

SINCE THE PLANT seldom has capacity to pasteurize milk at the rate it is delivered, holding tanks often equipped with refrigeration are used. Some plants cool all milk received to about 36° F. before the milk is transferred to the holding tanks.

Before pasteurization, milk is separated and blended to provide the butterfat content which is desirable in fluid milk.

After standardizing, the milk is

135

In coin-operated canteens, refrigeration plays a big role for milk, ice cream, and other food products.

pasteurized by heating it to 145° F. and holding it at that temperature for 30 minutes. High-temperature-short-time pasteurization is now commonly used. In this method the milk is heated to 161° F. and held at this temperature for 15 seconds. It is then cooled to 40° F. or lower.

COLD MILK to be pasteurized may be passed through a heat exchanger in which the cold milk is heated and the warm pasteurized milk is cooled. About 70 to 80 percent of the refrigeration which otherwise would be needed to recool the pasteurized milk can be saved in this manner.

From the pasteurizer, the cooled milk is passed to bottles or cartons. They are held in a storage room at 34° to 40° F. until loaded into refrigerated trucks for delivery.

If we assume that 80 percent of the milk production of 126.6 billion pounds is cooled from 90° to 50° F., and assign a specific heat of 1.0 to milk to allow for some inefficiencies in

cooling, the refrigeration load would be approximately 14.1 million tons.

Milk marketed as fluid milk—about 52.9 billion pounds in 1964—is heated to 145° or 161° F., depending on the pasteurizing process, and then it must be cooled to 40° F. or lower.

Assuming the milk is cooled a total of 100° F. and that the regeneration process of heating-cooling was 80 percent efficient, there would still remain about a 20° F. temperature reduction for which refrigeration would be required. This would take approximately 3.7 million tons of refrigeration, making a whopping total of 17.8 million tons for the milk cooling job before and following pasteurization.

Refrigeration is used in churning and storing butter, curing cheese, and to make ice cream, harden it, and transport it. These processes fall more into the field of manufacture and are not included in this chapter on how refrigeration protects the food supply.

Among the industries that developed to take care of the expanding perishable food business was the refrigerated warehousing industry.

By 1891, the industry had become large enough to have a trade association. The American Warehousemen's Association was formed in Chicago that year, consisting of 29 companies.

The U.S. Department of Commerce and Labor was requested to make a survey of cold storage plants. This was the forerunner of the report issued monthly since 1915 by the Agriculture Department on cold storage holdings of major perishable commodities.

Refrigerated warehouse capacity in 1963 was 1.1 billion cubic feet, excluding Alaska and Hawaii, representing a gain of 84 million cubic feet over the 1961 survey. Freezer capacity was 52 percent of the total. Per capita availability of space in 1963 of 5.88 cubic feet represented a gain of approximately 23 percent over 1943.

THE PERISHABLE food industry depended on transportation and refrigeration for its development, with the refrigerator car playing an essential role. But the total number of refrigerator cars available has declined in recent years because much traffic has moved to trucks.

As of July 1, 1965, the breakdown of the refrigerator car fleet was 65,020 ice bunker cars of all types; 10,945 mechanically refrigerated cars of all types; and 2,360 express refrigerator cars. This makes a total of 78,325 refrigerator cars.

In addition, there are 32,645 insulated bunkerless cars for transporting canned goods and other commodities that don't require refrigeration but do require protection from freezing during cold weather.

ABOUT 5,000 mechanically refrigerated cars are on order, which will soon make a fleet of almost 16,000 cars of this type.

Refrigerated trailers transported on flatcars are also owned by the railroads. The total is 5,451 regular service trailers, 728 meat trailers, and 1,499 insulated containers.

Perishable freight traffic of foods and beverages for the railroads in 1963 amounted to 1.4 million carloads, totaling 34.7 million tons.

The 1963 Census of Transportation indicates that 1.2 percent of all motor trucks registered were refrigerated, or 152,700 vehicles.

About 20,000 were classed as 35 feet or larger, and 17,000 as 25 to 34.9 feet. These are the size used for between-city carload traffic.

Many of the smaller refrigerated trucks are used primarily for in-city delivery service. The most popular size was 10 to 15.9 feet, with some 73,000 vehicles representing about 48 percent of the total.

Trucks carry 65 percent of the frozen food traffic, and about the same percentage of fresh fruit and vegetables.

Most broiler production is transported in trucks, and most milk.

Refrigerated trucks probably move more than 65 percent of perishable foods from farm to market. Long distance hauling is more likely to be by rail than by truck.

A HIGHLY ESSENTIAL part of the cold chain for food is refrigeration in the retail store. Without it, there would be little business in perishable foods.

Most of the retail food business is done in supermarkets in this country. The United States has approximately 28,000 supermarkets.

A well equipped market has refrigerated display cases for frozen foods, meats and dairy products, fruits and vegetables, and a battery of reach-in refrigerators for milk, cheese, and other refrigerated products. It usually has a produce cooler and a meat cooler near the preparation areas for these commodities where the reserve supplies can be held.

The store is air-conditioned for the comfort of the customers and this, too, is beneficial to the perishable foods.

Temperatures recommended for display cases used for meat are 28° to 38° F. and for produce and nonfrozen dairy products, 35° to 45° F. Frozen food cases should maintain 0° F. and ice cream cabinets −12° F.

RESTAURANTS and other firms that provide food services to the public have estimated sales of $20 to $26 billion, and rely heavily on refrigeration.

One meal in four is eaten away from home. Commercial restaurants make up 76 percent of the total annual sales. Clubs, airlines, schools, hospitals, and other institutions take care of the rest.

There are about 530,000 eating establishments in the Nation.

Recent surveys by *American Restaurant Magazine* indicated that all medium- to large-volume restaurants, serving 500 meals or more a day, had two reach-in refrigerators. Fifty-six percent had two walk-in coolers and 71 percent had ice cream cabinets. In addition, many had refrigerated beverage dispensers.

There were approximately 40,000 restaurants of this size. If each had two reach-in refrigerators of ½-horsepower size, a walk-in cooler of 1-horsepower size, and ice cream cabinets, milk cooler, and other fractional horsepower equipment that totaled 1 horsepower, a total of 3 horsepower or approximately 3 tons of refrigeration would be used. This would add up to just about 120,000 tons for medium to large restaurants.

THE LAST LINK in the cold chain is the home refrigerator and freezer. The estimate for 1965 sales of new farm and home freezers is 1.1 million. The 1960 census counted 9.8 million freezers in the 53 million households included in the census. This represented 18.4 percent of all the households. In the 5 years since 1960, with sales averaging over 1 million per year, consumers must have acquired almost 5 million homefreezers, making the total now over 14 million.

There are 9,900 commercial locker plants that are primarily engaged in provisioning homefreezers. The total 0° F. storage space contolled by consumers in locker plants and homefreezers is estimated at over 200 million cubic feet, capable of holding 6.5 million pounds of food.

It was expected that 4.7 million new household refrigerators would be sold in 1965. There is no current census estimate for home refrigerators in use. The last figure was in 1950 when the market was 80 percent saturated. In 1960 when the household market was estimated to be 90 percent saturated, there would have been 47.7 million refrigerators. Today the number is probably well over 50 million.

MANUFACTURERS of refrigeration equipment have worked closely with the food industry, making improvements and supplying new kinds of equipment as the need arose. Requirements of the food and beverage industry once dominated the market and they still do if household equipment is included.

The value of total shipments manufactured by the refrigeration equipment industry in 1963 was $1.9 billion. This figure did not include household refrigerators or home and farm freezers. Packaged air conditioning made up $611 million of the total. It is not possible to determine how much equipment in the remaining $1.3 billion is used for food refrigeration.

If you take only commercial refrigerators and related equipment, $279 million, and add to it household refrigerators, $688 million, and home and farm freezers, $143 million, the total would be approximately $1.1 billion for food refrigeration equipment manufactured in 1963. This is almost twice as much as the value of packaged air-conditioning equipment.

THIS IS THE STORY of the food refrigeration industry in the United States.

Links in the chain of refrigeration reaching from farm to kitchen are ice manufacturing plants, icemaking machines, milk coolers, vacuum coolers, hydrocoolers, poultry coolers, refrigerated warehouses, refrigerated trucks, refrigerated rail cars, walk-in and reach-in refrigerators, refrigerated display cases, locker plants, household refrigerators, and home and farm freezers.

The food industry uses over 20 million tons of refrigeration to chill and freeze fish, meat, fruits and vegetables, poultry, and eggs. The dairy industry uses an estimated 18 million tons just for cooling milk alone.

This country has 1.1 billion cubic feet of cold storage space, amounting to 5.88 cubic feet per capita.

The refrigerator car fleet totals 78,325 cars and 7,678 trailers for flatcar transport. There are approximately 152,700 refrigerated trucks.

Household refrigerators total about 50 million and home and farm freezers 5 million. There are 9,900 commercial locker plants. Manufacturing of refrigeration equipment for food is big business, amounting to an estimated $1.1 billion during 1963.

The future will bring new foods and new ways of refrigeration. Fresh quality will be captured by virtually instant cooling and freezing. It will be retained by continuous low temperature refrigeration. The variety of foods will continue to grow as fast transportation and refrigeration bring exotic foods to our markets from far-off places.

STORAGE

AND

WAREHOUSING

CALVIN GOLUMBIC
and HAMILTON LAUDANI

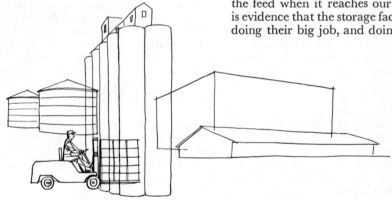

RETAIL value of food products sold in the United States in 1965 exceeded $90 billion. Of this, 60 percent or $54 billion worth of food was stored without refrigeration in warehouses and other facilities in our Nation's food pipeline.

Protecting this tremendous amount of stored food against insects, molds, rats, and other menaces calls for a warehouseman's broad shoulders and a scientist's pinpoint precision.

Feed grains for our animals must be safeguarded along with food grains for our own consumption—and 4.5 billion bushels of grains were marketed in 1964, equivalent to 300 billion pounds. Another 22 billion pounds of canned and dehydrated food products were marketed.

The quality and abundance of these foods when they reach our tables and the feed when it reaches our livestock is evidence that the storage facilities are doing their big job, and doing it well.

What does it take to do this job, to protect stored commodities against quality loss and damage from pests? It takes facilities that are built right, practices that deter spoilage and pest attacks, and exactly controlled use of gases and chemicals to create surroundings hostile to molds, insects, and other hazards.

Commodities are stored in a variety of facilities. Upright, tank, and flat structures are used for bulk storage of food and feed grains, flat or warehouse storage facilities for packaged products.

Upwards of half a billion square feet of wholesale warehouse space for foodstuffs is available in this country

Calvin Golumbic is *Chief*, Field Crops and Animal Products Research Branch, Agricultural Research Service.

Hamilton Laudani is *Director*, Research and Development Laboratory, Stored-Product Insects Research Branch, Agricultural Research Service.

exclusive of warehouse space of chain stores, food manufacturing plants, and food lockers.

The major hazards in nonrefrigerated storage are micro-organisms, insects, rodents, and other pests as well as the deteriorative effect of atmospheric oxygen and other chemical reactions.

Predominant micro-organisms attacking stored food and feedstuffs like grain, grain products, and oilseeds are fungi or molds, mainly of the *Aspergillus* and *Penicillium* genera. Among the fungi there are a large number of species, each so adapted to the environment that it can compete effectively against the others for the available food supply.

These storage fungi are widely prevalent on most grains at harvest as spores or superficial mycelium, but actual invasion of the grain by these organisms occurs later under storage conditions of high humidity and temperature. Spores, the reproductive units of fungi, germinate and develop into networks of long, hollow branched cells called mycelium, which are able to penetrate the seed.

Fungi are found in the bran and in the outer layers of the seed.

They attack with equal ease any section of the moist seed surface, but the xerophytic or drought-resistant fungi which have minimum moisture requirements seem to invade the germ more readily than the endosperm or the nutritive tissue of the seed. These fungi may be a cause of "black germ" or "sick" wheat.

Storage fungi colonies are also found at the site of insect and mechanical damage in the seed.

MOLD GROWTH produces a number of deteriorative effects on grain, grain products, and oilseeds. There is discoloration and loss of luster. Mustiness is introduced into the raw product and carried over into the processed product.

Processing quality is lowered. For example, it is more difficult to separate starch from protein in wet mill-

ing of corn. The fat acidity of oil from molded oilseeds is high, causing increased refining losses.

Fungi-induced deterioration may result in the loss of ½ percent of the world's grain production, according to a conservative estimate. Other estimates range up to 10 percent.

SPORADIC OUTBREAKS of poisoning by unknown causes in livestock have often been associated with the feeding of moldy grain.

The true nature of these moldy feed diseases became suddenly apparent to the scientific world and a matter of public concern as a result of the Turkey-X disease incident in England in 1960. One hundred thousand poults were poisoned after eating a Brazilian peanut meal.

Within a remarkably short time, scientists found that the causative agent, a toxic and cancer-producing substance called aflatoxin, was a metabolic product of some strains of the common storage mold *Aspergillus flavus*. Effective protective measures were quickly developed to prevent this toxin from getting into food and into feeds.

AFLATOXIN WAS FOUND to be a mixture of four closely related thermostable compounds named aflatoxin B_1, B_2, G_1, and G_2. The most toxic was aflatoxin B_1 which has a lethal dose (LD_{50}) of 18 micrograms in ducklings.

Animal species vary in their sensitivity to these toxins, but the general pattern of the disease in all species examined has been that of severe liver injury. Young animals like young pigs and calves are more susceptible than adults of the species.

Some other *Aspergillus* and *Penicillium* species are now known to have strains capable of producing aflatoxin and other toxic metabolites. The best defined of the latter are fumigatin and fumigacin from *Aspergillus fumigatus*, luteoskyrin from *Penicillium islandicum*, patulin from *Penicillium uriticae*, citrinin from *Penicillium citrinen*, maltoryzine from *Aspergillus oryzae* var. *microsporus*, ochratoxin from *Aspergillus ochraeous*.

140

Other mold genera also produce toxins. Some of these toxins have antibiotic activity against bacteria.

THE NATURAL FUNGI on stored grain and oilseeds contain a significant proportion of toxic strains of molds. The average toxin level in these crops, however, is usually extremely low because of protective procedures, and climatic and other factors.

Undamaged pods of farmers stock peanuts form an effective barrier to the entrance of these molds. Low daily temperatures during harvest also can reduce the risk of contamination even during wet weather.

MORE THAN 50 SPECIES of insects feed on grain and grain products. Most of the damage is done by four species: The granary weevil, rice weevil, lesser grain borer, and Angoumois grain moth. These insect species infest whole-kernel grain, and the larvae can live their entire lives within the kernel undetected.

Another group of insects feeds on broken grain and grain products. These include the saw-toothed grain beetle, red flour beetle, confused flour beetle, Indian-meal moth, flat grain beetle, and the cadelle beetle.

This second group of insects is usually present in grain with a significant amount of broken kernels, grain dust, and foreign matter. They are also commonly found in grain damaged by the four primary species.

Grain with high moisture content is infested by several species of fungus beetles and mites.

The insects that attack inshell peanuts consist of several species of beetles and of moths.

The more common beetles are the saw-toothed grain beetle, flour beetle, cigarette beetle, cadelle beetle, and corn sap beetle. The more important moths are the Indian-meal moth, almond moth, Mediterranean flour moth, and Angoumois grain moth.

Beetle infestations normally occur in bulk peanuts or within the bags of peanuts, and therefore are not usually visible. Most of the damage to peanuts is usually done by beetles.

Moths are found on the surface of bulk peanuts and on the outer surface of bagged peanuts.

A moth infestation is very noticeable because the larvae crawl about on the surface and leave a noticeable webbing. Furthermore, the adult moths fly freely, and they can become quite numerous.

The most serious pests of dried fruit are the Indian-meal moth, the saw-toothed grain beetle, various species of dried fruit moths, and flour beetles.

Insects may adversely affect the quality and the value of grain, peanuts, and other commodities in many ways. The most serious type of damage is by reducing the weight and nutritive value.

The internal feeders and some of the secondary species consume the endosperm. Others feed on the germ.

Such feeding reduces the yield of the milled or processed commodity, and when the infestation has been heavy and present for a long time, the yield may be too low for profitable processing.

INSECT INFESTATIONS frequently cause heating in small grains, which results in caking and spoilage.

A temperature over 120° F. may be produced in grain by insect activity. The hot air rises to the surface of the grain, and as it cools, moisture condenses and is deposited on the grain.

The wet condition becomes favorable for insects, mold, and fungi development. Caking and spoilage follow.

Some insects completely destroy the germination of seeds by eating the germ. Others eat the endosperm and deprive the seedling of sufficient food to develop properly.

PRESENCE OF INSECTS in bulk commodities may result in financial loss to the owner by having it downgraded. In the case of grain, it would be designated "weevily" by official graders. Downgrading will not only bring a lower price for the commodity but will also prevent the owner from securing a Government loan on certain products.

Insect-infested food commodities in interstate marketing channels are considered as containing filth and are subject to seizure under the Federal Food, Drug, and Cosmetic Act. This may result in a fine and in downgrading the product to animal feed.

Usual cleaning methods do not remove all the internal feeding insects in grain, peanuts, oilseeds, and dried fruit during processing. Presence of insect fragments in the processed commodities make these products unfit for human use under the Federal Food, Drug, and Cosmetic Act.

The most effective and economical way of maintaining the high quality of grain, oilseeds, peanuts, and their processed products is to take the necessary measures to prevent insect, fungi, mold, bacteria, and rodent damage. If action isn't taken until an infestation occurs, some damage has already been done to the quality of the product.

Many of the preventive measures that can be taken will help maintain quality of the products against most of the destructive organisms.

Others are specific for protection against insects, fungi, molds, bacteria, or against rodents.

A WIDE VARIETY of products are subject to deterioration from exposure to oxygen in the air. Stored fats, oils, oilseeds, and the fatty constituents in dehydrated products are particularly susceptible to this type of deterioration, which results in rancidity, off-flavors and odors, loss or change in color, and vitamin destruction.

Fat oxidation and the Maillard browning reaction have been implicated in the loss of nutritive value in storage of protein-rich foods from animal sources like milk powder.

The browning reaction, involving free amino groups and reducing sugars, is a common deteriorative chemical process that leads to undesirable appearance and quality changes and may be another causative factor of germ-damaged or "sick" wheat. Fungi are also implicated in this condition.

THE STORAGE PERIOD of bulk-stored commodities varies from a few weeks to a few years, sometimes more. The carryover in food and feed grains amounted to about 3.5 billion bushels in 1964, or about 90 percent of the total quantity marketed the previous year. The carryover of oils and fats is usually around 10 to 15 percent of the total supply.

AMONG THE BROAD measures for maintaining quality in stored foods, proper storage facilities are of the utmost importance.

Grain, peanuts, oilseeds, and other similar agricultural products are stored in every conceivable type of structure from a hole in the ground to modernistic skyscraper-type elevators.

A good storage structure should be well constructed with a minimum of cracks and crevices and no double walls or floors that could serve as reservoirs for insects, fungi, molds, and spoiled food. Concrete floors should be waterproof and vaporproof.

THE STORAGE STRUCTURE should be weathertight and contain screens to keep out insects, birds, rodents, and other animals.

It should be constructed to facilitate cleaning and the orderly movement of stored products.

Facilities used for long-term storage of grains should have a good recirculation system for aeration to keep the grain dry and cool as well as for fumigating the grain if this becomes necessary.

The structure should be built to provide reasonable safety against fire and storm damage. White paint on the roof and walls of metal buildings will help to keep the stored material several degrees cooler.

GOOD STORAGE PRACTICES are essential. Here are a few tips:
• Always thoroughly clean the premises before refilling—leftovers may contain insects, fungi, and other organisms that will infest new material.
• Clean the grain before it is stored.

142

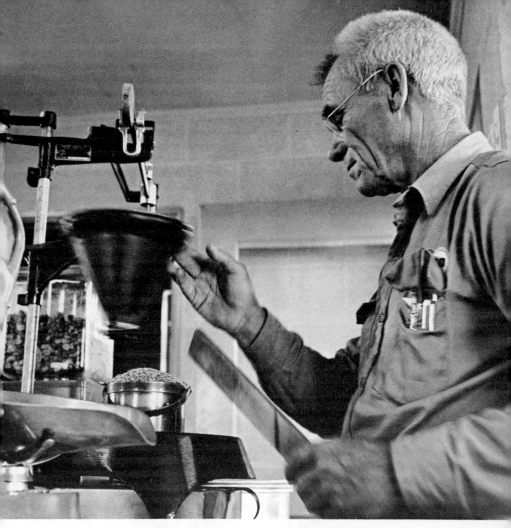

Testing wheat in country elevators near Garden City, Kans.

The elimination of grain dust, broken kernels, and foreign matter makes the grain less attractive and less susceptible to insect and mold infestations.

• Don't commingle new grain and other bulk agricultural commodities with old stock. Most likely the organisms that cause quality deterioration will be present in the old stock and introduced into the new crop if mixed.

• Never store high moisture grain. Have it machine-dried if necessary, with care not to heat-damage it. The drier the grain, the less susceptible it is to damage by insects, molds, fungi, and bacteria.

• Use the air recirculation system to maintain the grain cool and dry. At temperatures below 45° F. most grain insects become inactive and mold growth diminishes.

ONCE THE COMMODITY is stored, the appropriate treatment and quality control procedure to employ depends on periodic surveillance tests.

Elevator operators periodically check temperature for hot spots, note the odor of exhaust from aeration system, and examine samples for appearance, temperature, odor, damaged kernels, and insect activity.

Interior of an experimental automatic grain sampler is inspected during tests conducted by USDA in cooperation with a commercial grain company.

Quality surveillance in bulk-stored oils is fairly simple, since samples can be removed easily and then analyzed for peroxide value, fat acidity, color, and refining loss.

The proper sampling of grain can be a problem. If the bin is deep, insertion of a grain probe may be difficult and the probe may not reach as far as the bottom of the structure.

Pneumatic probes have been developed for this purpose and are undergoing evaluation. If possible, samples should be taken by a pelican or automatic grain sampling device whenever the grain is turned or moved from one bin to another.

IN STORAGE owned by the Agriculture Department's Commodity Credit Corporation, grain is inspected at monthly intervals—or more often if advisable. The grain is turned, screened, or fumigated when necessary.

Efficiency of this quality maintenance program is high, costing less than 3 cents per bushel in 1960. This cost totaled about $17 million in 1959 for a food and feed inventory worth about a billion dollars.

Success of the program is also shown by the outturn on grades of corn shipped from both binsites and from warehouses.

Shipments of corn from binsites

Stacks of commodities can be fumigated more economically and effectively under gasproof plastic films. Leaving the covers in place helps keep food clean and resists reinfestation by insects.

in all the major corn-producing States from 1957 through 1961 amounted to approximately 459 million bushels of corn, of which 73.4 percent graded Nos. 1, 2, and 3.

A SUBSTANTIAL AMOUNT of the Nation's grain and peanuts is infested when it goes into storage.

Fumigation is the most effective and sometimes the only way of controlling existing infestations. This is possible only when the storage structure is fairly airtight, or the commodity or the whole building can be covered with a tarpaulin.

Successful fumigation will kill an existing infestation but offers no protection to the commodity against reinfestation after treatment. Lasting protection against new infestations is obtained only by protective treatments.

There are many fumigants on the market for controlling insects in grain, peanuts, oilseeds, and processed food and feed products. The method of applying fumigants depends on type of fumigant used, commodity involved, and size and condition of the storage structure itself.

Fumigation can be very dangerous to the person applying the pesticide as

145

well as to other persons in the area. Only experienced operators should do the job.

Chemical means of controlling mold infestations in grain have not proven practical.

But residual surface treatments or protective sprays applied directly to the commodity can be used effectively in protecting bulk-stored commodities against insect infestation. Creation of unsuitable climatic or atmospheric conditions is effective against both insect and mold attack.

Residual treatment consists of spraying floor and wall surfaces of a storage structure with a persistent-type insecticide. The same spray should be applied to conveyors and other equipment inside the building.

Use of residual treatments is particularly important in storage buildings with wooden floors, loading platforms, and dead space under the building, as is the case with many of the peanut, feed, and oilseed warehouses. In such buildings both the top and bottom surfaces of the floors and the ground under and around the building should be sprayed.

Three of the most commonly used residual insecticides and their concentrations are 3 percent of malathion (premium grade only), 2.5 percent of methoxychlor, and 0.1 percent of synergized pyrethrins. It is best to apply these insecticides as wettable powder or water emulsion formulations.

PROTECTIVE SPRAYS can be applied directly to grain and inshell peanuts. Malathion and synergized pyrethrum have been approved by the U.S. Department of Agriculture for this purpose. The Food and Drug Administration has established a tolerance of 8 p.p.m. for malathion, 3 p.p.m. for pyrethrins, and 20 p.p.m. for piperonyl butoxide on peanuts and most grains.

Use of protective sprays on grain and inshell peanuts that are to remain in storage for any length of time has many advantages. The treatment is applied before any damage is done and prevents insect infestation for one storage season or longer. There is no adverse effect on germination, odor, taste, or any other quality factors.

Protective treatments offer about the only protection that can be given grain and peanuts stored in structures where fumigation is impractical or impossible.

Protective treatments should be applied to the grain or peanuts as they are moved into storage if stored either in bulk or bags.

The best time is when the commodities are being moved along the conveyor system.

A sprayer can be rigged so the spray hits the entire width of the conveyor belt at some convenient spot.

RATS ARE OFTEN serious pests in food warehouses. They eat an incredibly large amount of foodstuffs and damage or contaminate an even greater amount. A pair of rats may eat or destroy the equivalent of a 100-pound sack of grain a year.

Rats burrow through packaged food, causing spillage and spoilage of the food. They move about contaminating grain, dried fruit, peanuts, oil, partially or fully processed food—in fact, whatever food is in their path. As a result, each year large quantities of food are seized by Federal and State departments of health and condemned as unfit for human consumption because of rat contamination.

Rats may also cause serious property damage by gnawing on electric wires and pipes, causing fires and flooding.

The three common species of rats are the Norway rat, the black rat, and the roof rat.

A litter of Norway rats varies from 6 to 22, and a female averages 3 to 6 litters each year. Rats become sexually mature in about 3 months and the gestation period is from 21 to 25 days.

Droppings, runways, tracks, and gnawings are sure signs of rat infestations. Rat droppings are dark or black firm pellets, rod shaped, varying in size from one-fourth to three-fourths inch in length and from one-sixteenth to one-fourth inch in diameter.

Rats establish runways and use them

continually. Their dirty, greasy bodies leave characteristic marks on the surfaces with which they come in contact. In dusty locations, rat tracks can be identified by the trail of the tail, and the 4-toed front paws and 5-toed rear paws.

Rats gnaw through various types of materials to obtain food and water or to reach their nesting or hiding places. They will also gnaw on wood and soft metals to keep their ever-growing incisor teeth from becoming too long.

Sanitation measures prescribed for insect control are also effective for preventing rat infestation. Proper construction of the warehouse is essential. Double walls, spaces between floors and ceilings, and spaces beneath basement floors are an invitation to a rat problem. Ratproofing, which involves constructing and maintaining a building so rats can't gain entrance, is the most effective measure of keeping food warehouses free of rats.

RODENTICIDES SHOULD BE used as a supplement and not as a substitute for good sanitation, proper storage practices, and ratproofing.

Anticoagulant poisons have been the most widely used rodenticides during the last 10 years. These slow-acting rat poisons are preferred for use in most situations because of their high effectiveness against rats and mice and their low degree of hazard to humans and domestic animals. The anticoagulant poisons include Pival, warfarin, diphacinone, Fumarin, and PMP. Warfarin has been used most extensively.

These materials are prepared as solid baits mixed with grain or cereal products, or as liquid baits with water. Cereal baits should be checked carefully to make sure they are not infested with insects when placed in the warehouse, and replaced periodically so they do not become infested and serve as a source for insect infestations.

Rats like this destroy huge quantities of food each year.

Rat poisons should be used strictly according to the directions on the package, and all necessary precautions taken against contaminating food in the warehouse.

Much work has been done in developing hermetic or airtight storage for protecting grain against insects.

The principle of hermetic storage is an old one. People of the Mediterranean countries before the days of Christ used it to protect their grain against damage by insects.

Early airtight storage structures were simply underground pits, varying in size from small holes in the ground holding a few bushels of grain to some with a capacity of over 500 tons. The pits were lined with straw before being filled, so moisture from the walls and bottom would not contact the grain. After the pit was filled, straw was placed over the grain surface and then topped with a layer of soil. Stones were sometimes placed over the pit for maximum protection of the grain against animals.

In Malta, "fossae" or pits dug into solid limestone rock approximately 300 years ago are still being used for hermetic storage of grain.

In Argentina, airtight underground storage was started during World War II to protect surplus grain. This type of storage was so successful that the Argentines improved the design and construction of their underground storages, and are using them extensively today.

The French became interested in hermetic storage about a century ago, and their research in this field has led to development of aboveground storage structures. They are constructed of welded steel.

Most of the structures are octagon-shaped with 4 to 28 bins grouped together in a cluster.

Whether a primitive hole-in-the-ground or a sophisticated welded steel aboveground structure is involved, the principle that protects the grain against insect and mold damage is the same.

Oxygen present initially in the intergranular air is used up by the insects, molds, and the grain, and is replaced by carbon dioxide. When the oxygen falls below 2 to 2½ percent, the insects and molds are killed off and the damage stops. However, yeast growth becomes predominant under these conditions. Fermentation odors are imparted to the wheat that carry over to baked products, making them unsatisfactory for human use. The grain, however, is excellent for animal feed purposes.

This mode of storage is in common use by livestock feeders in the Midwest, even though it imparts fermentation odors and taints. There is a high-moisture storage capacity for 20 million bushels in Iowa alone.

In the United States most grain is relatively dry when stored, and it is the general belief that it is too expensive to make present day grain bins and elevators airtight. However, it is more economical to place high-moisture grain in airtight storage than to have it dried, stored, and protected against spoilage in the conventional way. For this reason airtight storage is being used today almost exclusively for high-moisture grain.

Research conducted by the Stored-Product Insects Research and Development Laboratory in Savannah, Ga., has shown that a controlled atmosphere with as high as 13 to 15 percent of oxygen can stop insect development if the proper concentrations of carbon dioxide and nitrogen are present. This discovery may open the way for utilization of some of our present concrete bins and the tighter metal bins for grain storage with controlled atmosphere.

Concentration of the three principal gases can be controlled by flushing or adding carbon dioxide and/or nitrogen to the intergranular air through the recirculation aeration system. These gases can be fed into the system either from tanks or by machines now available that manufacture these two gases by burning natural or manufactured coal gas.

Controlled atmospheric storage is one of the most promising nonpesticidal methods of protecting agricultural commodities against insect damage during storage.

This appears to be feasible not only for grains but also for peanuts, oilseeds, dried fruit, nuts, and for many other processed foods as well.

Oxidative deterioration is also prevented by hermetic storage. Such oxidation in bulk tank storage of fats and oils is retarded by the common practice of maintaining a layer of carbon dioxide or nitrogen over the oil's surface.

GOOD WAREHOUSING practices are essential if packaged food is to be properly protected during long-term storage. Effective surveillance, sanitation, and insect preventive programs depend on good warehouse practices.

Food should be thoroughly inspected before it is brought into the warehouse. If infested, food should be rejected. If it must be accepted, then it should be fumigated before being allowed in. In the warehouse, this food should be isolated, kept under constant surveillance, and used up as soon as possible.

PACKAGED FOOD should be on pallets and arranged neatly in stacks. Each stack should have a floor clearance of 8 inches or more and cover no more than 1,000 square feet of floorspace.

An aisle at least 3 feet wide should completely surround each stack. The four sides of every stack should be exposed and accessible at all times. Food should never be stacked against a wall.

Arrangements like these permit close inspection of a large percentage of packages, facilitate repair or removal of broken packages, allow more efficient stock rotation, make it easier to keep the premises clean, and increase the effectiveness of insect control and preventive programs.

GOOD SANITATION helps keep infestation and spoilage at a minimum. Insects, molds, and fungi can develop and multiply in a relatively small amount of food. Spilled food as well as accumulated food dust or sweepings can serve as the source for serious infestations.

All surfaces should be kept clean. Whenever possible, industrial vacuum cleaners should be used. They do a better cleaning job and help keep dust to an absolute minimum.

Broken packages should be repaired or removed immediately and spillings cleaned up.

Frequent inspections should be made of food in storage to determine whether an insect infestation exists or spoilage is taking place. Surface of the stacks and the spaces between packages should be inspected. The older stacks should be sampled periodically.

IF AN INFESTATION is found, its seriousness and extent should be determined. If only one bag or one lot is involved, the infested stack should be removed immediately and the remaining stacks watched closely to see if the infestation spreads.

If the infestation is widespread, the entire area should be fumigated or the infested stock removed as soon as these steps are possible.

If fumigation is not possible, more frequent space and residual treatments are advisable to keep the infestation under control. No new shipments should be placed in a warehouse while the infestation is out of control.

DESPITE EVERY PRECAUTION, insects show up in food warehouses. Protecting the food against |insect infestation is therefore necessary. This can be done by using insect-resistant packages or applying preventive insecticide treatments.

Proper packaging is the safest, most effective, and cheapest way to protect processed foods against insect infestation and mold spoilage during shipment and storage. Pennies spent on insect-resistant packages will return larger dividends than dollars spent on insect control.

Glass and sheet metal are the only food-packaging materials completely resistant to insect penetration. The cadelle beetle, lesser grain borer, cigarette beetle, and other stored-product insects can bore through packaging materials like cotton, paper, fiberboard, and foil.

Commonly available pliable packaging materials may be rated for their comparative resistance to penetration by insects. Polycarbonate film, polyester film, aluminum foil, polyethylene film, cellophane, and kraft paper are the most resistant, in that order. Rayon sheeting, cotton sheeting, and burlap offer very little resistance or none at all to penetration.

PACKAGES MADE OF materials with some natural resistance to insect penetration are vulnerable to invading insects like the saw-toothed grain beetle, various flour beetles, larvae of the flour and meal moths, and others that gain entrance into the package through openings that are already there.

Most package construction is so poor, especially the end closures, that these invading insects easily gain entrance. To be really insect-resistant, then, a package must be naturally resistant or chemically treated to prevent insect penetration as well as structurally designed to prevent insect invasion.

A chemical treatment has been developed that will prevent insect penetration of multiwall paper bags for 9 months or longer and of cotton sheeting for a shorter time. Pyrethrum and piperonyl butoxide are applied at 5 mg. and 50 mg. per square foot, respectively, on the package's outer surface.

The Food and Drug Administration has approved this treatment and established a tolerance of 1 p.p.m. for pyrethrum and 10 p.p.m. for piperonyl butoxide in foods packaged in treated multiwall paper bags.

STRUCTURAL TIGHTNESS of a package can be materially improved by means of proper closures.

The manufacturer's joint on bags and boxes should have a continuous glue line with the lips sealed as close as possible to the edges.

End closures of single ply and multiwall bags should have paste or tape over stitch closures. If the bag end is sewn, the tape should completely cover all needle punctures and the end of the thread itself. The tape should have a continuous glue line, with the adhesive extending as close as possible to the tape's edge. This type of construction completely seals all openings.

Tightly sealed overwraps greatly improve the insect resistance of shell cartons. Use of Van Buren ears at the end closures with continuous glue lines along the entire outer edge of the end flaps also helps. But until better designed fiberboard shipping cases are made, complete taping of all joints is about the only way of making this type of package more insect-tight.

Food in insect-resistant packages almost certainly will be insect-free when it arrives at the warehouse and will stay insect-free during storage. No other method safely protects food against insect infestation so well and for so long a time.

THERE ARE FOUR distinct ways of using pesticides to protect stored foods against insect infestation:

• Spraying floor and wall surfaces with a residual type insecticide to kill crawling insects.

• Periodic treatment of the airspace with aerosol, mist, or vapor formulations to kill flying insects and possibly some crawling insects.

• Periodic spraying of the surface of stacked commodities to form a protective layer against invading insects.

• Fumigation to kill out an existing insect infestation.

THE IDEAL residual treatment is toxic to a widespread range of insects, long lasting, does not react with the surface to which it is applied, and produces no undesirable effects on the food in storage or to the people who work in the warehouse.

The best time to apply residual insecticides to floor and wall surfaces is, of course, when the entire warehouse or a fairly large area is empty. This permits thorough spraying of all surfaces without contaminating food.

IF IT IS NECESSARY to apply residual spray in a full warehouse, care must be taken not to get the spray on food. Contamination of food from "bounce off" or drifting spray mist while walls or floors are being treated should be avoided. Equipment should be used that will produce a wet or coarse spray with a minimum of mist.

Sides and tops of stacked food should be covered with polyethylene sheets while applying residual treatments if any chance of contamination exists.

An emulsion spray containing either 5 percent of DDT or 3 percent of malathion is most commonly used for residual treatment of food warehouses. Since malathion breaks down rapidly on concrete surfaces, only the DDT should be used on these areas. The spray is applied at the rate of 2 gallons per 1,000 square feet, and a repeat application made every 3 to 4 months whenever this is possible.

Space treatments will kill flying insects or exposed crawling insects while the insecticide is suspended in the air or for a very short time on horizontal surfaces on which it has settled. To be effective as an insect preventive treatment, therefore, space treatments must be repeated often during the time insects are active. Because such treatments come in contact with food or containers, possibility of contamination is great if the proper chemical is not employed.

The only pesticide approved for this use is synergized pyrethrum. A tolerance of 1 p.p.m. of pyrethrins and 10 p.p.m. of the synergist piperonyl butoxide has been established for residues in milled cereal grain products.

Dichlorvos and other organic phosphate insecticides that deteriorate rapidly when exposed to air look very promising for space treatment in food warehouses. Research on use of these insecticides is going on currently at the Savannah, Ga., laboratory.

AN INSECTICIDE stack surface spray has been approved for use on dried citrus pulp, animal feed, oilseeds, other seeds, and some bagged raw food products like bagged inshell peanuts.

This treatment is effective in protecting insect-free food and feed against infestation. The treatment will suppress an existing infestation but may not eliminate it.

Sides and top of stacked bagged food or feed are sprayed with a wettable powder formulation containing 25 percent of premium-grade malathion or 2 percent of pyrethrins and 20 percent of piperonyl butoxide.

IF SERIOUS insect infestation develops in a food warehouse, fumigation is the only effective way to control it.

The fumigant should be approved for use on all food and other materials in the area to be treated. The dose used and the number of times a single item is fumigated must be carefully controlled so residue on the food does not exceed the established tolerance.

Methyl bromide and hydrogen cyanide have been approved for fumigating some foods, and tolerances have been established.

CONTROLLED TEMPERATURE and atmosphere are being investigated as possible nonpesticidal ways to protect food against insects and other harmful organisms.

Insect activity practically stops at temperatures below 45° F. Insects cannot survive in atmospheres that have less than 2 percent of oxygen. And atmospheres with as much as 13 to 15 percent of oxygen with specific concentrations of the other atmospheric gases are lethal to insects.

It may become economically feasible in the near future to use controlled temperature and/or atmosphere to protect packaged foods against insect damage during storage.

STORAGE LIFE of packaged commodities can be lengthened appreciably by even cursory attention to temperature and humidity control to slow down

151

spoilage and quality changes. This is especially important to manufacturers of grocery items like convenience foods and baked goods, since these items need a longer shelf life in their starting materials than is required in the food market.

Bakers in particular have to maintain in storage a great diversity of products and have developed guidelines for their safe storage. Flour should contain no more than 13.5 percent moisture and can be stored safely for several months at temperatures of 65° to 80° F. and relative humidities of 60 to 70 percent.

Under the same humidities, but at temperatures in the range of 40° to 50° F., nonfat milk powder can be stored for 6 months or more and powdered whole milk for 1 or 2 months. Similar conditions are recommended for dried fruits.

These temperatures and lower relative humidities of 40 to 60 percent are needed to store nut meats for periods of 2 months.

The same humidities, but higher temperatures of 60° to 70° F. to maintain plasticity, are recommended for lard and shortening.

With fats and oils, it is important to keep the containers well sealed and removed from foreign odors.

Sugar will keep indefinitely at temperatures of 60° to 80° F. and 40 to 55 percent relative humidity.

WHEN PACKAGED in consumer-sized containers and cans, refined vegetable oils and other oxidizable products often have their shelf life extended by adding antioxidants and packing the products in an inert gas.

Some of the permissible antioxidants are gum guaiac, butylated hydroxyanisole, butylated hydroxytoluene, and propyl gallate.

Further benefit can be obtained by treating the packaging material itself with the antioxidant.

Elimination of the deteriorative browning reaction is more complicated. In dehydrated food products, its effects can be minimized through extra drying, treatment with sulfur dioxide, and the removal of glucose.

PRESENT DAY packaged and canned goods require only a moderate shelf life because of their rapid turnover.

Storage time for many unrefrigerated items averages only 1 to 3 months in the wholesale warehouse and 2 and 4 weeks in the retail market, according to one study. In large food markets, grocery items have a turnover of 15 times per year at wholesale and 18 times per year at retail.

If the need arose, however, long storage lives for these products could be developed.

Dehydrated foods have a potential shelf life of 5 to 10 years if moisture content, oxidation, and browning reactions are controlled by appropriate formulation and packaging.

It is not uncommon for food and feed grains to be safely stored for such long periods in the Midwestern States. Wheat has been stored in Colorado for four decades with little loss in baking quality.

This is not the case in our warmer southern regions. The familiar round grain storage bins that dot the landscape in the Midwest are absent from the South. Insects and molds cannot be stopped here by measures effective in northern regions.

SAFE STORAGE of grains in the subtropical and tropical regions of the world is a major unsolved problem in protecting the human and animal food supply. It is particularly serious in the developing countries, which generally have tropical climates.

Recognition of the problem and its dimensions has been slow in coming. Now the Food and Agriculture Organization of the United Nations and its auxiliary organizations are defining the problem, and proposing international cooperative research efforts to cope with it. Fundamental research can pave the way for development of new principles and practices that will be needed for safe storage of foodstuffs in tropical climates.

PROCESSING—A PRIME PROTECTOR

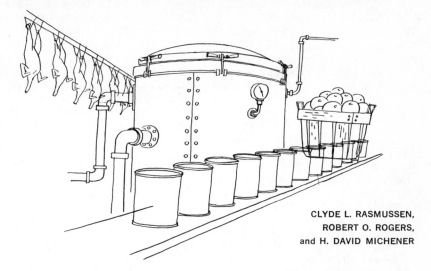

CLYDE L. RASMUSSEN,
ROBERT O. ROGERS,
and H. DAVID MICHENER

MAN'S expanding knowledge of food processing has enabled him to survive in growing numbers, and has made living far easier and more satisfying.

His inventiveness in extending the period of availability of foods and food combinations in forms that retain their nutritive and esthetic values has improved man's health, added variety to his diet, reduced the drudgery of food preparation, and increased his mobility. What's more, these results have been achieved at low cost.

Obviously, the benefits of food processing to consumers have been immense. Yet, processing has been a particular boon to farmers. Not only have farmers gained as consumers, but the technology of processing has greatly expanded the markets both at home and abroad for agricultural products of relatively high value.

Processed commercial vegetables have increased from around 6 million tons annually during 1950–1953 to 8.5 million tons during 1962–1965. During this same period, per capita annual consumption of processed citrus fruit has increased from 40 to 50 pounds,

and of processed noncitrus fruit from 48 to 53 pounds. American exports of fruit and fruit preparations have more than doubled.

The increased need for processed food has resulted from the rising standard of living, the desire for a more diversified diet the year round, an expanding urbanization, and an increase in the total population. Real income per consumer unit more than doubled from 1939 to 1965. While the U.S. population increased from 106 million in 1920 to 195 million in 1965, the percentage of the total population living on farms declined from 30 percent to less than 7 percent. Thus, off-farm

* * *

Clyde L. Rasmussen is an *Industrial Analyst* of the Product and Process Evaluation Staff, located at the Western Utilization Research and Development Division, Albany, Calif.

Robert O. Rogers is *Assistant Director* of the Product and Process Evaluation Staff, Office of the Administrator, Agricultural Research Service.

H. David Michener is a *Chemist* specializing in food microbiology at the Western Utilization Research and Development Division, Albany, Calif.

processing of foods is of great significance to both urban and rural people.

FOOD PROCESSING has many goals. Perishable foods are converted into stabilized products that can be stored for extended periods of time. Examples of the basic preserving processes are canning, freezing, dehydrating, and ionizing radiation.

Processing can change foods into new or more usable forms. Examples include winemaking, flour milling, olive brining, oil extracting, and butter churning.

Processing adds convenience or built-in maid services to products. This rapidly expanding phase of processing is typified by bakery products, frozen french fries, frozen TV dinners, frozen meat and fruit pies, canned soups, and instant dehydrated mashed potatoes.

After harvest or slaughter, unprotected food progressively loses quality and then completely deteriorates. Food is suitable for eating if used a relatively short time after harvest, but it becomes inedible and useless if allowed to exist without some kind of protection. In some cases, unprotected food is dangerous to human and animal life.

The chemical and physical nature of most foods and the environment in which they are normally placed provide excellent conditions for deterioration. In fact, fresh foods are among the most highly perishable substances in all of nature.

The ingredients in foods contributing to deterioration are water and chemicals such as proteins, carbohydrates, fats, minerals, and certain substances which are present in minute amounts, particularly enzymes.

Environmental factors especially favorable to food breakdown are microorganisms, heat, oxygen, moisture, and sunlight. Combine all of these and you have browning, rotting, souring, fermenting, and nutrient loss.

MICRO-ORGANISMS OF INTEREST in food processing are molds, yeasts, and bacteria. These are probably the most important agents of food spoilage.

Micro-organisms—often in the size range around one twenty-five thousandth of an inch—that contribute to food spoilage belong to the lowest order of plants. They contain no chlorophyll, the green coloring material essential in plants, hence they are dependent for their food substances on the plant or the animal materials upon which they live.

These minute organisms are everywhere—in the water we drink, in the air we breathe, and on all objects. All food products become exposed whenever they are left in an outside environment. As a result, foods brought into a plant for processing may contain many micro-organisms.

For their growth, micro-organisms require moisture, warmth, and food such as sugar, starch, and protein. Some require oxygen; others grow without it. Many micro-organisms can grow well even though the necessary nutrients and moisture are present in only minute quantities.

MICRO-ORGANISMS CAN BE destroyed with heat. Most molds and yeasts will be killed at temperatures of 140° to 190° F. Many bacteria can also be destroyed at these temperatures, as in milk pasteurization, but certain bacteria are very heat-resistant.

Freezing temperatures stop the growth of most micro-organisms, but a few strains can grow even at 10° F. These may spoil a food but do not make it poisonous. Removal of water also stops growth. Chemicals, such as salt, sugar, and acid, are used to prevent microbial growth, too.

Molds, yeasts, and bacteria may produce spores. These are tough and resistant resting cells often likened to a plant seed which at some later time becomes reactivated and grows vigorously after warmth, nutrients, and water are restored.

Certain spores which are much more difficult to kill than the growing cells can be killed by boiling for several hours. Some bacterial spores are resistant even to steam-pressure cooking at temperatures well above boiling.

Generally, bacteria are more difficult to destroy than molds and yeasts and are the most serious foes in heat processing, particularly on nonacid foods such as vegetables and meats.

MOLDS ARE OFTEN white or grayish in color and soft and fluffy. Later, they get darker and become blue, green, brown, black, or yellow. These colors appear as the mold ages and accumulates substances such as tannin compounds. The color is usually located in the fruiting bodies which produce the spores.

Spores may drop from the mold plant and blow or float to other places to start a new mold growth when conditions become just right. Then they will grow into new fluffy masses with great rapidity.

SOME MOLDS ARE CAPABLE of producing highly toxic substances that are called mycotoxins.

These molds occur throughout the world but are potentially more important in tropical and subtropical areas where high temperatures and moisture favor their growth. Under such conditions foods like cereals and nuts, if not properly dried after harvest, are subject to attack by the molds. These toxins are extremely dangerous to some animals.

The effects on human life have not yet been determined.

The U.S. Department of Agriculture's chemical, biological, and engineering research program on mycotoxins seeks to develop practical methods for preventing or minimizing mold growth in commodities, rapid methods for detection of the toxins, and processes for removing or destroying toxins in contaminated agricultural commodities.

The Food and Drug Administration's regulatory actions in this area have a twofold purpose: To help the manufacturers protect foods and feeds against mold infestation, and to remove any moldy foods and feeds from the market.

All molds are not necessarily bad for foods. Some molds are used to produce food constituents or modifications. For example, Roquefort cheese obtains its unique flavor from the growth of a mold. Citric acid, which is commonly used as a food ingredient, is produced by the growth of a mold on a sugar solution. The drug penicillin is produced by a mold originally found on cantaloup.

YEASTS ARE one-celled plants which reproduce by forming buds on the side of the cell. The bud grows into a fully developed cell and quickly breaks away from the mother cell. Under adverse conditions, yeasts may survive by forming spores.

Some yeasts are useful and some are harmful. Yeasts cause fermentation, which produces alcohol and carbon dioxide. This process can be used in making leavened or raised loaves of bread, for example. On the harmful side, yeasts cause unwanted fermentations which result in spoiled foods.

Yeasts are abundant in the air and on the skins of fruits and vegetables, and when the right conditions prevail they quickly go to work. But even when fermentation is desired, as in bread baking and in making beverage alcohol, only certain types of yeasts are desirable. Consequently, other types should be removed or avoided and the mix inoculated with the proper type of yeast.

BACTERIA ARE IMPORTANT micro-organisms in food spoilage. These minute, unicellular, simple organisms reproduce themselves very rapidly by dividing in two. These 2 divide into 4, 4 into 8, 8 into 16, and so on, with each division occurring in as little as 20 minutes. Thus, a single bacterium may produce millions in a matter of hours, as it has the ability to reproduce itself more rapidly than any other form of life.

Some bacteria prefer protein foods; others, sugar. Even small amounts of food and water may be enough to sustain the bacteria and help them grow. Few bacteria thrive in acids, so

155

foods such as tomatoes and other fruits are more easily processed than nonacid foods such as meats and vegetables.

Spores that are extremely heat resistant—more so than any other microorganism—are formed by some bacteria. Canned nonacid foods must be subjected to prolonged pressure sterilization at temperatures around 250° F. to destroy the spores. Because spores are more easily killed in an acid environment, fruits and tomatoes can be sterilized at 212° F.

Most bacteria are aerobic—they require oxygen for growth. But some can grow only in the absence of oxygen and are known as anaerobes. In the presence of air, they remain dormant. Inside a sealed can of food, or even in some plastic or paper containers, some surviving anaerobic bacteria may find conditions that are ideal for growth.

AN EXTREMELY DANGEROUS anaerobe is the one called *Clostridium botulinum*, because its spores are very heat resistant and during growth it produces a deadly poison. *C. botulinum* will not grow in foods containing over 10 percent salt and will not usually grow in acid foods.

The insidious danger rises where the attempted sterilization is not complete and only the *C. botulinum* spores survive. Such conditions have occurred in home-canned nonacid foods that did not receive sufficient pressure cooking. They could also arise in other foods that are heated sufficiently to kill most but not all of the bacteria. The harmless bacteria that would spoil the food and thus warn the user are easily killed and, if packaging prevents their reentry, the *C. botulinum* are left to develop without competition. Too often the toxin so produced is not detected and may be consumed unknowingly.

Some types of bacteria are useful. For example, cider and wine vinegars are made by the action of *acetobacter*, commonly called "mother of vinegar," on fermented fruit juices. Cheeses are made by the action of certain bacteria on milk. The manufacture of cultured buttermilk and yogurt also require bacterial action.

ENZYMES, ANOTHER perpetrator of deterioration, are chemicals naturally occurring within the food itself. All living matter contains enzymes. While the enzymes may enormously accelerate a reaction, they do not become a part of the reaction themselves and are not thereby changed or destroyed. Thus, they are catalysts.

In a living plant or animal, enzymatic activity is normal and necessary. In a harvested crop or slaughtered animal, enzymatic activity continues to promote certain of the life processes, but in the absence of life itself, undesirable products accumulate and ultimately cause deterioration.

A fruit may be harvested somewhat green so as to withstand shipping to a distant market. The fruit ripens in storage with the help of enzymes. But enzymatic action continues after the fruit becomes fully ripe and continues to promote chemical activity which ultimately destroys the fruit.

Meat is tenderized after slaughter by being hung for a matter of weeks. The tenderization is promoted by the presence of certain enzymes, but eventually the enzymatic activity will bring about deterioration.

Other enzymatic activity which produces desired changes in foods is found in cheesemaking, clarification of fruit juices, and in bread baking.

UNLESS THE ENZYMES present are necessary for such wanted reactions, their presence often serves only to speed up loss of nutrients and quality.

A typical example of an unwanted change occurs in harvested sugar cane. A natural enzyme changes cane sugar (sucrose) to glucose and fructose which cannot be recovered as crystalline sugar. These sugars thus remain in the molasses.

Other typical effects of enzymatic action are the off-flavor—often called hay flavor—in uncooked frozen vegetables, the darkening of green vegetables and the browning of light-colored fruits and vegetables, and destruction of vitamin C. The latter is an oxidative-type reaction which is speeded along by an enzyme and the presence of air.

Enzymes do their work most effectively in the presence of moisture and at moderate temperatures. Removal of water and lowering of temperature greatly reduce the rate of enzymatic action but do not completely stop it.

Enzymes may be destroyed by heat, the effectiveness of which depends upon the duration of heating, temperature, and nature of the enzyme. Other effective treatments include modification of the environment by the use of chemicals such as vitamin C, sulfur dioxide, or even just plain sugar which helps to prevent oxygen from getting into the fruit tissue to participate in the enzymatic reaction.

ANOTHER IMPORTANT CAUSE of food deterioration is oxidation, a chemical process in which oxygen combines with food constituents resulting in production of undesirable flavor and color. In some cases, enzymes are involved; in other cases, oxidation occurs without the aid of enzymes. Browning of cut fruit—peaches and apples, for example—is an illustration of enzymatic oxidation.

Fats and oils in foods may be particularly subject to oxidation. This type of oxidation is termed rancidity and may occur without the aid of enzymes. Typical of the results are the tallowy, painty, burned, fishy, grassy, and other off-flavors and odors that characterize rancidity.

In addition to the foods we usually recognize as containing fats—like cooking oils, meats, dairy products, eggs, fish, and nuts—many other foods contain sufficient fat to raise problems of rancidity during storage. Nearly all bakery products contain shortening. Many vegetables contain fats. Dehydrated potatoes contain only about 0.5 percent fat, yet oxidation of this minute component can cause serious flavor problems in the product.

Fats are composed of molecules of glycerin linked to fatty acids. They may be saturated or unsaturated, terms which refer to the ability of fatty acids to combine with other substances such as oxygen.

Saturated fatty acids are rather stable chemically and account for much of the firmness of fats at room temperatures. The unsaturated fatty acids which contain weak links in their chainlike structure are softer—some are even liquid at room temperature—and are much less stable. Hence, these are most subject to attack by oxygen.

ANTIOXIDANTS HELP prevent oxygen from attacking the fat molecule. They are present naturally in most vegetable oils. The American Indian added oak-bark extracts to rendered bear fat to keep it from becoming rancid.

The most common natural antioxidant is tocopherol, or vitamin E. Sesame oil contains one called sesamol. Gossypol is a natural antioxidant of crude cottonseed oil.

Fats contain other substances called synergists which increase the activity of true antioxidants but have no such activity themselves.

Both synergists and antioxidants are generally lost in the refining process which removes the objectionable colors and compounds naturally present. Hence, our desire to have vegetable oils that are clear and sparkling intensifies the problem of rancidity by requiring removal of part of their natural protective components.

Because oxygen is the villain in oxidation, the cure is the removal of oxygen or protection of the food so oxygen cannot attack it. Oxidation occurs more rapidly at higher temperatures. Storage of products in refrigerators and freezers helps to slow the reaction but does not completely stop it.

Other deteriorative actions are "browning," either with or without enzymes; irreversible changes in proteins; changes in pigments, vitamins, and carbohydrates; and physical changes such as separation of emulsions and precipitation of solids from a solution. Some of these changes occur independently of other reactions; some of the interrelations are understood, but many are still in the realm of mystery.

WHILE THE VARIOUS food processing measures appear quite different in application and in end products, they all approach the problem of food preservation in one or more of the following basic ways:

• Removal of water. Many reactions cannot occur if water is not present. Micro-organisms cannot grow and multiply without adequate moisture.

• Heat sterilizing. Enzymes and micro-organisms are destroyed or inactivated by sufficient heat. Entry of micro-organisms must be prevented by suitable packaging.

• Lowering temperature. Most reactions slow down as the temperature is lowered.

• Providing a chemical environment that will not permit certain deteriorative actions to proceed.

• Sterilizing with ionizing radiation. Special rays are used to achieve the same results as heat sterilizing. This process is not yet used widely on a commercial scale.

Each of these effectively preserves certain foods, but combinations of them do an even better job. Heat sterilizing effectively destroys micro-organisms, sealing in a container prevents further contamination, and storage of the canned product under refrigeration reduces deterioration normal for any canned product. Cold storage of dried products extends their storage life.

Preservation is clearly ineffective unless steps are taken to protect the processed foods from recontamination or exposure to moisture, air, or heat. The hermetically sealed can prevents entrance of micro-organisms and oxygen, thus keeping the product sterile and avoiding oxidation.

Dried foods must be protected from moisture pickup, and frozen foods safeguarded against moisture loss.

Some foods must be packed in an atmosphere free of oxygen. The air may be removed or replaced by an inert gas like nitrogen or carbon dioxide. The package is then sealed to prevent loss of inert gas and the entrance of air into the container.

In addition to the tin can which is ideal as an air and moisture barrier, plastic films and laminates are used as packing materials. The laminated bag or package may contain several layers, sealed together, of aluminum foil, kraft paper, plastic film, or cardboard.

DEHYDRATION OF FOODS accomplishes preservation in two major ways. It removes the water necessary for growth of micro-organisms and for enzymatic activity. And by removing water, it increases the concentration of sugars and acids, creating a chemical environment unfavorable to the growth of many micro-organisms.

Normally, most dehydrated vegetables must be dried to a very low moisture level for reasonable stability. But the usual sun-dried fruits high in sugar and acids are quite stable with moisture contents from 18 to 24 percent. However, if they are dried to a moisture range of 2 to 3 percent, they are even more stable.

The cereals are quite stable at 12 to 13 percent moisture content. And the dried legumes, beans, and peas normally have moisture contents in the range of 8 to 16 percent.

Another group of foods preserved by drying are nuts. The moisture range necessary for stability is around 3 to 6 percent. The high oil content, which runs from about 48 percent in peanuts to over 70 percent in pecans, is provided with some protection from rancidity by natural antioxidants.

THE HISTORY OF DRYING as a means of food preservation is about as long as the history of man because nature provided us with dried foods in the form of plant seeds. Many of the seeds were not only edible, but also highly nutritious and easy to produce. So seeds were probably man's first preserved foods.

In the maturing process of seeds, nature removes one of the main causes of deterioration—water. And if the seed is kept away from water, it may last for years. Explorers in ancient Egyptian ruins found well-preserved kernels of wheat, thousands of years old.

So, without much effort on man's part, the most important staple foods are preserved by nature. In the United States, only 20 percent of our calories come from cereals, but in many countries 70 to 80 percent of the calories are cereal-derived. Possibly more than half of the world's food supply, as measured by calories, is preserved in the field by nature, even before the crops are harvested.

NATURE PROVIDED MAN with another preserved food, sun-dried fruits. At first he probably found these preserved products under the trees, but later he reasoned that he could help matters along by picking the fruit and nuts and placing them out in the sun to dry.

Because weather is not always just right for drying cereals, legumes, nuts, and fruit, they were often spoiled and lost. So man embarked upon artificial drying, usually called "dehydration." In this process, air is heated and blown across the product. Cereals and nuts

not completely dried in the field can be brought quickly to the proper moisture content in a dryer. The sun-drying of some fruits was replaced by drying in dehydration plants.

Liquid products like fruit juices or milk are dried in several ways. Spray-drying involves atomization of the liquid into a hot air stream which removes water in a matter of seconds.

In drum-drying, a heated drum picks up a layer of puree or concentrate which dries within a few minutes as the drum rotates.

The dried product is removed by a scraper blade and then is ground or flaked as required.

The dehydration methods mentioned thus far involve drying at elevated temperatures. Often exposure to high temperatures results in undesirable changes in flavor, texture, color, and shape. Drying under a vacuum partially solves these problems because the evaporation of water takes place at much lower temperatures.

Frozen citrus juices can be economically concentrated in vacuum equipment in which pressure is so reduced

After being sized, dehydrated onions are inspected for any defects before packaging.

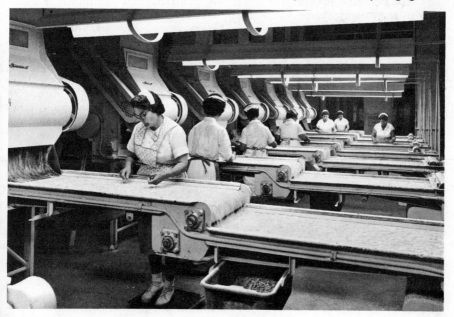

that the temperature of the product is kept under 100° F.

In freeze-drying, the product is kept frozen while it dries, thus avoiding the shrinkage that occurs in the course of ordinary dehydration.

A freeze-dried strawberry is just as large as the fresh strawberry, but weighs only a sixteenth as much.

Flavor changes are greatly reduced in vacuum drying. The burnt or caramelized flavor is practically eliminated. But the volatile flavoring components, like those you smell on fresh fruit, are nearly all removed—as they are in most forms of drying.

Vacuum concentration of liquids in multiple-effect evaporators is one of the least costly ways of removing water. But vacuum drying of piece-form foods—freeze-drying, for instance—is one of the most costly methods of water removal. Its use, therefore, is restricted to high value foods—for example, meats and seafoods—and to military or other logistic situations demanding such lightweight dried products.

While dehydration may slow down enzyme activity in the food, it does not entirely prevent this activity.

Thus, a dehydrating operation must usually incorporate some method of enzyme destruction.

For vegetables, heating to boiling temperature for a few minutes—called blanching—does the job. Blanching of cut fruits, like apples, apricots, and pears, has been generally impractical, however, because of the resultant softening and bleeding.

The cut fruit is exposed to the fumes of burning sulfur, or dipped into a solution containing sulfur dioxide. This effectively inactivates the enzymes, prevents discoloration, acts as an antioxidant, and thus makes possible the production of light, translucent products. Dried fruit not so treated becomes dark and may develop undesirable flavors. Most raisins and prunes are not treated with sulfur, and the products, while of good quality, are certainly quite unlike fresh grapes and prunes.

160

Other dehydrated products are benefited by the application of sulfur dioxide. Dehydrated potatoes, cabbage, carrots, and sweetpotatoes may be so treated to preserve the natural light color. This helps protect foods, such as vegetables, during drying by minimizing oxidative changes.

CARROTS ARE OFTEN coated with starch after blanching and before dehydration which helps protect the color from oxidative changes.

Removal of the small amount of glucose in egg—by either a fermentation or an enzymatic process—gives the dehydrated product good storage stability. In contrast, egg dried without this important step has a storage life at ordinary temperatures of only a few weeks. Cause of the deterioration is interaction between the glucose and the egg protein.

Skim milk to be dried must first be heated to improve its quality for use in baking.

Even higher temperatures and longer retention times are required to inactivate the fat-splitting enzymes in whole milk.

A DEHYDRATED PRODUCT remains stable only as long as it is protected from water, air, sunlight, and contaminants. Packaging, therefore, is very important.

The two major considerations in packaging are the exclusion of moisture and of oxygen.

Metal cans, plastic bags, and laminated bags and boxes effectively limit the passage of moisture and air through the package.

Elimination of oxygen initially is somewhat of a problem, however. Sometimes a vacuum pack is used. Or air may be replaced with an inert gas like nitrogen or carbon dioxide.

Some processors have found it expedient, however, to treat the product with an antioxidant.

The antioxidant is eventually used up in its fight with oxygen, so there is a practical limit to how long this protection can be provided.

IN PRACTICALLY ALL drying processes, removal of the last portions of water becomes increasingly costly and time consuming. So it is advisable to stop the process when cost and quality reach an optimum. The point at which each type of food becomes stable involves a complex relationship between water content and the nature of the food that is being dried.

ONE WAY to reach the desired low-moisture content in the product is to package it with an in-package desiccant—a chemical having an extremely high affinity for water. The desiccant or drying agent is placed in a porous bag to keep it apart from the food and then placed in the container, which is sealed. In this way, orange juice powder containing 3 percent moisture when packaged can be brought down to less than 1 percent in a matter of weeks while it is in storage.

For those foods that can be dried by conventional methods, dehydration has proved a good low-cost process of wide economic importance. If the naturally dried seeds are included, drying is the most important preservation process in the world. The usual dried products are low in bulk and weight. They can be packaged, stored, and distributed economically. And they have good storage stability.

IN CANNING, heat sterilizing performs two main functions: (1) destruction of micro-organisms and inactivation of enzymes, and (2) cooking the food. When a severe treatment is needed to destroy bacterial spores, the food may become overcooked.

Fortunately, sterilization and cooking occur at different rates. If a cooking temperature of 212° F. is increased only 18° F., the power to destroy bacteria increases about tenfold, but chemical changes—or cooking effect—are only doubled. Canning under pressure to achieve an equivalent sterilizing treatment, using 6 pounds of steam pressure to achieve 230° F. (instead of 212° F. in boiling water for 10 times longer) cuts chemical and physical changes by a factor of five. In commercial canning, even higher temperatures are employed.

The quality of the pressure-cooked and preserved food is thus greatly improved over food cooked in boiling water to give an equivalent sterilization.

Adoption of the pressure cooker made possible the successful canning of many nonacid foods that previously were not canned, or if canned, were done so with great risk. Pressure-cooking offers a practical means for destroying the dangerous bacterial spores of *Clostridium botuli..um*.

CERTAIN heat-resistant bacteria continued to cause trouble for many years, being responsible for the problems known to the trade as "swells" and "flat sours." Swells are caused by spoilage bacteria (sometimes also by chemical reactions) which produce gas causing ends of the can to bulge. In flat sours no gas is produced but the can contents acquire an off-flavor. This causes economic loss but is no hazard to health.

But *C. botulinum* also produces gas as well as a deadly toxin, hence the food from swelled cans should never be eaten.

Swells and flat sours have now been largely eliminated by proper cooking temperatures and times and by quickly cooling the canned products to temperatures below 100° F.

Employment of higher sterilizing temperatures coupled with shorter retention times—known in the trade as HTST for high-temperature short-time—is finding increasing application as necessary equipment and methods are developed.

New types of heat exchangers permit extremely rapid heating and cooling of liquid foods. A process known as "aseptic canning" makes use of this type of heating. The food is sterilized and cooled quickly and then put into cans under sterile conditions. The whole installation of filler, sealer, and can transport, as well as the cans and products, are sterilized and protected from further contamination.

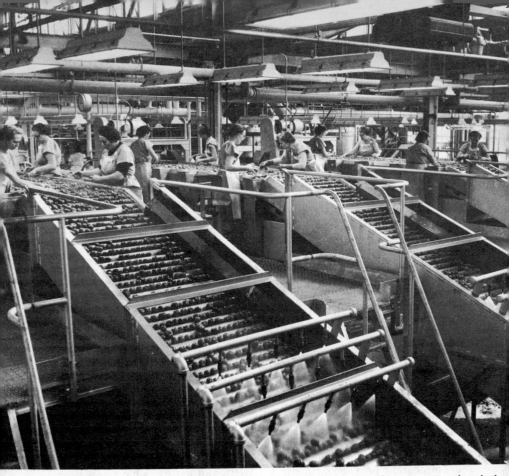

Elevator conveyors take tomatoes through spray washers to sorting tables at a processing plant.

This process works well with liquid-form foods. Piece-form foods are more difficult to heat and cool quickly, but progress is being made to process them, too, by HTST and aseptic canning.

EARLIER CANNING PROCEDURES made use of batch-type cookers.

Continuous cookers have largely replaced the "kettles" and the "autoclaves" and have improved operations, simplified control, and at the same time, significantly reduced the labor requirements and costs.

Cans are now machine-filled in contrast to hand-filling prevalent in earlier years. Materials are transported continuously about the plant on belts, in water flumes, or even pneumatically, thus minimizing delay and product deterioration before the final processing.

Whole canning operations are programed and controlled on central control panels where all phases of the processes are made known to the operators for immediate attention if corrective actions are needed.

In canning, as in other food processing methods, when scale of operation increases, many of the steps can be automated or made continuous.

As less and less of the canning process is left to chance or to an individual's decision or act, the better has been the product, the more consistent its quality, and the lower its cost.

ALTHOUGH FREEZING preservation has achieved greater economic importance rather recently, even the earliest man living in cold climates must have known something about holding meat and fish in frozen form.

One of the first commercial cold storage houses was built in New York in 1865. Fifteen hundred cold storage warehouses, capable of handling a million carloads of products a year, now serve the food industry.

Fish and poultry were first frozen on a commercial scale in the 1860's. In 1910, frozen berries were produced in the Pacific Northwest.

MODERN QUICK-FREEZING, however, did not become a reality until the 1920's when Clarence Birdseye's pioneering efforts resulted in its first commercial application to fish. In 1927, quick-freezing was extended to vegetables, and freezing as a major preservation process was on its way. Today, over 700 frozen items are found in supermarkets and more are coming.

Frozen foods have achieved popularity because their quality, particularly in flavor and color, is more like that of fresh counterparts than can be achieved by the other preservation methods.

In freezing, most vegetables require only light blanching. Of course, many convenience-type products like pies and TV dinners are cooked before they are frozen.

WITH LITTLE OR NO adverse processing conditions to remove volatile flavors or to destroy color, freezing's major quality problem involves texture.

Some fruits and vegetables, after thawing and cooking where required, do not have a crisp fresh texture. Strawberries become quite mushy, even though they have good flavor and color. Green beans may be rubbery, and asparagus wilted. Melons and cantaloups are rubbery after being thawed. Certain types of sauces separate badly after thawing and suspended solids may settle in juice made from frozen orange concentrate.

The solutions to these problems are many. Rapid freezing, as is possible with liquid nitrogen at —320° F., or

in fluidized-bed freezers, helps improve texture in strawberries, green beans, and asparagus. The texture breakdown seems to be related to damage to cell walls, and rapid freezing results in less damage.

As with all methods of food preservation, many factors determine the success of freezing as a method of preservation.

Quality of the product depends upon the quality of the raw material, of course. Hence only sound, wholesome raw material should be used for freezing. Furthermore, the variety or breed, the size and shape, and the degree of maturity including aging or seasoning, must be satisfactory for the product being made.

Processing conditions must be controlled so they provide the degree of protection required and minimize quality losses associated with the particular kind of freezing process.

Packaging must give the product the degree of protection needed, especially to avoid recontamination. The package must provide suitable moisture, oxygen, and light barriers, and should be durable to withstand handling from processor to user.

Storage conditions for frozen foods are extremely important.

While each food preserved by freezing has a different temperature tolerance, generally a change of approximately 5° F. doubles or halves the rate of quality changes. Thus, a frozen food that maintains top quality for a whole year at 0° F. may keep that quality for only 6 months at 5° F., 3 months at 10° F., and a day or so at 30° F.

For most frozen foods, a holding temperature of 0° F. is recommended at all levels of distribution. Lower temperatures are better but would be achieved at costs probably higher than most products can justify.

MAN HAS PRESERVED foods chemically for a long time. Next to drying, chemical preservation is probably the oldest form of food preservation; its beginning is lost in antiquity.

163

When early man discovered the use of fire for cooking, he also, no doubt, discovered that meats and fish were preserved by smoking. In this method, the meat is subjected to the fumes of burning wood. Smoking lowers moisture content of the meat, brings about an attractive color and aroma, and deposits on the meat minute amounts of phenols and resins which furnish some protection against both bacteria and oxidation.

In early days, smoking was about the only effective means available for preserving meats. Now, with refrigeration, freezing, and canning doing the major job of preservation, smoking is important mainly to develop the desired color and flavor in meats like ham, bacon, sausage, and fish.

Pickles, olives, sauerkraut, and even fruit preserves are partially or wholly preserved by chemicals. In pickles, the preservatives are salt and vinegar (acetic acid). Alcohol is a preservative in wines and liquors. Salt is a preservative in sauerkraut, and the high concentration of sugar helps preserve fruit jams and jellies. In foods like pickles and sauerkraut, an additional preservative is the lactic acid produced during bacterial fermentation.

Chemicals preserve foods in several ways. The chemical may be a poison to the micro-organisms that cause spoilage. The chemical may provide an environment in which micro-organisms cannot grow although it will not actually kill all of them, and in this category are salt and sugar solutions and acids.

The high sugar content also serves another purpose: It ties up the moisture, which is then not available to the micro-organisms.

As the science of food processing has progressed, important advances have been made. Controls have been improved so little is left to chance.

Processing procedures have been improved and products bettered as the food sciences have eliminated the use of undesirable chemicals and discovered or developed new chemicals which are effective in preserving food

164

without side effects harmful to man.

Trace amounts of noninjurious chemicals are being added more and more in conjunction with the other processing methods, such as canning, freezing, and dehydrating, to improve the products in many different ways. Ascorbic acid is added to frozen fruits and canned apple juice to preserve a light color. Benzoic acid and sorbic acid are used to prevent mold and yeast growth. Calcium chloride is added to canned tomatoes to help them retain firmness.

Laws and regulations governing the use of chemical additives have become progressively more strict. The 1958 amendment to the Federal Food, Drug, and Cosmetic Act provided that industry must prove the safety of chemicals used in food processing before the chemicals can be sold for use in foods. Prior to that time, it was necessary for the Food and Drug Administration to discover their use in foods already on sale and test them.

IONIZING RADIATION, a new food preservation method of great potential importance, advanced in only two decades from a laboratory curiosity to a commercially feasible method, and was first approved by the Food and Drug Administration in 1963 for use on bacon.

Most bacteria and other micro-organisms are destroyed by bombardment with ionizing particles or rays. Several kinds of rays have been tried, but gamma rays have certain advantages. They can penetrate further than alpha and beta rays. FDA has approved the use of gamma rays produced by cobalt 60.

Unfortunately, radiation cannot be administered without adverse changes in quality. High dosages affect the appearance, taste, texture, and nutritive value, but such changes can be minimized by keeping the radiation dosages as low as possible.

THE MAJOR PROBLEMS to be overcome before radiation is used on a large-scale basis for food preservation are high costs and undesirable side reactions from the ionizing bombardment. Methods for reducing these side reactions include reducing temperature and oxygen during treatment.

A PROMISING WAY of using radiation is with lower dosages in conjunction with other processing methods and for achieving only partial preservation, as extending the shelf life of fresh foods.

Storage life of fresh haddock at 32° F. can be increased from 6 to 9 days to 25 days with a radiation dosage of 250,000 rads and to 38 days with 400,000 rads.

This degree of preservation destroys the bulk of the nonsporeforming micro-organisms. But if fish so treated were accidentally stored at room temperature instead of 32° F., there would be danger that surviving *C. botulinum* spores would grow and produce toxin.

Radiation to destroy enzymes takes even higher dosages than required for micro-organisms.

On the other hand, enzymes are more easily destroyed by heat than are micro-organisms.

So both of the preservation methods might be used advantageously together in some cases; mild heat treatment to inactivate enzymes, and radiation to destroy heat-resistant bacteria.

IONIZING RADIATION should find limited use in the civilian markets in these ways:
• To rid wheat and other grain products of insects.
• To inhibit sprouting of potatoes and other tubers.
• To preserve certain protein foods like seafoods and meats (as described above for haddock).
• To improve the public health aspects of certain foods by destroying disease-producing organisms.
• To sterilize foods—like pork and pork products, particularly cured products—where the problem of undesirable side reactions is not acute.

WE HAVE BEEN TALKING about protecting foods through processing, using the basic methods of preservation. Recent developments and growth in the industry, however, have resulted from a different phase of processing, that of adding more convenience, built-in maid services, variety in form, combinations, and specialties.

Some call this a transfer of part of the food preparation job from the home to the factory.

This transfer, plus proliferation in the various sizes and types of packages and the expansion of labels or brands, have made possible the 7,000 or 8,000 food items currently found in the modern supermarket.

Packaging for many convenience products has necessitated both new types of containers and new materials. Boil-in-bag vegetables awaited the development of strong plastics that remain flexible and moisture-resistant at 0° F. and also withstand boiling temperatures.

A whole host of aluminum containers is now produced for the many convenience food items which require low-cost cooking and serving dishes. In addition to these features, protection must also be provided against recontamination, moisture and air transfer, damage, and the other demands of preservation.

The combining of foods in special dishes often raises problems which are not of concern when these foods are preserved separately.

Frozen sauces may be curdled, even after cooking, if they are not made with a waxy starch or flour. Oil in a frozen mayonnaise or salad dressing may cause separation problems if not of the right kind.

Special formulations are often necessary for frozen dishes to be served through automatic vending machines.

The whole package of dry cereal may have to be dehydrated to an extremely low moisture content to accommodate a few pieces of freeze-dried strawberry that have been added. Or the whole package of a dry cereal-meat dish may be packaged in nitrogen to prevent rancidity from developing in the small portion of dried meat.

SUPERMARKET

SAFEGUARDS

R. W. HOECKER

THE supermarket at your shopping center has an investment of $100,000 for temperature and humidity controls to keep the food you buy in top condition.

And as an added dividend for you, the air conditioning makes shopping more comfortable, too.

The clean, bright, and attractive store with its rows of refrigerated display cases is designed to attract you as a customer but repel the insects, molds, and bacteria that cause deterioration in the quality of your food.

This job of furnishing the highest quality foods at the lowest possible price starts at the farm and it ends in the retail store. The wholesaler and the retailer part of the job consists of purchasing a known quality of food and preventing any more than the minimum amount of physical and biological deterioration. Every retail firm has a quality maintenance program to help accomplish this.

QUALITY CONTROL in the retail firm starts with the purchase specifications—specifications usually developed and enforced by the U.S. Department of Agriculture. For perishables like fresh fruits, vegetables, meat, dairy products, and frozen food the specifications usually designate a quality that reflects either physical condition of the product, such as grade A potatoes, or palatability, such as choice meat. Inspectors check the arrival condition of perishables to be sure the buyers' minimum specifications have all been fulfilled.

R. W. Hoecker is *Chief* of the Wholesaling and Retailing Research Branch, Transportation and Facilities Research Division, Agricultural Research Service.

Treatment the perishables receive usually depends on this arrival condition. For example, tomatoes and bananas are separated into lots with the same degree of ripeness. The green ones are put aside for ripening while the ripe are sold immediately.

SOME ITEMS like frozen food are subject to regulations that govern how they are handled before they arrive at the warehouse or store. A few States have a frozen food code, while others are considering one. The code makes it unlawful to handle frozen food at temperatures above 0° F. Frozen food deteriorates at temperatures above 0° F. and will be of inferior quality even though it is again reduced to below 0° F.

Nonperishables like canned goods and mixes are also bought on the basis of samples and specifications. Upon arrival, samples are selected and inspected to be sure the lots meet minimum specifications. At the same time, samples of each lot are pulled and held at the central headquarters. Then if the firm has some difficulty later with the lot, the sample can be rechecked.

Some firms date food with a code mark or actual expiration date to be sure it is sold within a specified time.

RAPID TURNOVER makes it possible to sell food before it deteriorates in quality. Almost every item will deteriorate in time regardless of whether it is merchandised in fresh or processed form. Store managements stress rotation and turnover as part of a quality maintenance program. Quality control men police rotation of food items by inspecting stores.

Most merchandisers believe large displays stimulate customers to buy more than they would otherwise. But if sales from the display are not fast enough to keep the remaining food from decreasing in quality, the merchandiser defeats his purpose.

Usually displays are kept small for items that aren't in much demand, and for perishables during the slack shopping periods. Often containers are opened at the warehouse and only part of the contents sent to the store to minimize the excess stock carried at the retail level and thus speed stock turnover. In some instances perishables like milk, bread, and some produce items are delivered directly to the store rather than routed through the firm's warehouse, in order to obtain more shelf life for them.

Rapid turnover of nonperishables is desirable to decrease the cost of carrying inventory, to increase use of shelf space, and to assure that a fresh stock is on hand.

Firms have tight inventory control, using computers to increase turnovers and decrease the number of out-of-stock items. Firms maintain detailed records on the movement of each item in the store. These data are put on computer tapes and used to ascertain which products to stock, how large a shelf display to maintain, and when to order the item to be sure it will be available in the store when needed.

DISTRIBUTION CENTERS serving large metropolitan areas may have 75 to 125 large trailer trucks delivering to the firm's retail outlets. Trucks furnish some products with special atmospheric conditions during the trip from warehouse to retail store.

Generally, trucks must be heated in winter. And during the summer, frozen food, dairy products, produce, and meat usually have to be refrigerated.

Refrigeration is furnished by about 25 specially built trucks costing $10,000 to $20,000 each, equipped with mechanical units, or by use of ice and—in an increasing number of cases—with liquid nitrogen for frozen products.

Some truck bodies have compartments that can be cooled to different temperatures when mixed loads with various temperature requirements are handled.

Large insulated containers may permit frozen foods to be hauled on the same truck with products not requiring such low temperatures.

A supermarket in Arlington, Va., illustrates the wide choice of food products available to the consumer.

Supermarkets were among the first businesses to use air conditioning, both to make shopping more pleasant and to increase the shelf life of most of the 7,500 items carried by the store. About 45 percent of the retail dollar volume of food is refrigerated below 50° F. while being marketed. All these items are usually received at the warehouse refrigerated. They continue to receive some refrigeration at the warehouse, during delivery, and in the retail store.

Low temperatures retard development of harmful molds and bacteria, and in fresh fruits and vegetables slow up the maturing or ripening process. On the other hand, some perishables such as bananas, squash, and eggplant can be harmed by excessively low temperatures. Most perishables have an ideal humidity and temperature combination that will maintain quality for the longest possible time.

The warehouse has special holding rooms 20 feet high to furnish conditions best suited for perishables. Produce is held in two temperature and humidity controlled areas according to the product storage requirements— either 32° F. and 90 percent relative humidity for such products as apples, peaches, carrots, and lettuce or 50° F. and 85 percent relative humidity for such items as grapefruit, green beans, and potatoes.

Meat is held at 32° F.; frozen food at −10° F.; and dairy products (except ice cream) at 34° F. Bananas and tomatoes have special ripening rooms ranging in temperature between 55° and 70° F. and with relative humidity between 85 and 90 percent, depending upon the speed of ripening.

RETAIL STORES have specialized display or storage equipment to protect the quality and extend the shelf life of food products. Besides holding coolers and air conditioning, there are refrigerated cases for frozen food, fresh meat, dairy products, fresh fruits and vegetables, delicatessen items, and luncheon meat. Each case is designed to display and protect the particular food product.

A typical supermarket has separate holding coolers for a reserve stock of meat, fish, produce, dairy and frozen food. Special treatment is given some items. Live lobsters may be kept in tanks with chemically modified water. Store layouts are often planned so the ice cream display is near the end of the shopping pattern, and insulated bags are provided so you can get ice cream and frozen foods home before they thaw.

SPOTLESS TOOLS and equipment are keys to successful handling of perishables like fresh meat, dairy products, and fresh fruits and vegetables. In some instances special dips, sprays, and films are used to keep perishables free of dirt. One of the main reasons housewives give for preferring prepackaged fresh fruits and vegetables is that the food stays cleaner this way.

Operators use soapy water and chemicals in scrubbing and sanitizing tools and equipment for handling and displaying perishables. At times, special measures need to be taken. Rooms where cheese is prepackaged should have the air purified to control mold spores. Meat should never be packaged in the same room as produce.

Food attracts rodents and insects, and packages are designed to repel them. The food handler controls these pests through contracts with exterminator companies that follow systematic control programs. In addition, warehouses and stores have daily cleaning schedules to keep the facilities as dirt-free as possible.

Sanitary handling and facilities help keep bacteria and molds from causing food deterioration. In addition, some diseases—such as tuberculosis—can be transmitted to humans with food as the carrier. Most food store employees are required to have health cards signed by a medical official certifying they do not have tuberculosis. Good managers insist employees wear clean clothes and have clean personal habits. For some tasks women employees must wear hair nets. Clean washrooms are a must at both the store and the warehouse.

PHYSICAL DAMAGE to food products from breakage, bruising, and other mishaps in warehousing, delivery to retail stores, and in the stores is estimated at over $50 million annually. About three-fourths of this damage occurs in the store, with employees causing about 60 percent of it and customers about 40 percent. In addition to the physical damage apparent in the store, some bruising occurs that may not show up until after the customer gets the product home.

Great care is taken to minimize damage and offset losses like these. Glass jars are packed with shock-absorbing cardboard between them. Some produce items such as pears and citrus are individually wrapped with chemically treated paper, both to protect them from disease and to keep them from bruising.

Shipping containers are made with dimensions that allow for interlocking on pallets so they won't fall off. Fresh vegetables are prepackaged in consumer units to minimize bruising. Individual containers—like bleach bottles made of plastic—are designed to prevent breakage.

Stores are planned so easily crushed or damaged items like bread and baked goods are last in the shopping pattern, and can be placed atop other purchases. Checkout personnel are instructed in proper bagging to prevent crushing, bruising, and breakage.

SUPERMARKET management is everlastingly concerned with maintaining quality. It expresses this concern by furnishing optimum temperatures for perishables, fast turnover for all items, sanitary handling and facilities, and by preventing breakage and damage. You—the consumer—benefit.

GLADYS L. GILPIN and ANNABEL L. MERRILL

PROTECTING

FOOD QUALITY

IN THE HOME

Gladys L. Gilpin is a *Project Leader* in the Human Nutrition Research Division, Agricultural Research Service.

Annabel L. Merrill is a *Project Leader* in the Consumer and Food Economics Research Division, Agricultural Research Service.

IN the role of homemaker today, you need no Aladdin's lamp to provide for your table the luxury of strawberries in January and freshly squeezed orange juice any day of the year. A wide assortment of fresh and processed fruits, vegetables, cereals, dairy products, meats, and many other foods always awaits your selection. You need not be overly concerned about the safety and quality of the food you bring home from the store, and the opportunities for providing your family with both attractive and healthful meals are practically unlimited.

To help you achieve this seemingly magic goal, here are some guidelines for bringing food from store or garden to the table with maximum preservation of its original quality, safety, and nutritional value. First, fill your "market basket" wisely; select high quality foods either from market or garden. Store foods promptly under the proper conditions and use them within the recommended periods for storage. Finally, use preparation and serving procedures that are known to preserve food quality.

SELECT QUALITY FOODS. Choose only sound, fresh fruits and vegetables. Strawberries, tomatoes, and corn are particularly perishable; select these with special care. Watch for bruised, decayed, wilted, or yellow leaves on greens, lettuce, cabbage, cauliflower, and celery, and for soft and bruised spots in tomatoes, peppers, muskmelons, and other fruits. For you who have gardens, the selection of fresh produce will certainly be no problem.

Look for quality grades. This information is on the original containers of fresh fruits and vegetables and on the labels for many of these foods in their canned and dehydrated forms.

Buy graded eggs at a market that keeps them refrigerated. The grademark indicates the quality of the eggs when graded, but refrigeration is needed to hold their quality.

In meat, the grademark indicates a specific degree of quality to aid consumers in selecting meat suitable for cooking in different ways. The purple U.S. inspection stamp on the meat you purchase shows the meat came from healthy animals and was processed under sanitary conditions, but here again refrigeration is still essential for holding quality.

Information on the label sometimes includes the date a food was packed or the date by which it should be used to assure a good quality product.

When you buy frozen foods, select completely frozen packages. Check for evidences of previous thawing, as discoloration from juice, and for torn or crushed packaging material. Select frozen foods last and carry them home in an insulated or double paper bag.

CONSIDER THE STORAGE facilities in your home. They will determine largely the amounts and kinds of food which you should stock.

Storage temperature and humidity, and often the packaging used during storage, are major factors in protecting the quality of food.

Low temperature helps retain good quality in food by slowing the action of enzymes naturally present in food and the growth of spoilage organisms that cause fermentation and decay. Enzymes are chemical substances needed for normal growth and maturing of plants and animals. Enzyme action continues after harvest or slaughter and can cause quality losses unless slowed or stopped by treatments such as cold, heat, or drying. Spoilage organisms include bacteria, yeasts, and molds which are all around us—in the air, soil, water, and on food.

LOW HUMIDITY also retards growth of spoilage organisms. Some foods, however, must be held in a moist atmosphere to prevent drying and shriveling. This is the reason for using the hydrator or plastic bag for vegetables which are held in the refrigerator.

Protection from exposure to air can prevent oxidation which causes quality losses in foods such as rancid off-flavor of fat, darkening of color in fruits and vegetables, haylike flavor in vegetables,

and vitamin loss. The oxygen in the air reacts chemically with the food to produce these changes. The type of packaging needed for protection of a food from oxidation during storage depends on the food, the kind of storage, and the duration of storage.

IF YOUR HOME is equipped with both an adequate refrigerator and freezer, you have a good start toward protecting your food supply. Know your own equipment so that you can make the best use of it.

Since refrigerators are designed for storing food for only short periods of time and freezers for prolonged storage, they differ in the conditions they provide for protecting food. And there are also different conditions in the various types of equipment within these two categories.

Know where the cold or warmer spots are in your refrigerator—or whether the temperature is quite uniform throughout the storage space. Frost-free cabinets have a more uniform temperature distribution throughout the entire storage space, including doors, than those of other types, and consequently food will be equally well protected in any part of them.

THE TEMPERATURE of the general storage area in other types of refrigerators is less uniform, being lowest just below the freezing unit and highest at the bottom of the cabinet.

Temperatures in door-storage areas and in hydrators generally average several degrees higher than in the main storage spaces.

Foods that require the coldest storage should, therefore, be placed close to the freezing unit.

The average temperature in the storage area of refrigerators is usually between 38° and 42° F. when the control is set for normal operation. The control should be regulated to maintain a temperature no higher than 42° F. Check the temperatures in different parts of your refrigerator (and your freezer too) regularly. The cost of a reliable thermometer will be

171

repaid many times over in superior eating quality and in nutritive value of properly stored food.

FACILITIES AVAILABLE for storing frozen food in the home also vary. They may be a separate freezer, a refrigerator-freezer combination, or the freezer compartment or the ice cube section of a refrigerator.

Sometimes freezer compartments in refrigerators are confused with refrigerator-freezer combinations, and the frozen foods are not stored at the temperature expected. The freezer section of a refrigerator-freezer combination is isolated from the refrigerator section with a solid divider and has either a separate outside door or an insulated inner door. A freezer compartment of a refrigerator does not have these two features, although it may be in the same location and be the same size and shape.

Freezers and refrigerator-freezer combinations are designed to provide the o° F. or lower temperatures which are required to maintain quality in frozen foods.

Refrigerator-freezer compartments and ice cube compartments are not intended to provide this low temperature. It is best to buy frozen foods in the quantities that will be used within a few days if you do not have o° F. storage, as they become less palatable and nutritious over longer periods of storage at temperatures above zero.

MAKE YOUR EQUIPMENT serve you best by using it efficiently. Do not overcrowd the refrigerator; allow space around the food containers for air circulation.

An accumulation of ice on the coils insulates them and hinders their cooling action. Defrost the refrigerator whenever the ice becomes about a quarter of an inch thick.

In freezers, leave a little space between packages of newly purchased commercially frozen foods or foods to be home frozen, and put them in contact with a true freezing surface. When the foods reach storage temperature, move packages together to save space.

Frost on the walls of freezers has little effect on the operating efficiency but it takes up valuable storage space. It is well to remove frost before it becomes more than half an inch thick. To avoid the formation of frost and to maintain the required temperature, open the freezer door only when necessary and close it quickly.

Now LET's get down to the facts and figures which are the basis for these guides to safeguard your food until you are ready to prepare it for serving.

Management of your food supply to retain high quality and nutritive value includes stocking only the amounts and kinds of foods you can store properly and using at peak quality the foods you have on hand. Also, it is important to store without delay all perishable fresh and frozen foods.

The length of time that a food will retain its eating quality and nutritive value when properly stored in the home depends on the kind of food and its condition when stored.

Recommended storage periods can be only approximate and the maximum periods suggested here are for foods of high quality when placed in storage.

When the original quality of a food is unknown, it is advisable to limit the storage period.

Vitamin C, vitamin A value, and the B vitamins—thiamine and riboflavin—are nutrients that give particular concern during the period foods are stored in the home.

However, these relatively unstable nutrients are well retained provided the foods are held only for the recommended periods of time and under those conditions that assure the retention of food quality.

FOODS CAN BE CLASSIFIED into groups that require similar protection to help retain their nutritive value and good eating quality. Most fresh vegetables and fresh, ripe fruits will keep best in the refrigerator.

Sort all vegetables and store only the firm, ripe, sound ones.

Tomatoes often must be allowed to ripen before they are stored. They need light to develop vitamin A value and moderate temperature for bright red color. Tomatoes lose their nutritive value rapidly when they become overripe, so refrigerate them as soon as possible after they are ripened.

Put fresh vegetables that lose their crispness fast in the refrigerator in the vegetable crisper or a plastic bag; these include the vegetables for which storage periods are given below with the following exceptions. Store lima beans or peas in the pod, sweet corn in the husk, and ripe tomatoes uncovered in the refrigerator.

PLAN TO USE vegetables in time to get the best eating. Freshness and nutrients can be lost from vegetables that are kept too long even under the best storage conditions. For example, leafy green vegetables retain more than 90 percent of their vitamin C and vitamin A value for 24 hours when refrigerated properly; retention of these nutrients drops to 75 percent after storage for several days.

Suggested storage times for vegetables in the refrigerator are about 1 or 2 days for—asparagus, broccoli, brussels sprouts, spinach and similar greens, salad greens, mushrooms, green onions, corn (in husks); 3 to 5 days for—snap beans, cauliflower, celery, cucumbers, okra, green peppers, summer squash, ripe tomatoes; 1 to 2 weeks for—beets, carrots, and radishes (tops removed), cabbage, parsnips.

Before storing fruits, sort, wash, and dry those with smooth, firm skins like apples, pears, and plums. Leave underripe fruit in the room to ripen. Vitamin losses are small even at room temperature during the time required for ripening. Either use fruits as soon as they are ripe or transfer them to the refrigerator and use them within the recommended period.

Store berries whole, unstemmed, and unwashed. Berries are highly perishable and lose vitamin C and eating quality quickly when they are cleaned and prepared before storage. You need only to place them loosely in shallow containers so air can circulate around them and bottom layers will not be crushed by too much weight on top.

Refrigerate fully ripe pineapples in wrappings so other foods do not absorb the pineapple odor.

MAXIMUM STORAGE time in the refrigerator recommended for fruits is about 1 or 2 days for—berries (except cranberries), cherries, figs; 3 to 5 days for—apricots, avocados, grapes, nectarines, peaches, plums, pears, rhubarb; 1 week for—mellow apples, cranberries.

Storage at cool room temperature is best for some fruits and vegetables. Citrus fruits and melons keep quality best in a room at 60° to 70° F. but you can hold them up to a week in the refrigerator if they are not already overripe or bruised.

Citrus fruits are our most dependable sources of vitamin C. Their high initial content is remarkably stable; their flavor becomes unacceptable before much of the vitamin C is lost.

Bananas are best held at room temperature since they soften and brown quickly in the refrigerator.

Maximum storage time at cool room temperature is about 1 or 2 days for—ripe bananas; 3 to 5 days for—green-tipped bananas; up to 1 week for—melons, citrus fruits, pineapple.

POTATOES maintain quality best when stored in open containers at about 50° F., sweetpotatoes and mature onions at 60° F. You can store these vegetables and winter squash and rutabagas for several months in a cool room.

Under these conditions sweetpotatoes and winter squash will maintain a high vitamin A value until the time they are eaten.

If you do not have storage space in this temperature range, put the vegetables in the coolest room you have, inspect them often, and use them as soon as you can conveniently work them into your meal plans.

173

FRESH MEAT and poultry retain quality best if held in the coldest part of the refrigerator covered with only a loose wrapping. This will allow air to dry the surface slightly and retard growth of spoilage organisms. The thiamine in meats and poultry will remain essentially intact if you refrigerate these foods promptly.

Since meat and poultry take a large segment of the food dollar, be sure to use them before there is any important change in quality.

The following guide provides a basis for estimating how long you can hold some commonly used meats and meat products in a refrigerator with little or no quality or nutrient loss: 1 to 2 days for—ground meat, fresh pork sausage, variety meats, poultry, giblets, cooked meats; 3 to 5 days for—steaks, chops, roasts, halves or slices of cured ham, luncheon meats; 1 week for—whole cured ham, bacon, smoked sausage, and frankfurters.

MOST DAIRY PRODUCTS and eggs are best when held only briefly in the coldest part of the refrigerator in tightly covered containers. Protect the riboflavin in milk by refrigerating milk promptly; letting it stand in the sunlight hastens destruction of riboflavin. Use milk, cream, and cottage cheese within 3 to 5 days for the best eating quality.

Soft cheeses like cottage, cream, and Neufchatel are very perishable. Hard cheeses like Cheddar and Swiss keep their quality well if protected from drying out. Cover cut surfaces of hard cheeses tightly with waxed paper, foil, or plastic. Tightly wrap cheeses having strong odor to protect other foods stored with them. You should use refrigerated cream cheese and other soft cheeses within 2 weeks, but Cheddar, Swiss, and other hard cheeses will keep well for several months.

Refrigerate butter, margarine, and eggs in their original packaging or in covered containers. Eggs especially need protection to retard moisture loss and absorption of odors. For best eating quality, use butter and margarine within 2 weeks and eggs within 1 week.

Bread and most of the bakery products can be stored at room temperature for a few days. However, during hot, humid weather, you may need to hold them in the refrigerator for protection against mold. Refrigerate any baked products with cream or custard filling at all times because these are "favorite foods" of the spoilage organisms, and they can cause illness if not properly stored. Opaque packaging materials help retain the riboflavin in bread and in other bakery products.

Cereals, flours, and spices need protection from moisture, dust, and insects. Store them in tightly closed containers at room temperature.

STORE canned and bottled foods in a cool dry place; they need refrigeration only after the container is opened. These foods are safe to use as long as the seal is intact, but excessively long storage may impair their eating quality and nutritive value.

Dried foods are among the easiest foods to protect. Generally, you can hold them satisfactorily at room temperature in tightly closed containers for several months. In warm, humid weather dried fruit retains quality better if you refrigerate it.

Protect nonfat dry milk from the moisture in the air by closing the container after use. This way you prevent lumps and make reconstitution of the milk quick and easy.

Dry mixes from which you make baked products, and dehydrated soup mixes and combination main dishes store very well at room temperature. Many contain ingredients that help protect the food from quality losses during its storage.

If you have freezer storage space that provides a temperature of 0° F. or lower, a wide variety of frozen foods can be held for extended periods of time and still retain good eating quality and nutritive value.

FREEZE ONLY FOODS of high quality. The proper wrappings or containers

174

are essential in maintaining quality; when homefreezing foods, be sure to use those recommended for freezer storage and seal them tightly.

Frozen fruit stores very well at 0° F. and you can hold most kinds as long as a year with little or no damage to quality. Use home-frozen citrus fruits and citrus juices within 4 to 6 months for the best flavor.

Frozen vegetables have a comparatively long storage life when held at 0° F. as recommended. Generally, you should plan to use them within about 8 months. This will assure good eating and help to make room in your freezer for the new crop when it comes in season.

MANY KINDS of frozen meat hold their high quality well for many months as indicated by the following recommended storage periods: 12 months for—beef and lamb roasts, beef steaks, chicken, turkey; 8 months for—pork and veal roasts; 6 months for—duck, goose; 4 months for—lamb, veal, and pork chops; 3 months for—ground meat, giblets; 2 months for—cured ham, fresh pork sausage; less than 1 month for—bacon.

If you freeze homogenized milk, plan to use it within 4 or 5 months, for best results; homogenized whipping cream, within 2 to 3 months.

Frozen eggs will maintain good quality for 9 to 12 months.

Generally, cheeses do not freeze satisfactorily as they become crumbly and mealy. However, if this type of product is acceptable for your intended use, cheese can be held frozen for approximately 6 months.

ICE CREAM and other frozen desserts can be stored as long as 1 month at 0° F. with good results. If your storage space for frozen foods maintains freezing temperatures above 0° F., plan to hold these foods only 2 or 3 days.

Frozen bread and other bakery products can be held for the following periods: 2 to 3 months—bread, yeast rolls, cinnamon rolls, Danish pastry, doughnuts, angel and chiffon cakes; 4 months—chocolate cake; 6 months— pound and yellow cakes; 8 months— fruit pies (unbaked); 12 months— fruit cake.

So far we have given you some guides to follow in selecting your food and in protecting its quality, nutritive value, and safety during the interval of holding before it is used.

THE LAST STEP that cannot be overlooked in protecting food in the home is its final preparation for the family meal. Food preparation is both an art and a science. We are concerned here

The end result of it all: Food on the table.

mainly with the science of preparation as it affects the retention of nutrients and quality in food and the protection of food from spoilage.

You can conserve nutrients in a number of ways when preparing food. For example, wash foods only as necessary to clean them, make parings thin and trim foods as little as possible, save and use cooking liquids. You can prevent the oxidation which destroys nutrients by protecting foods from exposure to air.

In general, the preparation and cooking procedures that are best for retaining nutritive values are also effective in producing safe and palatable food.

MANY FOODS need thorough washing before they are prepared for cooking or serving. Dirt or soil on fresh fruits or vegetables is unpalatable and can carry spoilage organisms.

Some foods should not be washed. Rice is one of these.

By today's methods of handling, the consumer is assured clean packaged rice. Furthermore, washing rice is wasteful nutritionally, because most of the rice is enriched with iron and the B vitamins—thiamine, riboflavin, and niacin. These added nutrients are very easily removed.

Washing just once before cooking removes about 10 percent of the thiamine in brown and parboiled white rice and 25 percent in regular white rice; with additional washings, these losses of thiamine will be doubled. Losses of riboflavin and niacin are around 10 to 15 percent.

The practice of draining the cooking water and rinsing the cooked rice is also wasteful of these soluble nutrients.

Minimum trimming and paring is advisable practice both nutritionally and pennywise. Use the dark-green outer leaves of lettuce and cabbage and the tops of young green onions in salads. They add color to the salad and contribute more than their share of nutrients, particularly vitamin A value. Vitamin C is highly concentrated in the core of cabbage. Other nutrients like minerals are often concentrated in fruits and root vegetables in the part just under the skin.

Occasionally, removal of the less acceptable edible parts is justified. For example, the tough fibrous stems of greens contribute relatively little nutritionally and the nutritious part becomes more palatable by their removal.

VITAMIN destruction is accelerated in some fruits and vegetables when their tissues are cut or macerated. So whenever possible avoid cutting, slicing, or shredding them very far in advance in preparation of meals. Eating quality is better then, as well.

If it is necessary to get light-colored fruits for a salad or dessert ready ahead of serving time, you can keep color from darkening by holding them in citrus fruit juice.

This also shows the oxidation of vitamin C in the fruit and adds flavor to bland fruits. Refrigerating prepared fruits and salad greens until they are used also helps protect the nutrients and the eating quality.

Vitamins are destroyed by oxidation more readily in vegetables and fruits than in most other foods. In conserving nutrients in these two large food groups, vitamin C and the nutrients from which vitamin A is formed are of most concern to us. Vegetables and fruits contribute more than 90 percent of the vitamin C and around half of the vitamin A value in our national food supply.

HERE ARE SOME SIMPLE easy-to-follow cooking practices for conserving nutrients in foods while maintaining good eating quality: Keep the volume of cooking water small; cook foods until just tender; use low to moderate cooking temperatures; hold cooked food only briefly before serving.

Using a small amount of cooking water is very important. Water-soluble nutrients like vitamin C, the B vitamins, and minerals are lost in the cooking water along with color and flavor components of the food. Leafy vegetables cooked quickly in just enough

176

water to prevent scorching will lose only half as much vitamin C as when they are cooked with an excessive amount of water.

You can decrease losses of water-soluble nutrients by cooking food in a tightly covered pan. A tight lid reduces water loss by escaping steam so that the food can be cooked in a small amount of water. Many leafy vegetables can be cooked in this way in only the water that clings to the leaves. Cooking in a steamer or pressure saucepan are other acceptable methods for keeping to a minimum the amounts of nutrients that dissolve in the cooking water.

KEEPING THE COOKING period short holds vitamin destruction to a minimum and usually helps retain the color, flavor, and texture of the food. The longer a food is cooked the greater will be the destruction of vitamin C, vitamin A value, and thiamine, because these vitamins are not stable in heat.

Start vegetables in boiling water rather than cold water, because destruction of both vitamin C and vitamin A value is accelerated in some vegetables during the short interval before the water begins to boil. This rapid destruction results from enzyme activity which continues until the enzyme itself is destroyed by heat. By using boiling water, you shorten both the time of enzyme activity and the total cooking time which is required to make the vegetable tender.

Remember that most frozen vegetables take less cooking time than fresh ones. They were partially cooked before freezing to stop the action of enzymes that would impair the quality of the frozen food during storage.

Overcooking often develops undesirable color in vegetables. The colors are unstable in green, white, and red vegetables and undergo chemical changes during cooking with an accompanying loss or change in color.

Hard water helps to protect the color in green vegetables but not in white or red vegetables. White cabbage, onions, and other white vegetables turn yellow while red cabbage acquires a blue tinge. Adding a little vinegar, lemon juice, or cream of tartar to the cooking water will help these vegetables retain their natural color.

Use low or medium heat when cooking meats and other foods with high protein content. High temperatures and overcooking will produce tough, dry roasts or steaks and shrunken pieces of stew meat. In addition, this makes less meat for the family to eat.

Low heat is best for cooking eggs and cheese and for combination foods that contain large amounts of these foods, like custards and souffles. Too high heat toughens egg white and makes yolks mealy. It curdles custards and makes cheese stringy.

All this happens because high heat shrinks the protein in these foods.

Milk, too, requires low cooking temperatures, both to keep the protein from coagulating to form a scum on top and a coating on the pan and to protect the milk sugar from caramelizing and developing off-flavors and a brown color.

Another time to guard against overheating is when using fat in frying. When fat smokes, it is decomposing. This results in unpleasant flavors and odors and may even be a problem in digesting the food. Fats that have reached smoking temperature become rancid soon and add to the problems in storing a food.

If a food to be served hot is prepared too soon, holding until the rest of the meal is ready gives opportunity for additional destruction of vitamins. Color, flavor, and texture will suffer too.

EXCESSIVELY LONG holding of warm food, as 3 or 4 hours, also can result in danger from spoilage.

Temperatures ranging from 45° F. to 120° F. are conducive to growth of spoilage organisms.

Many foods, particularly poultry and meat, milk and eggs, and foods containing these are especially subject to spoilage when they are held at these temperatures.

Consider this when selecting foods to take on picnics or put in bag lunches since these meals sometimes must be held several hours before they are eaten.

To keep foods palatable and nutritious as well as to insure their safety from spoilage, it is necessary to keep hot foods hot and cold foods cold until they are served.

OFTEN LEFTOVERS are planned to save time and money, or if unplanned, may be used to advantage. Here are a few tips for keeping leftovers nutritious, palatable, and safe from spoilage.

Be selective in purchasing foods that are good nutritive sources, particularly of the less stable vitamins. These foods will still be good sources of the nutrients even if substantial vitamin or other nutrient losses occur before they are served.

Use, for example, enriched rather than unenriched cereal products for the extra B vitamins that enrichment provides, and citrus to supplement other fruits like pears, applesauce, and grapes that contain only small amounts of vitamin C.

The various kinds of cooked greens and the deeply colored varieties of sweetpotatoes and winter squash will still have a high vitamin A value when they are served in a later meal.

Use leftovers without reheating when possible. Many foods have a "warmed-over" flavor and lose some of their nutrients when they are reheated.

Cool hot foods quickly to slow down chemical changes that affect both vitamin retention and their eating quality. Shallow pans help cool foods fast. Place the pans in ice or in cold water to start the cooling, or use the refrigerator.

CONTRARY to common belief, refrigerating warm food does not cause it to spoil. But do not put so much warm food in the refrigerator that it raises the temperature above 45° F. and do not put deep containers of hot food in the refrigerator. Food cools too slowly at the center for this to be a safe procedure.

Also, do not depend on a refrigerator for cooling a whole stuffed turkey. Leftover turkey should be stored as follows to prevent possible spoilage:

The stuffing should be removed immediately and refrigerated in a shallow container to speed cooling. The meat should be removed from the carcass and refrigerated in single layers until it has cooled; then it can be packed closer to save space and prevent drying out.

Broth and gravy are especially subject to spoilage. They should be cooled quickly and put in a refrigerator but should be held for only a day or two.

If you plan for leftovers, always consider carefully ways to store and use them that will retain as much of the original quality as possible and that will not give spoilage organisms an opportunity to grow and multiply.

The protection of food brought into the home, therefore, means that the homemaker must provide suitable storage during the time it is held, use it before it loses eating quality and nutrients, and prepare and serve it in ways that preserve its natural goodness and food value.

Family satisfaction and well-being will make this job most worthwhile.

For further reading:
U.S. Department of Agriculture, *Conserving the Nutritive Values in Foods.* Home and Garden Bulletin 90, 1965.
———— *Freezing Meat and Fish in the Home.* Home and Garden Bulletin 93, 1963.
———— *Home Care of Purchased Frozen Foods.* Home and Garden Bulletin 69, 1960.
———— *Home Freezers, Their Selection and Use.* Home and Garden Bulletin 48, 1964.
———— *Home Freezing of Fruits and Vegetables.* Home and Garden Bulletin 10, 1965.
———— *Home Freezing of Poultry.* Home and Garden Bulletin 70, 1964.
———— *How To Buy Eggs by USDA Grades and Weight Classes.* Leaflet 442, 1966.
———— *How To Buy Poultry by USDA Grades.* Marketing Bulletin 1, 1963.
———— *Storing Perishable Foods in the Home.* Home and Garden Bulletin 78, 1965.
———— *Tips on Selecting Fruits and Vegetables.* Marketing Bulletin 13, 1961.
———— *U.S. Grades for Beef.* Marketing Bulletin 15, 1960.
———— *USDA Poultry Inspection—A Consumer's Safeguard.* Program Aid 299, 1965.

MEALS AWAY FROM HOME

AIMEE N. MOORE

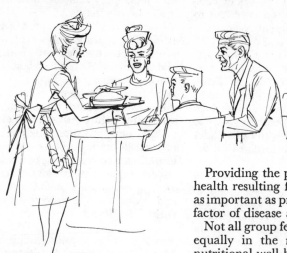

A LMOST everyone eats away from home occasionally; many people eat all their meals out at some time in their lifespan.

It is estimated that about a fourth of what we spend for food goes for meals eaten out of the home, and the proportion will probably continue to increase as more married women work, more young people go to college, and Medicare helps elderly people pay hospital and nursing home costs. Besides, Americans travel more and eat out more often for recreation as their standard of living increases.

PROTECTING THE consumer of food eaten away from home has two major facets. Instantly one thinks of safeguarding him from foodborne diseases, food poisoning, and foreign matter in the food, like bits of broken glass and sharp bone fragments. These are extremely important, of course. But it also means planning menus that are nutritionally adequate as well as attractive, purchasing forms of food high in nutritive value, then preparing the food so that nutrients are conserved until the food is finally eaten.

Providing the positive factor of good health resulting from good nutrition is as important as preventing the negative factor of disease and food poisoning.

Not all group feeding operators share equally in the responsibility for the nutritional well-being of their patrons, though each has some responsibility. Hospitals, nursing homes, university residence halls, penal institutions, and other similar organizations assume almost full responsibility.

Many persons, such as traveling salesmen, or the unmarried men and women who live in single rooms, eat practically all of their meals in commercial restaurants.

Of course, these people have a choice of restaurants and menus, but they still rely upon public facilities for adequate nutrition. Many other people eat at least their noon meal on working days in public restaurants.

The National School Lunch program was developed primarily as a nutrition measure. It provides a highly nutritious noon meal for children who may not otherwise have a good lunch, and it teaches children good food habits.

To maintain good health each person needs a sufficient supply of calories, protein, vitamins, and certain minerals. Recommended Daily Dietary

* * *

Aimee N. Moore is *Director*, Department of Nutrition and Dietetics, Medical Center, and *Professor* of Food and Nutrition, School of Home Economics, University of Missouri, Columbia, Mo.

Allowances have been established by the Food and Nutrition Board, National Academy of Sciences-National Research Council and are under constant surveillance to keep them up to date in the light of current research.

THE RECOMMENDED Daily Dietary Allowances are fairly technical. Therefore simplified charts, like A Daily Food Guide that indicates the number of servings of food in four main groups needed daily, have been devised to help nonprofessional people plan adequate meals for their families or for groups of people.

A section of *Food*, the 1959 Yearbook of Agriculture, discusses recommended allowances and tables of food values, and includes A Daily Food Guide. A Daily Food Guide is also carried on pages 394–5 in the 1965 Yearbook, *Consumers All*.

In addition, the U.S. Department of Agriculture issues a leaflet which carries the title "Food for Fitness: A Daily Food Guide."

Perhaps in the near future any dietitian or food service manager in the United States will be able to obtain nutritionally adequate menus, adapted to the food habits of his region and his clientele, at either a predetermined cost or a minimum cost by simply dialing a telephone linking him to a computer which is in a central location.

Research is now underway to develop such a computerized system.

PILOT STUDIES have shown that if data concerning recipes, size of servings, nutritive value of component foods (most of which is already available on magnetic tape that can be read by computers), and current or predicted costs of foods to be purchased are stored in the computer, programs can be written to produce menus in an incredibly short time which are as acceptable as those drawn up by dietitians.

The computer-planned menus always meet the nutritional requirements while the dietitian-planned menus occasionally do not, and besides the average cost is appreciably lower.

BOTH NUTRITIVE VALUE and the wholesomeness and safeness of food should be considered in selecting the source of the food supply and the form in which it will be purchased.

The United States has one of the safest food supplies in the world. We are protected by the Federal Food, Drug, and Cosmetic Act, the Meat Inspection Act, and by the Poultry Products Inspection Act—to mention a few of the most important laws enacted to prohibit the shipment of unwholesome, unsafe food in interstate commerce. Federal laws also protect us from misbranding, and from false or misleading advertising and packaging. State and local governments enact ordinances and codes that regulate these matters within the States.

THE 1962 U.S. Public Health Service Model Food Service Sanitation Ordinance and Code requires that "food in the food service establishment shall be from a source approved, or considered satisfactory, by the health authority and which is in compliance with applicable State and local laws and regulations." Among other things it specifically requires that all meat and poultry products be inspected for wholesomeness, that fluid milk be pasteurized, and all nonacid and low-acid canned foods be processed in food-processing establishments, not home-canned.

No State or local government is required to put into effect the Federal model code. However, the 1943 edition of the Ordinance and Code Regulating Eating and Drinking Establishments had been adopted by 37 States and over 1,100 county and municipal health jurisdictions.

Many of these jurisdictions have since adopted the 1962 revision which has just been described above.

MOST FOOD processors and distributors unstintingly support the concept of a safe, wholesome food supply, and actively assist public health officials in continuing to improve methods of processing, packaging materials, and the like. But there are some firms that barely meet the minimum standards set by law. It costs no more to purchase food from firms that maintain high standards of sanitation, and it may cost less. High standards of cleanliness may reduce the spoilage and waste and those firms may be able to pass along the savings to their customers in order to attract more business.

No FOOD purchaser can possibly visit all the firms processing or wholesaling the food he needs. But in many cases the institution purchaser may have several potential sources of supplies near enough to visit. It would be well worth his time to visit dairies, fresh produce wholesalers, bakeries, and other establishments to see firsthand the difference between firms and to select the best ones to patronize.

Nutritive value of food is affected by the method of processing. Some nutrients are destroyed by prolonged heat, others are dissolved in water used in processing. New processing techniques using high temperatures for short times or extremely low temperatures, for instance, tend to conserve more nutritive value than the methods now commonly used by the canning and freezing industry.

Many factors in processing affect nutritive value. The food purchaser can't keep up with all of them. But if he is aware of the possibility of a difference and has concern for the nutritive value of the food he purchases, he will consider nutritive value in making purchasing decisions.

AN EXAMPLE of this is enriched bread and flour. Some food purchasers think all flour, bread, and cereals are enriched; this is not true. More than half the States do require enrichment of flour and bread with thiamine, riboflavin, niacin, and iron—vitamins and minerals which were known to be inadequate in the diets of many Americans. Enriched bread, flour, and other cereals and cereal products do not cost the consumer any more than comparable products that are not enriched. In States where enrichment is not required, the purchaser of food for restaurants and institutions should specify that the bread, flour, and other cereal products be enriched. If a product is enriched, the term "enriched" will appear on the label.

Diseases transmitted through food are called foodborne diseases. These are divided into two major classifications: *Infections* transmitted through food, and *food poisoning*.

From 1952 to 1960 approximately 2,000 outbreaks of foodborne disease were reported involving almost 100,000 cases. No doubt numerous other outbreaks have occurred.

Foodborne disease is not reportable by law in many States, and health departments often become alerted to an outbreak by circuitous routes and too late either to secure samples or institute corrective measures.

DR. CARL DAUER of the Public Health Service says the actual number of foodborne and waterborne disease outbreaks is conservatively estimated to be at least 10 to 20 times larger than the reported number. This means the number of cases occurring annually would be somewhere in the order of 100,000 to 200,000.

Other public health officials believe it may be as high as a half million to a million cases annually.

Undoubtedly a far higher proportion of diseases like typhoid fever and botulism are reported than other types of foodborne diseases.

Typhoid and botulism are much more serious types of illnesses and consequently, they are likely to come to the attention of a physician and the public health authorities.

A high proportion of the foodborne disease that authorities *report* occurs in hospitals, colleges, and other institutions feeding many people three times a day. This does not mean sanitation standards are less rigid in those types of food service organizations than in hotels and restaurants— or homes, for that matter. The opposite is usually the case. It is much more noticeable when large numbers of

Type of disease	Outbreaks	Percent of outbreaks	Cases	Percent of cases
Typhoid fever	65	3. 4	603	0. 6
Salmonellosis	209	11. 0	10, 699	11. 7
Shigellosis	99	5. 3	10, 354	11. 0
Botulism	56	2. 9	116	0. 1
Staphylococcal food poisoning	633	33. 2	28, 331	30. 0
Gastroenteritis, undetermined cause	839	44. 2	44, 083	46. 6
Total	1, 901	100. 0	94, 186	100. 0

people who eat, work, and live together become ill within a short period of time, and this type of outbreak is usually reported.

People who pick up a foodborne disease in restaurants usually become ill after returning home. They may not connect their illness with the restaurant food—particularly if the illness occurs more than a few hours later. And even if they suspect the origin of the illness they may not report it.

Sources of contamination will become even more difficult to identify in the future. Many convenience foods like TV dinners, precooked and frozen entrees, and desserts are prepared in food processing factories and in central commissaries of large restaurant chains. Many restaurants and institutions as well as housewives purchase these foods. As a result food poisoning outbreaks occur that appear to be individual illnesses with no common location and frequently with no common food source to involve.

THE TABLE at the top of the page is adapted from Dauer's report.

Almost half the outbreaks reported were classified as of "undetermined cause." Many of these gastrointestinal (GI) upsets were suspected to be staphylococcal food poisoning and Salmonellosis.

Clostridium perfringens, not previously associated with foodborne disease, has been isolated in several outbreaks in recent years. It was reported separately for the first time in 1959, but is included here in the unknown category. Since this organism is an anaerobe (lives or is active in the absence of oxygen), it would not show up in the

procedures used to culture and identify most of the bacteria causing foodborne diseases. There are indications that *C. perfringens* may be implicated in many disease outbreaks.

THE PUBLIC HEALTH SERVICE lists 24 infectious diseases—also called contagious or communicable diseases—that can be transmitted through food and water. Here are a few of the most common: Colds, septic sore throat, flu (influenza), typhoid fever, diphtheria, scarlet fever, tuberculosis, undulant fever, and infectious hepatitis.

Some of these diseases are caused by bacteria, others by viruses.

Bacteria and viruses are living organisms much too small to be seen without powerful magnification. Hence outside the laboratory you never know when they are present. One need not be ill to transmit these diseases, although an ill person is much more likely to be a source of infection.

Bacteria and viruses are spread mostly by people, either directly by personal contact or indirectly. Because the most common way a person becomes infected is through the mouth, food and water—or the utensils they are served in—are frequently the carriers. But since there are so many possible avenues of contamination, most infectious diseases are not reported as foodborne or as waterborne diseases. Typhoid fever is an exception because it is frequently associated with a contaminated water supply. However, because of our wide use of municipal water supplies, the United States has relatively few cases of typhoid.

When anyone is nauseated and vomits or has stomach cramps and diarrhea, he usually blames it on food he has eaten. Food poisoning isn't the only thing that can cause vomiting and diarrhea, but it is often responsible for gastroenteritis.

THE MOST characteristic feature of food poisoning is the explosive nature of the illness. In most cases the victim feels all right for a while after eating, then suddenly becomes violently nauseated and has severe cramps and diarrhea. Afterwards he is exhausted. The onset may come within a few hours after eating or it may be delayed 72 hours or longer. The length of time before the onset may give the physician a clue about which type of organism to suspect and therefore what sources to suspect, because the different types of bacteria have different modes of operation.

Most types of food poisoning will not cause death, although the victim may feel so sick that for a short while he wishes he could die. However, if a person has severe heart disease or any other type of severe illness, the physical strain of vomiting and the emotional disturbance may cause fatal complications. Others who may suffer serious consequences are babies and elderly people who are very weak. Consequently it is especially important for hospitals and nursing homes to maintain high sanitation standards.

Unfortunately one cannot always tell by smelling and tasting food if it is not safe to eat. Food that is suspect should be thrown out, of course, but food that looks appetizing, smells good, and tastes delicious may still cause food poisoning.

APPROXIMATELY a third of the reported cases of food poisoning are known to be caused by Staphylococci; probably at least half the outbreaks are caused by this organism if the cause of all outbreaks were known. Staphylococci, or "staph" as they are commonly called, are extremely widespread. They are especially prevalent in nose and throat discharges and in the pus from infected cuts and boils.

During their growth in suitable food media these bacteria produce a heat stable toxin (poisonous substance) which is odorless, tasteless, and colorless. It is this toxin, rather than the bacteria themselves, that causes acute intestinal disturbance within 1 to 4 hours after eating.

If food has been grossly contaminated and allowed to remain at room temperature for 4 hours or longer, enough toxin may be produced to cause gastroenteritis (gastrointestinal upset).

The room temperature time is additive. For example, if a cook took 2 hours to make chicken salad for a picnic and refrigerated it overnight, then the next day it was left on the picnic table for 2 hours or longer, the total time at room temperature would be 4 hours or longer. Once the toxin is introduced into the food, it is not destroyed by boiling.

STAPH FOOD poisoning outbreaks are generally associated with foods handled after they are cooked. Cream pies and cream puffs, deviled eggs, ham sandwiches, or turkey salad are foods frequently involved.

Cream pies and cream-filled pastries may become soggy if refrigerated a long time, hence the temptation to leave them at room temperature. Turkey has to be stripped from the bone and diced, a time-consuming process, and often it is done during odd moments between other jobs. That is why these foods are frequently involved. The food is contaminated with "staph" bacteria from the food handlers and is left at room temperature long enough for the bacteria to produce the toxin.

There are innumerable types of Salmonella organisms that may cause food poisoning in man. Shigella are one common type, and Shigellosis is reported separately from Salmonellosis. Bacteria causing typhoid fever are another type of Salmonella.

WHEN living organisms of the food poisoning type are ingested, acute

183

gastroenteritis and fever may develop in 8 to 48 hours. The organisms multiply rapidly in the intestinal tract. The episode has a duration of 2 to 5 days. Once infected, individuals may become intestinal carriers and possible sources of infection for many months. Because the living organism causes the infection, foods causing outbreaks of Salmonellosis are most often contaminated after cooking.

Salmonella inhabit the intestinal tract of man and many animals, hence are found in the feces. They are spread easily if a person does not wash his hands after going to the toilet.

Poultry and processed eggs have often been the source of Salmonella contamination. In poultry processing, sometimes the intestines rupture and the cavity of the bird becomes contaminated. Or eggs become contaminated from dirty shells. Shellfish grown in contaminated water may become carriers and are also a potential source of contamination.

IF POULTRY is contaminated with Salmonella during processing, it is potentially hazardous even though poultry is usually cooked thoroughly and Salmonella are destroyed by heat.

In most kitchens, poultry is washed and inspected for pinfeathers before it is prepared for cooking; sometimes it is cut up. If the cook is interrupted in his work and does not wash his hands thoroughly, he can contaminate other food that has already been cooked. Or he can contaminate equipment—he may use the cutting board again before it is thoroughly washed.

Large turkeys may be stuffed before freezing, or stuffed with a warm dressing the day before they are to be cooked. If the cavity is contaminated with Salmonella, the dressing becomes contaminated; conditions are ideal for bacterial growth. The dressing or cavity may also be contaminated with Staphylococci in handling.

EVEN WHEN THE turkey is done, the dressing may not have reached a temperature high enough to kill the

bacteria (165° F.). Thick meat on the turkey effectively insulates the dressing from both heat and cold for relatively long times—long enough to grow a good crop of bacteria and for "staph" to produce a toxin.

Turkeys should be roasted unstuffed. The cavity of a large bird cannot hold enough dressing for the number of portions obtained from the turkey, so extra dressing has to be baked outside the turkey anyway. And of course it takes appreciably less time to roast an unstuffed turkey.

FROZEN AND DRIED eggs are used extensively in quantity food preparation because they save labor. Unless they are pasteurized after shelling, these products are often contaminated with Salmonella. A recent amendment of the identity standards for egg products requires that they be pasteurized or otherwise treated to result in finished products which are free of any viable Salmonella micro-organisms.

Eggs are sometimes eaten raw, as in eggnogs and some desserts. Frequently raw eggs are used in cooked products, like meringues or cream pies, that may not be heated thoroughly enough to kill bacteria if they are present. It is recommended that only clean, uncracked fresh eggs should be used for such food items as eggnogs and others requiring raw eggs. Eggs for such use should be cracked just before serving. Meringues should be made from pasteurized whites or from the whites of freshly cracked whole eggs.

SINCE cream pies with meringues are often involved in outbreaks of Salmonellosis, considerable research has been done to develop procedures for preparing these products to make them safe. Some recipes for cream pie fillings and puddings suggest heating the milk, adding the starch and cooking this mixture until the starch is done, then adding the eggs and cooking the mixture for a few minutes to cook the eggs. Using this procedure, called the three-step method, the eggs may not be cooked at a high enough temperature

184

for a long enough period to destroy Salmonella organisms.

K. Longrée and her associates at Cornell University developed a two-step method for preparing cream pie fillings and puddings that would result in cooking the eggs for a longer time. In this method the milk is heated with the sugar, then the eggs and starch are added at the same time and cooked until the product is thick and the starch is done. The two-step method is recommended for custard sauces, puddings, and cream pie fillings that are cooked in large quantities.

W. L. Mallman and associates at Michigan State University studied the effects of filling temperature, oven temperature, and baking time on safeness of meringues on cream pies. They recommend that the meringue be put on warm or hot filling, never on cold filling, and baked at a low temperature (325° to 350° F.) for a relatively long time (16 minutes or longer). Under these conditions all bacteria in the meringue will be killed.

ALTHOUGH relatively few cases of botulism occur in the United States, botulism is a public health hazard because a large proportion of the cases are fatal. *Clostridia botulini*, bacteria that form heat-resistant spores, are very widely distributed in nature. They grow in low acid and nonacid foods under anaerobic conditions (without air) and under these conditions they produce a toxin that is odorless, tasteless, and colorless. This is one of the most potent toxins known to man. Unlike the toxin produced by "staph" bacteria, however, it can easily be destroyed by boiling.

Most cases of botulism are caused by home-canned food that is not processed at a high enough temperature for a long enough time to kill the heat-resistant spores. The Public Health Service recommends that only commercially processed food be served in food service establishments.

Commercial canners establish elaborate safeguards to prevent botulism, but on rare occasions a commercially processed food is involved. In recent years canned tunafish was involved in one outbreak, smoked whitefish packaged in sealed plastic bags in another.

AS MENTIONED EARLIER, only recently has it been recognized that *C. perfringens* is the etiological or causative agent in some food poisoning outbreaks. This organism, like *C. botulinum*, is a spore-forming anaerobe, and there are many types. Some are heat-resistant, others are not. *C. perfringens* is widely distributed in feces, sewage, and soil. It is so widespread that researchers generally concede that it is a probable contaminant of nearly all foods.

H. E. Hall and R. Angelotti selected specimens of meat at random from retail stores in one community and isolated *C. perfringens* spores from about 45 percent of the specimens. Meat that had been handled—like chops, stew meat, or ground meat—had a higher incidence of contamination than other cuts of meat.

Fortunately, the incidence of *C. perfringens* in meats which required little or no cooking, or only light cooking, was lower than in meat that had to be fully cooked. Less than 1 percent of the samples yielded heat-resistant strains.

Symptoms of food poisoning by *C. perfringens* include diarrhea, acute abdominal pain, and nausea along with occasional vomiting.

These symptoms are first noticed 8 to 12 hours after eating the food and continue for 6 to 12 hours.

FOODS most frequently associated with outbreaks of food poisoning due to *C. perfringens* are meats, including fowl, and gravies that have been cooked and allowed to cool slowly. The potential hazard appears to be from contamination after cooking. If the spores are introduced while the food is between the temperatures of 158° to 176° F., these temperatures would heat-shock them and allow rapid germination. Extremely rapid growth would occur if the food were allowed to remain at temperatures between 110° and 116° F.

Microanaerobic conditions (no available oxygen in one portion of a mixture which otherwise has oxygen) can be created in containers that are not sealed. When a pot of gravy is boiled, for example, oxygen is driven out of the gravy. Oxygen can now permeate the gravy only from the top of the container. Anaerobic conditions could easily exist in the bottom of the pot if it were deep enough. The more viscous the food, the more difficult it is for oxygen from the air to penetrate.

Anaerobic conditions are more likely to be created in deep pots than shallow pans. A boned and rolled roast would be another example. Anaerobic conditions would be created in the center of the roast itself.

HALL AND ANGELOTTI stated that since a high percentage of meat samples can be expected to be contaminated with *C. perfringens*, the area where meat and meat dishes are prepared may become similarly contaminated.

They recommend that food, particularly meat, be cooked to a temperature above 140° F., cooled quickly to below 40°, and kept cold. Furthermore, if meat or meat dishes are to be reheated for subsequent use, they should be heated quickly to temperatures above 140° F. and, where possible, to boiling before serving.

UNTIL RECENTLY it has been assumed that common molds were not harmful. Moldy food, unfit for human consumption, was often fed to animals. Some molds are known to be beneficial, and many are known to be harmless. Some of these molds are introduced to foods purposefully in order to develop a desirable flavor, as in cheeses.

But apparently some common molds, under conditions not yet fully understood, can produce a toxin (aflatoxin) that is very harmful to man. Intensive research is being done on mycotoxins (toxins produced by molds) at the present time. Until more specific information on the subject is available, it is recommended that moldy foods be discarded in their entirety.

CONTROL OF FOODBORNE disease involves two main preventive measures in food handling whether the handling is in the food processing plant, the wholesaling firm, the institution kitchen, the home—or in transportation of the food product from one place to another:

• Prevent contamination.
• Establish conditions in which bacteria cannot grow.

DIRTY PEOPLE wearing dirty clothes and working with dirty equipment on dirty tables in a dirty kitchen can easily contaminate food or dishes. Clean people working in clean surroundings will be much less likely to contaminate food. People who are ill with infectious diseases or who have infected cuts or boils are very likely to contaminate food and dishes they handle. Ill people should not be allowed to work where food is being prepared or served, or where dishes are being washed.

However, many food service employees do not comprehend the meaning of the word *clean* as it is interpreted by a sanitarian. Many of these people come from our lowest socio-economic groups and live under conditions where real cleanliness is difficult to achieve.

The Model Ordinance and Code for Food Service Sanitation, 1962 Recommendations of the Public Health Service, requires that no one be allowed to work in a food service establishment in any capacity while he is "affected with any disease in a communicable form, or while a carrier of such disease, or while affected with boils, infected wounds, sores, or an acute respiratory infection."

THIS ORDINANCE further states that "all employees shall wear clean outer garments, maintain a high degree of personal cleanliness, and conform to hygienic practices while on duty. They shall wash their hands thoroughly in an approved hand-washing facility before starting work, and as often as necessary to remove soil and contamination. No employee shall resume

186

work after visiting the toilet room without first washing his hands."

To enforce these regulations, "at least once every 6 months, the health authority shall inspect each food service establishment . . . and shall make as many additional inspections and reinspections as are necessary for the enforcement of this ordinance."

Obviously an inspection once every 6 months will not be adequate to enforce satisfactory standards of sanitation unless the manager actively supports the principles involved and consistently requires his employees to follow accepted practices. But managers and supervisors are not always with the employee. That is why each food service employee also needs to know about sanitation.

Since we cannot assume that new food service employees know very much about this subject, new employees must be taught and must be supervised closely. This involves helping them break bad habits and teaching them enough about hygiene and bacteriology so they can understand the concept of sanitation.

It is not enough for these employees to follow blindly specific rules "do this" or "don't do that." There are just too many specifics. Good sanitary practices must become habitual and must invade every phase of his life if we hope to be effective in preventing contamination of food and utensils.

An effective way for employees to teach themselves about food service sanitation would be highly desirable. Many of these employees have little formal education and do not read well; in addition, they are unaccustomed to reading. Expecting them to study books or pamphlets is unrealistic. Programed instruction using teaching machines appears to offer a solution for the problem.

In 1963 research was begun at the University of Missouri Medical Center to assess the effectiveness of this new technique in teaching unskilled food service employees. A programed course,

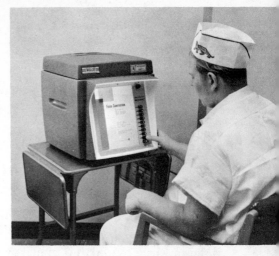

Using a self-teaching machine to study food sanitation.

Sanitation for Food Service Employees, was written and tested on all dietary employees under the level of supervisor.

At the experiment's end the employees in the experimental group who had seen the program on the teaching machine made significantly higher scores on a test about sanitation than the control group that was also given the test. The wide range in age, level of education, reading skill, and knowledge of the subject represented in the employees who participated in this study suggests the general applicability of programed instruction.

Subsequently this program has been used to instruct each new dietary employee at the University of Missouri Medical Center before he starts to work. Since the program is written for the seventh to eighth grade level, only four or five employees have been unable to complete the program.

Each employee is given a test about food sanitation, the same one used by the city sanitarian. With very few exceptions, employees have been able to pass this test after viewing the programed course one time. A dietitian or supervisor goes through the test with the employee afterwards to explain the correct answer to questions missed,

187

and to answer any others raised by the program. In addition, employees enjoy using the teaching machine.

SUCCESS IN MAINTAINING sanitation standards that reduce the likelihood of contamination revolves around teaching all food service employees the principles of personal hygiene and sanitary food handling. This probably will not be accomplished unless regular programs are established that are part of each new employee's orientation. If the new employee is to be instructed in food handling as a part of his on-the-job training, important points may be very easily left out.

In many institutions a new employee is shown where to work, his employer tells him what to do, but his fellow employees "teach" him his job. He receives little instruction in sanitary food handling principles.

Survey after survey shows few well organized training programs for food service employees.

Even in large institutions staffed by professionally trained managers who are aware of the need, the time element often precludes adequate training programs. It is frequently inconvenient to schedule employees for group teaching, and individual instruction often requires more supervisory time than can be spared to do an adequate job of training.

The magnitude of the job of training employees becomes apparent when one considers the number of new food service employees who have to be trained annually. The turnover rate among this group of employees is exceedingly high. The national average in fact is 40 percent.

IN MANY establishments the turnover rate exceeds 100 percent and in these establishments it may even be much higher in some job categories, like dishwashing machine operators or porters. Of course some of these employees may have worked in other food service jobs, but few have had adequate training in food sanitation.

Where the turnover rate is high,

supervisors spend a disproportionate amount of time rescheduling employees and interviewing new ones and have little time left for training.

In 1958 the Agricultural Marketing Service estimated that approximately 1.3 million persons were employed in public eating places. This number did not include establishments that serve meals but which are primarily engaged in other activities, like hotels, drug stores, and department stores. Nor did the figures include hospitals, college residence halls, prisons, schools, and similar institutions.

A FEW municipalities consider it so important for food service employees to have some knowledge of sanitation that they require each employee to attend and complete a course in food sanitation offered regularly by the local health authorities. Usually the employee must do this within a specified period and must demonstrate at the end of the course that he understands the principles of sanitary food handling.

Unfortunately, not many cities or towns have so enlightened a program. Even with this type of program a food service worker may be employed several months before he completes the required course in food sanitation.

PREVENTING contamination of food and utensils with micro-organisms capable of causing disease is obviously difficult, and total success is improbable. Therefore all food should be handled as if it were contaminated, and conditions set up that will either kill the bacteria that may be present or prevent them from multiplying at a rate that could result in food poisoning. This, too, is a very large order.

Bacteria are living organisms that require warmth and a suitable medium for growth and the development of their toxic products. Some foods, because of their composition, are more likely to support growth than others. Unfortunately most disease-causing bacteria find conditions and foods preferred by man suitable, even ideal, to support rapid multiplication.

188

Control of temperature and time is recognized to be the most dependable and practicable way to kill bacteria or prevent their growth. The Public Health Service's Food Service Sanitation Manual states that "safe temperatures, as applied to potentially hazardous food, shall mean temperatures of 45° or below, and 140° F. and above." Food should not be held at temperatures between 45° and 140° F.—called the Danger Zone because bacterial growth can take place in that range—except for necessary periods of preparation and service.

To maintain safe temperatures, perishable food should be refrigerated during transportation and storage. It is also much safer to thaw frozen foods at refrigerated temperatures, even though that takes a much longer time. Thawing at room temperature for prolonged periods is not safe because the surface may be warmed to room temperature while the center is still frozen.

If rapid thawing is required, thawing in cold running water or under a fan is recommended provided that the product is well wrapped.

Preparation time at room temperature should be kept to a minimum. The product being worked on should be stored in a refrigerator if the preparation has to be interrupted more than a few minutes.

The storage of leftover hot foods, and foods that have to be cooked and then cooled before serving, is one of the most hazardous of all conditions found in large quantity food service. Even when food is refrigerated promptly in "good" modern refrigerators, the food may cool so slowly that it remains in the Danger Zone for a prolonged time.

MANY FACTORS affect the rate of heat transfer in food. It is related to the mass in the container, the shape of the container, the density and viscosity of the product, the velocity of the cooling medium (air circulation, waterflow), whether or not the product is stirred, and may involve the molecular structure of the food. Even experts who have studied this problem for years

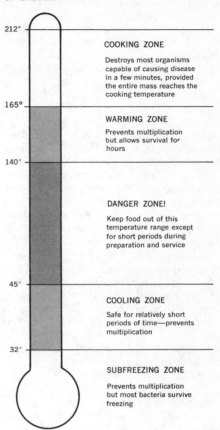

THERMOMETER FOR CONTROL OF BACTERIA

212°

COOKING ZONE

Destroys most organisms capable of causing disease in a few minutes, provided the entire mass reaches the cooking temperature

165°

WARMING ZONE

Prevents multiplication but allows survival for hours

140°

DANGER ZONE!

Keep food out of this temperature range except for short periods during preparation and service

45°

COOLING ZONE

Safe for relatively short periods of time—prevents multiplication

32°

SUBFREEZING ZONE

Prevents multiplication but most bacteria survive freezing

have not identified all of the variables.

Large masses of food, particularly viscous foods like cream puddings and white sauces, cool very slowly, even under refrigeration. This can be easily observed, and many studies to ascertain the cooling rates of different size batches give us precise temperature readings that verify our observations. Also, the temperature in a refrigerator fluctuates widely whenever hot food is placed in it. It is not unlikely that refrigerators in which large quantities of hot food are stored, like "leftover" refrigerators, may seldom reach 45° F. except for a few hours each day even though they may be set at 40° F. or at a lower temperature.

An example of this is reported in a

189

study by K. Longrée and J. C. White. In a refrigerator set at 38° F. and equipped with a fan to circulate the air, the temperature rose as high as 55° F. when hot food was put away at the end of a meal and remained at temperatures above 45° F. for at least 12 hours. Cooling rates on different batch sizes were determined. The researchers found that it took at least 20 hours for both 4 and 8 gallon containers of white sauce to cool from approximately 115° F. to 60° F. in a large refrigerator set at 47° F. and in which nothing else was stored.

Longrée and her associates at Cornell have sought ways to precool hot food before putting it into the refrigerator, which would lessen the danger of overloading refrigerators. A number of studies have been reported using techniques ranging from simple water baths with frequent stirring to prototypes of especially effective devices using refrigerated water running through a U-tube equipped with a scraper-lifter agitator. This Rube Goldberg-like gadget was very effective, and perhaps some day a food equipment manufacturer will market it.

Through use of the scraper-lifter agitator, the time to precool 4 gallons of a pudding from 140° to 60° F. was reduced from over 11 hours to an hour and 45 minutes. Less viscous foods can be precooled in shorter times.

Longrée and her associates studied the effect of several methods of increasing acidity in foods on bacterial growth. Potatoes and turkey meat were marinated (allowed to stand) in french dressing and mayonnaise. Various levels of pickles and mayonnaise were studied.

The researchers found that salads with high palatability ratings could be prepared which did inhibit bacterial growth when the acidity was increased in this manner.

Since these products are often the source of food poisoning, especially at picnics and church suppers, it seems a very practical method for reducing the danger of food poisoning.

CONDITIONS under which food is prepared and served in large quantity make it very difficult to eliminate the possibility of food poisoning. Many people have to handle the food and there are many opportunities to contaminate it. And it requires a lot of time to prepare large quantities of food; often the food has to be prepared several hours—or even a day—in advance of service.

The inescapable conclusion of this chapter is that effective means must be found to teach each food service worker more quickly and effectively the fundamentals of sanitary handling of food.

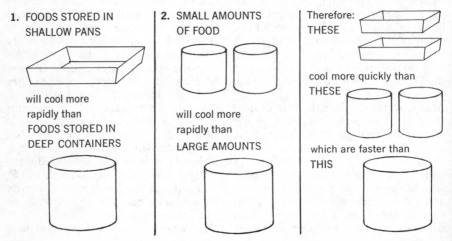

1. FOODS STORED IN SHALLOW PANS

will cool more rapidly than FOODS STORED IN DEEP CONTAINERS

2. SMALL AMOUNTS OF FOOD

will cool more rapidly than LARGE AMOUNTS

Therefore: THESE

cool more quickly than THESE

which are faster than THIS

MILITARY AND SPACE OPERATIONS

FERDINAND P. MEHRLICH and R. G. H. SIU

IT has been repeated by many a military leader throughout history that "An Army marches on its stomach," "Show me a fine messhall and I'll show you a tough fighting outfit," and so on regarding the *sine qua non* of good food for combat success. But the good food must be there, where the marching is, and then, when the fighting is. This becomes the crux of the military subsistence problem.

Subsistence operations of U.S. defense forces require over 100,000 personnel and annual expenditures of $2 billion. Typical annual purchases include 63 million dozen eggs, 336 million pounds of potatoes, and 385 million pounds of beef items.

Means have to be devised, and continually improved, to preserve the commodities from farms and processing plants for worldwide distribution under adverse environmental conditions and rough handling. Nutritive and sensory qualities must be retained so military meals reflect as close as possible the food preferences and standards cultivated by members of the Armed Forces during their prior civilian lives in a prosperous economy.

To UNDERSTAND the special nature of problems related to protection of food in military channels, one should know in general terms about the manner of subsisting Armed Forces personnel.

GOVERNMENT policy dictates that the freshest foods available and foods of good quality be used in meal preparation throughout the military establishment. The monetary level of meals is determined by statute and Executive order.

Nutritional requirements are set by the Surgeons General of the Army, Navy, and Air Force. All have agreed to the basic dietary standards, which have been recommended by the National Academy of Sciences.

Increases in the recommended levels of nutrition may be made—with the approval of local, authorized medical authorities—to compensate for the

*   *   *

Ferdinand P. Mehrlich is *Director*, Food Division, Natick, Mass., Laboratories, Army Materiel Command.

R. G. H. Siu is *Scientific Director*, Research Division, Army Materiel Command.

demands of cold weather, teenage growth, or unusually strenuous physical activity.

Military personnel in posts, camps, and stations eat a majority of their meals in organized dining facilities. Food service is usually cafeteria style. Food preparation is by trained military cooks and bakers in efficient kitchens. Recipes and menus are generally prescribed in official cookbooks and supplemental documents.

Food supplies are procured by requisition through established channels. Purchasing is generally centralized in the Defense Supply Agency, which cites either the Federal or the military specifications.

The latter are used when military requirements differ from those of other Government agencies.

Emphasis is placed on fresh foods in garrison feeding, although partially prepared convenience foods may also be used to a limited extent.

THE "A" RATION is served wherever tactical dispositions permit its use. A master menu, changed monthly by an official Menu Board, describes the meals to be served, deviations allowable, and the basis of issue of requisite components. The Army/Air Force's recipe book contains 1,000 entries; the Navy/Marines', 700.

In locations adjoining those of actual conflict, organized feeding depends in large part upon "B" ration meals, prepared from canned foods. Fresh produce and frozen meats are added as they are available.

The "B" ration consists of some 100 commodities, including fruits, vegetables, staples, meats, spices, garnishes, and desserts. Menus and recipes give directions for preparing 45 varied, tasty, and well-balanced hot meals.

Combat conditions impose a new array of stringent requirements upon military meals. They must be compact, light in weight, and nutritious and acceptable after years of adverse storage. Packaging also has to be much more rugged than the civilian counterpart. There are three classes of combat

meals under development, based on the size of the feeding groups.

The uncooked, 25-man combat meal has been designed to subsist groups of men in moderate numbers. The gross weight is less than 20 pounds for 25 men. Exclusive of bakery products, each 25-man meal is contained in a single factory-assembled package, less than 0.8 cubic foot in volume. This is in contrast to the "B" ration, with components shipped in more than 100 packages, requiring separate handling, storage, breakdown, and reassembly before issue to groups for meal preparation and consumption.

Each 25-man combat meal supplies 1,200 Calories per person. Comprised principally of dehydrated foods, the combat meal requires no refrigeration. Nor is it supplemented by perishables requiring refrigeration. Bread and cake products are furnished separately from continuous bakery equipment which uses instant mixes.

Eighteen menus, of a total of 30 under development, were available for a limited testing in Vietnam. These include *uncooked*, dehydrated steaks, pork chops, peas, fish sticks, fish squares, instant desserts, and salad bases. A typical supper consists of pork chops with cream gravy, green beans, applesauce, bread, margarine, mashed sweetpotatoes, coffee, cream, sugar, and cake.

To prepare this meal, the components are mixed with tepid water for 20 minutes. They are then prepared as if they were fresh foods.

COMBAT MEALS for small detachments are supplied in 6-man and 25-man modules. They consist of dehydrated, precooked foods which only require adding hot or cold water for eating.

There is no need for food preparation personnel, or for equipment other than a canteen cup and an expendable heating device supplied with the meal. An accessory packet is provided that includes coffee, sugar and cream, and salt. All food service equipment is expendable, such as trays, cups, knives, spoons, and serviettes.

The aluminum box containing the food components and accessories is overwrapped by an outer protective V-board carton.

The aluminum box protects against insect and rodent invasion, and it also serves as the vessel for reconstituting the dehydrated components.

Each meal provides 1,200 Calories of balanced nutrition. Twenty-one menus are available covering a 7-day cycle. No nutritional supplement is required for these small-detachment meals for as long as 120 days of subsistence.

New types of foods in considerable numbers have been developed in engineering these lightweight meals. Dehydrated products of high quality include precooked scrambled eggs, sliced beef and brown gravy, sliced pork, beef hash, beef and noodles, meat and spaghetti with tomato sauce, macaroni and cheese, sweet corn, carrots, peas, spinach, green beans, lima beans, rice, fruit cocktail, and pineapple.

A typical quick-serve dinner consists of meatballs and beans in tomato sauce, beef broth with noodles, fruit cocktail, applesauce, milk, bread, jelly, and a candy bar.

INDIVIDUALS whose duties preclude eating with a group are fed under battle conditions by means of newly developed meals and packets. These replace the "C" and "K" rations of World War II. The M-Packet illustrates these new types of ready-to-eat foods.

In the M-Packet the tin cans of civilian markets are replaced by flexible 3-ply containers. The inner ply is an inert film, such as polyethylene, to protect against food interaction with the package. The central ply is usually of aluminum to prevent light-induced deterioration, desiccation, and entry of oxygen. The outer ply for mechanical protection is a tough film, such as Mylar. The entire assemblage is overpacked in a lightweight, paperboard carton.

Foods like beef stew, ground beef in sauce, pork sausage, chicken loaf, beef with barbecue sauce, beef steak, and frankfurters are prepared as they

are for canning: "Flex-canning" might be an apt description of this new type of process. Hot filling and heat sealing are accomplished prior to retort cooking at temperatures of approximately 250° F., for long enough to achieve commercial sterility.

REDUCTION in the weight and volume of all meals has been a prime objective of military food development continuously since World War II.

It is noteworthy that the cruising range of atomic submarines may be determined more by the quantities of food the subs can carry than by refueling requirements, or the need to replenish oxygen and water. Reduction in dimensions and weight of all items carried by foot soldiers is equally important, especially in situations where resupply is difficult or not feasible.

Weight reductions of more than 50 percent compared to World War II rations have been achieved. This has been done by such means as eliminating the inedible parts of all foods, removing water through dehydration processes, infiltrating porous items with edible calorically dense emulsions, substituting lightweight flexible packages for heavier cans, and compressing under pressure. Each of these innovations, however, introduced new problems in palatability and in the assurance of long shelf life of the rations. As a result still higher demands were placed upon the qualitative features of food preservation techniques.

The minimum acceptable storage stability of military meals is 6 months at 100° F., or 2 years at 70° F. A majority of commercially available foods are not palatable after such periods of storage. Minimal nutritional levels must also be maintained.

Food likes and dislikes, important in predicting food acceptance, also play important roles in basic menu and recipe planning. Current rations need to be based on current findings. As eating habits among the general populace change, the composition of military rations should reflect these trends.

Foods, packages, and packing must

193

Technician tries out reconstituted orange drink in a Gemini capsule.

harsh requirements on food weight, dimensions, and stability but also will test packaging stamina. The Army's Natick, Mass., Laboratories, in support of the Manned Spacecraft Center of NASA at Houston, Tex., continues in the research and development of unique foods designed for use in all of this country's extraterrestrial flights and explorations.

Principal flights utilizing these foods during 1965 were Gemini 4, 5, and 7, with the rendezvous of Gemini 6.

Flight food for Gemini 4 consisted of a 4-day menu-cycle divided into 4 meals per day and providing 2,550 Calories per man-day. An average of 2,100 Calories per day was ingested during the flight.

The flight food for Gemini 5 was in the form of 3 meals daily for 3 days, providing 2,650 Calories per day. Average daily intake was less than 1,000 Calories owing to certain days of low food consumption.

Flight food for Gemini 7 was designed as a 4-day cycle of 3 meals daily, each supplying about 2,300 to 2,400 Calories.

Dehydrated foods were the principal components. Water for reconstitution was provided, but will be available as a fuel cell byproduct.

Space allotted to food stowage was extremely limited, ranging from 106 to 111 cubic inches per meal. Water used in food rehydration was supplied at a temperature of 80° F., and this low temperature posed palatability problems. Cabin temperatures were expected to rise as high as 135° F. for short periods of time; accelerations to equal 15 times the force of gravity during the blastoff.

On the moon the lack of atmosphere, so profound that a molecule could travel 30 million miles without colliding with another, will sorely test structural integrity of food and packaging. There, temperatures of −240° F. will be encountered.

THE SHAPE and form of space foods were designed initially to facilitate removal from their containers and

be resistant to the deteriorative effects of repeated freezing and thawing, as may be encountered in unprotected storage or in movement from polar to warmer areas. In the unpressurized holds of cargo planes, rations may be carried from one environmental extreme to another within hours.

MANY OF THE PROPERTIES of military foods are also desired for space foods.

Space missions of appreciable duration place a premium on weight savings, because each pound of payload placed in orbit requires the added weight and thrust of 1,000 pounds of fuel and booster to achieve the essential acceleration.

Conditions in space cabins and those anticipated on the moon not only place

Cereal cubes for space feeding.

consumption by astronauts encumbered in restrictive pressure suits, helmets, and gloves. Textural integrity had to be assured by overcoatings of high melting point emulsions or by gelatin infiltration, since crumbs floating free in the weightless environment of orbital flight could mean considerable discomfort for the astronaut.

Meats, vegetables, and fruits were freeze-dried mixtures. Puddings and soups were mixtures of essentially dehydrated ingredients. Typical of the beverages were citrus drink crystals, which have more utility than the conventional dehydrated natural juices for spacecraft environments. The latter fused under the conditions and defied attempts at proper rehydration. Also provided were freeze-dried shrimp cocktail of excellent quality, sausage patties, beef and vegetables, salmon salad, potato salad, corn chowder, and strawberry cereal cubes.

THE CEREAL CUBES were prepared from freeze-dried fruits mixed with a cereal resembling corn flakes. They were compressed into blocks and coated by an appropriate edible emulsion. Compression techniques were also employed in preparing bite-sized fruit cubes and toasted bread cubes.

Freeze-dried, bite-sized cheese, chicken, or beef sandwiches were prepared from bread soaked in gelatin solutions prior to freeze-drying to improve structure and aid in preventing crumbling.

MEAT BITES and sandwiches were dipped successively in fat preparations of high melting point, in the 136–141° F. range. In order to aid application, the fat was heated.

These coatings, while achieving structural reinforcement, still need improvement in "mouth feel."

They seem to leave a waxy feeling in the mouth after eating.

EIGHT MEAT ITEMS have been developed so far: Beef with gravy, beef pot roast, chicken stew with vegetables, veal in barbecue sauce, beef with vegetables, spaghetti with meat sauce, Canadian bacon with applesauce, and chicken with gravy.

According to the Natick Laboratories staff, all the fat should be trimmed from the meat so as to aid dehydration and rehydration.

Special gravies, rehydrating at 80° F. water, were added to the lean meat prior to freezing the mixes into blocks.

The blocks were then cut into uniform size and freeze-dried to assure even distribution of residual moisture throughout the mass.

195

791–476 O–66—15

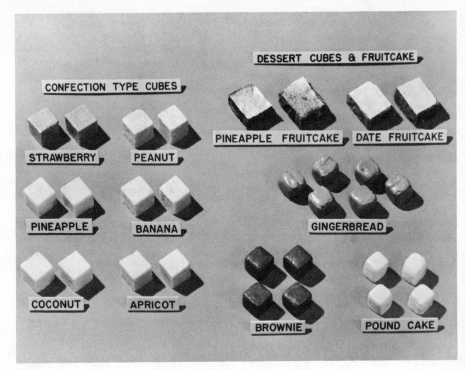

Bite-size desserts for space feeding.

Date and pineapple fruitcake pieces have been made acceptable for space flight use through enrobing the pieces in gelatin and coating them with "wafers" of edible starch. This "sandwich" was then dried to a moisture level of 7.0–9.5 percent to prevent the sirup from exuding into the protective vacuum package.

As SPACE MISSIONS become longer, astronaut crews larger, and flight cabins more spacious, shirt sleeve environments may begin to prevail. This will permit greater diversity of foods and feeding systems.

Already the planned feeding restrictions in the Apollo spacecraft appear to be less stringent in some degree than during the Gemini flights, but the food technologist and the scientist are still facing many challenges.

Food and packaging environmental testing for Apollo flights include the requirement that components remain wholesome, nutritious, and attractive for 400 hours at 75.5° F. and for 100 hours at temperatures ranging from 0° F. to 130° F. These are very tough standards to meet.

Partial pressures will be of the order of 10^{-4} torr for 100 hours, relative humidity 100 percent for 336 hours. Oxygen will represent 95 percent of the cabin atmosphere for up to 400 hours, at a total cabin pressure not exceeding ⅓ atmosphere. Acceleration forces will be essentially the same as in the Gemini flights but textural integrity of the foods must be preserved despite shock in any direction with a force of 30 times gravity, operating during the short times of 10 to 15 milliseconds.

THE U.S. ARMED SERVICES place great stress upon top quality food for their men and women.

Defense personnel who deal with specifications, procurement, storage, preparation, and service of food are

Gemini 7 Space Flight Menus

Menu I (Calories: 2,315)

Days 1, 5, 9, 13.*

Meal A:

Grapefruit drink.
Sausage patties.
Banana pudding.
Fruit cocktail.

Meal B:

Beef and vegetables.
Potato salad.
Cheese sandwiches.†
Strawberry cubes.†
Orange drink.

Meal C:

Orange-grapefruit drink.
Tuna salad.
Apricot pudding.
Date fruitcake.†

Menu II (Calories: 2,304)

Days 2, 6, 10, 14.

Meal A:

Chicken and gravy.
Beef sandwiches.†
Applesauce.
Peanut cubes.†

Meal B:

Orange-grapefruit drink.
Beef pot roast.
Bacon and egg bites.†
Chocolate pudding.

Meal C:

Potato soup.
Shrimp cocktail.
Date fruitcake.†
Orange drink.

Menu III (Calories: 2,322)

Days 3,‡ 7, 11.

Meal A:

Salmon salad.
Pea bar.
Gingerbread.†
Cocoa.

Meal B:

Grapefruit drink.
Bacon squares.†
Chicken and vegetables.
Apricot cubes.†
Pineapple fruitcake.†

Meal C:

Spaghetti and meat.
Cheese sandwiches.†
Butterscotch pudding.
Orange drink.

Menu IV (Calories: 2,297)

Days 4, 8,§ 12.

Meal A:

Bacon squares.†
Ham and applesauce.
Chocolate pudding.
Orange drink.

Meal B:

Beef and gravy.
Corn chowder.
Brownies.†
Peaches.

Meal C:

Coconut cubes.†
Cinnamon toast.†
Chicken salad.
Applesauce.
Grapefruit drink.

*Meal A also includes apricot cereal cubes, total Calories: 2,429.

†Nondehydrated, others are rehydratable.

‡Meal A also includes toasted bread cubes, total Calories: 2,429.

§Meal A also includes strawberry cereal cubes, total Calories: 2,411.

kept aware of the importance of maintaining high standards throughout the entire military supply line.

The impact of this attitude is readily observed in the armed services' relations with the American food producer. Their technical interests meet most clearly in the area of quality assurance—the specifications, inspections, and quality control involved in multimillion-dollar procurements.

FOOD SPECIFICATIONS include statements of the character of the materials, physical and chemical standards, the acceptable levels of defects, formula compositions and admixtures, and the types of packaging, as well as quality assurance procedures. At times, critical processing conditions and sequences are also stipulated in specifications.

Procurements involving new or unusual requirements are aided by Governmental evaluation of industry-supplied, preproduction samples. These permit differences in concept to be resolved in advance of any large-scale manufacture, and comprise another link in the long chain of safeguards of food quality.

Inspection of military foods utilizes the services of more than 700 inspectors. They are drawn from the Army and Air Force Veterinary Services and from the Defense Supply Agency. Programs that concern wholesomeness of foods, sanitation, or the health of the consumer are conducted jointly with the Surgeons General of the several armed services.

Effective, economical inspection of meal components is further assured by direct participation of the contractor. He performs acceptance examination and testing, in accordance with procedures agreed to contractually.

Contractor inspection is subject to verification by Government agencies, the initial level being 100 percent of the sample size as a rule.

When the reliability of the contractor inspection is confirmed, verification by the Government becomes less stringent. But if contractor unreliability is demonstrated, inspection is then performed by the Government, and the contractor is obligated, by contract, to reimburse these expenses.

IN VIEW of the possibilities of massive sneak attack, national survival may well depend upon the immediacy of our military response.

Even the potential of a quick and effective mobilization by this country is a strong deterrent to any aggressor.

To insure such action there must be early availability of ample quantities of necessary materiel, including an array of military foods.

Since these foods differ substantially from the civilian types, which are additionally subject to a seasonal supply, the United States is forced to stockpile a reasonable amount of them.

DURING THE 1950's, a series of comprehensive symposia were held to improve the means for describing and protecting the attributes of good food under long storage periods.

These discussions included the relationships of browning reactions to item stability, the stability of shortenings in cereal and baked goods, the stability of dehydrated eggs, the quality and stability of canned meats, and vacuum requirements for canned tomatoes and for dry milk products.

Considerable attention was directed to color, because in most foods it is an index of texture and taste, both in fresh and preserved foods.

SOME of the military standards have proven so reliable and useful that they are now used in specifications by all Federal agencies. Examples are glass-bead replicas of instant applesauce (Military Standard A–35045) and of instant potato granules (Military Standard P–1073A).

In like manner, grape juice grade standards are based on the color of carefully prepared chemical solutions of potassium permanganate and sodium dichromate, mixed in appropriate proportions. The fidelity of this color matching is so high that it has become the standard of reference in all Federal purchases of frozen, concentrated, sweetened grape juice (U.S. grade A Standard, Frozen, Concentrated, Sweetened Grape Juice).

Similar color references are under development for tomato ketchup, cake mixes, dried cheese, meat sauce, bread, and soup mixes. Progress in the sphere of objective color description, however, has been somewhat slower than is desirable.

As difficult as it is to define the color of foods, it is harder by far to protect them. Protection of such highly important colors requires knowledge of the chemistry of pigments as well as of the systems by which they are formed, modified, and/or destroyed.

Much has been learned about the chemistry of the orange and yellow carotenoids, and of the bluish, violet, pink, and red anthocyanins and astaxanthins. Brownish pigments of fruits and vegetables have also been studied in depth, but the stabilizing of a majority of these in processed foods has proven a formidable task.

In general, practical art and scientific studies agree that color can be protected by excluding light and oxygen from the preserved products, by proper salt balances, by very low moisture levels, and by low temperatures. ·

Not all color changes in foods are detrimental. Some are actually desirable. The characteristic flavor of roasted nuts, coffee, maple sirup, cocoa, bread, and cereal products is, in large degree, owing to Maillard-type reactions between the sugars and proteins or protein derivatives in the foods. We all know how savory the light brown crust of a freshly baked apple pie can be, and—on the other hand—how unattractive an underbaked crust is.

IMPROVEMENT in the storage stability of many military items stems from specification of proper containers, appropriate levels of acidity, freedom from unwanted sugars, and in-can oxygen-scavenging systems. Besides, moisture levels must be least conducive to nonmicrobiological deteriorations. For example, the flavor, appearance,

and shelf life of dehydrated eggs improve greatly when the reducing sugar glucose, normally present in eggs, is removed prior to drying. This is done either through a fermentation step or by the use of added enzymes.

During 1964–65 the Army tested a proprietary "Instant Egg Product," which combines USDA certified whole eggs, Grade A nonfat milk solids, and refined vegetable oils. This product is excellent in appearance, flavor, and convenience, and withstands storage at 100° F. very well. High taste panel scores have been accorded after storage for 1 year at 90° F., and the tests are still continuing.

One can see in this single successfully dried product the summation of scores of studies and of many important technological advancements achieved in and out of Government since World War II. This stable egg commodity is attractive both for its superior flavor and appearance, and for its logistic superiority. Refrigerated storage is not required, and 70 percent of the weight of shell eggs is saved through dehydration. The equivalent of 400 dozen eggs in this product weighs less than 150 pounds.

UNDER AN ARMY CONTRACT the University of Georgia conducted a study from 1951–61 of long-term storage of military rations.

Observations and tests were conducted on 209,265 units of ration components. These consisted of an assortment of 10 bakery and cereal items, 41 types of confections, 15 meat and fish products, 8 vegetable or fruit items, and 8 dairy products.

Storage temperatures ranged from −20° F. to 100°; relative humidity from 50 percent to 90. Some foods were subjected to alternate periods of storage at −10° to 100°, or from near freezing to 70° or 100° F.

Determinations were made of the changes in drained weight, appearance, color, aroma, texture, acidity, rancidity, and vitamin levels. Deterioration of containers and loss of vacuum in packs were also noted.

Thousands of taste tests were made to confirm flavor and textural changes, and to determine the effects of these on acceptability of the foods. Palatability, in general, was found the most sensitive index to quality of the stored foods.

Loss in vitamin B_1 and of vitamin C in certain products, however, exceeded the rate of loss of color and palatability. For this reason, vitamin assays should be relied upon to establish useful storage conditions in foods serving as primary sources of these water-soluble vitamins.

TEMPERATURE is the most important single factor governing food stability in impervious containers. It affects quality of the products in every aspect, including color, texture, aroma, flavor, and nutritional content.

The higher the temperature in general, and the longer the period of storage, the less acceptable are the rations. Exceptions were products like cheese, pork, and beef which benefit from brief periods at 32°, 47°, or 70° F., the University of Georgia researchers have discovered.

Storage-induced degradation was manifested by softening of meat products; leaking of oil from fatty components of such items as meat bars, chocolates, and peanut butter; drying out of bakery goods; development of stale and rancid odors and flavors; darkening or bleaching of colors; and diminution of the level of both naturally occurring and added vitamins. Vitamin A losses in general were considerably less than losses of vitamin C or the vitamin B complex.

At temperatures above the freezing point, interactions occurred between the foods and packages, or among the several components enclosed in a single package. Off-flavors, unattractive colors, rusting, and separation of container components often resulted.

Some products became unpalatable within 6 months at 100° F. Among them were cereal bars, processed cheese, steamed fruitcake, and meat bars.

Storage life of rations can be prolonged up to several years by storage at low temperatures. Frozen storage, however, is to be avoided for commodities whose texture is degraded by freezing, like tomatoes and salmon.

Dampness or high humidity were most detrimental to the packages and containers. As a consequence, built-in resistance to moisture, corrosion, leakage, and package-fatigue are specified for containers for military use.

A number of studies have shown that storage conditions which are excellent for one group of foods may be far from ideal for others. Accordingly, where practical, individual components of military meals should be stored separately and assembled when needed.

A PRACTICAL RESULT of storage studies has been extension of the usable life of military rations wherever control of environment is feasible. It is not always possible, of course, to afford such control. In many areas of the world the prevailing temperatures, rainfall, and humidity are highly adverse.

For example, canned foods in open warehouses in New Guinea were reported to have attained temperatures as high as 118° F. during 1945. Rainfall in areas of South Vietnam approximates 150 inches per year, and virtually all of it falls within a 6-month period.

It has been necessary, therefore, to seek means for stabilizing military foods, to the degree possible, by devices other than the control of storage environment. These efforts have led to development of antioxidants, stable shortenings, high-vacuum or nitrogen fill processes, instant coffee, and whole families of dried foods of excellent quality which are just now appearing on supermarket shelves.

DURING RECENT decades military needs have been the primary stimulant to improved drying processes for a large array of foods. In World War II, shipping losses attributable to submarine warfare in the Atlantic and the restriction of tin for can manufacturing related to adverse actions in the far Pacific made it imperative to test in depth the advantages of dehydration.

Every class of food commodity important in sustaining civilian and military populations was dried by the best means at hand. Some of these were rather primitive at the time. Almost every GI of those days recalls the greenish cast of the dried eggs, the haylike effluvium of the dried cabbage, the violet-scented dried carrots, and the hard pellets of dried beef. These items sustained life, but that's about all that could be said for them.

Sophisticated technological innovations were occurring during those same years in the drug industry. Antibiotics were being discovered and developed, which had to be dried with great care to preserve potency. Blood plasma, first sent to field hospitals under refrigeration, was shipped in powder form before the end of the war.

Freeze-drying was the process by which these sensitive biological products were preserved in almost unchanged condition. Before long this process had found its way into the U.S. food industry.

Foods preserved by freeze-drying are light in weight. Up to 90 percent of the fresh weight is removed. Freeze-dried foods are highly porous and have a high affinity for moisture. Accordingly, they reconstitute readily with a freshlike taste.

Their texture may be modified in some degree, however, during the freeze-drying process. These changes can be either tenderizing or toughening. In general, toughening is undesirable, so that procedures for preventing such changes have been under continuing study.

The high porosity of freeze-dehydrated foods permits their infiltration with emulsions or solutions to increase caloric levels, modify texture, or add flavor or vitamins. On the other hand, the high porosity also predisposes the food to rapid oxidative deterioration unless impervious packages are used and residual oxygen within the package is reduced to very low levels.

Foods to be freeze-dried are prepared essentially as for canning or home cooking. Inedible portions are separated and waste is discarded; the rest is sliced, diced, or cut into pieces ready for serving. A mild heat treatment generally follows to inactivate enzymes, which otherwise would aggravate deteriorative changes.

The foods are then frozen rapidly to produce only small ice crystals throughout their cellular mass. Freezing may be accomplished by a turbulent stream of very cold air, at temperatures ranging around $-45°$ F., by plunging them into or spraying with liquid nitrogen, or by use of solid carbon dioxide. Blast freezing using chilled turbulent air is the common procedure.

Water is removed from the food in vacuum chambers by sublimation. The frozen mass is not thawed during this step, since thawing destroys texture and leads to unacceptable toughness.

Moisture removal, which is assisted by mild heating of the food, is carried out generally through the employment of vacuum pumps and refrigerated condensers.

Desiccation is continued until the residual moisture level falls below the 2 percent point.

The new generation of military meals depends largely upon dehydrated meats, fruits, vegetables, and mixed, dehydrated entree preparations. Some 80 new food items have been developed so far and even more are due to make their appearance.

The level of residual moisture conducive to the longest shelf life of dehydrated foods differs from item to item. Mixtures of meats and vegetables in dishes like stews or chili con carne present special problems in moisture relationships. Some of the ingredients exert high moisture-vapor pressures while others do not.

Moisture-vapor pressure is expressed in terms of the relative humidity of the atmosphere in equilibrium with the food in an impervious container.

In ground beef and potato hash, the relative humidity of the beef at room temperature is approximately 5 percent. But the vegetable constituents have a relative humidity equilibrium in the range of 20 to 35 percent. Under these conditions moisture will migrate from the vegetables to the meats to the detriment of the overall stability of the product.

Moisture sorption curves are used as a basic means for studying the mode of water binding, which substantially affects chemical and textural changes in such dried foods.

Sorption curves depict the relationship between the moisture content of a food and the relative humidity of the atmosphere in equilibrium with it in a closed container. An illustration shows a generalized sorption curve indicating the approximate relative humidities *above which* various types of damage may occur in dehydrated foods.

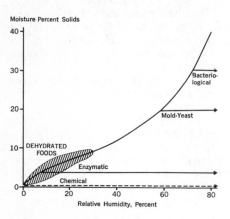

Moisture Percent Solids

Each of the different foods generates a curve typical of the mean of its constituents. Computation of the sorption curve of each component in theory should allow the construction of a curve for the food mixture and a prediction of the commodity's probable shelf life. In practice, however, factors as yet unweighed have vitiated predicted sorption curves and it remains necessary in all cases to confirm them experimentally.

Typical food sorption curves are shown in another illustration. Starchy foods, like potato, and foods high in protein, like beef, have reasonably similar curves. Fruits high in sugar,

like peaches, present curves of a different and low profile. Foods rich both in sugars and in compounds of high molecular weight, like green peppers, exhibit an intermediate type.

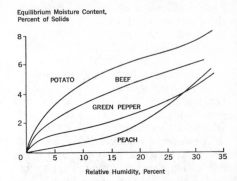

Equilibrium Moisture Content, Percent of Solids

Analyses of such curves by the Quartermaster Food and Container Institute directed attention to the relationship between moisture sorption and the stability of dehydrated foods.

Practical lessons learned from a study of food sorption curves include the novel concept that it is undesirable to dry dehydrated foods too dry.

Stemming largely from Army studies, another important application of food moisture sorption curves has emerged. This use has greatly enhanced the shelf life of the mixed dehydrated components of composite foods. It has lowered the costs of packaging such foods and has greatly increased their convenience.

Reference to the curves for beef, potatoes, and green peppers in the illustration shows that if such constituents were placed together in a single container, for example, as components of a stew, moisture would be exchanged among them, changing moisture content of each of the ingredients.

Rather simple mathematical procedures can be applied to determine the acceptable ingoing moisture levels of the component ingredients and assure the most suitable equilibrium end point.

Today's use of the sorption curve in research is thus being expanded to provide guidance to food processors, who can through this means place superior dried products in military as well as civilian channels.

The large surface area in the porous interior of freeze-dried foods renders them especially prone to oxidative deterioration. Exposure to oxygen is difficult to avoid unless unusual precautions are exercised during their preparation and processing.

Oxidation which starts during the earliest steps of processing is temperature-dependent, and can under suitable conditions proceed at such a pace that even spontaneous combustion can be engendered. Oxidation rates are also moisture-related, as noted earlier.

OXIDATIVE DETERIORATION in foods causes rancidity, vitamin loss, and undesirable color changes. Examples are the disappearance of the fresh greenish hues from dried vegetables. In dried meats the red myoglobin may be changed to grayish hemichromes.

Effort is being directed along several lines to increase our knowledge of pro-oxidizing conditions and mechanisms and to isolate, study, and hopefully, to employ both naturally occurring and added antioxidants when required.

Research is now underway in the Natick Laboratories to understand and exploit protection against oxidation which appears to be related to the orientation of oxidizable fats upon other food components, and especially upon the proteins.

When they are completed, these studies will provide the guidance for reformulating many ration items.

The rate of development of brown discoloration in dehydrated meat increases with moisture content up to 57 percent relative humidity (5.5 percent moisture in meat with 40 percent fat), and decreases as the moisture content increases up to relative humidity levels of 70 percent (7.5 percent moisture in meat with 40 percent fat).

Inhibition of browning deterioration requires moisture levels not exceeding 3.5 percent on a dry, fat-free basis, or 2 percent in meat with 40 percent fat. Partial inhibition can be achieved by removing free sugars from the meat prior to the drying process.

CONTROL OF UNWANTED micro-organisms has been a major objective since Pasteur. The Food Division of the Natick Laboratories, which is the Department of Defense principal food research and development organization, has maintained a strong continuing program in this direction.

Microbiological problems related to freeze drying were studied, to aid in designing adequate control procedures. Fruits, meats, and vegetables were inoculated with strains of pathogenic bacteria and their survival observed. *Salmonella oranienburg, Staphylococcus aureus, Aerobacter aerogenes, Escherichia coli, Alcaligenes faecalis*, and spores of *Clostridium botulinum* were used, at populations ranging from 34,000 to 8,000,000 per gram of food. Peas, corn, spinach, pears, chicken, fish, and beef were the food test media.

The death of spores was not convincingly clear cut, owing possibly to leakage among some of the containers. Vegetative cell destruction was of the order of 95 percent, attributable to processing conditions during the freeze drying.

A continuing decline of vegetative cells occurred in storage, the level depending upon temperatures, atmospheres, and types of product. Survival was highest in the meats. Unfortunately, the conditions of storage at 100° F. and 70° F., although most effective in reducing bacterial numbers, were often those most adverse to the quality of the food itself.

Until much more work is done on the microbiology of freeze-dried foods, emphasis must be placed on meticulous sanitation, from initial preparation of product through packaging. Positive microbiological controls need to be effected for all classes of dehydrated foods and especially for freeze-dried commodities.

Bridging the freeze-dehydration processing technique and the other modern innovation of radiation preservation of food are current studies by Thomas J. Lipton, Inc. on irradiation of dehydrated food products.

The rehydration and cooking times of dehydrated vegetables appear to be foreshortened dramatically by irradiation up to levels of 6 megarads. (A megarad is a radiation dose equivalent to the absorption of 100 million ergs of energy by the irradiated material.) The time required for rehydration of dehydrated diced potatoes, for example, is reduced from 20 minutes to 5. Quality of the product is substantially degraded under the conditions of exposure. This limitation appears to be under control, however, as a result of tests conducted at the Natick Laboratories, and at other laboratories both in this country and in England.

DEVELOPMENT of the process of preserving foods by use of nuclear radiation represents a highly concerted effort. Cooperating with the Army have been the Atomic Energy Commission, the Departments of Agriculture, Commerce, Interior, and Health, Education, and Welfare, the food technological community in this country, and laboratories in England, France, Germany, Denmark, and Canada.

The radiation preservation process involves exposing food to electrons or gamma rays. There is a rise in temperature of only a few degrees, so the food itself is not cooked in the process. Raw foods remain raw. Different effects are obtained, depending on the level of radiation provided.

At the lowest levels, in the order of 7,500 rads, sprouting of potatoes and onions is inhibited, extending their postharvest storage life well into the next harvest. At slightly higher levels, human pathogens like trichinosis-causing worms and liver flukes are destroyed, making infested pork and fish safe for human consumption. At still higher levels, insect larvae and eggs are destroyed, eliminating insect damage in packaged cereal and permitting previously infested fruits across quarantine barriers.

At even higher levels, pathogenic bacteria like Salmonella are inactivated. At the same time so are most of the bacteria present, thereby extending the refrigerated shelf life and marketing radius of fresh foods.

Finally, at the highest levels, in the order of 4.5 million rads, all bacteria are killed and prepackaged food can be kept without bacterial spoilage, in the absence of refrigeration. The military and civilian advantages of such a process are readily apparent.

THE UNIQUE facilities of the Army Food Irradiation Laboratory which became available at Natick during 1963 have provided improved tools for irradiation studies. Radiation sources at the laboratory have given appreciably higher dose rates than available heretofore, and permitted large numbers of reasonably complex tests to be completed under favorable conditions.

Foremost among the efforts to establish the feasibility of this process has been the effort led by the Office of the Surgeon General of the Army to test the wholesomeness of a wide array of irradiated foods. Initiated during 1954, these studies—the most extensive of their kind concerned with any food process—were continued throughout an 11-year period.

Thousands of animals have been involved in feeding studies concerned with testing the safety of 21 foods selected as representative of the military diet. More than $6 million has been expended in this effort alone. It has dealt with thousands of animals of four species: Rats, mice, dogs, and monkeys. Long-term feeding studies have extended over 2 years with the animals receiving up to 35 percent of total ingested dry solids as food, sterilized by the gamma rays of cobalt 60.

Human volunteer studies have been completed. Also involved in these studies were some 273 dogs and more than 3,000 rats on which tissue examination was made by the Armed Forces Institute of Pathology. Results have shown the safety of some 40 foods, including such animal products as beef, corned beef, ham, and shrimp.

It has been established that gamma irradiation from cobalt 60 does not induce radioactivity in foods exposed to it, nor does that from cesium 137. The Surgeon General has noted that foods irradiated with cobalt 60 and found to be wholesome are also wholesome when preserved by electrons at energies up to 10 Mev. (a measure of electrical energy equivalent to an electron with a million volts).

The Food and Drug Administration will consider petitions for clearance of foods only if there is no measurable radioactivity above the background level. There is, in contrast, the theoretical potential that electrons at sufficiently high energies may induce a degree of radioactivity in treated foods. The thresholds of activation lie in the range of from 10 to 16 Mev. Accordingly, studies must be continued to determine the maximum permissible energies, since the thickness of product which can be penetrated and preserved by electrons is dependent upon their energy.

According to theoretical calculations, a man might receive an added level of total body irradiation amounting to 0.26 milliroentgen (mr) per year if his entire diet were irradiated with electrons at an energy level of 24 Mev., and if the food were ingested immediately following irradiation. This compares to 150 mr per year which men in general receive from naturally occurring radioisotopes in their normal nonirradiated foods.

A NUMBER of irradiated foods have been approved by the Food and Drug Administration so far. Bacon processed to sterilizing levels of 4.5 megarads by either the gamma of cobalt 60 or by accelerated electrons up to energies of 10 Mev. has been approved for production in aluminum containers or in cans of tinned steel plate. The Army is planning a trial procurement of this meat commodity.

Wheat and wheat products have been cleared at levels of 0.2–0.5 megarad, which will assure insect de-

infestation. A facility to accomplish such processing is under construction at Savannah River, Ga.

In the United States, Canada, and Russia, clearances have also been granted for treating potatoes to inhibit sprouting. Canada has led the rest of the world in the actual operation of a commercial facility.

Early work on extending the shelf life of freshly caught fish and certain other seafood has culminated in the building of the Marine Products Development Irradiator source and laboratories at Gloucester, Mass., for the Bureau of Fisheries by the Atomic Energy Commission. Seaborne irradiators in processing ships would appear as a logical extension of the studies which are due to be carried out by the Gloucester facility.

PRACTICAL USES of irradiation in improving the availability of selected fruits and vegetables as well as seafoods appear within sight.

One type of flexible packaging material (nylon) has been cleared for use on foods preserved by the gamma rays of cobalt 60 or cesium 137. Five other types have been submitted for clearance.

Future plans by the Army envisage completion of petitions to the Food and Drug Administration for some 35 additional foods within the next 5-year period. The list includes chicken, ham, pork, beef, shrimp, hamburger, corned beef, pork sausage, frankfurters, luncheon meats, lamb, baked fish, and duck at sterilization doses. Also included is a wide array of radiopasteurized marine and fruit products, which will be submitted jointly by the Army and by the Atomic Energy Commission.

In technical areas, two of the more important recent findings may go a long way in assuring development of irradiated foods of superior quality. Some evidence is developing which appears to indicate that dose-rate may also be of great importance in providing radiation-sterilized foods which have superior quality.

Extensive investigations are confirming substantial benefits from employing extremely low temperatures during the irradiation of foods at sterilizing levels.

A CONCERTED EFFORT to test the benefits of low temperature irradiation was initiated during January 1961 by the Quartermaster Food and Container Institute.

Typical of early efforts was the testing of boneless beef loins. These had been irradiated some 6 weeks earlier in the gamma source of the Cook Electric Co. of Morton Grove, Ill., to a sterilizing dose of 4.5 megarads, at liquid nitrogen temperatures of —300° F.

Evaluated by a panel of 13 experienced technologists, the irradiated beef received an acceptance score of 7.76 on the 9-point hedonic scale of Peryam and Pilgrim.

Very few meats, raw or processed by any means, ever receive scores much higher than this.

CONSISTENTLY excellent meat items are produced even at the low flux rates of the Natick laboratory cobalt source.

A balance must be drawn between the economics of high flux machines operating perhaps under room temperature conditions and extremely low temperature irradiation using cobalt 60 or other isotopes.

Extensive panel appraisals of recently produced beef items confirm the optimism of the early years.

Experiments in low temperature irradiation of pork, chicken, lamb, and veal have also been carried out. Results confirm that fresh meats irradiated at low temperatures are superior in color, texture, flavor, and nutritional value compared to those treated at room temperatures. Further studies indicate the benefits of low temperature irradiation may be extended to other classes of food as well.

IT IS HARDLY to be expected that all problems, or even all the problems of major proportions, have been solved once and for all.

The fact that vigorous research and development is continuing on the century-old process of thermal canning and the millennium-old process of dehydration should inject considerable modesty into our claims after only 11 years of work on a process discovered barely 20 years ago.

Many problems remain. Nevertheless, the technical feasibility of the irradiation process has been demonstrated beyond any reasonable doubt.

The nadir of the research is past. The pioneering venture has been brought to a new plateau—pilot plant experience and cost calculations.

AT THE INVITATION of Assistant Secretary of Commerce Alexander B. Trowbridge, with the support of Assistant Secretary of the Army Willis M. Hawkins, and Atomic Energy Commissioner James T. Ramey, representatives of 50 commercial meat and poultry packers, radiation equipment manufacturers, and engineers met in Washington, D.C., on September 24, 1965.

They considered the best arrangement for joint Government-industry collaboration on semicommercial pilot plant studies involving fresh foods cleared by the Food and Drug Administration for unlimited consumption by humans.

THE Atomic Energy Commission representative indicated that if a satisfactory agreement could be worked out, the Commission would supply an appropriate source of cobalt 60 without cost for this work.

The Army representative indicated that if a joint venture can be agreed upon, it would underwrite a reasonable fraction of the million-pound annual production for a number of years of a commercially built, owned, and operated facility.

An Interagency Government Task Force is now working with interested industrialists to establish firm plans, which will assure an early availability of radiation-preserved foods to American military personnel overseas and their relatives at home.

Government and Industry Roles

EXTENSION AND PESTICIDE KNOW-HOW

L. C. GIBBS and HOWARD F. LEHNERT, JR.

TO those who work in agriculture, the benefits of agricultural chemicals in producing the world's most plentiful, most wholesome, and most economical food supply are obvious. On the other hand, the possibilities of harmful residues, accidental contamination, and other hazards of chemical usage can cause alarm or panic in persons outside of agriculture.

The responsibility and challenge of helping educate all segments of the public about using pesticides safely and effectively to produce our food is the job of the Cooperative Extension Service, working with other agencies and organizations.

With its tie to the great centers of agricultural research and knowledge, Extension has provided the means of distributing the scientific know-how that has contributed to America's ability to provide—and protect—our unparalleled food abundance.

In the early days of Extension, producers were given information largely by word of mouth and personal visits. That was also the day when one farmer produced enough food for himself and three others. Extension now

uses the latest techniques to carry its educational message to an increasingly broader audience. In 1965, as a result of improved technology, 1 farmer produced enough food for himself and 30 other Americans plus enough for export to feed 6 persons in foreign countries.

THE SUCCESS of our agricultural system was pointed up by Vice President Humphrey who said, "If I were to try to put my finger upon the secret of the productive abundance of American agriculture, I would point to the Land-Grant colleges and the Extension system."

Safe use of pesticides is not new to Cooperative Extension Service programs. In the early 1900's, Government workers—the predecessors of today's county agents—held demonstrations showing how to control

* * *

L. C. Gibbs is *Coordinator*, Agricultural Chemicals Programs, Federal Extension Service.

Howard F. Lehnert, Jr., is an *Information Specialist*, Federal Extension Service.

208

Colorado potato beetles safely and effectively with paris green. In the 1930's, county agents taught proper application methods to avoid arsenic and lead residues on fruit.

Extension activity on the safe use of chemicals in food production increased considerably after World War II. That was when modern pesticides reached the American farm.

Since 1950, Federal Extension Service (FES) personnel have mailed announcements of pesticides that were newly registered by the U.S. Department of Agriculture to all the State extension specialists needing them. The specialists, in turn, relay this information to county agents. Notices on residue tolerance have been mailed to State workers since 1954.

In 1957, Extension workers organized a national campaign to eliminate residues of antibiotics in milk. Cooperating in this effort were FES, four regional committees of State extension dairymen, their State extension directors, and county agents in dairy areas. Residues dropped sharply because of this intensive program.

Months before residues on cranberries came to public attention in 1959, State extension services had sent out more than 900 news stories on safe use of chemicals. Between 1953 and 1956, all States producing wheat carried on an intensive clean grain campaign to keep grain up to required standards. Almost all information used by the States in these two programs came from FES.

Agriculture and household chemicals are important projects in the Nation's 4–H Clubs, which have more than 2 million members. Under leadership of the State Extension Agricultural Chemicals Coordinator, Pennsylvania issued a series of publications to help 4–H members and their leaders fully understand safe and effective use of pesticides. Such youth participation is a key part of Extension's pesticide-chemical education program.

In Virginia, meat and milk supplies are safe because of a three-way cooperative effort underway to test alfalfa and other samples of forage for pesticide residues.

County extension agents obtain samples of alfalfa and other hays at the farmer's request. Samples are sent to the biochemistry department at Virginia Polytechnic Institute where researchers prepare the samples for testing by the State department of agriculture. The department reports test results directly to the farmer and copies are sent to the county agent and the university. The Extension Service then follows up with educational and advisory work on hay handling.

The University of Maryland also has an effective program dealing with pesticide residues. The university's Department of Dairy Science trained county extension agents and fieldmen of dairy marketing cooperatives on methods of taking forage samples. These samples are tested by the Dairy Science Department, and results in feeding recommendations are then sent to the farmer on a confidential basis. County agents receive reports of all recommendations for their counties.

Control of the many pests that challenge farmers and our food supply, and the safe use of chemicals and other pest control measures are major educational assignments of the Cooperative Extension Service.

Grasshopper on a wheat head, Custer County, Colorado.

PLANT AND ANIMAL diseases, insects, and weeds could quickly put us back into the age of wormy rotten apples, scrawny vegetables, and low farm yields if allowed to go unchecked. Pest control is a basic part of the good farm management that helps us produce an abundance of the foods we are able to enjoy today.

Needed is wide understanding of the pests, alternative control measures, and the responsibility for safe use of control measures. This need is widespread among farmers, nonfarm users of pesticides, dealers and custom applicators, home gardeners, local agencies, and the general public. Helping inform this vast audience is a major function of the Cooperative Extension Service.

EACH STATE extension office has a pesticide-chemical program leader and specialists on insects, plant and animal diseases, livestock, crops, farm management, and other fields. They all work together as a team to help agriculture maintain an adequate supply of food. Similar specialists in FES and other USDA agencies provide the latest facts and help county extension agents meet local problems.

An important aspect of FES' chemical education program is encouragement and development of Extension, University, and State and County Advisory Committees. These committees serve as advisory and planning bodies for educational programs concerned with the safe and proper handling, storage, and use of pesticides.

ALL STATES have a Central Chemicals Information Center in one or more locations. Florida and California are examples that other States are patterning their organizations around.

The Florida Chemicals Information Center founded by the Extension Service gathers information from reliable sources and immediately relays it to growers, processors, county agents, and fieldmen. These groups in turn are responsible for getting the facts to others who need them.

One organization reproduced 2,000 copies of "Buyers' and Shippers' Guide to FDA Tolerances on Citrus," and another group sent out 500 copies of an Extension statement on "Revised Pest Control Recommendations on Vegetables" and brought this new information to the attention of growers before a booklet could be printed.

MOST STATES have a newsletter that lists booklets and releases, petitions for tolerances, newly established tolerances and exemptions, recent pesticide label registrations, and reports on meetings and conferences. These letters go to key persons and organizations. They in turn relay the information to their clientele. Cooperation between industry and the county agents is an important part of this effort.

County extension agents carry on a very specialized and localized educational program with the assistance and backup of Federal and State agencies. These agents work with farmers who must fit pest control into their farm operations, make it pay, and at the same time, avoid harmful residues in the soil and in feed or food products.

EACH SEGMENT of agriculture has its own and different management problems, tests, and customer requirements. In any county there may be livestock producers, dairymen, field crop and fruit and vegetable producers. Extension agents help explain research results, identify pests, describe new pesticide regulations and residue tolerances, make management control suggestions, and stress using the right chemical at the right time in line with instructions on the label of the pesticide.

The Extension Service audience has traditionally been the people of rural America, but today suburbanites are asking their county agents about a wide range of subjects which include home gardening.

In Nassau County in New York, with a population of 1.3 million, the county agent trains garden center operators at wintertime schools to answer homeowners' questions directly.

New Jersey State Extension specialist tells fruitgrowers meeting in an orchard about methods used to evaluate herbicides in orchard weed control.

Since 1961, more than 500 sets of two reference notebooks developed by the Nassau office have been sold. One set, which sells for $4, contains about 100 Cornell University and USDA booklets. The other, which was available at no cost, contains mimeographed and printed sheets prepared by the agents as new information is available. The agents mail this information to the owners to keep their reference lists up to the minute.

Agents in Nassau County also mail more than 1,000 "Garden Guides" each week to garden centers and commercial concerns dealing with the public. For the homeowners, they provide five 1-minute telephone recorded messages telling how to handle current garden problems. Similar programs are also underway in Michigan, Louisiana, and other States.

A small but highly important Extension audience is the processor who cans, freezes, or otherwise converts our raw farm produce into the variety of readily usable foods that today's housewife insists upon.

To facilitate this program, FES specialists prepared and distributed materials for State extension entomologists, horticulturists, and plant pathologists about the use of pesticides on canning crops.

BASIC OBJECTIVES of Extension programs are to place in proper perspective the economic, scientific, health, and other factors involved in the complex agricultural pest control problem, and to report the progress which is accomplished.

The programs also stress the balanced approach used in modern day agri-

211

culture for pest control. Included are chemical, biological, cultural, and mechanical pest control measures.

To help meet these objectives, Federal pesticide registration regulations have been tightened.

Federal and State research programs are aimed at developing less hazardous agricultural chemicals, as well as nonchemical control techniques that will provide greater pest control flexibility. Monitoring programs, such as the Federal program in the lower Mississippi Valley, are being expanded to keep a close watch on pesticide levels in our environment—water, air, food, soil, and wildlife. The Extension Service cooperates closely with each of these efforts.

An increasing number of in-depth training schools and short courses are being held in all States. The audiences include Extension agents, vocational agricultural teachers, producers, dealers, physicians, veterinarians, fieldmen, and custom aerial and ground applicators. These training sessions range from one to several days duration depending on the interest, problems, and needs of the various audiences which are involved.

HOME GARDENERS are a growing group of chemical users. Because of this the Extension Service is increasing its educational work with urban and suburban dwellers, using all forms of mass media publications, and working with existing organizations and groups—all directed to safe and proper use of chemicals in food production and in safeguarding our health and environment.

Vocational agriculture teacher A. L. Hutton demonstrates spraying against cabbage leaf worm. His classes at Purcellville, Va., include out-of-school young farmers besides regular students.

Spraying a lettuce field against insect pests.

This educational effort also provides information about selecting chemicals.

Extension agents who work in local governments with local public agencies are in a good position to give them the latest pest control and safety precaution facts regarding a specific local problem.

FES has increased its efforts to get pesticide facts to the general public through the press, through many specialized groups, and by cooperation with wildlife, health, and garden groups. As part of this job, the Coordinator, Agricultural Chemicals program of FES distributes more than 125,000 pieces of literature relating to pesticide chemicals to State counterparts each year. This includes information on regulations, tolerances, residues, safe use, and other data the State extension chemical leaders or program coordinators use in their intensive educational work.

The public obtains the information through localized news releases, radio and television broadcasts, direct mail letters from county extension agents, exhibits, slide presentations, meetings, and personal conferences. The accent is on methods that help eliminate the cost of unnecessary amounts of pesticides as well as those that reduce the chemical hazards.

Another example of Federal support of State work was an FES slide set on "Safe Use of Pesticides." The original artwork for this set was adapted for use in a slide set in Ohio and by a commercial concern that sells and rents visuals to schools and others on a regular or subscription basis. In addition to these two examples, almost all of the States have added selected slides to the FES set to localize and give more impact to local programs concerned with the use of pesticides. The wide acceptance of the FES developed slide set is indicated by the fact that over 600 sets have been sold since its release during 1963.

Chemical residues on meat animals and crops can generally be attributed to illegal, improper, or careless use of pesticides. Foods free of residues or within allowable tolerances can be produced if growers, processors, and others cooperate and take the necessary precautions to see that all pesticides are used as specified. Careless use can result in contaminated foods that are subject to seizure.

Used improperly, pesticides can be dangerous, result in food contamination, cause crop damage, lower quality, and cause death in animals. Each pesticide has its own merits and limitations and must be put to work accordingly. Used properly, pesticides can do a worthwhile job. Extension provides the know-how to get the job done.

An FES survey showed that the States have produced more than 1,000 publications mentioning pesticide use. Of these, 640 publications were primarily intended for commercial farmers or producers, 320 for nonfarm use such as home gardens, 44 for use by dealers and industry representatives, and 50 intended for the general public.

Many publications are meant mainly for farmers or ranchers. Even so, local pesticide supply dealers, custom sprayers, and homeowners request large numbers of the publications.

Cultural and other pest control methods are recommended where appropriate. For example, the New York booklet "Tree Fruit Production Recommendations" discusses pest control through orchard location, resistant varieties, and soil management practices, as well as giving information on chemicals. The section on chemicals stresses safety, residue tolerances, time of last application before harvest, and information about the poison control centers.

A California Extension booklet, "1965 Pest and Disease Control Program for Peaches and Nectarines,"

contains sections about pesticide residues, USDA limitations on use of chemicals, warnings, regulations on injurious materials, hazards to honeybees and other beneficial insects, and special problems of processed fruit.

Extension also prepares materials which stress the hazardous aspects of pesticides. The Florida Extension booklet, "Better Fruit Programs," emphasizes these hazards and tells how to offset them.

The April 1965 Extension Service Review, an FES publication, was devoted to safe use of pesticides, including the types of safe-use educational activities being carried out in the States. More than 600 copies of this publication were distributed to key government officials and national organizations. It also went to all State and county extension workers.

The trade associations are important Extension audiences also.

These organizations relay information to specific segments of the national audience. Normally, FES works with the national trade associations, and State extension personnel work with the State units.

At the national level the Extension Service maintains liaison and cooperates with organizations and groups like the National Agricultural Chemicals Association, National Safety Council, National Cotton Council, National Canners Association, Manufacturing Chemists Association, National Wildlife Federation, National Pest Control Association, Chemical Specialties Manufacturing Association, the National Sprayer and Duster Association, and the Aerial Applicators Association.

Safety kits to be used by Extension agents as training guides for their agricultural chemicals programs have been put together by the Extension Services of Florida and Louisiana. These kits are used in training groups or individuals in the safe use of pesticides around the home and in agriculture. The kit developed by Florida was also distributed to vocational agriculture teachers and county health officers within the State.

Partly due to increased educational effort by the Florida Extension Service, Florida growers have adopted the practice of testing their crops for pesticide residues before harvest. More than 600 persons were instructed on safe and proper use of pesticides by the Florida State Extension specialists during eleven 1-day schools in the State. Much of the subject matter and materials used in this training effort came from FES.

Two pickle processing companies planned to leave Arkansas in 1958–1959 because of unstable production resulting primarily from cucumber diseases. To meet the problem, a disease control program was devised by State research and Extension plant pathologists with the backing of company representatives. Because growers adopted the program, the companies had to expand processing facilities to handle the increased production. FES cooperated with the Arkansas Extension Service in supplying Extension know-how and the technical subject matter.

FES works closely with States to develop regional programs that give the maximum educational results at minimum cost. Specialists in FES worked with the Northeastern States to produce radio and television announcements that promote safe and effective use of pesticides by both agriculture and the general public.

Red River Valley potato growers will soon have a disease warning system operating through the county extension offices. This will help prevent damage to a crop worth $30 million annually. Weather stations are being set up in 13 North Dakota and Minnesota counties that will tell county agents the "right" conditions for late potato blight. Once a favorable blight point is reached, county agents can advise growers when to spray to minimize late blight damage to their crops.

FES supplied subject matter and educational leadership for an intensified educational effort by the Loui-

A sampling machine like a vacuum cleaner sucks insects into a removable nylon bag. In a laboratory later they will be anesthetized and removed for counting.

siana Extension Service to reduce damage to fish in 1962. Growers were cautioned through circulars, letters, radio broadcasts, newspaper articles, and at meetings on the safe use of insecticides for control of the sugarcane borer.

Extension's past displays a record of unparalleled success that helped lead to our abundance of nutritious, high-quality, safe food, and a good environment in which to live. All levels of Extension—Federal, the State, and the county—will continue to meet the challenge of a rapidly advancing technology, an expanding population, and an increasing awareness of the problems facing the people in our Nation.

QUARANTINES—FIRST LINE OF DEFENSE

H IVAN RAINWATER and CLAUDE A. SMITH

ORIGINALLY, the word quarantine meant "a term of 40 days during which a ship arriving from a foreign area, suspected of being infected with a malignant or contagious disease, is restrained from contact with the shore."

Today, in relation to agriculture, quarantine refers to the restraints or restrictions placed upon the transportation of animals, livestock, poultry, plants, fruits and vegetables, plant and animal products, or other material, which are suspected of being carriers of agricultural pests.

PLANT AND ANIMAL quarantines, like health quarantines, were born of necessity. An adequate supply of food is as essential to the well-being of people as good health is, since it affects every individual.

Today's plant quarantine system is America's first line of defense against foreign plant pests.

To safeguard the Nation's plant, food, forest, and fiber resources, Federal regulations prohibit or restrict the entry of foreign plant pests, plants, plant products, soil, or other material or conveyances carrying plant pests or constituting a pest hazard.

Basic aims of plant quarantine regulations are the same today as when the system was first established—to provide the needed protection along with a minimum of inconvenience to everyone concerned.

Since its beginning in 1912, the plant quarantine system has benefited farmers and consumers by reducing sharply the rate at which destructive plant pests formerly gained entry into this country from other lands. Plant quarantine laws and regulations provide the authority and machinery for effective enforcement activities.

Today's agricultural quarantines protect our food supply by stopping the destructive plant and animal pests at our country's borders.

Quarantine laws and regulations

* * *

H Ivan Rainwater is *Assistant Chief* of the Methods and Procedures Section, Plant Quarantine Division, Agricultural Research Service.

Claude A. Smith is *Senior Staff Veterinarian*, Animal Health Division, Agricultural Research Service.

give the U.S. Department of Agriculture authority to regulate entry of plants, animals, and plant and animal products. By this means we can help prevent the entry of plant and animal pests that are new to this country.

Yet plant pests cause big losses every year despite the fact the United States is generally recognized as having the most effective plant pest control program of any large nation in the world.

Major responsibility for the heavy loss is traceable to alien pests brought into this country on plants introduced by man, chiefly during early development of this country.

An inventory of the foreign insect pests now in the United States shows that approximately 94 different kinds gained entry prior to enactment of the Plant Quarantine Act of 1912. Additional data assembled by the Federal Horticultural Board show 110 foreign plant diseases had been introduced up to the year 1919.

Some injurious pests established here during the many years preceding the first quarantine laws included the codling moth, hessian fly, stem rust of wheat, asparagus beetle, San Jose scale, greenbug, Argentine ant, European corn borer, and alfalfa weevil.

UNTIL WELL within the 20th century the United States was the only major nation which was not protected by law from importation of plant pests. As a result, this country was said to have been the dumping ground for substandard nursery stock. Failure to obtain necessary controlling legislation resulted in great losses to agriculture and permitted introduction into this country of scores of the world's most destructive plant pests.

Early defense measures against invading plant pests were made on a local basis by individual communities, colonies, and later by States.

As the population grew and the tempo of both domestic and foreign trade in agricultural products increased, the foreign pest problem became increasingly a national one.

In 1905, an act prohibiting importation of certain plant pests was passed by Congress. This early legislation was not strong enough to stop the pest invasions. It lacked adequate provisions for administering and enforcing the ban on plant pest entries.

IN 1912 CONGRESS passed the Plant Quarantine Act to meet the serious pest threat facing the Nation's farms, ranches, gardens, and forests. This act has provided the legal basis for the development of our present-day system of quarantine.

From 1917 to 1942 Congress granted authority to the Agriculture Department on a year-to-year basis to prevent the pink bollworm and other pests from being brought across the Mexican border into the United States.

In 1942 Congress passed the Mexican Border Act. Under this legislation, inspection is conducted on the Mexican border and all infested carriers such as trucks are cleaned and decontaminated before being permitted to enter this country.

In 1926, export inspection and certification were authorized as a service to domestic growers wishing to meet plant quarantine requirements of foreign countries. The Organic Act of 1944 contains additional legislation that pertains to certifying domestic products for export purposes.

The Honeybee Act of 1922, as amended in 1962, restricts the entry of adult honeybees to prevent the introduction and spread of certain bee diseases.

In 1957 the Federal Plant Pest Act was enacted to give more effective control over entry and movement of plant pests. It superseded the act of 1905.

SOME FOREIGN crop pests are capable of inflicting great losses to major segments of American agriculture. Plant quarantine inspectors intercept many of these pests frequently at the border entry ports.

Because we travel more and faster these days and move plants, food, forest and fiber products, and miscellaneous cargoes in greater quantities,

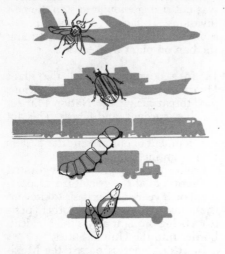

Many foreign plant pests have not become established in the United States. If allowed unrestricted entry, new invasions of plant enemies from foreign countries could cost the United States additional lost and damaged crops, reduced production efficiency of our farms and forests, and increased expenditures for pesticides and for pest control measures.

THE PLANT QUARANTINE Division of the Agricultural Research Service, with its technically trained staff of more than 500 inspectors, administers the laws and regulations designed to stop foreign plant pests.

Inspection service is maintained at 75 major ocean, Great Lakes, air and border ports of entry in the continental United States, Hawaii, Alaska, Puerto Rico, American Virgin Islands, Nassau, and Bermuda.

the danger of spreading plant pests is greatly increased.

Pests that can move only a few inches a year under their own power may be moved in bits of soil, on souvenirs, or as live pet curiosities—like live jeweled beetles sold in Mexico and worn on a lady's dress—from a foreign country by jet aircraft in a few hours.

Plant pests are readily spread by the movement of diseased or infested plants, seeds, bulbs, fruits, or crops. They also may travel as "hitchhikers" on farm machinery, vehicles, ships, aircraft, nonagricultural cargoes, and on other products not usually thought of as representing a pest risk.

Many of our worst plant pests came from other countries and thrived here because of abundant food and few natural enemies.

Estimated cost through fiscal year 1964 of the control programs resulting from a few of the worst introduced pests, and dates when first reported in the United States are listed below with the crops which they attack:

Inspectors also work in the Netherlands, Belgium, Germany, Italy, France, and South Africa in preshipment clearance of flower bulbs, and in Mexico to supervise fumigation of citrus and other fruits before they are exported to this country.

In addition, services are provided on a regular or on-call basis at approximately 526 outlying ports and military installations throughout the United States.

Plant quarantine inspectors examine imported cargoes of plants and plant products and require treatments or other safeguards, when necessary, to free them from pests.

Working in close cooperation and collaboration with other Federal and State agencies, they inspect incoming planes, ships, automobiles, trains, freight cars, travelers and their baggage, miscellaneous nonagricultural cargoes, mail, and other items to prevent the entry of pests.

Date first reported	Pest	Crop	Cumulative control costs
1726	Stem rust	Wheat, Small grains	$35, 122, 400
1916	Japanese beetle	Farm-Orchard crops	37, 078, 200
1926	Burrowing nematode	Citrus	7, 791, 100
1936	White-fringed beetle	Field-Garden crops	30, 914, 100

Imported plant propagative material is examined and treated by trained personnel at specially equipped inspection stations.

Through a cooperative arrangement with the States, a number of plant species are held under postentry quarantine for further observation.

An additional responsibility of the Plant Quarantine Division is the inspection and certification of domestically grown plants and plant products to meet the import requirements of foreign countries. Although in a somewhat different category than plant quarantine restrictions on imports, export certification helps strengthen the international fight against dissemination of plant pests. Thus it indirectly reinforces our national defense against the invasion of foreign pests.

THE ANNUAL VALUE of crops, forests, and forage in the United States is assessed at more than $23 billion for crop products, more than $2 billion for forage products, and more than $20 billion for forest products.

This is a total of approximately $45 billion for U.S. crop, forest, and grazing lands being given plant quarantine protection from foreign pests.

Total cost of protection for these re-

POTENTIAL CARRIERS OF PLANT PESTS

186,000,000 travelers cross our borders yearly

36,000,000 pieces of luggage

sources by the plant quarantine inspectors stationed at this country's international airports, seaports, and border crossings is estimated as less than 5 cents per person each year.

During the past 55 years, $556 million in Federal and State funds was spent to control or eradicate 23 plant pest introductions which had occurred in the past 200 years.

For the 10-year period 1954–1963, Federal funds for entomological research totaled approximately $58 million. Of this, about $35 million was used for research on eradicating, controlling, and reducing losses resulting from introduced insect pests. Several million dollars was also allotted for research to develop methods to control plant diseases and nematodes introduced into this country.

THE AVERAGE TRAVELER who knows about agricultural quarantines will readily give his support in observing quarantine restrictions.

An estimated 186 million foreign travelers and returning Americans now enter or reenter the United States each year. They bring with them over 36 million pieces of baggage—all potential carriers of plant pests.

Cooperation by these travelers who have learned how they can help protect this country's food supply is a tremendous contribution in efforts to reduce accidental introductions of foreign agricultural pests.

GUARDIANS OF U.S. PORTS

500 inspectors

219

Information on quarantine restrictions reaches travelers in this country through notices distributed aboard ships, in airline ticket folders, and in U.S. passports; through public service TV and radio announcements; through attractive exhibits in international airport terminals, garden shows, and area fairs; and through brochures and leaflets and other publications.

The Armed Forces cooperate by distributing notices of military regulations that support agricultural quarantine laws to persons traveling on military planes and ships.

Notices in foreign languages are distributed outside the United States by U.S. consular offices to foreign travelers applying for U.S. visas abroad. A notice in Spanish and English, supplied by the Plant Quarantine Division, is distributed throughout Mexico and Central America by the governments of these countries as an aid in preventing movement of plant pests within the North American Continent.

Introduction of a new plant pest may mean the use of additional quantities of pesticides to stamp it out.

Hitchhiking bug symbol developed by USDA to warn travelers against spreading agricultural pests. Her name is "Pestina."

When the Mediterranean fruit fly became established in Florida in 1956, a total of 14 million pounds of insecticides was applied over a 2-year period to 7 million acres within the infested area before eradication was accomplished.

Problems still attend the use of pesticides despite continued improvement in methods of using and applying them. Because of their wide use, the manner in which they are applied and the residues that may remain, hazards to human health, wildlife, beneficial insects, and biological control projects could possibly result.

Agricultural quarantines are a real help in reducing these hazards by stopping foreign pests at America's borders and thereby reducing the need for control programs which require the use of pesticides.

That agricultural quarantines do prevent the entry of many dangerous foreign agricultural pests into this country is shown by the fact that in

1965, a total of 32,572 separate plant pest interceptions were made by plant quarantine inspectors—an average of one plant pest stopped every 16 minutes around the clock.

By preventing the introduction of foreign plant pests, agricultural quarantine protection means the consumer is receiving more abundant and wholesome foods, is receiving greater money savings when purchasing foods, and is subject to fewer pesticide hazards.

The spread of animal diseases has plagued mankind since ancient times.

Then as now, animal diseases tended to spread along the trade routes of the world, sometimes jumping thousands of miles across deserts and mountains to invade new regions after trade was established between the areas. Hence, the massive increase in trade and travel throughout the world in recent years has compounded the problem of preventing their spread.

Only in relatively recent times has the technique of detecting animal diseases and preventing their spread forged ahead of the ever-growing technology of trade and transportation. Application of modern techniques to keep out animal diseases now has made the United States one of the safest countries in the world in which to produce livestock and poultry.

Our Federal animal inspection and quarantine system is based on the idea that it is better to prevent the introduction of new and costly animal diseases than to contend with them later.

For example, U.S. livestock producers had to fight nine different outbreaks of foot-and-mouth disease between 1870 and 1930.

Some countries that have failed to eradicate this disease have undertaken tedious and costly vaccination programs to control it. However, foot-and-mouth outbreaks in the United States were stamped out by enforcing strict procedures including slaughter of infected and exposed animals.

This difficult procedure—still the

Some dangerous plant pests and the number of 1965 interceptions.

INSECTS

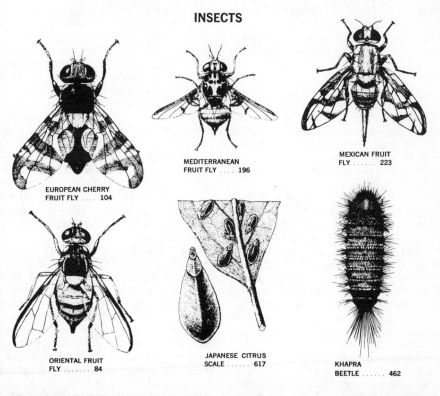

EUROPEAN CHERRY
FRUIT FLY 104

MEDITERRANEAN
FRUIT FLY 196

MEXICAN FRUIT
FLY 223

ORIENTAL FRUIT
FLY 84

JAPANESE CITRUS
SCALE 617

KHAPRA
BEETLE 462

DISEASES

BLACK SPOT OF CITRUS	571	GOLDEN NEMATODE	101
CITRUS CANKER	245	SWEET ORANGE SCAB	299

only known way to eradicate the damaging disease—was also used to eliminate foot-and-mouth from Mexico following an outbreak there in 1946.

To safeguard animals and meat production in both countries, the United States and Mexico jointly waged a 7-year war against the virulent disease. The United States spent $135 million to help Mexico eradicate foot-and-mouth and thus avoid even greater costs that could have resulted if the disease had crossed the 2,100-mile international boundary and entered U.S. herds.

Our animal quarantine defenses have successfully kept out of the United States a highly fatal disease of ruminant animals known as rinderpest. This virus disease which many Americans have never even heard of has been killing cattle in the Old World ever since Biblical times.

TWO OF THE MANY other serious diseases that are spreading in the Old World today are African swine fever and African horse sickness. Both, like rinderpest, have been successfully excluded from this country by our animal quarantine system.

African swine fever, a highly virulent disease that is usually 100 percent fatal to infected pigs, was long confined to Africa where it has prevented commercial production of hogs in some areas. Changes in many African countries since World War II, coupled with expanding trade, triggered the spread of African swine fever to Europe. Portugal became infected in the late 1950's, and the disease has since been found in Spain and France.

The first livestock killer to arouse unified action was contagious bovine pleuropneumonia. This lung-sickness of cattle had arrived in 1843 when a New York milkman innocently bought an ailing cow from a British ship captain. This "bargain" cow started an epidemic of pleuropneumonia that spread through several valuable herds. Additional cattle importations from Europe also brought the disease to other areas of the United States.

By the 1880's, European countries were refusing to buy U.S. cattle for fear of spreading pleuropneumonia. This trade crisis led to the animal quarantine system that exists today.

Acting to protect American herds from disease and to salvage this country's foreign markets for livestock, Congress in 1884 established the Bureau of Animal Industry in the Agriculture Department. Congress also transferred responsibility for enforcing animal quarantine laws to the Secretary of Agriculture, and passed the first Federal quarantine law for detaining and testing livestock entering and leaving the United States.

Similar conditions caused the spread of African horse sickness from historically infected areas of Africa to Asia as recently as 1961. Since then it has killed more than 300,000 horses, mules, and donkeys in eight countries of the Near East and southeastern Asia.

Animal diseases spread in many ways. The most obvious is the movement from country to country of sick animals or of "carriers"—infected animals that show no outward symptoms of the diseases they carry. Such animals have moved along trade routes of the world for centuries, spreading as they go new and unknown animal diseases to previously healthy herds in distant areas.

Less obvious methods of disease transmission are shipments of infected meat, hides, and other animal by-products, meat scraps in ship and airplane garbage, or the careless disposal of food, litter, and manure from infected animals. Foreign meat sent by mail or carried by travelers can also contain viruses of such animal diseases as foot-and-mouth or rinderpest.

OUR MODERN animal quarantine system dates back to the 1880's. (Earlier laws regulating the importation of livestock were administered by the Secretary of the Treasury and were not under veterinary control.)

At the same time the Agriculture Department developed an underlying philosophy that has governed agricultural quarantine laws and practice to this day. It is that agricultural quarantines should be applied only on a scientific basis according to the disease or the pest problem involved.

Through the years this philosophy has successfully resisted pressures occasionally applied to use quarantine laws or regulations as trade controls instead of disease-prevention measures. Tariffs and import quotas are enforced by the Bureau of Customs separately from agricultural quarantine laws.

In 1884 the newly formed Bureau of Animal Industry, in cooperation with the States, undertook eradication of contagious bovine pleuropneumonia.

It cost the United States 5 years of work and more than a million dollars to wipe out this disease, but our livestock raisers have never again had to fight contagious pleuropneumonia. Instead, it is now a quarantine problem, because the disease is still prevalent in some foreign countries.

Another disease that started as an animal health problem and became—after its successful eradication—a quarantine problem is bovine piroplasmosis, or cattle tick fever. Tick fever got into the southern United States from the West Indies and Mexico during Spanish colonial times. The cattle industry in the South was severely affected by the disease.

Tick fever spread slowly northward during the days when cattle were moved on the hoof, then more rapidly after the railroads began moving livestock over longer distances.

Early in this century Agriculture Department scientists learned that a specific tick was the vector of piroplasmosis, and cattlemen were forced to turn to an organized dipping and inspection program to eradicate the disease by eliminating the ticks.

Now, cattle fever ticks have been eliminated from the United States. But many times each year agricultural quarantine inspectors find them on cattle or other animals arriving at U.S. ports, or on animals straying from Mexico or smuggled into the United States from there.

Less obvious methods of disease transmission were recognized by law in 1890. In that year Congress passed a law bringing sheep, other ruminants, and swine under more stringent quarantine restrictions. This law recognized that feed, litter, manure, clothing, and other items that have been in contact with infected animals can also spread disease. It provided authority to the Secretary of Agriculture to make necessary regulations to prevent such items from introducing animal diseases into the United States.

This and other animal quarantine laws also gave the Agriculture Department authority to place restrictions on animal products that might introduce disease into our country.

LAWS RELATING to livestock and meats from countries infected with foot-and-mouth disease remained inadequate to deal with this highly virulent, hard-to-detect virus.

Six outbreaks of foot-and-mouth occurred in the United States during the first 30 years of this century. Two of the last outbreaks, which occurred in California in 1924 and 1929, resulted from feeding uncooked ship garbage to hogs.

Then in June 1930, Congress passed a law that contained an absolute prohibition against the importation into the United States of cattle, other domestic ruminants or swine, or fresh, chilled, or frozen beef, veal, mutton, lamb, or pork from countries where the Secretary of Agriculture determined that foot-and-mouth disease or rinderpest existed.

The same law, as amended in 1958, allows the Secretary to establish stringent controls over wild ruminants imported from foot-and-mouth or rinderpest infected countries. The controls involve extensive quarantine periods abroad and in the United States. While in quarantine here the animals are subject to blood tests and other diagnostic examinations.

These animals then are allowed to go only to approved zoos where they remain under permanent control of

223

the U.S. Department of Agriculture. To get on the approved list, a zoo must isolate its animals from domestic livestock, have acceptable methods of disposing of all wastes to prevent the spread of diseases by this avenue, and must meet other rigid standards of operation.

Effectiveness of the 1930 act is demonstrated by the fact the United States has never had to contend with foot-and-mouth during the 36 years the law has been in effect. This is true although foot-and-mouth, like rinderpest, now occurs in most of the countries outside North and Central America, and despite an immense increase which has occurred in world travel and trade during recent years.

Poultry came under animal quarantine restrictions in 1950 after an outbreak of Asiatic Newcastle disease in California that year. The source of the outbreak was a shipment of game birds from China that were infected with a highly lethal strain of the disease. The 1950 outbreak was quickly eradicated, but now any foreign poultry that may harbor Asiatic Newcastle are quarantined at the U.S. port of entry for 21 days or longer under the supervision of a veterinarian.

TODAY'S ANIMAL QUARANTINE laws are designed to permit the maximum free movement of animals and of animal products in international commerce consistent with the protection of our Nation's $21 billion livestock and poultry industries.

Animals and poultry from certain areas of the world known to be free of serious diseases are allowed to enter the United States without having to be quarantined.

In other cases, negative results to tests are necessary for entry. Dourine and glanders, two diseases that infect horses abroad, can be detected by tests. So can tuberculosis and brucellosis, two diseases of humans, and animals such as cattle and swine. Visual inspection and precautionary dipping of cattle and other animals from fever tick-infested areas effectively protect

U.S. cattle against ticks which can carry piroplasmosis.

Another degree of control involves quarantine periods of varying lengths. For example, horses from areas where African horse sickness is known or suspected to exist are quarantined on arrival in this country for at least 60 days under insect-controlled conditions.

Animals from foot-and-mouth or rinderpest-infested countries come under the most stringent degree of quarantine control. Domestic ruminants and swine from any of these countries are excluded under the provisions of the 1930 law.

As WORLD TRAVEL increases along with global trade, agricultural quarantine inspectors have had to devote more attention to travelers' baggage and international mail to prevent the entry of animal diseases by these avenues.

Home-canned, partially cured, or improperly cooked meat carried in personal baggage as a gift to a friend in this country, or mailed to people in the United States by well-meaning relatives abroad, could bring in animal diseases if the scraps are discarded in a place where domestic animals can eat them. Agricultural quarantine inspectors, working with customs and postal officials, must block off these avenues of animal disease entry.

THUS, agricultural quarantine inspectors appear in many different places wearing many uniforms.

Sometimes these inspectors work side by side with other Government officials at international seaports or airports; and sometimes they work alone in sweaty coveralls examining cattle at a dusty and remote border station.

But wherever their post, they form this country's first line of defense against foreign animal diseases. That line of defense has prevented a major outbreak of these diseases in the United States for over three and a half decades—an accomplishment which the American consumer benefits from every time he chooses his favorite cuts of meat in a supermarket.

HOW NEWS MEDIA GET THE WORD OUT

JOSEPH F. SILBAUGH

WORKERS trying to rid the Southwest of livestock-destroying screw-worms faced a crisis in the fall of 1963. How the crisis was met and overcome is a classic American example of cooperation between the public news media and agriculture in getting the word out.

Infestations were beginning to flare again in parts of Texas where livestock had been free of the flesh-eating screw-worm for months on end.

On September 19, the Associated Press reported 42 cases in 14 counties—which was the largest number since the middle of July.

THE PEST was threatening to follow its usual pattern of building up explosively after a spell of cool, rainy weather. Furthermore, the release of hundreds of millions of screw-worm flies sterilized by cobalt 60 irradiation had been so successful in pushing the pest out of Texas and neighboring States that complacency was beginning to set in. Many producers had stopped inspecting their livestock regularly. Some had thrown away their smears and sprays and were branding, castrating, and shearing animals without properly treating the wounds.

Such neglect could give stray screw-worm flies an opportunity to lay their eggs and reinfest cleared areas—and each undetected case could erupt into thousands in a few weeks' time.

It was vital to protect the gains that had already been made. A barrier of sterile flies up to 160 miles in depth was being maintained for 1,250 miles along the border to prevent reinfestation from Mexico.

A FALL BUILDUP of screw-worms might spread throughout southern Texas and survive the winter. This could jeopardize the entire effort at a time when screw-worm eradication was almost within sight.

". . . officials view the next 60 to 90 days as the most critical in the program," United Press International reported in late September. "To accomplish early eradication, the officials hope to enter the winter with most of southern Texas completely free of screw-worms."

THAT CALLED FOR reaching farmers and ranchers at once with information on the status of the campaign, and the strategy to be followed in the months which lay ahead.

* * *

Joseph F. Silbaugh is *Chief* of the Reports Branch, Information Division, Agricultural Research Service.

And every livestock producer had to be made aware that he held the key to early eradication:

He must examine his livestock regularly for screw-worms. He must treat all open wounds to prevent cases from developing. And he must collect samples of insects found in wounds and mail them in for laboratory identification, so the area could be given "hot-spot" treatment if necessary.

Livestock producers got the word that fall. And it was mainly the public news media that got the word out.

NEWS SERVICES and daily newspapers helped to keep the public up to date on developments in the campaign. It was strongly supported in editorial columns of newspapers.

Weekly newspapers carried the word on the outlook and problems, along with stories from county agents and vo-ag teachers giving local angles and encouraging producers to cooperate.

Radio stations broadcast Extension farm flashes on the current picture, spot announcements from the county screw-worm committees urging support, interviews with campaign officials, and reports of progress.

Television stations showed filmed interviews and reports on eradication activities, as well as spots asking livestock producers to do their part.

Farm magazines reviewed progress in the campaign, outlined future steps, and called upon ranchers to be alert for possible new cases.

All media regularly carried round-ups on the eradication effort.

The result was that nearly everybody in Texas—even city people—knew about the screw-worm by December 1963. Most important, the number of reported cases had been cut by nearly 98 percent compared with the same time the year before, and the eradication effort was no longer under any serious threat.

This was by no means the first important contribution to screw-worm eradication by the public news media.

The media had reported on successful use of the atomic sterility technique to wipe out screw-worms in the Southeast in the late 1950's. Southwestern stockmen, who were then losing millions of dollars a year from screw-worm attacks, began to wonder whether the same weapon couldn't be used in their part of the country.

These stockmen organized a foundation in 1961 to take the lead in raising $3 million in matching funds for a cooperative eradication program with the U.S. Department of Agriculture and the States.

Newspapers and farm magazines, radio and television stations supported farmers and ranchers in organizing nearly 250 local committees of the foundation. These committees raised the bulk of the necessary $3 million through voluntary contributions from producers. The State of Texas appropriated an additional $2.5 million for the eradication effort.

THE CAMPAIGN got underway in February 1962, following a hard freeze that greatly reduced the number of overwintering screw-worms and gave the workers a headstart.

Public news media continued their support. For example, they emphasized the responsibility of each livestock producer in the campaign. And they explained to the public the need for establishing an inspection line across Texas to keep screw-worms from escaping north and east via truck or train.

The campaign moved so well that only 274 cases were reported in Texas in July 1963, over an area where the infestations at that time of the year ordinarily ran as high as 50,000.

IT IS APPROPRIATE that public news media helped put the sterility technique to work in Texas: The concept had originated there in the mind of a young USDA entomologist, E. F. Knipling, and was communicated to scientists in the 1930's by technical journals. A long series of laboratory and field experiments culminated in 1959 with the spectacular screw-worm eradication campaign in the Southeast.

Through public news media,
he got the word . . . and
joined an atomic age
battle against the
screw-worm fly

TARGET:

Eradication of This County Screwworm Livestock Pest

THE SCREWWORM

Screwworm Eradication Has Changed Southwest's Sheep Industry

SCREWWORMS Are on the Run.

SEX and SCIENCE DOOM a PEST

By BYRON W. DALRYMPLE

Screwworm Outbreaks Bring On Precautions

SCREWWORM STAMP-OUT
...how it will affect your ranch

MAGAZINES

provided detailed coverage of the effort to rid the Southwest of screw-worms. By telling a stockman about cobalt 60 sterilization of screw-worm flies, magazines helped to gain his confidence, support, and cooperation. They published progress reports during the campaign, told about the job ahead, and gave ranchers the word on how to examine and treat animals and report new infestations.

County agents and vo-ag teachers were important sources of information for public news media during the campaign to eradicate the screw-worm.

PRESS
coverage kept the public informed on the screw-worm campaign. Wire services and daily papers reported events like Secretary Freeman's press conference (right) at Mission, Texas, where sterile flies are produced. Weeklies carried local angles and encouraged producers to take part. News and editorial support helped raise necessary funds.

Mission Screwworm Plant Buzzing Busily

Eradication Hatchery Produces
100 Million Sterile Flies Weekly

By SEL DETERLING

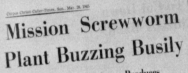

Treatment On The Scene

They Don't Plan To Quit Until Last Worm Is Gone

By SEL DETERLING

FAMILIAR FLY CARTONS
Shown by D. C. Bruce, inspector

VISITORS FROM MEXI...

Mexico Next Battleground In Screwworm Campaign

By BOB M. GASSWAY

Fight Against Screwworm May Extend Into Mexico

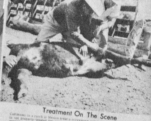

Screwworm Eradication Workers Report Infestation at Zero Again

Livestock Men Alerted After Screwworm Case Found

RADIO & TV
gave producers up-to-the-minute coverage of screw-worm outbreaks and pinpointed areas that were imperiled. Farmers got spot news radio reports right in their own field.

Television showed the new sterility technique at work. Interviews with campaign officials and members of county screw-worm committees were effective in educating producers and gaining cooperation.

THE SAME SORT of communication that helped achieve conquest of the screwworm is going on every day in the United States. Indeed, protection of the Nation's food supply would be impossible without the aid of these public news media.

First of all, our abundance of safe, high-quality, reasonably priced food depends upon technology.

New information must be developed through research, and it must be passed along promptly to producers, processors, and distributors.

Then, too, technology has also revolutionized transportation, which means that devastating insects and other pests are never more than a few hours away from our fields, flocks, herds, and food distribution pipelines. The necessary protective measures can be taken only with the support of an informed public.

Citizens may ask questions like these: Why are we spending public funds to develop better ways of controlling an insect that attacks farmers' crops or food in a warehouse? Is it really necessary to hold me up at a highway quarantine station to search my car for infested fruit? What about the vegetables I buy—are they safe from hazardous pesticide residues?

The answer to a basic question of how to protect our food supply has been generally clear to the majority of Americans for more than a hundred years: The foundation of protection is knowledge, gained through research.

Gathering and disseminating useful information was the main job assigned by Congress to the Department of Agriculture when "the people's Department"—as Lincoln called it—was established in 1862. The Nation took another important step in 1887 by providing Federal funds to help the States set up agricultural experiment stations.

From these beginnings has grown a partnership of State and Federal scientists who amaze the world with their contributions toward making our food the best ever. In addition, industry has become a major partner in this country's agricultural research.

But all of this research is not of much value to most people unless the findings are put to practical use.

That means, to begin with, publishing results in a scientific or technical journal. This not only adds the findings to mankind's literature of science but also makes the information available at once to the technicians and advisers who serve industry and agriculture.

Agriculture Department scientists publish about 4,500 reports every year in scientific and technical journals. This includes about 3,000 on farm and marketing research, and about 800 on nutrition, consumer use, and utilization investigations.

As many or even more reports are published by additional researchers in the States and in private industry.

WHEN FURTHER RESEARCH and development have transformed scientific discoveries into useful practices, they must then be put into the hands of farmers and other citizens for practical application.

Farm magazines, newspapers, radio, and television all help do the job. These media are relied on by State and Federal agencies as well as the Cooperative Extension Service.

EXTENSION WORK was set up by Congress in 1914 to serve farmers and consumers in what has become the largest adult education enterprise in the world. Some 6,600 county agents, 4,200 home economics agents, and 3,200 subject-matter specialists are currently working in 3,000 counties in the 50 States and Puerto Rico on a cooperative basis.

Extension workers write three-quarters of a million newspaper articles each year, and make two-thirds of a million radio broadcasts.

State Extension editors are one of the main sources of agriculture information for the Nation's 9,000 weekly newspapers. Most States have radio and television specialists who prepare programs regularly and work with local agents. In North Dakota, for example, the land-grant university and

231

television stations cooperate each winter in a television school for farmers.

RESEARCH and how to use it account for a great deal of important news and information which originates with the Agriculture Department.

More than 300 press releases dealing with research are issued by the Department over the course of a year. Washington correspondents of the wire services report on these and other Department announcements for about 1,800 daily newspapers.

Close ties have been established by the Department with newspaper farm-page editors who reach about 10 million readers. New developments in agriculture are also watched by the science writers now found on many newspaper, magazine, and wire service staffs. Other outlets for Department news, photographs, and publications include trade magazines, and periodicals issued by commercial firms, farm organizations, and cooperatives.

MOST OF THE Nation's farm radio audience is covered by about 400 stations which receive the Department's recorded Agri-Tape releases every week, at their request. A half-hour farm program is broadcast weekly on more than 60 stations of a major radio network.

Stories about Department work of value to city people and suburbanites reach them on a 15-minute weekly program carried by some 200 stations and a half-hour consumer show that 100 stations use each week. Some 350 radio stations employ professional farm broadcasters doing local farm programing.

Some 200 television stations have regular farm telecasts, or consumer programs, or both. Those receive photo package feature material, film shorts, and video tapes, upon request.

The Agriculture Department also works closely with 150 farm magazines that have a readership of 22 million.

IT IS THROUGH these public media that farmers get much of their information

on the ever-changing technology that helps protect our food: The feeding, sanitation, and housing that help keep livestock healthy; the diagnostic tests, vaccines, antibiotics, and drugs that aid in controlling diseases of poultry; the fertilizers and growth regulators that make crops highly productive; the pesticides that prevent serious damage by insects, nematodes, and weeds; the specially bred resistant varieties that keep diseases from destroying some crops; the biological and cultural methods that control some insects without the use of chemicals; the management practices that help safeguard farm products against deterioration after harvest.

MOST OF THESE practices are put to use by each farmer on his own farm as he sees fit.

But there are some situations in which the protection of our food supply cannot be left to chance. Organized effort becomes necessary.

The news media are essential in giving the general public an understanding of actions that may involve a great many of us, and that may even call for our direct cooperation.

TAKE THE DEFENSE LINE the Agriculture Department maintains at air, sea, and border ports of entry to prevent destructive pests of crops and livestock from getting into the country. Keep these pests out if you possibly can—this is fundamental. We know from experience that it can cost tens of millions of dollars to eradicate pests or live with them, once they get in.

Inspectors must check the live animals, commercial cargoes, mail shipments—and also the personal baggage of travelers. Annoying, perhaps, but essential. Foot-and-mouth disease can reach our shores in the salami innocently packed away in a traveler's suitcase; fruit flies can arrive in the coffee berries which are knowingly concealed inside a handbag.

More and more people are going abroad each year. This increases the chance that some returning traveler

232

will introduce a dangerous foreign insect or disease. The Agriculture Department must have the public's help to keep these pests from slipping past our Nation's guard.

That message went out through spot announcements to millions of television viewers around the country as the annual travel season got underway during 1965.

Radio interviewed national officials on the state of our border defenses, and reported on threats like the golden nematode invasion of Canada.

DAILY NEWSPAPERS carried stories of important interceptions—for example, the discovery at Dulles International Airport, near Washington, D.C., of 18 khapra beetles in mixed grain carried by passengers as feed for pet hamsters.

Inspectors in charge at port cities make it a point to see that all local news media get the word concerning interceptions of pests which could have a serious impact upon the economy of the surrounding area.

This often leads to additional coverage, like it did in Savannah, Ga., where a television station produced a series of three programs in 1965 on the Nation's port inspection work.

Organized effort also is required to get rid of the long-established livestock diseases that will give way only to a persistent campaign, State by State.

Hog cholera is just such a disease. It has plagued us since 1833.

THE HOG CHOLERA eradication program owes its beginning in no small way to public news media, particularly the farm magazines.

They told producers what scientists and leaders of the industry were saying in the 1950's—that it was time for the United States to stop living with hog cholera.

This disease was costing us millions of dollars a year and cutting us out of export markets for pork in countries that did not want to run the chance of bringing in the disease. We had the weapons and experience to stamp out hog cholera. All we needed was the will to carry out the job.

CONGRESS TOLD the Agriculture Department in 1961 to organize a campaign in cooperation with the States to eradicate hog cholera.

Magazines, newspapers, and radio announced and explained the eradication effort, which builds up gradually through four phases until the disease is finally wiped out.

Progress from phase to phase in each State, along with other important developments in the campaign, are well reported at the local, State, and national level by public media. The media also encourage hog producers to help keep the disease from spreading by reporting suspected cases, protecting swine by proper vaccination, feeding table scraps only if they have been cooked, keeping visitors out of hog lots, and following shipping rules in buying and selling pigs.

ONE OF THE outstanding contributions of farm magazines and other media to the hog cholera campaign is their aid in establishing Iowa's "Minute Man" warning system in other States across the country.

This system goes into effect the moment an outbreak is reported: A livestock inspector personally notifies all farmers within a 3-mile radius and warns them to take precautions to protect their swine. At the same time, the county agent gives local newspapers and radio stations the news, as well as information on what producers should do to keep the disease from spreading.

The Nation cannot afford to leave to chance a matter like the regulation of pesticides, either.

Pesticides make it possible for us to produce plenty of wholesome, high-quality food.

Yet today's pesticides are powerful materials, and they can harm man and his environment if they are misused.

The Agriculture Department registers a pesticide for interstate sale only if the material will be safe as well as effective when used according to directions and warnings on the label. If the pesticide leaves residues on a food, registration is granted only after the Food and Drug Administration of the Department of Health, Education, and Welfare has established a safe tolerance for it.

BUT WE CANNOT stop there, because pesticides are used by virtually everyone—farmers and gardeners, homeowners and housewives, supermarket operators and public health workers. All our people must understand the necessity for using such materials safely.

That is the goal of nationwide educational campaigns conducted by the Agriculture Department and other public agencies and private organizations. Public news media have made a tremendous contribution to these efforts by carrying the message on safe use of pesticides to mass audiences— millions of people who could not be reached in any other way.

For example, every radio and television station in the United States has been supplied by the Agriculture Department with spot announcements urging people to "Read the Label— Use Pesticides Safely." National magazines tell consumers about Department publications that spell out how to use pesticides safely. Picture stories on safe use are distributed to thousands of newspapers, photo syndicates, and magazines.

Two award-winning motion pictures issued by the Department on the subject of safe, effective pest control have been screened widely on television stations across the Nation and before many local, State, and national groups. "The Safe Use of Pesticides," a 21-minute color film produced jointly by the Agriculture Department and the Food and Drug Administration, tells the farmer how to use pesticides so as to minimize residues on food crops. "Pests or Plenty?" is a 13-minute consumer-oriented color movie which shows how modern pest control tools and techniques protect our food supply safely and efficiently.

Newspapers and radio give a great deal of specific information on choosing the right pesticide, applying it properly, and disposing of containers in a safe manner. Farm magazines emphasize that producers must follow recommendations, directions, and precautions down to the last detail so as to protect themselves as well as the Nation's consumers.

Another essential service that people call upon their Government to organize is weather forecasting. Providing reliable information requires a network of observers stationed all over the country and on ships at sea, along with a skilled staff of scientists and technicians to man the meteorological center of the Weather Bureau in the Department of Commerce.

The forecasts help farmers plan many of the operations on which our food supply depends, including plowing, planting, and harvesting. Then, too, warnings that frost is expected often enable growers to save a fruit or vegetable crop.

Weather conditions also affect insects and diseases—late blight of potatoes, for example, follows cool, rainy periods—and adequate protection depends on getting the word in advance.

WEATHER INFORMATION goes out 24 hours a day by teletypewriter to newspapers, radio, and television, which pass the information along to the public. Magazines and newspapers regularly give farmers the weather outlook for the month ahead.

In addition, public news media often step in to provide special services. A radio station in Chico, Calif., helps fruit and nut producers of seven surrounding counties by staying on the air all night when frost threatens. Each grower calls in if the wind or cloud cover changes in his area, or the thermometer shifts a vital degree or two. These reports form a pattern and reveal the slight air movements that can raise the temperature out of the danger zone or lower it to where

234

producers must fire the smudge pots. Organized efforts like these go on year after year—constantly safeguarding the public in vital ways but rarely making sensational news.

Sometimes, however, organized action must be taken on an emergency basis. It is in this area that public news media perform their most spectacular service. When the alarm has to be sounded, they can reach many people, and reach them fast and often.

Even an hour can make a difference. Modern marketing facilities increase the opportunity for exposure to new pests, and cross-country transportation can spread trouble more rapidly than ever before in our history.

RADIO WAS MEETING emergencies as long ago as the 1920's, when on three occasions it gave stockmen the word that foot-and-mouth disease had again invaded the United States. Broadcast warnings helped hold this highly infectious malady in check by keeping diseased animals from being sent to stockyards or turned out on the range along with healthy stock.

Television had come to many communities by 1952, when vesicular exanthema of hogs broke out of California and spread rapidly throughout the United States.

A farmer near Little Rock, Ark., was watching television on February 3, 1954, when he viewed a 4-minute film showing the symptoms of VE. He telephoned an inspector, who confirmed the farmer's suspicions that his hogs had the disease. As a result, this outbreak was soon eradicated.

The need for measures like quarantine, slaughter, and disinfection in the Federal-State campaign against VE was explained to the Nation's farmers by public news media. They also helped gain passage of State laws that put a stop to feeding hogs uncooked garbage—found to be the main reason behind the explosive spread of this costly livestock disease.

NEWSPAPERS, radio, and television all aided the conquest of the Mediterranean fruit fly in 1956, when it invaded Florida and threatened fruit and vegetable producing areas of other southern States.

Discovery of the Medfly and the organization of a Federal-State effort to combat the pest were quickly made known through the public news media. Then the media prepared people for the inconvenience resulting from eradication operations, including roadblocks to keep infested fruits, vegetables, and plants from spreading the insect, and aerial spraying of infested areas, both urban and rural.

Announcement of local spray schedules by press, radio, and television at least 1 day ahead enabled people to protect their clothes and cars from the sticky insecticide-bait mixture used to fight the Medfly. Providing this advance notice was a feat in itself, considering that at one time some half a million acres in 21 counties were being treated by 23 aircraft, and new infestations were being found almost every day in the week.

Important developments in the campaign were regularly covered by the public news media. Reporters investigated and squelched rumors about such matters as property damage and use of unsafe planes. Citizens were urged to back the eradication effort by picking and destroying all fruit that might offer the Medfly a place to lay its eggs. And many editors gave the campaign strong support. In a little over a year, the Medfly invasion had been completely wiped out.

Similar information coverage helps workers deal with other pests, including the gypsy moth, which destroys hardwoods in the Northeast.

EXPERIENCES like these campaigns bring new appreciation of how much the public news media can mean to the Nation's efforts in protecting our food supply.

This is the public's business, and the people are entitled to know what is going on. Newspapers, magazines, radio, and television are ready to tell the story—to get the word out.

EDUCATION

FOR

500 CAREERS

H. W. SCHULTZ

PROTECTION of our food supply is entrusted to people—trained people who handle or deal with food as it is being grown or produced in the soil, on the land, and in water; as it is harvested, stored, processed, transported, and sold; and as it is being cooked or otherwise prepared for eating. Other people, even though they do not so directly handle food, have a profound influence on the abundance and safety of our food supply through their participation in research and development, regulation and control, education and communications, and the business aspects of producing, marketing, and utilization.

The education or training of these influential people is described in this chapter. It is their education which makes them particularly suited or qualified to participate in the struggle against insects, rodents, or other pests,

plant and livestock diseases, weeds, and weather, and spoilage due to micro-organisms, chemical reactions, and mechanical damage, all of which constantly threaten the quantity and quality of our usable food supply.

The education of persons engaged in the public health and public interest aspects of food through programs on sanitation, inspection, control, grading, nutrition, and various consumer services also will be described.

It would be a kind fate, indeed, which would make it possible to describe one program for educating or training "food protectionists." Such is not our good fortune, however, and the reader will soon recognize the

H. W. Schultz is *Professor and Head* of the Department of Food Science and Technology at Oregon State University. He was trained in biochemistry and nutrition and was employed in the research laboratories of a large food company before taking his present post.

processes for preparing people to protect our foods is very involved. As a matter of fact it is improper to try to simplify the situation by using a term like "food protectionist" unless it is used as a very nonspecific designation of the entire group of persons engaged in protecting our food supply. Certainly there must then be individual or smaller groups to represent one or another of about 500 professional or occupational job titles.

ALL "FOOD PROTECTIONISTS" do not have the same education, of course. One's preparation, which includes both his education and training, will generally determine the nature of his employment. Conversely, the kind of job one performs is usually determined by the nature of the preparation, formally planned or not, which precedes that employment.

Usually people try to plan their education and training for particular occupations of their choosing. Frequently, however, necessity requires one's engaging in a new field of endeavor for which there is no established or specific educational or training program. An excellent example is the need which suddenly arose only a few years ago for many "experts" in the various aspects of pesticides. In such instances, persons with the most suitable backgrounds are selected to perform the new tasks until a more formalized preparation is devised and made available.

Obviously, then, although there are well established programs for preparing people to do most of the things which contribute to protecting our food, there are instances in which this is not the case. Here again the complexity and perhaps some weaknesses are revealed. Nevertheless, the total accomplishment in providing us with the most abundant and the safest food supply in the world speaks well for the educational system in the United States.

Our educational programs provide a broad foundation of knowledge. Even in colleges and universities where specialization in certain fields is sought, for example in land-grant institutions, students are taught fundamental subjects which permit them a rather wide choice of jobs. As a result, they become capable of undertaking assignments which are not necessarily in their field of specialization as students. In total, students are educated and trained to be adaptable to more than just one occupation.

An understanding of educational needs requires knowledge of what our foods must be protected against. Summarized a little later are the principal things which threaten our food supply. Utilization of basic knowledge of genetics, cellular biochemistry, growth and physiology of living organisms, as well as abnormalities and diseases, has made it possible to produce plants and animals for food with the greatest adaptability, efficiency, and economy.

IN A SENSE, our food sources are protected by such knowledge from the forces which could prevent our having the most and best food possible. The adverse forces include poor nutrition, insects and other pests, drought, depleted soils, and diseases. Thus, we protect our food capabilities with applications of knowledge of nutrition, entomology and pesticides, conservation of water, fertilizers, and prevention of diseases in plants or animals.

A wide range of soils, climates, and growing conditions, a long continental shoreline, and large lakes and streams permit the United States to adapt and produce a diverse assortment of foods to provide a high level of nutritional adequacy and to satisfy our individual desires. We may acquire new tastes and rather liberally import foods we cannot produce to satisfy these tastes.

IT IS NOT POSSIBLE to produce all foods at all places at all times as needed. Consequently, foods are moved from areas of production to points of consumption and must be kept from deteriorating, sometimes for long periods of time. We protect foods by various means from spoiling or becoming unusable during these periods of transportation or holding.

FOODS ARE VULNERABLE to spoilage which impairs or destroys their value, salability, usefulness, acceptability, enjoyableness, or appearance. Spoilage may render the food inedible. However, not all spoiled food is harmful; that is, not all spoiled food is poisonous and would make one sick if eaten. For example, sour milk is "spoiled fresh milk," but it may still be usable as an ingredient in cooking.

BRIEFLY, foods are spoiled by one or more of the following:
• Micro-organisms growing in or on the food. These tiny organisms multiply and can cause changes in general appearance, color, texture, and flavor which may make the food undesirable. Dangerous micro-organisms, like *Clostridium botulinum*, *Staphylococcus aureus*, and *Salmonella typhosa*, rarely appear in food. When they do they may produce toxins capable of causing extreme illness and even death. By application of proper sanitation in the production, storage, and handling of foods and use of today's very effective methods of processing and preserving, we protect our foods from both harmless and harmful undesirable micro-organisms.
• Chemical changes can alter food color, texture, and flavor in such a way as to spoil the food. Discoloration of fresh meat, browning of a freshly cut apple, and oxidation of fats causing rancidity and off-flavors are common recognizable examples. These and other undesirable changes can be prevented through proper handling, by processing, or by use of chemical additives which prevent the changes.
• Physical abuse or improper handling and storage can also spoil foods. Examples are breakage of crackers, cookies, and shells of eggs; "drying out" of cake, bread, or marshmallows; picking up of moisture to make candy sticky and crackers soggy, and to cause salt to "cake"; freezing of certain fruits and vegetables; and melting of ice cream. Packaging and temperature control are principal ways to protect foods from physical damage.

Much has been written and said in recent years which infers our foods are deleterious to health because they may contain certain chemicals. The chemicals referred to most are the insecticides and other specially selected or synthesized compounds which are used to kill or control insects, rodents, weeds, and other pests. These substances, called "pesticides," are necessary to protect our food supply from the ravages of pests and aid tremendously in our maintaining a high production in agriculture and minimizing losses from pests during storage, transportation, and handling.

The use of pesticides brings a need to protect our food so pesticides or other potentially harmful substances do not get into foods or do not persist in them to harm individuals in any way when the foods are eaten.

Finally, in the overall picture of food and agriculture, we protect our food supply from unfavorable market or economic conditions. This is achieved largely through assembling information on production, stocks on hand, market demand, consumption, uses, and prices, and communicating it to farmers and other producers, to food distributors, and to consumers.

THE PROCESSES of supplying foods to consumers are far from simple. The U.S. food industry is the largest industry in the world in terms of dollars and numbers of people engaged. More than 40 percent of the over 70 million people employed in the United States work in the field of agriculture and food. Everywhere people are on the supply routes helping to get food to consumers. Some are specially prepared through years of education, some are trained quickly on the job, but all are involved in one way or another so that we can have an abundant and safe supply of food.

TODAY most food is consumed after passing through food processing companies where it is altered in numerous ways, primarily so it may be usable at another time, and at another place. Certain fresh foods, including eggs, are handled by produce companies. Retail

238

HOW FOODS GET TO THE CONSUMER—THE PRINCIPAL SUPPLY ROUTES

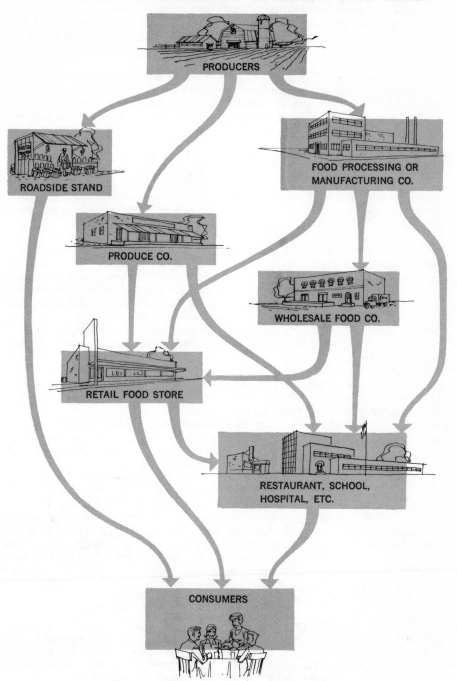

food stores handle the largest amount of our food before consumption, but restaurants, schools, hospitals, and the like serve an ever-increasing quantity.

CONSUMERS themselves are also involved in food protection. There can be wastage and spoilage in their homes, reduced, of course, by use of modern equipment such as refrigerators and deep-freeze cabinets.

Informational programs directed to housewives help protect and conserve foods within the home.

People are employed at each step from growing and production to consumption, and consequently there are thousands of employment opportunities with innumerable responsibilities in a wide variety of places. Each of these jobs requires some kind of education or training.

SPECIALISTS are prevalent in the field of food protection.

These are persons devoted to some particular line of study, occupation, or professional work.

In food and agriculture the specialists are many because of the wide diversity of activities in private industry, government, universities, research organizations, and elsewhere that are involved all along the line from production through utilization.

LET'S LOOK at a list of the professional or occupational titles of some of the 500 or more specialists who may work in food and agriculture.

This list reveals once again how diverse the protection of our food supply actually is and consequently, how broad must be the education and training of the people engaged in doing the job.

• Specialists concerned with soil and water:

Soil scientist, agricultural engineer, agronomist, soil conservationist, water conservationist, civil engineer, sanitary engineer, hydraulic engineer, agricultural chemist, microbiologist, physicist, agricultural economist, physical oceanographer, meteorologist, statistician, extension specialist.

• Specialists concerned with growing or producing food:

Agronomist, horticulturist, animal scientist, dairy scientist, poultry scientist, fisheries scientist, range management specialist, biological oceanographer, wildlife scientist, biologist, botanist, zoologist, geneticist, animal physiologist, animal nutritionist, plant physiologist, plant nutritionist, veterinarian, plant pathologist, entomologist, parasitologist, nematologist, toxicologist, microbiologist, agricultural chemist, agricultural engineer, mechanical engineer, civil engineer, sanitary engineer, sanitarian, agricultural economist, market specialist, statistician, extension specialist.

• Specialists concerned with processing, manufacturing, and storing food:

Food technologist, dairy technologist, food scientist, dairy scientist, microbiologist, chemist, physicist, biologist, toxicologist, nutritionist, home economist, horticulturist, plant physiologist, animal physiologist, food inspector, sanitarian, grading specialist, veterinarian, entomologist, fisheries specialist, quality control specialist, statistician, agricultural economist, marketing specialist, industrial engineer, mechanical engineer, refrigeration engineer, civil engineer, electrical engineer, agricultural engineer, sanitary engineer, packaging specialist, extension specialist.

• Specialists concerned with consumer use of food:

Home economist, nutritionist, dietitian, institutional food service specialist, chef, sanitarian, hygienist, public health specialist, toxicologist, microbiologist, food technologist, dairy technologist, food scientist, marketing specialist, agricultural economist, extension specialist.

In addition to those on the lists above, there are persons who handle administrative or fiscal matters as business managers, personnel managers, accountants, purchasing agents, salesmen, and secretaries. Most of them require special education or considerable training so that they can fulfill their responsibilities.

PROGRAMS RELATED to food protection provide another way to gain an appreciation of the vastness of educational and training requirements to supply the people engaged in protecting the abundance and quality of our country's food supply.

THE FOLLOWING LIST of many of the programs serves this purpose even though terminology is used to denote general functions or objectives and not necessarily titled programs. It may not always be clear where the activities are centered—that is, in consumer-producer organizations; foundations; Federal, State, county, or city governments; in universities; or in industry. Furthermore, it should be recognized that some government-centered programs influence the quantity or the quality of our food supply through regulatory laws while others do so through assistance programs. Also, there are many voluntary activities among segments of the food industry which are very effective indeed.

HERE IS the program list:

Farmer cooperatives, loans to farmers, small business assistance, price supports, commodity marketing orders, soil and water conservation, land retirement, food and feed surplus storage and inventory management, defense and defense mobilization, commodity exchanges, marketing information, agricultural outlook, market development, commodity commissions, foreign trade balances, foreign aid, Food for Peace, rural areas development, rural electrification, crop insurance, economic research, utilization research.

Marketing research, agricultural production research, fisheries management, wildlife management, meat inspection, poultry and egg inspection, dairy plant inspection, food import inspection, Federal Food, Drug, and Cosmetic Act, food grades and standards, food plant inspection, food warehouse inspection, public eating place inspection, water supplies, water and air pollution, pest control, foods contaminated by disaster, public health research, food research, and consumer research.

Simplifying the look at education is not easy. We have learned there are many things that foods are protected against, that food is protected at all of the many stages of the food distribution chain from production to consumption, that there are many different specialists—500 or more—engaged in the numerous phases of protecting the food supply, and there are many "programs" aimed entirely or in part at helping insure an abundant and safe food supply. It should thus be clearly evident the education or training of all these different people must be very involved indeed. And it is, but not as hopelessly as it might seem.

FROM OUR OWN observations we know some people with a high school education or less find employment on farms, on fishing vessels, in food processing companies, in retail stores, and many other places, including important administrative positions. We all know, in a general way at least, what they were taught and what special skills each must have developed through participation and self-learning.

We recognize, too, that most of the specialists which were listed earlier have at least 4 years of university or college education.

ALSO, it is appreciated that advanced knowledge and development of skills not attainable during just 4 years in college are required for many specialists, especially those who do research and development work, teach scientific or technical subjects in universities and elsewhere, or administer and manage scientific and technical programs. Such specialists are awarded master's and doctor's degrees upon completing prescribed study programs.

Finally, we hear more and more about shortened technical study programs in the so-called technical schools and also in universities and on the job. These require 1, 2, or 3 years to complete and are adequate and appropriate to prepare men and women to play

241

certain important roles in supplying and protecting our foods.

STUDY AT THE UNIVERSITY is the principal source of specialists.

Increased enrollment of students and greatly expanded research programs have resulted in universities and colleges becoming very large. However, growth has not altered to any appreciable extent the basic organization of most institutions of higher learning.

Those institutions called universities are usually made up of a number of colleges or schools, sometimes as many as 10. If the institution as a whole is called a college, its main subdivisions are usually called schools. Examples are Colleges or Schools of Agriculture, Arts and Sciences, Engineering, Business Administration, Home Economics, Education, Medicine, Veterinary Medicine, Pharmacy, and Public Health.

Each college or school within a university offers several curricula—a curriculum being a whole body of subject matter courses arranged in an orderly sequence for pursuit by students which, if satisfactorily completed, lead to a bachelor's degree (B.A., bachelor of arts; B.S., bachelor of science), usually after 4 years of study but sometimes after a longer period.

In each college or school there are departments whose faculties do the actual teaching of specialized subject matter within the general area of the college or school. Students declare a particular interest in a department and then they become "majors" in that specific department.

EXAMPLES of departments in schools of agriculture are Agricultural Economics, Agricultural Engineering, Agronomy or Soils, Animal Science, Dairy Science, Entomology, Food Science and Technology, Horticulture, Fisheries and Wildlife, Plant Pathology, Veterinary Science, Agricultural Chemistry, Microbiology, and Agricultural Education.

A student may wish to take employment in agriculture, industry, government, a university, or elsewhere after

he receives his bachelor's degree. If so, he will find plenty of good-paying, worthwhile, and challenging opportunities for a career.

The student may, however, wish to expand his knowledge and develop his skills still more. If so, he will gain admission to the Graduate School of his university, or of another one, where he will study under the tutelage of an accomplished specialist who serves as the student's major professor. The student will also have faculty committees to help in selecting graduate courses to prepare him as a specialist, to guide his research for the required independent study called a thesis, and to give him examinations which finally determine if he meets the requirements for advanced degrees, like the M.S., master of science, and the Ph.D., doctor of philosophy. The emphasis in graduate schools today is on training for careers in research.

Even though advanced study is within the jurisdiction of the Graduate School, the graduate student has a major department, whose requirements for degrees must be met. Major departments serving the graduate school usually are the same as those of the university and school, and they offer the major fields in which appropriate advanced degrees are given.

SOME UNIVERSITIES offer programs of less than 4 years' duration. Common ones have been for 2 years and train persons in the technology of agriculture. Others are termed short courses since they may be for periods of only a few days or at most a few weeks and are intended primarily to help people, including those with degrees, remain up to date on knowledge of food and agriculture. Extension specialists usually arrange short courses as part of their programs to transmit technical and scientific information to those who can make use of it.

THE LAND-GRANT colleges and universities were born on July 2, 1862— more than 100 years ago—when President Abraham Lincoln signed the

Morrill Land-Grant College Act. This act authorized giving each State free public land which it could sell or use for the creation or development of institutions of higher learning where "The leading object shall be, without excluding other scientific and classical studies and including military tactics, to teach such branches of learning as are related to agriculture and the mechanic arts. . . ."

A CENTURY AGO colleges and universities were attended by only a privileged few, and were not much interested in agriculture and industry. A goal of the Morrill Act was to have at least one institution of higher learning "in every State . . . accessible to all . . . where all the needed sciences for the practical avocations of life shall be taught." This goal was reached a long time ago and has put agriculture in the United States far ahead of where it is in other countries, with only a very few exceptions.

As would be expected, the 70 land-grant colleges and universities graduate most of the men and women who are employed in the 500 or more different kinds of jobs in agriculture and food.

These institutions of higher learning offer curricula related to our food supply not only in their schools of agriculture, but also in practically all other fields including science (where chemists, microbiologists, physicists, biologists, and others are trained), in engineering (where agricultural engineers and others are taught), and in business administration (where training can be directed toward the commercial aspects of food).

MANY land-grant colleges and universities have schools of veterinary medicine which teach in large part the subjects pertaining to diseases of livestock and poultry.

Some land-grant institutions have schools of forestry and public health.

All of the land-grant colleges and universities can give good undergraduate preparation for graduate studies in the professional specialties.

TODAY'S CONCEPT of agricultural education in the university is that there are three general areas which need a somewhat independent emphasis. These areas are:

Agricultural science where the emphasis is on the physical and biological sciences and often is preparatory to graduate study; agricultural business where business management and economics are emphasized and may also prepare the student for graduate study; and agricultural technology where technology or applications of science receive the most emphasis.

Where this concept is adopted formally or in practice, as at most schools of agriculture, the various departments in the school elect to offer curricula in only one or two of these areas, or in all three. Courses are selected from their own department and elsewhere in the university and arranged in curricula to prepare the students for employment in one of the areas.

SCHOOLS OF agriculture usually establish a "core" of courses required in each of the options, as they are often called, and these must be completed by all students under each option regardless of the department in which he has his major.

These basic requirements are appropriate to each option. They invariably give all students solid backgrounds in biological and physical sciences, English and communications, humanities and social studies. In addition they insure opportunities for election by the student of nonrequired courses of special interest to him.

Honors programs in agriculture for superior students have been introduced in some universities. In these programs students are assigned special advisers and given unusual consideration in degree requirements. Special honors courses are offered for these students.

There is one kind of curriculum offered in more than 20 universities, usually in schools of agriculture, which deserves special mention because it is concerned with many of the most important phases of food protection. It

243

791–476 O–66—18

deals with the broad field of commercially preserving and processing food.

THIS IS CALLED, by different universities, food technology, food science, or food science and technology. Dairy technology and dairy science curricula offered in some institutions are similar and give specialized training exclusively in the processing and preserving of milk and milk products.

Usually the curricula fall in the optional category of "agricultural science" although some are under the "agricultural business" option. In each instance, however, the student majoring in this field receives a thorough background in the fundamental sciences, as well as an understanding of the composition of foods, the changes which occur in foods to spoil them, the processes by which spoilage can be prevented or minimized, and the manufacture, storage, transportation, and consumer use of foods.

Food technologists, because of their broad training in the chemical, physical, and microbiological aspects, find unusual employment opportunities in food processing plants, regulatory agencies, supply companies, and elsewhere. Some go on to graduate school where they become specialists (food scientists) in particular aspects of foods and are trained to do research and development work in university, industry, and government laboratories.

CLEARLY, EDUCATION in agriculture today goes far beyond just training young people to engage in farming or the raising of crops and livestock. Agriculture is recognized for what it is—the largest industry in the world—which includes, besides farming and farm management, scientific, technical and business occupations in research, education, industry, business, services, communications, and conservation and recreation.

Students in agriculture are appropriately educated to become research scientists, industrial executives, authorities in marketing, banking and credit officers, university professors, government officials, editors and publishers, radio and television executives, conservation authorities, regulatory officials, and the managers of very large as well as smaller operations for the production of food.

Curricula in agriculture can give young people the kind of background of knowledge, skill, creativity, and inspiration which—when followed by experience—will raise them to positions that are the counterpart of the most important and rewarding positions in any other industrial occupation in the United States.

SCHOOLS OF ENGINEERING train many of the specialists listed earlier. These schools have departments just as do schools of agriculture. Usually they have departments of civil, chemical, electrical, general, industrial, mechanical, sanitary, and agricultural engineering. Some schools have departments of aeronautical, architectural, metallurgical engineering, and others. Bachelor's, master's, and doctor's degrees are offered.

ALTHOUGH almost all fields of engineering have a relationship to food protection in one way or another, three fields have the closest relationship. These are agricultural engineering, sanitary engineering, and chemical engineering.

• Students majoring in agricultural engineering take the same basic courses in mathematics, physics, chemistry, English, and mechanical drawing, usually during the first 2 years, which are required in other fields of engineering. In addition, they take fundamental courses in agriculture and may specialize in farm structures, electrical power and processing, power and machinery, and soil and water.

Some departments of agricultural engineering offer curricula in the school of agriculture as well as in the school of engineering. The agriculture curricula, sometimes called "mechanical technology in agriculture," may be offered under both the "agricultural technology" option and "agricultural business" option. These enable the students to acquire a background in agricultural sciences, the manipulative skills for operating machinery, and business as well as elementary engineering principles.

• Sanitary engineering, which could be called public health engineering and is sometimes a branch of civil engineering, has its association with our food supply because it deals with problems of community water supply, sewage, industrial waste disposal, and public health engineering.

The sanitary engineer is required to have a basic knowledge of chemistry, physics, bacteriology, and other biological sciences such as hygiene. Curricula prepare him to meet diverse situations like chlorination of water for drinking, keeping harmful wastes and impurities out of water, design of milk pasteurizing equipment, protection of oyster beds from sewage, cleaning and sanitizing systems in food plants, design, construction and inspection of buildings for food processing, or to serve as government employees protecting the public health through law enforcement.

• Chemical engineering, dealing with large-scale commercial chemical processes, is employed more and more in the food industry. Chemical engineers design and operate plants and processes used in concentrating foods like citrus juices, dehydrating foods like coffee extracts, potatoes, meats, fruits and vegétables, and in fermentation industries producing certain beverages.

OTHER ENGINEERING specialists are also very important in protecting our food supply. Included are the refrigeration engineers who help preserve our foods in warehouses, trucks, railway cars, retail stores, institutions, and homes. They are usually trained in departments of mechanical engineering. Industrial engineers, among other activities, find new and more efficient ways to do things in commercial plants. Food engineering, as a separate curriculum, is offered in only a few universities.

CURRICULA IN SCIENCE educate additional specialists in foods. Schools of agriculture are now graduating something over 9,000 trained persons per year, and it is estimated there are about 15,000 jobs available yearly for such persons in agriculture and food.

WHERE DO the additional people all come from?

Part come from schools of engineering, but many more are graduates of other schools and their departments of chemistry, microbiology, physics, botany and plant pathology, entomology, zoology, physiology, and nutrition. When industry, government, and universities cannot fill positions with agriculture graduates they employ these people and train them on the job to specialize in foods.

Students in the sciences are thoroughly trained in the fundamentals of their particular science while in the university, and many enter graduate schools for advanced study in specialized fields of knowledge.

FROM THE undergraduates—even some who do not complete a full 4-year course—come the technicians, analytical chemists, bacteriologists, biologists, sanitarians, and inspectors who work in food laboratories of industry and government and in the field to safeguard the quality of foods from the standpoint of uniformity, sanitation, and protection of the public's health.

They receive on-the-job training to give them skills to enable them to perform their special duties.

From the supply of those with master's and doctor's degrees in the sciences come the biochemists, agricultural chemists, entomologists, toxicologists, and others who deal with problems relating to the use of pesticides in protecting our food from insects and other pests. Many of these scientists are employed in research laboratories of industry, universities, and government to improve the effectiveness of pest control and at the same time keep the control procedures from being hazardous to the general public.

245

Some scientists deal, for example, with aspects of regulating pesticides by the U.S. Department of Agriculture under authority of the Federal Insecticide, Fungicide, and Rodenticide Act, and the Pesticide Chemicals Amendment to the Federal Food, Drug, and Cosmetic Act. Others work in the Food and Drug Administration, which among other things regulates additives in processed foods under authority of the Food Additives Amendment to the Federal Food, Drug, and Cosmetic Act.

Also, from the graduate scientists come those who do the research on bacteria and other micro-organisms to learn more fundamental facts about those capable of producing toxins which might endanger consumers.

OTHER TRAINING for food protection is also available. The various segments of what is termed public health are extremely important in educating people to keep our food safe. There are several schools of public health that train people especially for this kind of work. However, one does not necessarily have to study in or graduate from such a school to be adequately prepared for some positions in public health agencies. Schools of agriculture, engineering, and science also provide adequate training in some fields, as has been noted earlier.

Public health workers accomplish their tasks of protecting man from sickness and death by working more or less directly with the population through public health departments of Federal, State, county, and city governments. Curricula in nutritional sciences and dietetics are, of course, directly related to the public's use of food.

The field of medicine deals with food in several ways but this does not need to be elaborated here.

MOST OF THE food inspectors employed in meat and poultry inspection work of the U.S. Department of Agriculture and similar State agencies are graduates of schools of veterinary medicine,

although some are chemists and bacteriologists. Veterinarians, having studied diseases in livestock and poultry, are excellently qualified to discover and prevent products from diseased animals from being consumed.

The work of veterinarians throughout the country in controlling and eradicating animal diseases helps immensely in providing all of us with a safe supply of meat and poultry.

Technical schools are preparing technicians in several categories which relate to foods. Curricula of these schools consist of courses teaching applied skills along with some fundamental scientific knowledge in production, processing, and business. They train people for those occupations requiring training beyond high school but not necessarily 4 years in college. Usually technical schools offer curricula of about 2 years' duration and are not intended to be the first 2 years of a university education.

On-the-job training to some degree is required by all jobs. Training of some sort must at least familiarize a new employee with his duties and responsibilities. Industry and government agencies provide some excellent training programs which go much beyond this. Some are conducted within the organization. Some consist of arranging and possibly financing special or regular study programs outside, often leading to academic degrees from universities.

The Federal Training Act of 1958 encourages training for the maximum in professional development.

PROTECTING OUR FOOD supply so it remains the most abundant and safest of any in the world depends upon people.

- Education of all these people cannot be described simply. But with a description of how the system of higher education operates and what curricula are offered, especially in the land-grant colleges and universities, it becomes more understandable how people are trained to fill all the available occupations.

INDUSTRY: PROFIT AND PROTECTION

JAMES E. REYNOLDS

MAKING an honest dollar through honest effort has, historically in these United States, been considered as American as Mom's apple pie.

That's what the food industry in this country does. It makes an honest dollar. It makes that dollar through an honest effort to protect your food and mine against all hazards.

It's a multibillion-dollar, almost unbelievably complicated operation, this business of protecting our food as it makes its several ways from the production area to the shopping cart we wheel to the checkout counter in the food store.

It's a successful business, as well.

Food, animal and vegetable, presents itself to us in many forms today. It comes fresh, frozen, dried, concentrated, milled, processed in a profusion of forms. It comes by truck, train, water, and air. It is safe to eat.

The principal reason our food is safe to eat is because the industry supplying it to us could not make a profit furnishing us unsafe food. We would not buy it. We would transfer our food dollar away from that segment of the food industry that failed us.

So, each segment of the ruggedly competitive food industry fights to protect our food in the area in which its profit lies, to the ultimate benefit of the industry and the consumer. This, actually, has been the story and the history of the food industry.

Reaching back a long way for an illustration, it was a man wanting to make money who got the canning end of the food industry underway. France in the closing years of the 18th century was fighting most of Europe, by land and by sea. She was not able to keep her soldiers and sailors adequately provisioned. So, her governing body of five men—The Directory—offered a 12,000-franc prize to the citizen who could devise a method of preserving food for transport on campaigns.

NICOLAS APPERT, an obscure chef and confectioner with no knowledge of biology, came up with the method. It took him 14 years to develop and fully test his process, but in January 1810 Appert was awarded the prize by Count Montalivet, French Minister of the Interior.

In June of the same year Appert published "The Book of All Households; or the Art of Preserving Animal and Vegetable Substances for Many Years." It set forth procedures used in

* * *

James E. Reynolds is *Chief* of the Current Information Branch, Information Division, Agricultural Research Service.

canning more than 50 different canned foods and was immediately widely distributed and translated into many European languages.

So, Appert found a way to keep food safely—won 12,000 francs—and the whole world benefited.

THE CANNING INDUSTRY has changed since the days of Appert, and it continues to change. People like Louis Pasteur of France, H. L. Russell of Wisconsin, and Samuel C. Prescott and W. Lyman Underwood of Massachusetts pioneered in demonstrating the importance of destroying bacteria, to make food keep. Other people developed the equipment that led to today's sanitary, high-volume output.

But Appert's simple theory, that food sufficiently heated while sealed in a container that excludes air will keep, is still the fundamental modern principle of canning as practiced today.

A LOT OF OTHER theories have been developed into principle in the century and a half since Appert made his great contribution to the food industry. In Appert's day, little fresh produce traveled more than one day's wagon journey to the market.

Today, whole railroad cars of lettuce are sent through a vacuum-cooling process in California, then dispatched eastward to markets 3,000 miles away. Fresh pineapple arrives in Kansas City from Hawaii. Florida citrus, as fresh as you would find it in your own supermarket, is on sale in Switzerland.

The average retail food store in the United States has some 46 various fresh vegetables on display at one time or another throughout the year. When you include fresh fruit, the number of fresh produce items is about 75.

These day-to-day happenings are possible because the food industry protects these foods.

Lettuce, for instance, is field wrapped in film, packed 24 heads per box, vacuum-cooled, shipped to terminal markets in rail cars or trucks in which temperature and humidity are controlled, placed in similarly controlled

storages, and transferred swiftly to the retail outlet, where trained personnel keep it in top quality condition until you purchase it.

Much the same is true of the handling of fresh peaches, except that peaches have for a number of years now been hydrocooled—bathed in ice water before shipment. More recently, shippers have also been dunking the peaches for just a couple of minutes in hot water. This doesn't cook or change the taste or temperature of the peaches. It simply cuts down the incidence of rots and extends the shelf life of the peaches.

Industry has for many years used flood-type hydrocooling for cooling asparagus, celery, and sweet corn.

Oranges, in whatever form, are similarly protected. Fresh oranges are protected against adverse temperatures, against bruising. Chilled orange juice frequently travels in giant tanker cars, under controlled temperature. Frozen concentrate goes in refrigerated trucks or railroad cars that maintain the concentrate's temperature at 0° F., or below.

In some cases, as in winter shipment of potatoes from northern States, insulated cars equipped with heaters protect the commodity against cold.

THE HISTORY of protecting commodities against heat and cold during transit is quite a story in itself, and one the food industry delights in relating. As in many a good story, a detail or two is lacking, but the story is there nonetheless.

The name of the shipper seems to have vanished into the mists of time, but generally accepted as fact is that on July 1, 1851, a freight train pulled out of Ogdensburg, N.Y., on the Ogdensburg & Lake Champlain Railroad (now the Rutland). The train trundled across the northern part of New York State, close to the Canadian border, then all the way down the east side of Lake Champlain and southeastward to a connection with what is now the Boston & Maine at Bellows Falls, in Vermont.

This was an ordinary freight train of the period, hauling the usual number of cars. But one boxcar carried an unusual load, an experimental shipment, bound for Boston. The 30-foot wooden boxcar, constructed upon the same principle as the home icebox of the period, was insulated and iced, for it was carrying 8 tons of butter—the earliest known successful use of refrigeration on a long haul by railroad.

The car was twice replenished with ice during the journey and the butter reached Boston as fresh as when it left Ogdensburg, far up on the St. Lawrence River, hundreds of miles away.

OTHER SHIPMENTS followed as Bostonians developed a taste for New York State butter. The operation became so successful that more cars had to be built to handle the traffic in butter which developed all the way across northern New York. And according to press reports of the day, the "Butter Train" that ran every week "brought immeasurable financial benefits to the towns along the line, as well as to people everywhere."

The first successful refrigerator car was patented in 1868 by William Davis of Detroit, and the Davis cars were used with some success for the shipment of fruits and dressed beef. But as early as 1857 W. W. Chandler had added an inside lining to each of 30 ordinary boxcars for the Pennsylvania Railroad, filled the airspaces with sawdust, and installed iceboxes in the boxcar doorways.

It was really in the late 1880's, when the ammonia compression machine for making artificial ice emerged from the experimental stage, that railway refrigeration became truly practical throughout the United States. And it was in June of 1889 that California shipped its first car of deciduous fruits all the way to New York City.

CONTRIBUTING GREATLY to protection by industry of fresh fruits and vegetables in transit is the early knowledge which had been gained in the ocean shipment of bananas.

Ships were designed and built specifically for carrying bananas as early as 1904, and shippers learned that the process of protecting them was more properly one of air conditioning than simply of refrigeration.

They learned that the safest carrying temperature is about 55° F., and that the carbon dioxide content in the holds should be no greater than $\frac{3}{10}$ of 1 percent.

Today shippers recognize that fresh fruits and vegetables are living organisms and both in storage and shipment are heedful of their total environment. Day-to-day application of this principle is what helps us in this country, in city or in village, in the producing area or 3,000 miles distant from the producing area, to have the variety and quality of the fresh fruits and the vegetables we enjoy.

SAFE TRANSPORTATION has been a major factor in protecting our grain shipments, as it has been in protecting the more perishable commodities.

Behind every slice of bread we eat is an interesting story of transportation. That slice of bread may have started in the wheatfields of Kansas, Montana, the Dakotas, or any one of the many States in the grain belt. It may have run through several States, traveling as grain or flour from country elevator to the terminal, from terminal to mill, from mill to the grocery or bakery.

The farmer's immediate market for his wheat ordinarily is the country elevator. From the country elevator the wheat may be shipped to one of the big terminal elevators. Terminal elevators are usually equipped for cleaning, clipping, drying, grading, and mixing the grain, as well as storing or sacking it.

The grain may travel from the terminal elevator to a mill for grinding into flour, or to a feed mill. Again, it may go as grain, flour, meal, or breakfast cereal to foreign countries.

An average carload of wheat is just under 1,900 bushels, or about 57 tons. But in 1961 the Southern Railway

Freshly harvested potatoes arrive by truck for storage at a processing plant in Presque Isle, Maine, while others leave in a train especially built to carry potatoes.

System came out with what has been known ever since as its "Big John" covered hopper car. This aluminum car carries about 118 tons of wheat and can be loaded and unloaded as easily as you fill and empty a bathtub.

The car is watertight and self-cleaning. One receiver, in the Southeast, says the feed grains he orders from the Midwest come to him in cars that are "kitchen pan clean."

CARS CARRYING grain haven't always been "kitchen pan clean," but the railroads have made continuing efforts through the years to maintain and improve the cars that haul grain. And, in the case of wheat, the grain got cleaner in every separate movement toward the ultimate consumer.

Standards of cleanliness in today's flour mills would seem fantastic to the miller of Civil War days. So would the standards of the bakery supplying the needs of the food store, and those of the breakfast food and "mix" manufacturer in their giant plants.

But these two basic laws of the trade are what have made our food supply

250

in the United States what it is today: A high quality product from the producer; a well protected product through the channels of marketing.

THE TRUCKING INDUSTRY, which came on the American scene some time after the railroads, has carved out for itself a healthy share of the food transporting market. The truckers say that in 1965, by conservative estimates, there were at least 25,000 U.S. communities served by no other form of transport, communities that depended on the motor truck for all they consumed and for all they marketed.

Progress in the development of equipment and techniques used by truckers to transport food during the post World War II years was truly remarkable. This was particularly so during the 1950's and 1960's.

Perhaps the greatest catalyst in the development of trucks as food carriers has been the surging growth of the American broiler industry.

In 1941, total broiler production in the United States was only 560 million pounds, with about 50 percent of it coming out of the Delmarva peninsula of Delaware, Maryland, and Virginia. By 1964, U.S. broiler production had jumped more than 13 times to just over 7.5 billion pounds. Georgia, accounting for only about 10 percent in 1941, had by 1964 skyrocketed into first place with 1.3 billion pounds. Nine Southern States—North and South Carolina, Georgia, Florida, Alabama, Mississippi, Louisiana, Arkansas, and Texas—accounted for just under 5 billion pounds or 66 percent of total broiler production.

THE DELMARVA production was first marketed, and still largely is marketed, in the heavy population centers of the East, with Cleveland perhaps its extreme western limit of distribution. The broilers moved to market by truck, as did those shipped from Maine to Boston and New York. The trucking industry improved its refrigerated equipment to meet the developing demands of the broiler producers. These demands became steadily more pressing as broiler production surged upward in the South during the years following World War II.

Birds from Arkansas and Mississippi now commonly ship to the West Coast and those from Georgia and North Carolina ship to the Great Lakes region and even on as far as the West Coast. They move today from processing plant to retailer in trucks that can protect their quality and wholesomeness on the short haul from Delaware to New York, or the long haul from Georgia to California.

TO PROTECT broilers in transit from processor to retail food store, the trucking industry drew on its early, struggling experience with red meat and with frozen concentrated orange juice. This involved trial-and-error experimentation with various types of mechanical refrigeration processes and with different types and degrees of insulation. Progress, if sometimes seemingly slow, was nonetheless steady.

Frozen foods, truly a growth industry, also spurred the trucking industry

as it developed its equipment. Much of this equipment is now so sophisticated it can carry two different types of commodities at two different temperatures. For example, it can transport half a load at 0° F. and the other half at 35° to 40° F. by use of a portable seal-type divider.

TRAILER DESIGN is constantly being changed. Like the railroads, the trucking industry has cut gross weight by using lighter metals such as aluminum. And it has solved the problem of heat transfer in transit by using a foamed-in-place insulating technique. This involves injecting a polyurethane resin between the walls of a trailer, then expanding it by adding a catalyst and so filling all voids. The technique increases the efficiency of refrigeration while at the same time it decreases the weight and the thickness required for trailer walls.

Another significant technological development in protecting food in transit has been the use of liquid nitrogen as a substitute for mechanical refrigeration systems. With liquid freezing equipment, the trucker loads cargo immediately upon receipt, freezes it down to a temperature determined by the length of the trip, and is assured of arrival temperatures that will meet shippers' requirements.

THE RAILROADS and the trucks compete aggressively for the business of bringing food in all forms to us who drop into our shopping carts the head of lettuce from California, the baking potato from Idaho, the grapefruit from Texas, and the lobster from Maine. Now and again their differences turn up in print as each bemoans alleged concessions granted the other.

But ordinarily this is a silent struggle of technologists, engineers, cost managers, and others pitted in a continuing contest to determine which of these transportation channels—or sometimes which combination of them—can, at a profit, bring to us a high quality food product.

It would not be proper to discuss

either the railroads or the truckers without noting the innovation of "piggyback," which brings together rail car and truck, and of "fishyback," which adds water transportation into the transit equation.

BOTH "PIGGYBACK" AND "FISHYBACK" have become possible through the increasing standardization within the trucking industry, which allows for the interchange of trailers between carriers.

Use of the "piggyback" technique lets shippers load a trailer, refrigerated or otherwise, at the processing plant, haul the trailer to a railway, and there put the trailer on a flatcar. The railroad then hauls the trailer to the city of destination, where the trailer is offloaded, coupled to a tractor, and driven over the road to its final destination.

"FISHYBACK" transportation is when the trailer is loaded at a shipping point, goes then directly over the road to a port—or goes from the loading point to a railroad where it is loaded on a flatcar and hauled to the port. In either case, it is offloaded at the port and put aboard a freighter that carries it across the ocean. At the port of entry the trailer is offloaded from the freighter and driven over the road to the ultimate consignee.

In some instances, as in the shipment of fresh citrus from Florida to Switzerland, the trailer may have to be sent "piggyback" from the port of entry, because bridges or highway tunnels will not permit over-the-road movement.

USE OF THIS "fishyback" technique of overseas containerized shipment is on the increase. It reduces handling costs, reduces pilferage, and keeps the food in top quality condition.

While developed primarily to protect our food products for export, this technique is also expected to protect Hawaii's pineapple and Alaska's king crab as well as other products coming into our 48 contiguous States.

Through the kaleidoscopic pattern of America's evolving process of food production and food marketing one

element—a high quality product— has remained constant. It has remained constant because the customer has demanded it. The frozen food industry, constantly growing, is an outstanding example of industry meeting this customer challenge.

First the processors had to learn how to handle the raw products coming into their plants. Then they had to determine the best method of retaining raw product quality during processing. And they had to learn how to protect the processed product during storage and transportation.

NEXT CAME protection at the retail food store level; how long and at what temperatures retailers could hold the product, what type of cold boxes would protect the product and afford the customer free access to it. And then the industry had to take one step beyond the retail sales level and tell the customer how to handle the product in the home, from refrigerator or freezer storage on through preparing it for a family meal.

The processors started out with a scattered assortment of fruits and vegetables. Now they can supply you a complete meal in one package, or if you like, in a number of packages.

THE FROZEN FOOD INDUSTRY, along with many other segments of the food industry, comes into the ken of most of its customers at the retail food store level. And the retail food store today plays an integral part in protecting your food and mine.

The cat no longer suns herself on the carrots in the storefront window. That's because the mice no longer scamper from behind the flour barrel. And the flour barrel, too, has departed. Flour is packaged in sizes to meet consumer requirements, the carrots are in refrigerated trays, and— generally—those refrigerated trays are in an air-conditioned store that not only contributes to customer comfort, but helps establish an environment in which it is less difficult to maintain food product quality.

Shoppers at a refrigerated meat display case in a Washington, D.C., supermarket.

Refrigerated walk-in cold rooms and refrigerated showcases preserve the quality and appearance of meats, of dairy products, and of frozen foods. And all of the cold rooms and the showcases, along with the storage rooms the customer never sees, are as clean and sanitary as the shelves that display the product to the customer's critical appraisal.

TODAY WE TAKE for granted good sanitary conditions in the food industry. Yet those conditions which are elementary in the protection of our food result only from continuing efforts of industry to improve what is already good. We might cast our thoughts back for just a moment to the meat for which William Davis designed the early refrigerator railroad cars, during the year of 1868.

The animals from which that meat came were slaughtered under dreadfully unsanitary conditions. The carcasses that went into those cars were bruised and accumulated more bruises in transit. They were loaded out of Mr. Davis' primitively refrigerated railroad car into a horse-drawn wagon.

The carcasses were delivered to a butchershop where the retailer cut them up under unsanitary conditions, and the meat was not refrigerated when displayed to the customer. Those were the days when the meatmen said "Sell it or smell it."

Today's meat supply is slaughtered humanely, under rigidly enforced rules of sanitation. It moves from slaughterhouse to the retail customer's shopping basket through channels that protect it from all danger of quality deterioration. And meat comes to the ultimate consumer clean, unbruised, still possessing its bloom, and—importantly— safe to eat. In general terms, that process of protecting our meat supply can be called quality control.

Quality control, of course, is broader than this. Take the American hotdog as an everyday example. Your favorite

253

brand of wieners doesn't just happen to taste the same every time you buy it.

The processor samples the ingredients going into your wiener before, during, and after processing and runs these samples through a battery of tests to maintain a proper balance of nutrients and flavors. Automatic thermometers check and record room temperatures. Both humidity and air circulation are carefully supervised.

AIR IS CHECKED not only for its circulation, but for its cleanliness as well. Trained personnel perform bacteriological tests on the air, walls, ceilings, and the equipment to assure sanitary conditions.

Plastic-coated light bulbs, special formula paints and cleaning compounds, and regulations on building materials and construction are other safeguards against contamination.

Electronic detectors remove any possible metal from the product, and electronic devices detect possible nonmagnetic foreign substances. Complicated high-speed scales weigh the product and automatically discard improperly filled containers.

And, before the product leaves the plant, the processor reverts from machine to human. He has a taste panel determine that the product tastes good.

Then the wiener, tested by machine and man, starts on its refrigerated way to complement the sauerkraut, to acquire a charcoal smoke patina over your backyard grill, or to help the hungry fan through a baseball game.

IT HAS LONG BEEN traditional to refer to the American farmer as a rugged individualist and, in recent years, to refer to him as "the last of the truly independent individualists." This well may be so, but the American farmer has also historically been a man who knew how to work with his neighbors for the common good of the community.

Farmers helped each other build cabins, raise barns, clear land. They shared pasture and range land, traded use of equipment and labor.

Out of their early spirit of neighborliness came the notion of forming farm cooperatives. Most were informally conceived and not much more formally initiated. Some were made up of farmers who pooled their fertilizer orders to get the advantage of carlot prices. Others were the cattlemen of the Southwest who pooled their cattle into the great herds which they drove up the Chisholm Trail.

All of them were formed, initially, to profit the individual producer.

That's still the basis for existence of the highly organized, extremely efficient, very businesslike cooperatives that start your food and mine from the farm or ranch to market today. But, over time, these cooperatives have had considerable to do with the quality of that food. And they have had a lot to do with the Nation's marketing system.

MOST CONSUMERS would recognize these names among the ones pioneered and developed over many years by cooperatives: Sunkist citrus of Sunkist Growers, Welch grape products of National Grape Cooperative Association, Land O'Lakes dairy products of Land O'Lakes Creameries, Rockingham Poultry Marketing Cooperative, Sun Maid Raisins, and the Arkansas Rice Growers Association.

The farm cooperatives, large and small, run clear through the country. On the marketing side, they have helped the farmer get better prices for his product. They have done this by setting standards of quality a member must meet before the cooperative will accept his product for marketing. They have met the demands of the quantity buyer by assembling products of like quality in large enough lots so he can count on continuing supplies of the quality and quantity he requires.

THIS HAS MEANT the people concerned with supplying food to the market have been able to make efficient use of their processing and distributing equipment and channels.

In the process, the farmer has profited. So have the processor and the distributor. And so have you and I.

254

THE CHEMICAL MANUFACTURERS whose activities range throughout all the industry of the Nation make a tremendous contribution toward protecting our food industry, from the wiener on through shredded coconut.

Wieners, like other sausages, require flavoring agents. Canned shredded coconut requires a humectant, to keep it moist. Table salt, powdered sugar, and malted milk powder all require anticaking agents.

WITHOUT ADDED antioxidants, frozen peaches would be brown and unattractive. Some cake mixes could not be used unless antioxidants were employed to keep the shortening in them as fresh as possible.

Pectin added to fruits naturally low in this thickening agent makes possible the production of jams and jellies of consistent and desirable thickness. Emulsifiers prevent the oil and vinegar in today's prepared salad dressings from separating.

Salt and sugar, along with some spices, were the original food preservatives. Still used, these are now supplemented both as flavoring and preservative agents by a long list of chemicals. Food additives enhance the flavor of certain foods, maintain the appearance, palatability, and wholesomeness of many others. Use of all is rigidly controlled, in order to protect the Nation's health.

THE CHEMICAL MANUFACTURERS have contributed also to the growth of America's packaging industry that has put cuts of meat in transparent plastic film and cottage cheese and countless other foods into the convenient-size containers that have significantly lessened the problems, sanitary and otherwise, of the bulk handling of food products.

And, all along the line, the chemical manufacturers have contributed to the wholesomeness of our food supply by furnishing the materials with which equipment is cleaned, floors are swept, and the food industry generally kept tidy and sanitary.

This phase of their operations, of course, concerns our food supply only from the point of harvest on to its ultimate consumption.

THEN THERE'S THE STORY of how the chemical manufacturers protect our continuing food supply in the production phase of crops, vegetable and animal. It ranges from the fertilizer going into the soil on through insecticides, fungicides, herbicides, rodenticides, nematocides, molluscicides that kill snails and other injurious mollusks, desiccants and defoliators, and a long list of plant growth regulators. It includes the systemic insecticides, given internally to destroy the insects which attack animals. The systemics range from those that successfully kill cattle grubs without harming the animal, its meat, or its hide, to those which kill the fleas that plague the family dog.

WITHOUT CHEMICALS it would be an almost impossible task to support the broiler industry of this country. Chemicals are used in keeping clean the floors, the walls, and the other parts of the broiler plant. A safe chemical cleanses the plant equipment. And other chemicals clean the trucks that transport the broilers.

This is true also of the dairy industry, an industry which early went to steam-cleaning its equipment and has taken advantage of further protection afforded by modern-day chemicals as it has developed.

Human beings being human, little heed is paid by the average person to the day-to-day benefits which he derives from the chemicals that help make the modern food marvel possible.

Junior probably wouldn't stand still long enough for you to explain to him that without an added stabilizer he couldn't enjoy chocolate milk as he knows it.

Nor would many of the young marrieds of the mid-1960's pause long to listen while you explained that the addition of potassium iodide to table salt has practically eradicated simple goiter in this country.

So far as Junior and the young marrieds are concerned, milk is milk and salt is salt. It's nice to live in a time and a country where we can all take this for granted, and take for granted that the products are safe to eat and drink.

BUT THE HARD TRUTH is we would be in a sad situation if the people who furnish us our food took very much for granted.

Violently allergic to criticism, the strictly regulated—by law—American food industry polices its own operations rigidly. It wants to keep its $57 billion (in 1965) industry a profitable, growing enterprise. It can keep its business profitable just so long as Junior and the young marrieds and the rest of us have no complaints.

How it works at insuring itself against any complaints might be illustrated by a look in some depth at the canning segment of the food industry.

INVENTIVE GENIUS has made food canning one of the most highly mechanized of all American industries. Scientific developments and their application have provided means of evaluating and controlling various steps in the procedure that today cans more than 1,200 different foods and food combinations.

Certain basic operations are common to practically all canned food products.

One of the first and most important steps in commercial canning is the thorough cleaning of the raw food material immediately upon its receipt at the cannery.

Methods of cleaning vary with the nature of the food, but all the foods are freed of foreign or undesirable material which may be attached, and they are carefully inspected and trimmed free of any imperfections.

AFTER THE raw foods have been as expertly and thoroughly cleaned as you could clean them in your kitchen, they are prepared for canning.

Many fruits and vegetables are first sorted for size and maturity. They are sorted for size by a series of moving screens with different mesh sizes, or by passage over differently spaced rollers. Hand sorters separate them into groups, according to the degree of ripeness or the perfection of shape. Peas and lima beans often are machine-separated into more and less mature portions by flotation in a salt solution.

Operators trained in locating and removing blemishes do by hand any necessary trimming, sometimes the only cutting necessary to prepare the foods in the desired style of pack. When the foods are to be canned other than whole, machines especially designed for each product cut, slice, dice, halve, or peel them.

IN EACH OF these steps the raw food is continuously under inspection. Further, experienced persons make a final inspection, to pick out mashed or broken pieces that are off-color, and any foreign matter that may elude the cleaning, washing, and trimming operations.

Some foods are blanched. This means they are immersed in hot water or exposed to live steam. The operation expels air and gases, inactivates enzymes and so arrests changes in flavor, and wilts products—such as spinach—so that more can be filled into the container.

Proper blanching reduces strain on the seams of cans during processing, particularly where exhausting is not employed.

MACHINES DO the filling whenever the nature of the product permits, as with peas, corn, juices, and soups. Foods canned in larger pieces, like peaches, pears, and salmon, are usually filled into containers by hand. In some cases, mechanical filling proceeds at speeds up to 1,200 containers a minute. Closing machines keep pace.

Because internal pressure following the process and cooling needs to be less than atmospheric, a vacuum is obtained in the containers. The degree of vacuum in the processed, cooled container varies with the size and style of the container and product.

The vacuum helps keep can ends drawn in—indicating a sound package. It reduces strain on containers during processing, minimizes discoloration or flavor effects of remaining oxygen, prolongs shelf life of some products, prevents bulging at high altitudes or in high temperatures, and is necessary to keep some styles of lids on glass containers.

WHEN NICOLAS APPERT was carrying on his work, glass jars were the only available containers. They were blown to shape individually on the end of a pipe. Today's glass containers—their use greatly expanded during World War II when tin was hard to come by—are manufactured by automatic machinery. Their large-scale use was made possible by the development in the 1930's of machinery for vacuum packing products.

Plastics also have made great strides and help provide the vital competition for other methods of packaging which keeps industry dynamic. In another way the plastics, as resin linings in tin cans, are a further factor in increased safety in the use of that particular type of container.

THE "PROCESS" is the heat treatment to which foods are subjected after hermetic—airtight—sealing in containers. During the process, heat destroys micro-organisms which would otherwise cause food spoilage.

The degree of heat and length of exposure to heat to which the product is subjected vary with the product being processed and with the size of container.

Appropriate times and temperatures have been determined through years of continuing research.

Few people casually opening a can of soup ever give a thought to whether that canned product is completely safe to open and use in any climate. Even fewer are aware of the lucid, step-by-step instructions—distilled from research findings—that the canner has followed in making his product safe for use in all climates.

DEVELOPMENT of equipment that removes much of the hand labor from canning has contributed to the protection of wholesomeness in the final food product itself.

Machines cut out the pits of peaches and apricots, peel and core apples and pears. Others husk ears of sweet corn, trim and wash them, and cut the kernels from the cobs.

Green peas go through the canning operations from the field to the can without ever being touched by hand.

In canning, as in other phases of the food industry, the first line of continuing defense in protecting your food and mine is strict, unwavering obedience to the laws of sanitation. How successful are the canners and the rest of the food industry in this effort?

WE MIGHT DRAW as good an illustrative answer to this question as any from the dairy industry.

Blessed with abundant supplies, the American dairy industry thought to convert some of its product into ghee, for export purposes.

Ghee is a butter oil type commodity widely used in Asia. The first step in its manufacture is to let milk just stand for a sufficient period of time, then when enough natural change has taken place, put the material through the final stages necessary to develop the product known as ghee.

The American dairy industry was unable to come up with ghee, despite quite a prolonged effort. The obstacle it could not overcome was that the American dairy environment was simply too sanitary for the expected natural changes—which were necessary before the milk could be converted into ghee—to take place.

So, THE AMERICAN dairy folk had to go back to their sanitary laboratories, and try to develop a culture that could be introduced into our sanitary American milk, which then in turn could be converted into ghee, that Asian product which through 1965 had proved sturdily resistant to a sanitary environment.

257

THE FEDERAL-STATE WAR ON PESTS

EMORY D. BURGESS

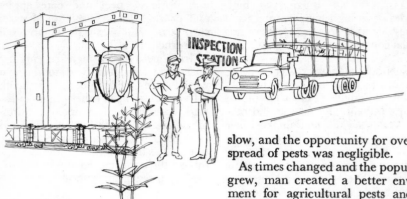

ORGANIZED plant pest control in the early days of this country was unknown and largely unnecessary. Today, cooperative efforts are vital to agriculture and to the consumer. They protect our food supply against attack by a wide variety of pests.

When the colonists began to settle North America, agricultural pests were not a matter of great concern. Crops were cultivated only in sufficient quantities to provide a simple existence. Highly specialized agricultural production was unheard of and much of the colonists' food was grown for family use. The number of inhabitants was not great; hence, there was little need to produce large quantities of foodstuffs over extensive areas which create a bug heaven for those species that infest it.

PASSAGE FROM foreign countries was slow, with sailing ships taking months to cross the oceans. So the opportunity for bringing new foreign pests to America was virtually nonexistent. Unless conditions were exactly right most would perish during the long trip. Land transportation also was slow, and the opportunity for overland spread of pests was negligible.

As times changed and the population grew, man created a better environment for agricultural pests and developed speedier transport. This made it much simpler for both insects and plant diseases to invade new territory and to thrive there.

Need soon arose for cooperative programs with the States to suppress or prevent the spread of serious agricultural pests which from time to time invaded the North American continent. The first of these was the cooperative gypsy moth program that got underway in the State of Massachusetts in the year 1907.

MORE THAN 125 of our most troublesome plant pests in this country are insect aliens. This number would be greatly increased if plant diseases, nematodes, and other injurious species were included in the total.

There was no deterrent to free entry until 1912 when the Plant Quarantine Act took effect. This act has done much to curtail invasion from abroad and to slow the spread of pests at home.

Since the turn of the century, agricultural experts have supported an all-out war on new pest invaders before they can expand their beach-

* * *

Emory D. Burgess is *Director* of the Plant Pest Control Division, Agricultural Research Service.

head. If successful, this technique spares producers from having to battle the pests over a broad front. It also lessens the need for the widespread use of pesticides.

DELAY OR FAILURE to attack a new pest following detection increases the difficulties in handling the problem, and may even result in abandoning a cooperative effort if the situation gets out of hand. This can result in placing the entire responsibility for suppression upon farmers over increasingly larger areas where host crops are being produced.

Usually this is a heavy burden for the farmer to bear. Current consumer standards demand freedom from pest blemish or contamination; fruits and vegetables must be essentially insect-free before they are acceptable to the modern housewife. In today's age of commodity grades and quality standards, a producer must strive towards high quality produce in order to demand the prices that will make his farming operation profitable.

TO RECEIVE sufficient return for his efforts the farmer must suppress a variety of plant pests by including cultural, biological, or chemical control practices in his production procedures. New pests make his job a lot tougher, and his costs higher. He must avoid excess pesticide residues, staying within legal limits. Penalties for failure are extremely severe.

There have been times when these increased production costs or the nature of the insect, plant disease, or nematode have forced abandonment of a crop. The boll weevil forced growers of long-staple cotton in the Southeast out of that variety of fiber. Potatogrowers in England can produce a crop of potatoes but once every 4 or 5 years because of the golden nematode.

When it is possible, therefore, to protect large areas of the country from a plant pest by confining an attack on a new problem to a local area, Federal and State pest control agencies quickly join their forces to do so.

Problems involving agricultural plant pests are handled in the U.S. Department of Agriculture under the authority of its Organic Act, the Plant Quarantine Act of 1912, and other legislation, by the Plant Pest Control Division of the Agricultural Research Service.

When a pest of foreign origin is first found in the United States, State and Federal agricultural agencies must reach a prompt decision on the best ways of handling the situation. The subsequent action may have far-reaching effects. It may impinge on the economy of a local area, a State, a region, or perhaps the entire country.

Planning must from the beginning be based upon the soundest biological and other factors available, even though background information at the time may leave something to be desired.

OVER THE YEARS the Agriculture Department has maintained cooperative agreements with the States to provide machinery and lines of communications for gathering, compiling, and reporting pest abundance data. This system is geared to report the early discovery of new insect pests that may be capable of creating extensive damage.

Under the agreements each State provides a central point to which pest information is funneled continually. Each year thousands of records of insect pest occurrence and abundance are processed and made public in State and national releases.

WHEN INSECTS are unfamiliar to field observers, specimens are collected and identified. Specimens may be identified by specialists in the States, but where this is not possible they are sent to the National Museum in Washington for determination as to species. Those new to this country are always verified by Federal specialists, and the information is passed on to the appropriate State and Federal officials.

Each year a hundred or more new species of insects, plant diseases, and nematodes are uncovered and classified through this and other survey and

259

detection efforts. Fortunately, most of these new records concern species with little or no economic importance. However, some insects not known to occur here are regarded as particularly harmful, and attention in the detection effort is principally focused on them.

In recent years a number of new pest species have turned up in the United States that have threatened to create additional burdens on producers and, in turn, on consumers. In each case prompt detection has enabled the State plant protection agencies and the Plant Pest Control Division to minimize their impact.

The khapra beetle, a despoiler of stored feed and food products, was discovered in a grain warehouse in southern California in 1953. This beetle occurs generally throughout much of the world except in North America. It is one of the most destructive grain pests as well as one of the most difficult to kill.

Following its establishment here and despite early regulatory and eradication efforts, the khapra beetle spread into Arizona, New Mexico, eastern Texas, and Mexico before it could be brought fully under control. By 1965 there were no known infestations on the North American Continent despite a continuing record number of interceptions at many ports of entry in the United States, Canada, and Mexico.

Khapra beetle and larvae infestation of spaghetti. The khapra beetle is called the world's worst pest of stored grain and grain products.

THE MEDITERRANEAN fruit fly is one of the most feared and destructive citrus pests in subtropical areas throughout much of the world. It first appeared in the United States in Florida in 1929, invading 20 southern counties before it was eradicated. It showed up for the second time in Florida in 1956. The Medfly was successfully banished from Florida in about 18 months following a massive cooperative eradication and regulatory campaign.

Constant vigilance through cooperative trapping work uncovered subsequent introductions in 1962 and 1963. These were also eliminated—each time more expeditiously due to the fact that discovery was made shortly after reentry, which denied the fly the time necessary for population expansion and spread.

The melon fly, a serious pest of citrus and vegetables, appeared in the Los Angeles area in 1956.

Constant vigilance in cooperation with the State of California permitted early discovery of the melon fly and its subsequent elimination.

WHILE IT IS OFTEN possible to deal with some species aggressively and to eliminate them, many pests such as witchweed and the cereal leaf beetle are much more stubborn.

Witchweed—a parasitic plant attacking corn, sorghum, and sugarcane—was found in this country for the first time in 1956 in contiguous counties in North Carolina and South Carolina. It is of South African origin. Without some sort of control, a profitable crop cannot be grown if witchweed attacks it.

THE PARASITE attaches itself to the roots of host plants from which it obtains nourishment, depleting the benefactor of vigor. Each witchweed plant produces some 50,000 to 500,000 microscopic seeds that may remain dormant in the absence of its hosts for as long as 20 years.

In addition to attacking commercially valuable hosts, witchweed attacks weeds like crabgrass, so that seed production goes on even in the absence of corn or of other economically desirable plants.

Although witchweed is one of the most difficult plant pests to combat, cooperative regulatory and control action has prevented the pattern and area of infestation from increasing geographically beyond those Carolina counties where it was discovered.

The principal corn growing areas in the Midwest and cane production in the South have been spared the costly and troublesome chore of annual control. What's more, intensive suppressive work has reduced witchweed seed production to a minimum, permitting profitable corn culture in its presence.

OTHER PLANT PESTS create similar tough problems. The cereal leaf beetle was first discovered in southern Michigan and northern Indiana in 1962. It is a pest of grain, particularly oats, and seriously impairs or prevents the production of host crops without some type of control program.

Following its discovery the beetle caused severe damage at the focal points of infestation. In some cases its depredations were severe enough to cause some growers to plow up their grainfields and accept a complete loss for that particular season.

Incomplete research data brought about by insufficient foreign references and the lack of time necessary to obtain pertinent data in this country has made containment of the cereal leaf beetle a tremendously difficult task.

Yet progress has been made and long-distance spread of the beetle is being averted, while new information is being developed that may lead to far more effective control.

Following the discovery and positive identification of a plant pest intruder from beyond U.S. borders, a determination must be made on the potential economic damage which the species may inflict upon the agricultural community.

This requires a review of available domestic and foreign literature, and also consultation with biologists and research scientists—both in the United States and in other countries.

Over the years, more and more background information on species not known to exist in the United States is being collected and made available. Much information has been cataloged for ready reference as needed.

This is important data. On it, and on the familiarity of research scientists all over the world, may hinge the determination of whether a species will create a serious impact on our Nation's agricultural economy.

As important as this information is, however, it must be tempered by the fact that often relatively insignificant pests react far differently in a new environment. Sometimes this is because the intruder doesn't bring along the parasites and predators that normally impinge on its development. In other cases a species may adapt to its new home more favorably because of genetic changes or of environmental conditions more to its liking.

ONE OF THE MOST spectacular adjustments to a new environment was the recent adaptation of the boll weevil to more arid areas in the Southwest, long thought to be a barrier to its spread from the Southeast where it settled many years before.

This adaptation has provoked a new look at the boll weevil problem, with particular focus on the extensive noninfested cotton-growing areas in southern New Mexico, Arizona, and southern California. Cooperative fall insecticide treatment programs have been undertaken in both areas to create a barrier zone free of overwintering weevils. Repeated treatments prior to frost are designed to eliminate weevil populations that are preparing to overwinter.

ONCE A NEW PEST is determined capable of doing extensive damage to its host crop, consideration must then be given to the host crop's value to the economy of the United States. Obviously, an enemy of a nonessential crop does not get the same attention

as one attacking a more economically important host. The value of the host crop, the degree of damage the new pest may be expected to cause, and the costs of control provide an estimate of the impact of the species on agriculture.

DURING THE APPRAISAL process, information is gathered on the availability of control, eradication, or regulatory measures that might be employed if a decision is made to take cooperative action. In many cases up-to-date information is not at hand and the State and Federal research agencies are then called on to provide it.

If the expected benefits are not sufficiently great, compared with the initial and continuing costs of confinement and suppression, the matter may be dropped after consultation with State regulatory agencies.

But even in the absence of cooperative containment and control programs, State and Federal agencies frequently undertake research aimed at simplifying the control problem for producers. Sometimes their efforts alter the cost-benefit relationship to the extent that regulatory people may once again become interested and finally establish corrective programs.

ASSUMING THE PROBLEM appears to call for cooperative action to prevent spread of the pest, or to seek suppression or eradication, the problem is reviewed by Federal officials with cooperating agencies, both State and private. These include organizations like producer and industrial associations.

In the United States there are four Regional Plant Boards composed of representatives from the State agencies with responsibility in plant protection. The National Plant Board consists of two members elected from each of the four regional boards.

These organizations meet annually and on special call to discuss mutual plant protection interests. Membership of the plant boards is kept constantly advised of developments involving newly introduced plant pests.

As a matter of fact, preliminary

plans are usually developed by Plant Pest Control Division personnel with the State regulatory officials residing in the area where a new pest discovery is made. From the review with the Regional or National Plant Board evolves a recommendation for joint action.

Since these problems generally concern insects, plant diseases, or nematodes of foreign origin inhabiting only a portion of their potential range in this country, initial efforts are designed to restrict further movement of the pest. This requires development of State or Federal quarantines which provide the legal basis for regulating the movement of commodities capable of spreading the pest through normal channels of trade.

FEDERAL QUARANTINES and often those administered by States require public hearings before they may be adopted. If a Federal quarantine is in order, a notice of hearing is published in the Federal Register seeking the views of interested parties on the need for it.

At the hearing the Agriculture Department presents facts about the discovery and gives information on the biology of the pest, its potential destructiveness, the estimated area involved, and the commodities that may be placed under regulation.

The interested States, the affected industry, or anyone else wishing to be heard place their views in the record. These views are studied before the Department makes its determination of whether a Federal plant quarantine should be put into effect.

ONCE A QUARANTINE is decided upon, public notice is given and administrative instructions issued outlining the specific areas to be regulated.

The instructions describe the regulated commodities. They also exempt from certification types of articles that present no pest risk. For instance, manufactured timber products are exempt from the gypsy moth quarantine, while timber with bark attached must be certified prior to movement into nonquarantined areas. This is because gypsy moth eggs are laid on the bark of trees. Where the bark is removed during sawing or manufacturing, there is no hazard in the movement of the finished wood products.

WHEN A QUARANTINE has been established, Federal and State inspectors make sure that all quarantine-affected commodities destined to move outside the regulated area are free from living forms of the pest, before the commodities are certified for movement.

Many articles besides agricultural commodities may require certification for movement under domestic plant quarantines. Among them are cable reels, farm machinery, and soil.

The kinds of regulated articles depend, of course, on whether they can serve as carriers to spread the pest. Quarry products in the Northeast provide an excellent vehicle for transportation of eggs of the gypsy moth. Scrap iron or junk in the Southeast can carry hitchhiking eggs of the white-fringed beetle. Farm machinery and other vehicles often become contaminated with soil-infesting organisms such as the golden or soybean cyst nematodes. Equipment used for harvesting cotton can carry pink bollworm larvae from place to place.

AIRCRAFT may transport adults of pests that spend part of their life cycle underground in turfed areas. Three of the most important of these potential plane passengers are the Japanese beetle, the white-fringed beetle, and the European chafer.

This urge to hitchhike by air has prompted efforts by the Federal Government, the States, and airport authorities to treat the grassy portions of landing fields and environs to deny these species their nearby breeding grounds.

CONTROL OF THE MOVEMENT of infestable articles from areas under regulation has become a complicated and time-consuming effort. It taxes the ingenuity of State and Federal officials to keep abreast of the many avenues of

263

escape and to adopt countermeasures to avoid it. They must make sure that commodities and other regulated articles moving into free areas are in a certifiable condition and yet provide this service without greatly impeding the normal flow of commercial traffic.

ERADICATION is most aggressively sought if it can be obtained safely with the available tools at hand.

Success stories in elimination of pests include the khapra beetle, which has been virtually eradicated from the North American Continent. Eradication of the Mediterranean fruit fly from the United States has been accomplished four times. Hall scale, a serious pest of nuts and stone fruits in California, has been eliminated. Citrus canker, a disease of citrus in the Southeast, was banished many years ago. And the golden nematode, among the world's most destructive pests of potatoes and tomatoes, is well on its way towards elimination from the only known U.S. infestation, on Long Island.

Once eradication is accomplished, the quarantine can then be lifted.

IN PEST CONTROL PROGRAMS advantage is taken of all known control methods. While chemicals appear most often in the plant protection operator's arsenal, other techniques also are gaining in prominence.

Regulations governing cotton planting and stalk destruction in some areas in the Far South have for many years provided long winter host-free periods which have proved exceedingly effective in keeping the pink bollworm of cotton in check.

Moths continuing to emerge throughout much of the winter have been denied available hosts on which to reproduce their kind.

Only in those years where cultural practices break down does the pink bollworm develop in sufficient numbers to cause appreciable injury; yet it is one of the world's most feared cotton pests. When buildups occur, during the summer large numbers of adult pink bollworms can be carried by the

wind into previously uninfested cotton hundreds of miles away.

The sterile male technique was put on an operational basis in 1964 to prevent the Mexican fruit fly from establishing a solid foothold in southwestern California and northwestern Mexico. It involves multiple releases of sterile male flies in overpowering numbers into the natural population. As normal females mated with sterile males produce infertile eggs, the chances of self preservation are remote.

This technique has been highly effective. It has superseded the arduous and unpopular task of making multiple applications of insecticide following the periodic reappearance of the flies in fruit that evades quarantine barriers.

FOLLOWING THE discovery of an effective synthetic gypsy moth sex attractant, a systematic aerial trap drop procedure was initiated in 1964. Specially designed traps were dropped on a grid pattern at one-sixteenth of a mile intervals. These traps are so constructed that male moths attracted to them cannot escape and are thus not available to mate with females in the native population. Because the male moths generally precede female emergence, this effort is aimed at depleting the male population in sparsely infested or isolated areas.

The technique is designed to make it more difficult for the moth, a destructive hardwood forest pest, to sustain itself. Increasingly greater emphasis has been placed on the rearing and redistribution of gypsy moth parasites and predators to deplete low population densities even more.

UNFORTUNATELY, biological or cultural control won't always do the job. Chemicals still remain essential tools in keeping pest populations in check, particularly where efforts are being made to eliminate outlying focal points of infestation remote from those generally infested and under regulation.

Where chemical pesticides are required in cooperative control programs, operational plans are submitted to the Federal Committee on Pest Control for concurrence or for suggestions.

The Committee was established in 1961—it was then called the Federal Pest Control Review Board—through an agreement between the Secretaries of Agriculture; Interior; Health, Education, and Welfare; and Defense. High level officials from each Department are appointed to the Committee and they meet frequently to review the work of all agencies in Government where pesticidal chemicals are used to meet program objectives.

Representatives of the operating units in each of the agencies appear before the Committee each year to discuss their treatment plans. Besides covering program objectives and the need for such activities, their review also goes over in detail the areas involved, kinds and dosages of chemicals to be used, the methods of application, and the safeguards which are to be observed.

IN MANY INSTANCES the review outlines the agency's intention to cooperate with other Federal, State, or local agencies. Particular reference is made to monitoring possible side effects that may result from the use of pesticides.

Virtually all the plant protection efforts in which the Agriculture Department cooperates with the States, and which use significant amounts of pesticides, are being monitored. Monitoring is directed towards determining any likely impact of the pesticide on fish and game, beneficial insects, water, and public health. State and private agencies such as privately endowed chemical diagnostic laboratories are engaged to make the observations.

COOPERATIVE PLANT PEST control programs are carried on under the supervision of the trained and experienced Federal and State plant protection personnel.

When aircraft are used to apply insecticides, rigid specifications are set forth in the contracts with the operators. Aircraft must not only meet Federal Aviation Agency specifica-

tions, they must also conform to Agriculture Department requirements that are carefully checked by plant pest control specialists.

Pilot qualifications are spelled out regarding experience in aerial spraying work. Tests are made to assure proper application rates. Each batch of the pesticide to be used is tested to assure its composition meets the standards in the purchase specifications.

Plant pest control aerial supervisors observe the operation and immediately ground any operator who does not carry out the job properly.

THE PLANT PEST Control Division of the Agriculture Department cooperates with State authorities on 22 programs to prevent the spread of imported agricultural pests from their restricted areas of infestation. These programs involve not only insects and plant diseases, but nematodes as well.

The Department's cooperative work on grasshoppers and Mormon crickets differs from these other programs.

Many species of grasshoppers are native to North America and outbreaks periodically do great damage to rangeland grass and agricultural crops. The Agriculture Department's cooperative work on grasshoppers is limited to the suppression of outbreaks that occur periodically in large numbers on the extensive low-value rangelands in the Western States. Much of this is in the Federal domain.

Grasshoppers can decimate the grass and browse over large grazing areas. Winged adults of some species migrate long distances, laying waste to everything edible in their paths when they alight to feed in new areas of crops or of rangelands.

When buildups are imminent the ranchers, States, and the Federal Government share the expense of suppression to avoid depletion of the range and prevent migration to previously unaffected areas. Some years this is an extensive operation; in others, relatively small acreage is involved. It depends on whether conditions during the year favor grasshopper development.

VETERINARY

BIOLOGICS

JOHN M. HEJL

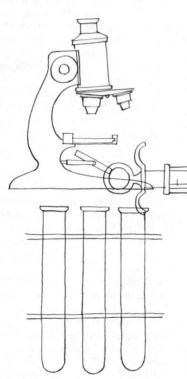

USING diseases against disease—that's one way we keep our herds and flocks healthy, and assure the consumer that the meat, milk, and eggs he purchases are good to eat.

Veterinary biologics do the job, and revolutionary new techniques are commonplace. Biologics are made from the organisms, or derivatives, that cause the livestock and poultry diseases they help diagnose, prevent, or treat.

Making sure that biologics are both safe and effective is the mission of the Veterinary Biologics Division of the Agricultural Research Service.

This mission is most important to the consumer, whose food supply is safeguarded, and to the livestock and poultry industry, which produces about $50 billion of livestock and livestock products each year.

Animal protein currently makes up the major part of our diets. The demand for livestock products will become much greater as our population swells and as more and more people learn about proper nutrition.

IN PROVIDING the millions of steaks and broilers needed, the U.S. producer may have to deal with 58 animal diseases—that's the number we know enough about to take action against. Many of the diseases are highly contagious, and can wipe out our herds and flocks if unchecked.

The producer's weapons against disease include biologics—vaccines, serums, bacterins—and drugs. The producer must know they are safe and will do the job. In this he relies on the integrity of the manufacturer and the watchful concern of Federal agencies.

Poorly produced biologics and drugs can be unsafe or useless. These are concerns that are shared by the producer, manufacturer, consumer, and the Federal Government.

John M. Hejl is *Director* of the Veterinary Biologics Division, Agricultural Research Service.

THE ANIMAL Virus-Serum-Toxin Act of March 4, 1913, authorizes the Secretary of Agriculture to regulate animal biologics. The Federal Food, Drug, and Cosmetic Act authorizes the Secretary of Health, Education, and Welfare to regulate animal drugs. Animal biologics are usually immunological—pertaining to immunity—in nature, while animal drugs are usually proprietary—medicine, chemical, or similar preparations—in nature. Regulation of animal drugs by the Food and Drug Administration of HEW is described in another chapter.

THE VIRUS-SERUM-TOXIN ACT provides that vaccines, serums, toxins, or similar biologics marketed interstate must be produced under a U.S. Veterinary License issued by the Secretary of Agriculture. No products may be marketed if worthless, contaminated, dangerous, or harmful; they must be safe, pure, and effective.

The act provides for inspection of establishments and the biologics which they are licensed to produce.

The Secretary of Agriculture is authorized to develop regulations to carry out the Virus-Serum-Toxin Act. The Veterinary Biologics Division is responsible for administering the regulatory program in the U.S. Department of Agriculture.

The regulatory process for animal biologics begins when the manufacturer applies to the Secretary of Agriculture for a license. The application must list the establishment's name and address, names of company officers, the biologic itself, and estimated annual production. It must be signed by an authorized officer of the firm. By the officer's signature, the firm agrees to observe the regulations.

THE APPLICANT must show his facilities are adequate to produce biologics. Facility blueprints are submitted, giving construction, plumbing, drainage, sewage, and other details. They include floor plans of laboratory rooms and the general building layout. A plot plan of the premises showing plant buildings and the nature and use of adjoining properties is also required. All equipment and its location are listed, along with the kinds of products to be handled in each room.

In addition the applicant must describe his methods of producing and testing the biologic, giving procedures in complete detail.

WITH THE APPLICATION must come copies of labels, package literature, and claims to be made in advertising or other promotional material.

Labels have to show the name of the product; container contents in liquid, solid, or potency measurements; dosage and direction for use; serial number; the expiration date; establishment license number; name and address; and warnings to keep the product under refrigeration, not to save unused contents, and so on as required.

Labels and package literature may show other information as long as it is not false or misleading.

Advertising claims have to be based upon supporting data.

Research data are submitted to prove the safety and the effectiveness of the biologic.

Data must include how the product was developed, and results of testing it under laboratory conditions. Results of field testing under controlled experiments also are supplied.

The burden of proof is on the manufacturer for the quality and safety of the biologics. Samples may be requested if Veterinary Biologics Division tests are needed to aid licensing decisions.

UNTIL IT IS LICENSED, the biologic is called an experimental product. Distribution for field evaluation is not authorized by the Division unless the prior laboratory work indicates the product to be safe and of value. The manufacturer must also obtain the consent of State veterinarians in States where the product will be field checked. The biologic must be labeled "For Experimental Use—Not for Sale."

A license is not issued until it is found the applicant is a bona fide

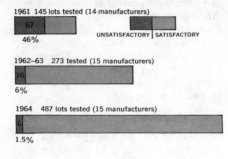

1961 145 lots tested (14 manufacturers)

67

46% UNSATISFACTORY | SATISFACTORY

1962–63 273 tested (15 manufacturers)

16

6%

1964 487 lots tested (15 manufacturers)

6

1.5%

manufacturer, his facilities adequate, and his professional staff competent and experienced in biologics production. In addition, methods of production and testing must conform to standards, labels and advertising comply with regulations, and the research data show the product to be safe, pure, and effective.

If a license is denied, the applicant is given the reasons and a list of needed corrective measures. The Division may prescribe certain tests, give technical guidance, or suggest more research to further evaluate the product. Most manufacturers' tests and field experiments are observed by Division field veterinarians.

AFTER A PRODUCT is licensed, it receives inspection and testing surveillance from the Veterinary Biologics Division. All production lots of licensed biologics must be tested for sterility, safety, and effectiveness by manufacturers, and found satisfactory before marketing. The Division prescribes methods for testing, and sets standards

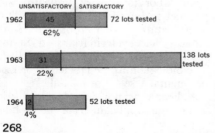

BOVINE RHINOTRACHEITIS Vaccine Testing

UNSATISFACTORY | SATISFACTORY

1962 45 72 lots tested

62%

1963 31 138 lots tested

22%

1964 2 52 lots tested

4%

for the release of biologics based on the test results.

Inspection of licensed establishments is on a continuing basis. Division veterinarians assigned to the biologics inspection program operate from a field headquarters in Ames, Iowa.

The manufacturer's records of production, results of his tests, and samples of each production lot are sent to this headquarters. Records of production and testing are reviewed.

Checks on the validity of records, tests, and samples are made by unannounced visits to the establishments. Thorough inspections are made of production and testing methods, and the adequacy of production, testing, and distribution records. Personnel and sanitary practices are also reviewed.

EFFECTIVENESS of the inspection program is greatly enhanced by the Veterinary Biologics Division's own ability to test commercially produced biologics. Division tests check on validity of the manufacturer's tests. Capability of the Division to develop new methods for evaluating biologics also improves the program's effectiveness.

The Division has a laboratory unit at the National Animal Disease Laboratory at Ames, Iowa. The unit checks products to detect problem areas that manufacturers may have in producing and testing biologics.

SAMPLES OF all lots produced under license are sent and held under refrigeration at the Ames inspection headquarters. Many of these samples are tested by the Division.

Priority is given to testing products used in national disease eradication programs. An example is *Brucella abortus* vaccine used against brucellosis. Others are pullorum antigens used to detect pullorum disease in poultry, tuberculin used to detect tuberculosis, and hog-cholera serum and vaccines.

Testing priorities for other biologics are based on the demand for the biologics by veterinarians and livestock and poultry raisers.

Products found unsatisfactory before

licensing are not marketed, of course. Products that are found unsatisfactory on reexamination after licensing are immediately recalled from marketing channels.

TEST SCHEDULES are designed so two or three lots of each product produced by each manufacturer are tested at the same time. If test results show a lot to be unsatisfactory, more samples of that firm's products are scheduled for further testing. Thus, the firm's tests are checked, problem areas or weaknesses in production and testing detected, and laboratory support and information provided for the field inspection program.

Inspection is coordinated with laboratory testing. To correct lab-detected faults at the plant level, inspectors visit the firms to observe production and testing.

If the fault is in testing methods, on the spot corrections are made. If the trouble is in production, the manufacturer is advised. It is his responsibility to correct the faulty methods.

Until the manufacturer can adequately demonstrate his ability to again produce a safe and effective product, marketing is prohibited.

THE EFFECTIVENESS of biologics is best shown by testing them with the type of animals on which they are to be used by the farmer—the host animals. A group of host animals is treated with the product under test. Later, along with a set of untreated control animals, they are exposed to the disease the product should protect against. A product is satisfactory if the untreated control animals sicken or die from the disease, while the treated animals survive and remain well.

Laboratory and laboratory animal tests also can be used. However, the scientific validity of these tests must be determined first.

The value of certain products can be determined only by tests in host animals. Most others can be tested by laboratory procedures or in host or laboratory animals.

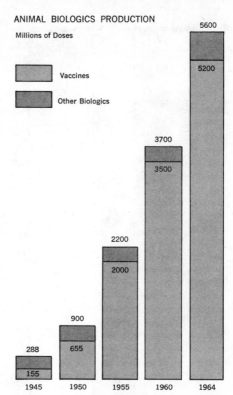

ANIMAL BIOLOGICS PRODUCTION
Millions of Doses

Vaccines

Other Biologics

| | 288 | 900 | 2200 | 3700 | 5600 |
| 1945 | 1950 | 1955 | 1960 | 1964 |

(155 / 655 / 2000 / 3500 / 5200)

Testing costs vary greatly. It may cost $500 to $5,000 to test a product in cattle or swine. A test in mice or guinea pigs may cost as little as $50.

The total testing cost is reflected in the purchase price of biologics. Less costly tests obviously are preferred, especially because of the vast quantities of products produced and tested. About 15,000 lots of over 5 billion doses of animal vaccines, serums, bacterins, and similar products are produced and tested annually.

MANY CHANGES have occurred in evolution of the veterinary biologics program to its present form. Production has risen from 288 million doses in 1945 to 5.6 billion doses in 1964, an increase of 2,000 percent.

Before 1950, products regulated under the Virus-Serum-Toxin Act were a small variety of serums, and inactivated virus and bacterial vaccines. These were produced and tested under methods

269

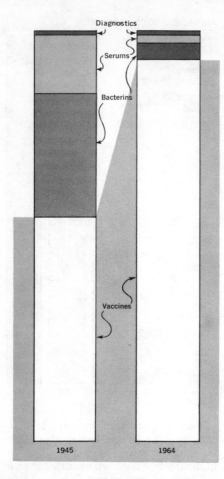

Diagnostics

Serums

Bacterins

Vaccines

1945   1964

sheep, and many other animal diseases.

Another development is the production of modified live virus vaccines on tissue culture. Tissue culture vaccines to date have proved superior to other kinds in quality. These vaccines also are cheaper to produce.

Live and modified live virus vaccines have increased from 155 million doses in 1945 to 5.2 billion doses in 1964. Vaccines now account for 93 percent of the total veterinary biologics production.

OTHER CHANGES occurred in biologics testing methods. Prior to 1950, each manufacturer devised his own. After the licensing of modified live virus vaccines, there soon were as many kinds of test methods as establishments producing the vaccines.

Uniform test methods for comparing each firm's products and to assure that each product exceeded minimum standards were lacking.

Uniformity in testing was needed for the Agriculture Department to meet its responsibility under the Virus-Serum-Toxin Act.

At the time the Veterinary Biologics Division had no laboratory facilities for the job. But by working with industry scientists, reviewing scientific literature, and consulting with scientists at universities, the Division initiated development and enforcement of standard test requirements for some of the licensed vaccines.

After the Division acquired laboratory facilities in 1961, great progress was made in improving and validating existing standards and developing new ones. Today over 50 standards are in effect. Many more are being developed.

TODAY'S BIOLOGICS used in diagnosing, preventing, and treating animal diseases are the best science can offer. Nowhere in the world are there better products to be found.

Millions of dollars are spent each year in research to improve existing products and develop new ones.

And our forward-looking farmers are making good use of these weapons against animal disease.

developed many years previous. Progress in biologics had remained static. And most of the products were only mediocre in their effectiveness.

About 1955 striking changes took place in the development of new kinds of veterinary biologics. Advancements were made to change the nature of live viruses by adapting and growing viruses in chicken embryos, unnatural hosts like rabbits, and by other ingenious methods. With the new techniques, disease-producing potential of the viruses was eliminated but their immunizing ability was retained.

THESE PRODUCTS, known as modified live virus vaccines, are now used to prevent hog cholera in swine, rabies in dogs and cattle, bluetongue in

JUSTUS C. WARD

A DYNAMIC

STATUTE

FOR

PESTICIDES

Justus C. Ward served as *Director* of the Pesticides Regulation Division, Agricultural Research Service from 1957 to July 1966.

IT may surprise you to learn that many pesticides have been subject to Federal and State regulations for more than half a century.

The first Federal statute involving pesticides was the Insecticide Act of 1910. This law was passed during a drive to stop unethical persons from merchandising ineffective or adulterated products. In fact, the law was described as "An Act for preventing the manufacture, sale, or transportation of adulterated or misbranded Paris greens, lead arsenates, and other insecticides, and also fungicides, and for regulating traffic therein, and for other purposes."

It also required that labels carry the name of the manufacturer or distributor, an ingredient statement in proper form, and a net weight declaration.

The act provided regulations describing how it should be enforced.

For example, the regulations stipulated that samples be collected only by official inspectors. They were to make investigations to locate shipments of products which might be in violation of the law, and obtain shipping records needed in order to establish that interstate movement of the products had taken place.

The regulations outlined how a product should be examined to determine whether or not it and its labeling were in compliance with the law. They stated that the methods of testing might include chemical, microscopical, physical, and bacteriological methods, and tests in orchard, field, garden, and greenhouse, on animals, in or around premises, in cages, in the laboratory, and in any other necessary areas.

The regulations provided that when examination of a product showed it to be adulterated or misbranded under the law, the shipper was to be notified in writing and given an opportunity to provide an explanation. It was clearly stated, however, that when a shipment was to be seized no such hearing would be required.

Finally, the regulations explained how legal actions were to be handled. The U.S. Department of Agriculture

271

was to request the Attorney General of the United States to institute appropriate legal action, except where delay would risk losing effective action on a proposed seizure. In the latter situation, the Secretary of Agriculture was authorized to communicate directly with the U.S. District Attorney in the jurisdiction where the illegal goods were located.

FROM 1910 UNTIL World War II the pesticide evolution in the chemical age was a very slow and deliberate process. New means of controlling insects did not appear frequently and even new fungicides were hard for the research specialists to find.

Consequently, regulatory officials had little trouble in keeping up with developments. And since the law did not cover evaluation of hazards of the economic poisons it controlled, chemical analysis was the most important enforcement procedure.

In that period there was little public concern about these useful chemicals. There was a rather general feeling that pests needed to be controlled and usually the best way to do the job was with one of the economic poisons. Effective protection against the health hazard or the economic damage caused by the pest was the principal factor considered.

As a logical consequence of that emphasis, the Insecticide Act of 1910 was most useful in protecting the public against the possible loss of crops or damage to property from useless and misbranded products.

During an era when arsenicals, fluorides, nicotine, rotenone, and related simple products were the primary pesticides, this law was adequate. And it provided the foundation for all of the modern improvements in the Federal pesticide laws.

As WARTIME chemical discoveries began to be adapted to civilian use during the later years of World War II and the use of pesticides increased, it very soon became obvious that new and stronger laws were needed.

272

The Agriculture Department took the initiative in preparing legislation. Help came first from the U.S. Department of the Interior, which strongly endorsed the inclusion of rodenticides—or rodent killers—in the new law. And invaluable assistance came from the pesticide industry. The industry realized the time for modernizing Federal laws had arrived.

As a result of careful and extensive cooperation, the Federal Insecticide, Fungicide, and Rodenticide Act (FIFRA) was passed, and signed into law on June 25, 1947.

THIS LAW extended the principle that a pesticidal formulation should meet proper standards. Among those standards was still the presence on the label of the name and address of the manufacturer or distributor, an informative ingredient statement, a net weight or a volume declaration, and accurate instructions for use. In addition, an adequate caution was required.

All of these standards dealt with the pesticide as it was accepted for interstate shipment and public sale. No other Federal law has authority over the pesticide itself and its labeling.

The Pesticide Chemicals Amendment to the Federal Food, Drug, and Cosmetic Act—an amendment passed in 1954—deals with the safety of food on which pesticides have been used, but that law has no control over the pesticidal formulation as does FIFRA.

FIFRA RETAINED key portions of the Insecticide Act of 1910, and it added two new ideas.

First, all pesticides intended for shipment in interstate commerce must be registered with the Secretary of Agriculture before shipment. Second, the Agriculture Department was given control over all precautionary statements in the labeling of pesticides—in other words, the review of the safety features so important in the proper use of the chemicals.

Registration requirement promptly stopped introduction of untested products into interstate pesticide retail marketing. This was done simply by applying the general provision in the statute which required that labeling be adequate—when complied with—to protect the public.

This was made very effective by refusing to register any product without proper labeling supported by scientific data on performance, composition, and safety. Since shipment of an unregistered pesticide was a violation of the law, withholding of registration was found to be a rather effective way of stopping shipment of untried economic poisons.

UNDER THE NEW LAW, registration could be withheld until data was supplied to prove that the pesticide would give the degree of pest control claimed or implied on the label.

Registration could also be held up to await submission of adequate toxicological evidence to prove the product could be used safely when all cautions on the label were followed.

And finally, extensive chemical residue studies had to be supplied and summarized to show the product could be used as directed on a specific food crop without leaving illegal residues before a use on a food could be registered. An "illegal residue" is any detectable amount of a pesticide on a food unless that amount is the same as or less than a "tolerance" established by the Food and Drug Administration.

The law covers pest control products which are used in agriculture for the production and protection of food crops and meat animals.

It covers products used in the home to control destructive, disease-bearing, and nuisance insects, rodents, molds, mildews, and bacteria.

FIFRA covers materials used in the general environment to destroy unwanted fish and undesirable wildlife; and to repel mosquitoes, ticks, lice, and other vermin from the human body and from pets and livestock.

And it also covers chemicals used to modify plant growth and to desiccate or defoliate plants to aid in harvesting a crop with machines. The value of desiccants and defoliants in mechanical harvesting is due to the fact that the desiccants dry up the plant tissues and the defoliants cause the leaves to fall off, thus keeping those unwanted plant parts out of the combines and out of the cottonpickers.

Sometimes the data needed to justify registration of a pesticide are extensive, but it must all be studied carefully by the Government regulatory scientist.

REGISTRATION CONTROL provides the best present means under Federal law for preventing the distribution of inadequately labeled, ineffective, or unsafe pesticides.

However, FIFRA has no control over the actual user of the product. Its major protection of the public comes from the strict control over every feature of labeling. It leaves with the user the responsibility for reading and following the label, if he is to avoid future difficulty.

Misuse is just as dangerous when the product being handled is a pesticide as it is with a drug, a household chemical, a gun, or an automobile.

DURING THE EARLY YEARS of FIFRA, questions arose repeatedly on the need for expanding its coverage. So on August 7, 1959, Congress amended the law to include nematocides, defoliants, desiccants, and plant regulators. Plant regulators are the chemicals which will change the way in which a plant grows—for example, the chemicals which prevent "fruit drop," as well as those which "thin" the fruit set, are plant regulators.

Symbol developed by USDA to encourage safe and effective use of pesticides.

Use Pesticides Safely

FOLLOW THE LABEL

274

This amendment was sponsored both by the trade and interested Government departments. It merely recognized legally that these agricultural chemicals deserved controls similar to those in effect on insecticides, rodenticides, and other economic poisons, since all these chemicals moved in the same channels of trade to the very same customers.

This broadened scope of the law, however, did not satisfy Fish and Wildlife Service (FWS) officials who had long urged that chemicals sold for control of moles, birds, predatory animals, and other forms of nonrodent wildlife pests be covered by FIFRA. Study of the FWS proposal resulted in inclusion of these pesticides under the law by a Secretary of Agriculture's "declaration of pests" dated March 27, 1962. This action completed the act's coverage.

BECAUSE OF THE LAW'S wide range of coverage, specialists in other governmental agencies can often give advice on the complex registration problems that may arise.

With this in mind, administrative officials responsible for enforcing the law set up informal lines of liaison with other departments as early as the years 1949 and 1950.

Pharmacologists of the Agriculture Department became responsible for contact with Food and Drug Administration (FDA) pharmacologists and with medical officers of the Public Health Service (PHS). Bacteriologists of the Agriculture Department worked directly with those of FDA and PHS.

Rodent control officials at Agriculture established liaison with research specialists studying pest mammal control in the Fish and Wildlife Service. And, finally, Agriculture biologists conferred frequently with fishery and wildlife personnel in that Service.

In this way, regulatory scientists of the Agriculture Department kept informed on the thinking of experts in other Departments. However, the technicians in these other Departments could only give advice on registration matters and had no legal obligation to develop data which could be used for enforcement purposes under FIFRA, since administration of the law was centered in the Agriculture Department by Congress.

BETWEEN 1947 AND 1957 several actions were taken with far-reaching effects on the regulation of pesticides.

The first of these was not related directly to FIFRA. It came from the yearlong hearing held in 1950 by FDA on pesticides in food. The hearing's purpose was to obtain the essential scientific data upon which official tolerances for specific pesticides on food crops could be based.

Soon after these hearings were completed, a select committee of the House of Representatives was appointed with Congressman Delaney of New York as Chairman to investigate chemicals in food and in cosmetics.

The Delaney committee held extensive hearings in 1950 and 1951 and learned that while pesticides were essential to insure an adequate and nutritious food supply for the American public, they could be misused with very serious results.

The committee also decided that a better way to establish tolerances on food crops was needed, and assumed the initiative to find that way. Congressman Miller of Nebraska, a member of the Delaney committee, took primary interest in the search.

AS A RESULT of these two series of hearings and the findings of the Delaney committee, the second major development of the decade came with passage in 1954 of the Pesticide Chemicals Amendment to the Federal Food, Drug, and Cosmetic Act, an amendment mentioned briefly before.

Under this amendment a "pesticide chemical" means any substance which alone, in chemical combination, or in formulation with one or more other substances, is an "economic poison" within the meaning of FIFRA as now in force or as hereafter amended, and which is used in the production, the

storage, or the transportation of raw agricultural commodities.

This amendment revised the cumbersome "Hearing" procedures for the obtaining of tolerances which were a part of the basic food and drug law and it assigned two functions to the Agriculture Department.

The first of these functions required the Secretary of Agriculture, or his designated representative, to certify to the FDA that the chemical for which a petition for tolerance had been filed would be useful for the purposes described. The second required the Agriculture Department to express an opinion as to whether the tolerance requested reasonably reflected the residues likely to remain upon the treated food crop when the chemical was used as directed.

THIS AMENDMENT was a change in a food and drug law and did not modify the wording of the FIFRA.

It actually made few immediate changes in the existing registrations. This was because during the period from 1947 to the year the Food and Drug amendment became effective, in 1955, registrations of food crop pesticides had been based on uses which would not leave detectable residues. Or, if residues were known to be present, they were at such low levels they were deemed by FDA liaison officials to be inconsequential.

In virtually all cases the chemical methods available for detecting residues were less accurate than 0.1 part per million, which was generally felt to be a practical cutoff point for most residue methods.

The Pesticide Chemicals Amendment, however, caused changes in new registrations for pesticides on food crops since it provided firm standards whenever tolerances were set. It also became possible for the Agriculture Department to inform an applicant for registration of a pesticide on a food crop that his application would be delayed until a tolerance had been established by FDA.

This delay was justified when the

275

Ground boom sprayers apply insecticide to corn, Orlando, Fla.

chemical analyses showed residues present. The legal basis for this was that the applicant could not—pending the setting of a tolerance by FDA—propose labeling for his product which would be adequate to protect a customer from likely economic loss through a seizure of the treated food crop by FDA. This principle was easy to understand and it was readily accepted.

THERE WERE MANY uses of pesticides, like seed treatments, preplanting soil application, and use before edible parts begin to form, which did not leave detectable residues on the harvested crop, however.

The chemical trade soon asked FDA officials what should be done when the analysts could prove there were no residues provided their products were used as directed.

In reply, FDA spokesmen stated repeatedly that if there were no residues, a petition for a tolerance would be unproductive since no tolerance above zero would be justified. In addition to

this clear-cut comment, FDA officials often advised the petitioner to apply directly to the Agriculture Department for a registration upon a "no residue" basis.

IN THIS WAY, the industry learned that "no-residue" registrations might be obtained to justify interstate shipment and sale of pesticides.

Such registrations were often requested when a pattern of use was shown to leave no detectable residues on the crop at the time of harvest.

Sometimes this type of registration was used to permit introduction of a pesticide while further work was being done on its toxicology. When this was the case, a petition for tolerance usually followed completion of the pharmacological program. And when tolerances were established it was always possible to use the pesticide with fewer restrictions upon it.

In addition, the "no-residue" registration became popular for justifying directions for minor uses for which a larger market could not be expected.

With these incentives supporting this type of registration, many registrations for food uses of pesticides were issued on a "no-residue" basis.

Since "no-residue" was dependent on the sensitivity of the methods available, it became inevitable that improved chemical analytical methods would create legal problems. This has indeed happened.

THE STAGE had been set, meanwhile, for the part FIFRA and its enforcement was to play in the dramatic developments which started on November 9, 1959. That was the day the Secretary of Health, Education, and Welfare announced seizure of cranberries contaminated through misuse of aminotriazole.

This chemical is a herbicide which was first used on nonfood areas to control grassy weeds. It was then found to be effective in removing weeds from cranberry bogs, and an application for its registration for that usage was filed with the Agriculture Department.

Extensive toxicological work was required, and a petition for a tolerance for aminotriazole on cranberries was presented to FDA. The tolerances were requested at levels which would permit use during the spring months. After careful consideration of all the toxicological facts, the petition was denied and the use on cranberries—in accordance with the spring pattern of application—was not registered.

THE COMPANY then carried out extensive tests using the material in the fall within 10 days after the berries were picked. This use was shown not to leave any residue on the succeeding crop—and to give good weed control. With the concurrence of FDA this use was then registered.

Unfortunately, some cranberry growers applied the herbicide in the spring and harvested contaminated berries. This type of misuse brought about the "cranberry episode" of 1959.

The Department of Health, Education, and Welfare (HEW) news release emphasized that the problem was directly related to a pattern of use not registered by the Agriculture Department. All subsequent investigations upheld that announcement.

THIS SITUATION pinpointed—in a way which could never have been done as effectively otherwise—the importance of following directions on the label. It also emphasized the extent of the public protection built into the registration review as handled by a conscientious Agriculture Department staff with the assistance of its informal liaison advisers.

With the importance of the registration function so openly recognized for the first time, it was possible to obtain increased support for the Agriculture Department agency responsible for the program, and it began to grow and to become more precise and critical in its own operations.

WHILE THIS GROWTH of the regulatory function was underway, President Kennedy appointed a Life Sciences Panel to study pesticides. This group first met in August of 1962, and after intensive study for 9 months issued a report on "The Use of Pesticides."

Immediately following release of the report on May 14, 1963, a Senate committee opened a lengthy series of new hearings. This committee was the Subcommittee on Reorganization and International Organizations of the Committee on Government Operations. Its report was a ten-volume document supported by several appendices and covered the general subject "Interagency Coordination in Environmental Hazards (Pesticides)."

As A CONSEQUENCE of all this attention to pesticides and their hazards, the law and its effectiveness in protecting the public came under close scrutiny.

The most searching questions were asked about protecting fish and wildlife, about uses on food registered on a "no-residue" basis, and about broadscale uses in the environment.

Since the law did not specifically

refer to any wild species, the first assumption by critics was that no consideration had ever been given to wildlife values in the label review procedure. This was proved to be untrue, since wildlife cautions had been required for several years on hazardous pesticides.

The question then shifted to whether warning statements were giving adequate protection or needed strengthening and greater emphasis.

IN THE "NO-RESIDUE" registration area, improved analytical methods resulted in seizures of food crops analyzed by the more sensitive procedures.

For example, cauliflower grown in the Northeast was found to contain small residues of endrin when the improved chemical procedures were used. The crops were seized by FDA since there were no tolerances for endrin on cauliflower.

In the area of environmental uses of pesticides, growing concern over anticipated hazards of chemicals led to reappraisal of the safety of the established patterns of use.

IN THIS ERA of changing public attitudes toward pesticides a new chapter in regulation has commenced.

The report on the "Use of Pesticides" recommended that the Federal agencies with responsibilities for any phases of pesticide research, use, or control, reexamine their functions and agree on how best to keep each other informed of progress, particularly in pesticide registration and tolerance setting.

Considerable study was given to wording of a formal Interdepartmental Agreement. Finally in May of 1964 an agreement was signed by the Secretaries of Agriculture, Interior, and Health, Education, and Welfare. Under it the Agriculture Department, HEW, and the Interior Department set up procedures for cooperation in registering pesticides and establishing tolerances for them.

To fulfill its responsibilities in enforcing FIFRA, the Pesticides Regulation Division of the Agricultural Research Service has chemical laboratories at the research center at Beltsville, Md., at New York City, San Francisco, Gulfport, Miss., and at Denver, Colo.

In addition, the Division has its own testing facilities to check the effectiveness of insecticides, fungicides, herbicides, rodenticides, bird and mammal poisons and repellents, bactericides, and related products at the Beltsville research center. It has a fungicide and herbicide laboratory at Corvallis, Oreg. And a new livestock product testing unit has been established by the Division at Kerrville, Tex.

These Government stations under direct control of the Division have not proved to be fully adequate for many large-scale studies.

Consequently, Federal-State cooperation in pesticide legal testing is being undertaken to permit utilization of large cropped areas at experiment stations for studies on the effectiveness of official samples.

Forty-eight States have laws closely resembling FIFRA, so that very close working relationships are possible.

The general enforcement plan of the Department today is patterned closely after that described in the discussion of the Insecticide Act of 1910. The Pesticides Regulation Division to which enforcement of FIFRA is delegated has an inspector staff of 20 men. The work of these inspectors is supplemented by about 120 State employees who are deputized to check shipping records and collect official samples.

THESE PRODUCTS are then submitted for analysis and testing to the Federal laboratories discussed previously. Some of the findings have led to significant action.

In the past few years, for example, it has been discovered that a fairly large number of disinfectants distributed for hospital use are too low in effectiveness. Enforcement actions were taken to remove them from the market. This protected the public and hospital staffs from false confidence in products used widely to treat surgical instruments, bedpans, and other surfaces.

CROSS CONTAMINATION of products is a major problem in current pesticide production.

Detailed controls over the labeling of pesticides are a part of the law and are applied during the registration process.

The product, however, must be exactly as it is shown in the ingredient statement before scientific review of the labeling is most valuable. Enforcement analyses are disclosing that this is not always the situation. In fact, we have found that adulteration of pesticides occurs far too frequently.

Contamination has been so serious in some cases that seizure of the product has been necessary to protect users against personal hazards in using the materials, to avoid danger to livestock, or to prevent illegal residues on crops.

Aggressive enforcement action to take such dangerous pesticides off the market has been a significant part of the protection being given the public under FIFRA.

GOVERNMENTWIDE MOVES toward more cooperation in pesticide management are aided by several new committees and subcommittees.

One of the most important is the Federal Committee on Pest Control which held its first meeting in August of 1964, with two representatives from each of the Departments of Agriculture, Defense, HEW, and Interior. The members have designated alternates, so the business of the Committee can be handled without delay at any meeting called by the Chairman.

This Committee replaced the Federal Pest Control Review Board, which was established in the summer of 1961. Dr. Robert J. Anderson, Assistant Surgeon General of the U.S. Public Health Service, has served as Chairman of both the Board and the Committee.

Responsibilities of the Board were limited to the consideration of the programs of the Federal Government using pesticides. The Committee has been given a much wider range of authority.

Due to the broad scope of the Committee's responsibilities, some of its functions have been assigned to subcommittees which operate under the titles "Monitoring," "Research," and "Information."

The Monitoring Subcommittee is further subdivided into areas covering people, fish and wildlife, soils, water, and air.

The Federal Committee on Pest Control has not yet taken an active part in giving advice on registration matters. But it is available for such action if the basic cooperating Department staffs need its services.

TO SUM UP: The Federal Insecticide, Fungicide, and Rodenticide Act through its registration and enforcement features provides the primary public protection against improperly labeled or adulterated pesticides under Federal law.

The registered label always has been and still is the best guide available to the user of a pesticide.

This means the registered label must be subject to prompt revision whenever new scientific data become available to justify any changes. It must also be subject to rapid modification when any new standards of safety or of performance are set.

These requirements are well recognized by both regulatory officials and the regulated industry. The most effective public protection has come through mutual respect and wholehearted cooperation.

FIFRA is a dynamic statute and its enforcement an eternal challenge. This challenge must be met so the public will continue to have dependable guidance in using the modern pesticides needed to insure an adequate and nutritious food supply, and to protect human and animal health.

For further reading:
Harris, T. H. and Cummings, J. C., "Enforcement of the Federal Insecticide, Fungicide, and Rodenticide Act in the United States." *Residue Reviews*, Vol. 6, pp. 104–135, 1964.
Ward, Justus C., "The Functions of the Federal Insecticide, Fungicide, and Rodenticide Act." *American Journal of Public Health*, Vol. 55, No. 7, 1965.

MEAT AND POULTRY INSPECTION

ROBERT J. LEE and HENRY W. HARPER

THE round stamps or marks of Federal inspection found on meat and poultry products are the consumer's guarantee of wholesomeness. The wording "U.S. Inspected and Passed by Department of Agriculture" on processed meat items, "U.S. INSP'D & P'S'D" on fresh meat, and "Inspected for Wholesomeness by U.S. Department of Agriculture" on poultry and poultry products certifies that meat and poultry products came from healthy animals and birds, and passed the high standards of the Federal Government for wholesomeness and for cleanliness.

These inspection marks also certify that meat and poultry products are truthfully labeled.

The Meat Inspection Act became law in 1906, and the Poultry Products Inspection Act in 1957. Both acts are administered by the Consumer and Marketing Service.

The cost of inspection is only pennies a year per person. This is low-cost insurance for a continuing supply of clean and wholesome meat and poultry.

Federal inspection is required for all meat and poultry prepared in plants that sell their products in interstate and foreign commerce. It includes inspection of cattle, calves, sheep, hogs, goats, horses, chickens, turkeys, ducks, geese, and guinea fowl.

Today about 85 percent of commercially slaughtered livestock, and 86 percent of poultry sold off farms, are federally inspected. In addition, about 19.5 billion pounds of meat and 1.7 billion pounds of poultry are processed into various food products under Federal supervision each year.

Special exemptions are granted to the farmers who slaughter their own livestock on their farms. Meat and poultry products shipped in interstate or foreign commerce under this exemption must be identified with the name and address of the farmer or poultry producer, as a protection to the purchaser of the products.

In addition, farmers or poultry producers who ship for human consumption unwholesome or otherwise unfit meat or poultry products across a State line are subject to a fine or to imprisonment, or both.

Meat and poultry plants that sell all of their products within the same State in which they are produced,

* * *

Robert J. Lee is *Training Officer* of the Inspection Branch, Poultry Division, Consumer and Marketing Service.

Henry W. Harper is *Staff Officer* for Planning and Appraisal, Meat Inspection Division, Consumer and Marketing Service.

and to non-Federal inspected establishments or to nongovernmental agencies within the same State, are not subject to Federal inspection.

U.S. MEAT AND POULTRY industries are the world's largest, with a yearly output of over 31 billion pounds of meat and 10 billion pounds of poultry. Americans eat an average of over 174 pounds of red meat and over 38 pounds of poultry a year. About 40 percent of our food dollars go for meat and poultry—they are leading items in family food budgets.

Thirty-six percent of our protein is supplied by meat from cattle, calves, sheep, hogs, and poultry. In addition, meat and poultry provide 29 percent of the thiamine in our food, 28 percent of the iron, 41 percent of the niacin, 22 percent of the riboflavin, 22 percent of the vitamin A, 34 percent of the fat, and 19 percent of the calories.

MEAT INSPECTION as we know it today began with passage of the Meat Inspection Act of 1906. It was a result of public clamor following Upton Sinclair's description of a Chicago packinghouse in his novel "The Jungle."

The act extended Federal inspection of meat by making inspection mandatory—rather than voluntary—for meat entering interstate commerce. It also added provisions for sanitary control of the plants to assure cleanliness in their operations.

THE NUMBER OF animals slaughtered under Federal inspection increased from some 42.9 million in the fiscal year ending June 30, 1906 to over 111 million in fiscal 1965. During 1906, inspections were made in 163 establishments in 58 cities. In 1965, Federal inspectors serviced 1,775 establishments in 743 cities.

Early legislation for Federal meat inspection included an 1890 measure providing inspection of salted pork and bacon for export. Its purpose was to relieve the economic distress of livestock producers who were suffering from loss of exports to Europe.

The export market for American meat and meat products, particularly bacon, was well established by 1879. Then, alarmed by the widespread appearance of trichinae (minute roundworms which inhabit principally the muscles of hogs and when transmitted to man cause trichinosis) which was attributed to hog products, various countries put prohibitions on imports of pork from the United States.

ITALY WAS the first country to prohibit imports (1879). Others quickly followed. By the end of 1881, Portugal, Hungary, Germany, Spain, France, Turkey, and Rumania had placed embargoes on pork. Great Britain put restrictions upon cattle in 1882 by ordering immediate slaughter at the port of entry.

Hardships caused by these restrictions continued for a decade, but the restrictions were a potent force in starting the United States on its way to Federal meat inspection.

The 1890 act was limited. It referred chiefly to the manner in which export products were packed and their appearance immediately prior to shipment. Condition of animals at time of slaughter was not included. Because it was not sufficiently inclusive, the measure failed to achieve its goal.

Six months later, Congress approved legislation providing for examination before and after slaughter of all cattle and hogs intended for export and for interstate commerce.

Special emphasis was placed on post mortem inspection of cattle from which meat was exported. The legislation provided for microscopic examination of all pork for export and certification of freedom from trichinosis, condemnation of diseased animals, marking or stamping of inspected carcasses, and labeling of food products made from the carcasses and intended for export or interstate trade.

THE FIRST INSPECTION under the new law was made in New York City on May 12, 1891. This was inspection of dressed beef for export. A month later, inspection began in Chicago, and soon afterwards in Omaha, Kansas City, Milwaukee, and Jersey City.

Germany's restrictions on U.S. pork were removed in September 1891. Italy, France, Denmark, and Austria all followed suit.

Several additions were made in 1895 to the then existing program. Calves and sheep were added to the act, and Congress authorized the Secretary of Agriculture to set up regulations for disposal of condemned carcasses.

THE MEAT INSPECTION ACT of 1906 set up sanitary regulations and standards of cleanliness for personnel and facilities. In addition, it extended inspection to canned meats and meat products.

This act gave assurance that the meat inspected was from a healthy animal, and that the animal was slaughtered and the meat prepared under sanitary conditions. No harmful preservative, chemical, dye, or contaminant was allowed in the preparation. The name of the product had to be accurate, and preparation of the product was supervised from "hoof to can."

The act carried a special exemption for meat and meat food products prepared by farmers. They were required to furnish a certificate in duplicate to the shipper showing the animal was healthy and wholesome if it was to enter interstate trade. The law provided penalties for falsification.

THE LAW has been extended and modified since 1906. The act of 1906 was essentially a 1-year appropriation act. The measure was reenacted in 1907 with inclusion of the word "hereafter." This extended provisions of the law for an indefinite period.

Horses were added in 1919 to the list of animals covered by the law, with a provision for separate slaughter.

POULTRY INSPECTION had a somewhat similar beginning.

During the early 1920's, trainloads of live poultry arrived each week in New York City. Most of this poultry was shipped from the Midwest and was

loaded on special railroad cars which had living quarters for an attendant. These cars also had watering and feeding facilities for the poultry.

THE ATTENDANTS were experts in their field and took pride in their ability to bring the poultry great distances with little loss in weight. This was encouraged by means of bonuses.

Finally, competition became so intense that shady methods evolved. These included feeding ingredients to the poultry to bind the lower intestinal tract, followed by feeding of salt to encourage heavy water consumption. Another practice was to feed large amounts of corn prior to unloading.

As a result many of the birds were sick by the time they had arrived at the local slaughterhouses.

THE NEW YORK CITY Department of Health took an active interest in these practices during 1926. Local poultry buyers also became alarmed because of losses suffered due to the artificially induced weight.

Consequently, the Agriculture Department was requested to establish an inspection program in New York City for live poultry.

INSPECTION of live poultry by the Agriculture Department was inaugurated on November 15, 1926. At first, this consisted of inspecting poultry at railroad terminals and markets in and around New York City.

This inspection was conducted under an agreement between the Bureau of Agricultural Economics of the Department and two cooperating organizations, the Greater New York Live Poultry Chamber of Commerce and the New York Live Poultry Commission Merchants Association.

Live poultry inspection accomplished two purposes.

Inspectors were able to determine by touch the average amount of feed in the crop. A sample of birds in each railroad car or truck was checked before the unloading and delivery to buyers. Limitations were established.

If feed in the crop was more than permitted, the poultry was held for reinspection. Cars of live poultry could not be unloaded until the birds had passed inspection.

Inspectors also were able to determine if any prohibited materials were included in the feed on the morning the birds were to be unloaded. All such poultry found at the time of inspection was removed and it was destroyed as unfit for human food.

RAIL SHIPMENTS of live poultry to New York City reached a peak of 200 million pounds in 1930, but shipments were sharply cut by 1935. This was due to development of year-round broiler production in localities close to New York City and a lessening demand.

Demand fell because many consumers who purchased live poultry and had it slaughtered under supervision of local religious officials were now able to purchase birds slaughtered outside the city. This had become acceptable under religious dietary laws.

As a consequence, inspection of live poultry by the Agriculture Department was discontinued in 1935.

The first inspection by the Department of dressed and eviscerated poultry—slaughtered birds with the head, feet, feathers, and internal organs removed—was on a voluntary basis.

THE SERVICE was supplied in 1927 to a large soup company in the East. This company exported some of its products to Canada. The Canadian Government required that canned poultry products exported to Canada be accompanied by a Federal export certificate indicating the product had been inspected and found wholesome.

New York City followed Canada's lead in 1928. It required inspection of canned poultry products sold in the city.

Five additional plants requested poultry inspection from the Agriculture Department to meet these requirements. Thus by the end of 1928 a total of six plants operated under the voluntary poultry inspection service. During that year, 3,150,423 pounds

of poultry were inspected under the program with 11.72 percent condemned. Subsequently, the percentage of inspected poultry condemned markedly decreased as the plants under inspection soon found it profitable to present healthy poultry for inspection.

CANNING PLANTS received a very large percentage of inspection service furnished during the early years since direct sale to consumers of ready-to-cook poultry was just beginning to get underway.

Practically all slaughtered poultry sold consumers in the United States before 1928 was "New York dressed," poultry with the feet, head, and internal organs not removed.

Actually, development of poultry inspection has kept pace with the rise of the ready-to-cook poultry market, because poultry cannot be properly inspected for wholesomeness except at the time of evisceration.

But it was not until 1945 that the amount of ready-to-cook poultry inspected for direct consumer consumption exceeded the quantity inspected for use in canned poultry products.

WORLD WAR II made a heavy impact both on the poultry industry and on poultry inspection.

Besides increased civilian demand, military needs for poultry proved greater than the industry could supply. New plants were built. Unused plants reopened to provide additional facilities for the rapid increases in broiler production.

Military purchase specifications required inspection of all poultry products either by the Army's Veterinary Corps or the Agriculture Department. Most of the military purchases during the war years consisted of New York dressed poultry.

AT FIRST, the military examined the frozen, dressed poultry at the point of delivery. However, it soon became obvious that the most careful examination at this point would not prevent some unsatisfactory product reaching mess halls. Consequently, the military began to survey prospective poultry processing plants. Bidding on military contracts was limited to approved plants only.

POULTRY INSPECTION activities during the war made the poultry industry and the American housewife far more conscious of inspection than ever before.

Sales value of the inspection mark received more recognition. Thus, even though users of the inspection service bore the full costs of inspection, the program continued to grow.

More and more retailers acquired holding facilities for frozen ready-to-cook poultry. As a result, demand for New York dressed poultry disappeared. At the same time demand increased for inspected convenience food products, like chicken pies and dinners.

Poultry production continued to expand during the years between the close of the war and 1950. Commercial broiler production almost doubled. The turkey crop also increased, but not as markedly. Hundreds of new poultry processing plants started up to handle the increased production.

MOST POULTRY during the early years of inspection work was slaughtered and plucked in dressing plants. It was then shipped from those plants as New York dressed.

Eviscerating and canning plants purchased the dressed poultry, generally from brokers, for evisceration and further processing. There was no chance to examine the live poultry or observe slaughter and dressing conditions.

A TREND DEVELOPED during the 1940's to move eviscerating operations to the dressing plant, or build new combination dressing and eviscerating plants. The objective was to combine these activities into one continuous dressing and eviscerating operation.

This development reached a peak by 1950 when it was considered practicable to issue regulations on sanitary conditions for slaughtering and dressing of poultry.

Sanitation inspection was furnished to dressing plants that applied and that met the sanitary requirements. Eviscerating plants which operated under inspection were not permitted to receive dressed poultry for evisceration unless it had been slaughtered in an official plant.

The military began purchasing only ready-to-cook poultry by 1955. Similarly, civilian supplies, except for a few areas, consisted almost entirely of eviscerated poultry.

THE ATTENTION OF Congressional leaders was directed during the mid-1950's toward the problem of unwholesome poultry being shipped across State lines. The Poultry Products Inspection Act, which was signed by the President on August 28, 1957, was the result of many hearings with consumer, industry, and governmental groups.

This act required all slaughtered poultry moving in interstate or foreign commerce to be inspected. The act became fully effective on January 1, 1959.

The Secretary of Agriculture assigned responsibility for administering the act to the Agricultural Marketing Service, now the Consumer and Marketing Service. Experience gained during the years 1927 through 1957 in developing and applying inspection techniques and criteria was of great value in preparing regulations for administering the new compulsory poultry inspection service.

PRESENT INSPECTION PROGRAMS, based on the Meat Inspection Act of 1906 with modifications and amendments, and the Poultry Products Inspection Act, consist of these essential functions:

Sanitation of the establishment; inspection of animals and birds before slaughter; careful inspection of the carcass and internal organs at time of slaughter; processing inspection; disposal of condemned material; marking and labeling; and inspecting imported meat and poultry products.

Sanitation of the establishment is of primary importance in providing a clean and wholesome product. Federal

284

inspection begins with approval of a plant's construction and equipment.

Rigid rules of sanitation include things like ample supplies of hot and cold water under pressure and distributed throughout the plant to meet operating needs, efficient lighting, good drainage and ventilation, adequate facilities for sewage disposal, convenient locations to clean or sterilize instruments, and cleaning facilities for workers. The equipment—which includes cutters, hangers, hooks, and trays—must be of easily cleaned, rust-resistant material.

Inspection by the Agriculture Department means the plant passed the initial examination for sanitation, and that standards are being maintained constantly. The plant is subject to a continuing inspection.

INSPECTION OF ANIMALS and birds before slaughter provides a way to identify and eliminate diseased animals and birds from food channels. About 2.2 billion birds and 112 million animals were checked in federally inspected plants during the fiscal year ending June 30, 1965.

Inspection begins in the stockyards before the animals are driven in for slaughter or, in the case of poultry, on the trucks as the birds arrive at the processing plant.

Experienced veterinarians check the animals and birds carefully. Any animal that looks abnormal in any way is

SCOPE OF FEDERAL MEAT AND POULTRY INSPECTION

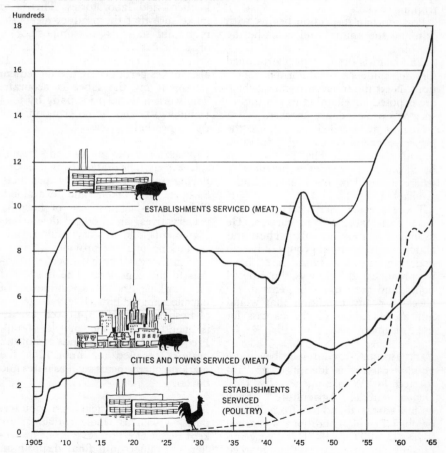

tagged. It may be either with a "U.S. Condemned" or "U.S. Suspect" tag, depending on how serious the condition appears. This tag has a serial number for followthrough identification.

An animal tagged as condemned is not taken to the slaughter floor, but is killed separately and disposed of under supervision to prevent contamination of healthy, wholesome meat.

An animal or a lot of birds that is questionable is also kept apart and is slaughtered separately. Only animals and birds which appear completely healthy are sent along for normal slaughter.

INSPECTION of carcasses and internal organs is made by veterinarians and their assistants—meat or poultry inspectors—who have received special training.

Post mortem inspection begins with skinning the animal and defeathering the bird.

The head is the first part examined for any evidence of abnormal conditions. Next the internal organs, which are exposed for examination in the inspector's presence, are checked.

Guided by detailed regulations, the inspector examines by sight, incision, touch, and smell. His procedure is based on long experience in knowing where diseased or harmful conditions are likely to exist.

The inspector then checks all surfaces and parts of the carcass. He examines membranes of the chest and abdomen, the various groups of lymph nodes in animals (birds don't have lymph nodes), the kidneys, the exposed bones, and the carcass in general. He checks for any condition that would indicate unfitness of the carcass for use as human food.

EACH IMMEDIATE container bearing a poultry carcass is identified as "Inspected for Wholesomeness by U.S. Department of Agriculture." Each animal carcass found free from diseases or objectionable conditions is marked "U.S. INSP'D & P'S'D." Every important cut of meat is then marked

with the Federal purple meat inspection stamp.

Any animal or poultry carcass not obviously wholesome is segregated for a closer veterinary examination.

PROCESSING INSPECTION is a continuation of inspection of meats, including poultry meat, through curing, smoking, canning, and many other types of processing.

This includes processing of sausage, cured meats, potted and canned meats, poultry roasts and rolls, and frozen products like pies and dinners.

The goal is to assure use of wholesome ingredients and accurate labels so the purchaser may obtain a product that is honestly labeled as well as pure.

Processed products are examined and evaluated scientifically in test kitchens and laboratories. This is to make sure that the product meets the minimum standard of composition—or in the case of poultry products, the minimum meat content standard. It also makes certain that the ingredient statement on the label is accurate. The work is done principally by food technologists and home economists of the inspection services.

CHEMISTS test the purity and safety of spices and other materials used in preparing meat and poultry products. Samples are taken and examined. This guards against use of harmful preservatives and other deleterious ingredients, and against adulteration.

Marking of meat provides a means of identifying federally inspected products to the consumer. The fluid used for marking meats is composed of harmless ingredients. Every large cut of fresh meat of an approved carcass is marked with the purple stamp. Frequently, burning brands or hot ink brands are used for imprinting the mark on cured meats such as hams and bacon.

ALL CONDEMNED meat and poultry, parts as well as whole carcasses, are kept under close supervision of inspection personnel until final disposition.

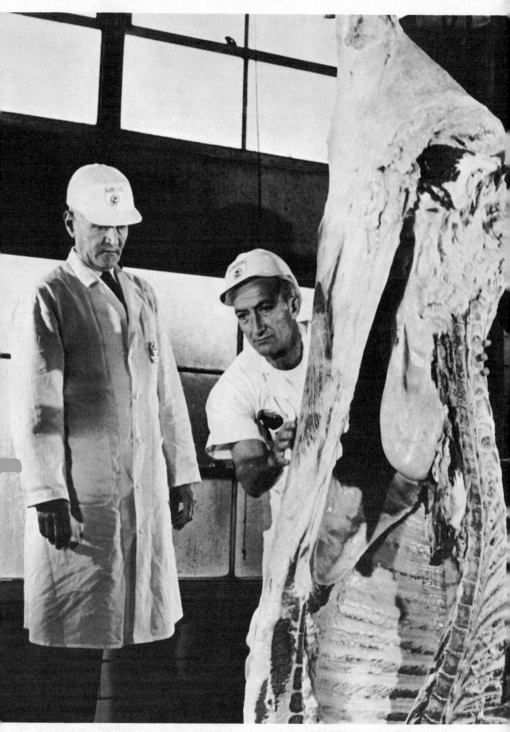

USDA meat inspectors check a side of beef at a packing plant in Bristol, Va.

They must be destroyed in the presence of an inspector and he files a report on their destruction.

One method of treating condemned carcasses and parts is to convert them into industrial grease and fertilizer. Some plants destroy the condemned meat by incineration or by addition of crude carbolic acid or other denaturing agents.

OFFICIAL APPROVAL of labels intended for use on canned or packaged meat and poultry food products is required by the inspection services.

Each year thousands of proposed new labels are submitted to the Agriculture Department for its approval. Some 61,915 new labels were approved in the fiscal year ending June 30, 1965. Each label passed an accuracy test to be sure pictures and wording supplied an exact description of the contents.

Approval was withheld from a total of 5,679 labels and sketches.

Required features of a label include the accurate name of the product; a list of the ingredients if anything was added to the basic product; the name and place of business of the manufacturer, packer, or person for whom the product is prepared; an accurate statement about the amount of the product; and the inspection legend (including the plant number).

ALL IMPORTED MEAT and poultry products are subject to requirements of the Imported Meat Act and the Poultry Products Inspection Act.

This further protects the American consumer against unwholesome and adulterated meat and poultry products which might otherwise be offered for sale in the United States.

These acts cover meat, meat food products, slaughtered poultry, and poultry products. None of these may be imported unless they are healthful, wholesome, fit for human food, and unadulterated. They must contain no dye, chemical, preservative, or ingredient which render them unhealthful, unwholesome, adulterated, or unfit for human food purposes.

288

Regulations issued under the acts provide that no such products may be imported unless they have been prepared under an official national system of meat or of poultry inspection substantially equivalent to that in the United States.

Before any foreign meat or poultry inspection service is approved, regulations of the foreign country are carefully reviewed to assure they provide adequate safeguards to assure a wholesome supply of meat and poultry.

Veterinarians from the United States make plant surveys in the foreign country which is involved.

And once a foreign inspection system has been approved, followup visits are made to assure continued compliance with U.S. requirements.

SHIPMENTS OF meat and poultry products from an approved foreign country must be accompanied by foreign certificates attesting that products in the shipment received an adequate ante and post mortem inspection and are wholesome and free from adulteration.

Import inspectors are stationed by USDA at strategic locations throughout the United States.

They inspect each shipment of meat and poultry products offered for importation into the United States to assure that a certificate accompanies the shipment and that the product actually is wholesome and free from adulteration. They also check out the product's label to assure it has been approved. They submit samples of the meat or poultry offered for importation into the United States to a laboratory when there is any reason for doubt about its wholesomeness.

Once an imported meat or poultry product enters the United States, it is treated as a federally inspected product.

IN THE U.S. INSPECTION program, graduate veterinarians supervise inspection in plants where slaughtering is being conducted.

Besides having six or more years of study in an accredited veterinary college, they must demonstrate a keen sense of smell, touch, and sight, which are important faculties in this work. After employment, the trainee works as an assistant to an experienced man before qualifying to pass on the condition of eviscerated carcasses.

Inspectors assist the veterinarian in the ante and post mortem examinations and in supervising the processing operations.

SALARIES and other costs of the Federal meat and poultry inspection service are paid by the Government. The industry reimburses the Government for the cost of performing any overtime and holiday service.

Savings in medical expense and protection of the Nation's health have resulted from contributions of the inspection programs in eradicating animal diseases.

Bovine tuberculosis, a major disease communicable to humans, has declined 85 percent in humans since the tuberculosis eradication program in cattle began in 1917. Tuberculosis in farm herds has been reduced from 5 percent in 1918 to 0.08 percent in 1965 as a result of the effective eradication measures, including detection at meat inspection points.

THE INDUSTRY in the fiscal year ending June 30, 1965 sought approval of the Agriculture Department for 2,529 new or remodeled structures. Of this total, 1,947 were approved as complying with requirements for slaughtering and processing establishments operating under Federal inspection.

Livestock and poultry producers are major beneficiaries of the inspection programs. They gain in two ways— from disease control and because the inspection program itself encourages a steady consumer demand for meat and poultry products.

It is important economically to the producer to know if his flock, herd, or other flocks or herds in his locality are infected with a disease.

Early knowledge of infection is essential to any plan for its elimination. And the Federal inspection service is equipped to supply this information as well as to direct attention to the locality of infection.

Production costs are lowered when the producers can control the causes of infection and improve conditions on their farms.

When a veterinary meat or poultry inspector finds a diseased animal, he diagnoses the disease and records it in his daily reports. This report and livestock shipping records are sufficient in most cases to identify the territory of origin.

The inspector reports his findings directly to the State or Federal disease control officials with jurisdiction in the region from which the infected animal came. Then, by the means of eartags, earmarks, brands, tattoo marks, and descriptions of animals, the farm and herd that supplied the diseased animal for slaughter can often be located.

THE CONSUMER and Marketing Service reported over 1,350 cattle with tubercular lesions in the fiscal year ending June 30, 1965. This led to the testing of 42,762 cattle in 718 herds. A total of 567 cattle were disclosed as reactors, and 77 herds included reactors.

Heavy losses from diseases have gradually been reduced through eradication programs and contributions of meat and poultry inspection to them. Examples are progress being made in eradicating brucellosis and in controlling actinomycosis, anthrax, hog cholera, Johne's disease, Texas fever, and the complex respiratory diseases of poultry.

LESS THAN 0.25 percent of the animals and 2.41 percent of the birds which were federally examined were condemned in the fiscal year 1965. This evidence of the good health of the Nation's farm stock is encouraging to both domestic and foreign buyers.

The homemaker gets assurance from the Federal mark of inspection that his meat and poultry have been handled under strict standards of cleanliness.

Processed meat and poultry get the same cleanliness check.

THE FOOD AND DRUG

ADMINISTRATION

FRANCIS E. McLAUGHLIN

THE average American has perhaps only a vague idea of the activities and responsibilities of the Food and Drug Administration, but the chances are good that he equates the name with enforcement of the "Pure Food Law." Pure food is of paramount concern to the public and to keep it pure requires a major portion of the resources of the Food and Drug Administration (FDA) of the U.S. Department of Health, Education, and Welfare.

Each year inspections of food plants, collections and examinations of food samples, and removal from the market of adulterated or misbranded foods lead the list of FDA field programs and of FDA assignments.

FDA ADMINISTERS several Federal acts that deal in whole or in part with food regulation. These include the Federal Food, Drug, and Cosmetic Act, with which we will be primarily concerned, the Tea Importation Act, the Filled Milk Act, and the Import Milk Act.

The Federal Food, Drug, and Cosmetic Act, enacted in 1938, deals in part with the prohibition in interstate commerce of adulterated and mis-

branded foods. The act also provides authority for preclearance review of food additives, color additives, and pesticide residues, and establishment of safe tolerances for them.

The Tea Importation Act of 1897 prohibits importation of any tea which is inferior in purity, quality, and fitness for consumption as determined by standards established under authority of the act.

The Filled Milk Act of 1923 prohibits substitution of any fat or oil for milk fat in milk or cream, with certain exceptions for infant foods.

The Import Milk Act, enacted in 1927, prohibits importation of milk or cream into the United States unless the shipper involved possesses a permit from the Secretary of Health, Education, and Welfare.

For violations proscribed by the Federal Food, Drug, and Cosmetic Act, there are provisions for criminal prosecution, with imprisonment and fines

* * *

Francis E. McLaughlin is *Assistant* to the Assistant Commissioner for Operations, Food and Drug Administration, Department of Health, Education, and Welfare.

for conviction, seizure of goods, and injunction proceedings.

THE FOOD AND DRUG ADMINISTRATION is not one of the larger Federal agencies, but its increase in responsibilities and rate of growth parallel the development and tremendous diversification in the food, drug, cosmetic, and related industries in recent years.

In an article in the 1959 Yearbook of Agriculture, George P. Larrick, then Commissioner of Food and Drugs, said FDA had a staff of about 1,400. By June 30, 1965, FDA personnel numbered over 4,100. During the same period, the enforcement appropriations had grown from $10.9 million to more than $40 million.

Approximately 55 percent of FDA personnel are assigned to the field service, which consists of 18 district office and laboratory units and 46 resident inspection stations. Remaining personnel are assigned to headquarters scientific and administrative units in Washington, D.C., and nearby Virginia and Maryland.

FDA SEEKS to bring about compliance with the Federal Food, Drug, and Cosmetic Act and the other related food laws which it administers through its activities in these following four categories:
• Providing advice and technical data to the industry, interested law enforcement agencies, and the public.
• Making regulatory checks.
• Setting specific standards for compliance.
• Conducting basic and applied scientific research needed to do all this.

IN COMPANY with other Federal agencies, FDA takes the position that effective administration of law is aided by supplying industry with advisory opinions on applicability of the law, and on its requirements.

Over the years FDA has operated on the theory that a manufacturer seeking to market a legal food product should be able to rely on the advice given him by an FDA staff member, and that voluntary compliance with the law is promoted when the industry will rely on and follow the agency's advice.

The type of advice offered industry may range from an answer to an inquiry on the suitability of a food additive to the conduct of a seminar on proper food manufacturing practices.

Information on methods of analysis for detecting natural or artificial impurities and contaminants in food products is also a recurring subject of dialogue between FDA and industry.

FDA SEEKS to keep the consuming public constantly apprised of additions to the food protection laws, proposed actions or completed actions under the existing law, and the results of recent scientific studies.

Letters in response to consumer inquiries, FDA Memos for Consumers, talks given by consumer consultants, and press releases are used by FDA for this purpose.

Topics may range from a proposal to reduce the amount of vitamin D which may be legally added to food products to an invitation to consumers to comment on the amount of peanut ingredient they think should be required in a proposed standard for peanut butter.

In addition to informing interested consumers on requirements of the existing food law, FDA seeks to elicit the broadest type of consumer response on any proposed action having significant impact on the consuming public. FDA is especially anxious to hear from the consumer with a good common-sense approach to the subject, as well as the expert or scientist who can supply highly technical comments on the action which is proposed.

FDA IS PRIMARILY a law enforcement agency and, as such, is in constant contact and collaboration with Federal, State, and local agencies carrying on similar or related activities.

There is continuous exchange of information between FDA and State agricultural and health departments. State chemists, officials, inspectors,

291

791–476 O–66–21

and technicians are constantly being trained in FDA's analytical, inspectional, and other law enforcement procedures.

METHODS FOR detecting natural and artificial food contaminants developed in FDA laboratories are routinely passed on to State agricultural and health departments. Recently, FDA districts have begun to coordinate closely the development of inspectional work plans with State agencies having similar responsibilities in order to avoid inspectional gaps and duplication of effort.

FDA carries on special informational campaigns on such diverse topics as the proper use of pesticides by growers and consumers, necessary storage practices by food warehousemen, grain sanitation, and legal use of medicated feeds and food additives.

The degree of compliance with requirements of the food laws administered by FDA can be assessed only through a system of continuous regulatory checking.

Over 800 field inspectors carry on periodic inspections of food plants and warehouses. They examine and collect samples of food commodities prior to shipment in interstate commerce, during interstate shipment, and while the commodities are being held for sale following shipment.

THESE MEN carry out thousands of inspections each year in establishments ranging from bakeries doing a small amount of interstate business, to canneries making shipments to all parts of the United States. Their scene of activities may vary from a cabbage field to the office of the president of a large food corporation.

Other specially trained FDA inspectors examine and collect samples of products which have been offered for importation into the United States.

Food and Drug Administration chemists, in a mobile trailer laboratory, analyze raw products for pesticide residues.

Scientists in each FDA district laboratory have electronic equipment capable of conducting the most sophisticated types of food analyses.

From the observations of the inspector and the analytical results obtained on any sample collected, a picture of compliance or of noncompliance is drawn.

Observations of the inspector may result in nothing more than a few suggestions on how the manufacturer can improve the sanitary safeguards in his operation.

On occasion, however, the inspector's report coupled with laboratory examination may show a picture of extremely poor manufacturing practices which result in adulterated food products.

Then it becomes necessary to track down the food lots suspected of being contaminated and to take appropriate regulatory action.

With many thousands of manufacturers, distributors, and storers of foods, drugs, therapeutic devices, and cosmetics carrying on businesses which have a substantial effect on interstate commerce, each district office must carefully program its plans for regulatory checking.

This has led to installation in district offices of an automated system to handle the district's inventory of regulated industries.

EACH DISTRICT is assigned quotas for sampling and inspection in such food projects as grains, dairy products, beverages, bakery goods, fish, fruits, and other commodities.

The districts have considerable autonomy in programing the assignments necessary to fill quotas. This helps avoid inspectional gaps in the coverage of the regulated industries over an area which may include several States.

EACH DISTRICT OFFICE and resident inspection station keeps in close contact with the State health and regulatory officials.

It is not unusual for a food plant to receive an unannounced visit from an inspection team made up of State and FDA personnel. State officials have used their special embargo powers against goods found contaminated during such inspections.

Assistance to State and local health officials in times of natural disaster is classed under the head of regulatory checking. That's because in the inspection and reconditioning of food stocks which have been exposed to floods, hurricanes, and fires, health and disaster workers occasionally encounter an individual who seeks to take advantage of the emergency conditions.

For this reason the destruction of contaminated and exposed foodstuffs must be carefully supervised.

FDA INSTITUTES legal actions like seizure, injunction, and prosecution to bring about compliance with the Federal Food, Drug, and Cosmetic Act.

During the fiscal year ending June 30, 1965, a total of $206,700 in fines were imposed by U.S. courts for violations of the act. During the same period, 11 injunctions were granted and 238 prosecutions terminated.

Many of these actions involved food that had become decomposed, moldy, insect-infested, or otherwise contaminated. Large fines were assessed against individuals responsible for preparing or holding foods under such insanitary conditions.

A prime factor in the Government's decision to bring a legal action is the degree of seriousness of adulteration or misbranding involved in a particular case.

THE LAWS administered by FDA provide that the Government set the standard for compliance for a number of foods and components of foods. Foods or food components that do not comply with the legally established standard are classified as illegal.

An example of standard-setting or rulemaking can be found in section 401 of the act. It provides for establishment of reasonable standards of identity, quality, and fill of container for foods, with butter, fresh and dried fruits, and vegetables exempted. The goal is to promote honesty and fair dealing in the interest of consumers.

STANDARDS define what a particular food product shall consist of, setting minimum figures for valuable ingredients and in some instances maximum figures for less valuable ingredients which are also common to the product.

Standards have been established for cocoa products, cereal flour and related products, macaroni and noodle products, cheeses, dressings for foods, food flavors, tomato products, and many other foods. The standards may include enriched varieties of foods, insuring that the amount of enrichment is a substantial one.

MOST OF THE STANDARDS established thus far have been standards of identity, specifying permissible ingredients and quantities of ingredients to be present.

However, standards of quality have been established for a number of canned fruits and vegetables.

Standards of fill of container have been established for seafoods, tomato products, and for some canned fruits and vegetables.

ANY FOOD purporting to be a standardized food must comply with specifications established under the standard.

Substandard fill of container or substandard quality must be indicated on the label.

Proposed standards meeting the requirement of section 401 of the act offered by the food industry, the Government, or some interested person are formally published in the Federal Register in order to get comments and suggestions from all interested parties, including consumers.

After evaluation of the comments and other pertinent facts involved, an order is published which adopts, modifies, or rejects the proposal.

An order or a "rule" may be stayed upon the basis of an objection made by an adversely affected party who requests a public hearing, and in addition, there are provisions in the law for carrying an appeal to a Federal Circuit Court of Appeals.

Keystone of these standards is the promotion of honesty and fair dealing in the interest of consumers. Thus, as already indicated, it is vitally important to obtain the broadest possible consumer response to any proposed food standards.

THE STANDARD of compliance for color additives used in foods is established through promulgation by FDA of regulations listing the safe color additives and their permitted uses.

Establishment of a color additive listing for food use is supported by extensive chemical and pharmacological testing carried out by a petitioner who desires FDA clearance for this particular level of use.

Petitioners normally ask FDA's advice and approval on protocols for animal feeding studies, which will produce the necessary pharmacological proof of safety.

WHERE IT IS deemed necessary to protect the public's health, the standards for compliance require certification by FDA of each batch of certain color additives listed to insure they conform with requirements specified.

In the fiscal year ending June 30, 1965, FDA laboratories tested 3,224 batches of color additives to insure their compliance with the specified standards.

The procedure for making effective standards for compliance for color additives in foods is similar to the procedure governing establishment of food standards.

UNDER THE FEDERAL Food, Drug, and Cosmetic Act, any additive used in a food intended for public consumption must be either generally recognized as safe or it must conform with a regulation spelling out safe conditions for the use of the additive.

The food additives section of the act became law in 1958, and is designed to provide the public health safeguards made necessary by the postwar advent of numerous new preservatives, neutralizers, foaming agents, and other food additives which produce beneficial technical effects in foods.

THE LAW broadly defines a food additive to include any substance used in and around food which may reasonably be expected to become a component of food.

This includes medications administered to animals which may leave residues in tissues after slaughter. Other sections of the law provide that such medications must be proven safe and effective for treated animals under standards set by FDA before being marketed.

THE TERM FOOD ADDITIVE also includes substances added directly to food for technical effect, from flavoring agents to fruit coatings; substances used in food containers, from paper components to plastics; and even atomic energy, which may some day have widespread commercial application in food preservation and processing.

All of these must be shown to have the intended physical or other technical effect.

And of more importance to the consumer, they must be proven safe for use in or around foods according to standards set by FDA.

The standards include information on the chemistry of the additive, the effect produced, the methods for determining the presence of the additive, and the necessary tests to establish the additive's safety.

THE LAW provides that an additive having cancer-producing properties when ingested by man or animal cannot be considered safe.

The time and efforts of many scientists in Government and in private industry are represented in each additive use given clearance in the form of an FDA regulation.

THROUGH INTEGRATION of Federal law and cooperation between Departments of the Federal Government, the job of insuring that pesticides are used safely has become a team effort. One example of this cooperative effort is the governmental screening procedure for residue-producing pesticide chemicals proposed for use upon raw agricultural commodities.

The U.S. Department of Agriculture, if convinced of the usefulness of a residue-producing pesticide, will certify that fact to the Department of Health, Education, and Welfare along with a statement covering the amount of residue that will remain on the crop from the proposed use.

It then becomes a responsibility of FDA to see that the tolerance supporting data presented by industry equal or exceed a standard for compliance set by FDA to insure that the amount of residue will be safe for consumers.

IF THE DATA satisfy the standard, a tolerance—the legally permitted residue—is set by FDA.

These data comprise a practical analytical method for measuring the amount of the residue. They include information about the chemistry and the structure of the pesticide chemical, and about any metabolite (biological conversion product) formed on plant life.

Animal feeding studies are required to measure acute or chronic effects of the pesticide, including any effects on the animal's reproductive cycle.

PHYSICIANS, pharmacologists, and other scientists in FDA must be satisfied that the chemical and pharmacological data are up to standard in terms of quantity of tests run and caliber of research represented. These scientists then check to see that the data fully support the establishment of a tolerance.

The tolerance is set at a small fraction of a level found to have no significance to the health of the test animals. A wide margin of safety is needed to allow for differences in sensitivity between people and animals, as well as sensitivity differences among people.

295

If the data do not justify establishing a greater tolerance, a tolerance of zero in or on any crop may be set.

THE PRESIDENT'S Science Advisory Committee issued a report on "The Use of Pesticides" in 1963. It concluded that establishment of pesticide tolerances and the enforcement of them upon raw agricultural commodities through the inspection and analysis by FDA were key factors in permitting the continued usage of pesticides without danger to consumers.

The work of FDA inspectors and scientists results in the examination for pesticide residues of better than 1 percent of the estimated 2.5 million shipments of raw agricultural commodities in the United States annually.

BESIDES RUNNING regulatory checks on interstate shipments of raw agricultural commodities, FDA also maintains surveillance of pesticide residue levels in the U.S. food supply through "market basket" surveys in five geographical locations.

The market basket list is made up of 82 food items representing a 2-week diet of a 19-year-old male.

SURVEY RESULTS have presented a consistently low level of pesticide residues

Miniature white piglet at Beltsville, Md., is a new type of research animal being used in USDA and Food and Drug Administration scientific research programs.

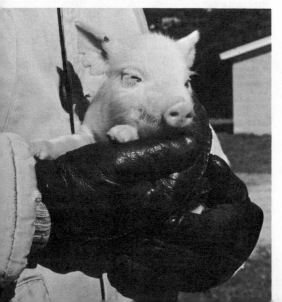

in food ready for consumption. This level is, in fact, a small fraction of the safe, legal tolerances which have been established under the Federal Food, Drug, and Cosmetic Act.

Progressive and diversified programs of pure and applied scientific research make it possible for the FDA district field laboratories to carry out highly sensitive pesticide residue analyses on raw agricultural commodities.

THESE programs also enable the laboratories to analyze for direct and indirect food additives, to check food products for substitution of inferior ingredients, to isolate bacterial organisms responsible for food poisoning, to examine food samples for radioactivity, and to run a hundred and one other tests upon foods.

Without the necessary support research, it would not be possible to set standards for compliance. Backup research is essential to evaluation of petitions for pesticide tolerances and exemptions, food additive petitions, color additive petitions, and proposed standards for foods.

On any given day, the scientists in FDA's Washington and field laboratories can be found working on such research projects as development of new methods or refinement of old ones for testing chemical and biological contamination of food.

Other scientists are observing the effects of processing and storage on the characteristics of food products, carrying on animal feeding studies dealing with the carryover of drug residues from animal feed to animal tissue and byproducts, or conducting studies showing the effects of chemicals on animal organ systems.

THE ADMINISTRATOR advising industry on the requirements of the act, the inspector engaged in running down the source of a food poisoning, and the FDA scientist engaged in a food research project are, in fact, all engaged in the same task—making sure the U.S. food supply is consistently safe, pure, and wholesome.

GRADING—ASSURANCE OF QUALITY

GEORGE R. GRANGE

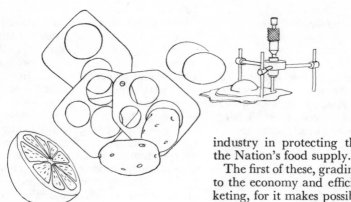

GETTING food products from farm to consumer is a complex task. The amazing efficiency of this marketing process is one of the marvels of the 20th century.

Billions of pounds of food are produced, sold, processed, distributed, and resold annually in a vast, pulsating complex of man and machinery. Modern marketing involves sending lettuce by air 3,000 miles from the west coast to the East. Marketing ships tons of grain from the Great Plains to the great metropolitan centers of the Nation. It places a cut of meat on your supermarket counter within hours after the meat was processed a hundred miles away.

Part of the credit for the efficiency of today's marketing structure lies in the voluntary system of Federal and Federal-State grading and inspection—which gives meaning to food and food product transactions.

This program basically has two parts: Voluntary grading programs which furnish a common language for the marketplace, and voluntary inspection programs which aid the food industry in protecting the quality of the Nation's food supply.

The first of these, grading, is essential to the economy and efficiency of marketing, for it makes possible the sale of commodities across great distances, allows a processor to control the quality of his product, and gives the consumer a choice in purchasing food.

Grading, as old as civilization itself, safeguards the quality of the Nation's food supply by setting up an accurate standard by which food is sold.

THE PURPOSE of grading a product is to identify the degrees or gradations in its value or usability.

Farm products unavoidably vary in quality because something grown in the field or raised on the hoof cannot be controlled like any manufactured item. Grading has been a part of the marketing process for farm commodities since the earliest times.

As GRADING is a language of marketing, so standards are the "words" used in that language.

Standards have to be established before a product can be graded in any meaningful, understandable, and consistent manner. Sorting eggs by size is a simple kind of grading operation. However, standards are needed to establish different size classes to assure

* * *

George R. Grange is a *Deputy Administrator* of the Consumer and Marketing Service.

uniformity among graders. Determining the dividing line between a "large" egg and a "medium" egg exemplifies the function a standard plays in defining and classifying every separate grade factor for a product.

STANDARDS, therefore, go hand in hand with grading—though they are an earlier development. The Egyptians established "standards" of length, and the Romans required a set of standards of weights and measures which was to be used throughout the known world. These were early developments leading toward establishment of "standards of identity," which differ from grade standards in that they decree only the minimum standard a product must meet to be accepted in the marketplace as a product under that name.

Such standards were developed as early as the 12th century in Great Britain—standards for bread (the "assize of bread" which became a factor even in colonial marketing), for spices, for wines, and for many other products.

THE EARLY STANDARDS in Britain had some of the characteristics of modern grading standardization. The assize of bread, for instance, established prices based on the quality of the bread as determined by contents. These standards were the forerunners of activities carried on today by the National Bureau of Standards, the Food and Drug Administration, and the meat and poultry inspection services of the Consumer and Marketing Service (C&MS).

Voluntary inspection programs—as for egg products, dairy products, and processed fruits and vegetables—are similar programs in that they identify products by minimum standards. The voluntary programs differ, however, in that they are not required by law.

ONE ASPECT of these early standardization attempts has a direct relation to quality grading operations of today. As far back as the late medieval period in British marketing, there were three basic means by which a standard was established. First, it was often established primarily as a customary standard which authorities later declared to have the weight of law. In this case, enforcement of the standard by custom and social ostracism was supplanted by the third-party enforcement by legal authorities.

Second, establishment of a standard by statute was often done at the request or insistence of the merchant guilds concerned in marketing the product. This was to protect guild members—who were subject to guild enforcement—from outside merchants, who were subject to no such restraints.

Third, standards were often established by statute on the insistence of the consuming public that they be protected from the unscrupulous merchant. This principle of market regulation for protection of the "commonalty" was an early responsibility accepted by the Crown.

Thus, we have historical evidence of three basic criteria for standards of marketability: Customary industry use of standards, demands of industry for standards to improve the marketing of their products, and needs of the public to have a guideline to purchasing. These three forces are constantly at play, even to this day, in establishing standards for marketing.

THE FIRST "GRADING" in the sense we use today probably arose as a result of the first of the above points—customary use by industry. Cotton grades as we know them today are similar to the early grades used by cotton traders; even the terms, like "good middling," reflect the fact that these grades were used as early as the 18th century.

Such grades served the same purpose as grades do today—they established common terminology on which trading could be based.

But to serve a function in marketing, a customary grade had to be uniformly accepted by the persons doing the trading. Often custom developed different sets of grade terminology for different markets. In these cases, neither set of terminology could function in trade between such markets. This situation in the cotton industry at the beginning of the 20th century led to passage of the Cotton Futures Act, which established uniform grade terminology for cotton to be traded in the futures markets.

The Cotton Futures Act of 1914 was the first legal authority for establishment of standards within the U.S. Department of Agriculture (USDA).

Two years later, the Grain Standards Act was passed, the second such law, but with a different purpose. The Grain Standards Act required the use of Federal standards when grain was sold by grade in interstate commerce. It did not make Federal grading compulsory but outlawed use of any grades other than the official grades.

Perhaps both of these laws are progeny of the Nation's first law regulating food products—the Tea Importation Act. The act, passed in 1897, provided for a board of tea experts who evaluated samples of tea, established a number of different "samples" or standards which were acceptable, and then distributed these samples to examiners at U.S. ports.

Although this law is similar to the Federal Food, Drug, and Cosmetic Act and to the Meat Inspection Act in that it establishes minimum standards a product must meet, it is comparable with many of the present-day quality grading operations in that actual samples or standards of various types of tea were developed and used in the inspection process.

Quality standards and quality grading go one step beyond the simple establishment of a minimum standard of identity.

Standardization for grading involves classifying all samples of a product into distinct levels or gradations of a product's characteristics or qualities which lie above the minimum required for identification.

Where inspection determines whether a product ought to be marketed at all, and standards of identity determine whether it is marketed under the proper name, grading recognizes the value in the marketplace of each level of that product above the minimum which is allowed in the market under the particular name.

U.S. grade standards for quality complement other mandatory standards designed for protection of the consumer.

Minimum standards of quality—commonly referred to as food and drug standards—have been established by the Food and Drug Administration (FDA) for many food products. These products must meet the minimum food and drug standards or otherwise be labeled to indicate that they fail to meet such minimum quality levels.

For products for which food and drug minimum standards of quality have been established, the Agriculture Department adopts—as the minimum level for the lowest U.S. grade—specifications that are at least as high as these mandatory requirements. In establishing U.S. grade standards it is customary to have one or more levels of quality above the lowest grade: for example, grades A, B, and C. Thus, the Department provides two or more grade levels for marketing purposes and at the same time recognizes the minimum mandatory standards which have been established by FDA.

Among the first quality grades for food were those promulgated for fruits and vegetables during World War I, under authority of the emergency Food Production Act. This inspection work was performed in the major markets in the country at the request of industry—either buyer or seller—and for foods which were purchased by the military for the war effort.

The Food Products Inspection Service, to perform this work, was started in 1917. In 1918, its work was expanded so "certificates could be made as to quality and grade, as well as condition of soundness" as had been specified in earlier legislation. The first specific standards to be published under this authority were for potatoes.

Official standards for agricultural commodities have been established by the Agriculture Department for a wide range of products: Cotton—1909, corn—1916, wheat—1917, potatoes—1917, butter—1919, shell eggs—1923, beef—1927, canned fruits and vegetables—1928, frozen peas (the first for a frozen product)—1939.

GRADING, then, is simply classifying farm products into uniform categories of quality. It is a sorting process. All acceptable categories of a farm product are identified in terms of their market value, that is, their size, end use, abstract quality (taste, color, freedom from blemishes, odor, shape), and the like, which measure a product's relative value or market price.

GRADING—so long as it is accepted by the marketplace—may be performed by anyone, the manufacturer, the marketer, a private agency, or the local, State, or Federal Government. Much grading in our own country, however, is performed by the Federal Government—which offers two advantages: Nationwide uniformity of standards and third-party impartiality.

Under the voluntary grading programs during 1965, the Agriculture Department and cooperating States graded and certified three-fifths of the beef produced in the United States; two-thirds of the ready-to-cook poultry; one-fifth of the shell eggs; four-

A USDA meat grader marks the quality grade on beef carcasses at an Omaha packing plant.

fifths of the dried or frozen eggs; half of the lamb; three-fourths of the frozen fruits and vegetables; one-fourth of the canned fruits and vegetables; two-thirds of the potatoes; and many other types of foods.

Users of the service in 1965 paid the Department and cooperating State agencies about $50 million in grading fees. Six thousand Federal and State graders provided grading service at hundreds of shipping points, processing plants, storage warehouses, and receiving markets throughout the United States.

THERE ARE TWO TYPES of grading—producers' and consumers' grading. More precisely, there are three situations of grade use—consumer labeled, consumer unlabeled, and commercial.

A producer's standard is one applied to the farm product at the point of first sale, or when sold by the first handler.

Such standards are used by marketers as useful tools in trading—particularly at great distances—up to the point of retail distribution.

A CONSUMER'S STANDARD is one applied to the product in the form in which the product is going to be sold to the consumer.

Its primary purpose is to measure differences in quality that are important to the average consumer and to convey this information to him.

Such a simplification of the use of grades is not universally applicable in today's marketing system. Some grading which is properly "consumer grading" is never labeled as such—and the consumer never sees this grademark upon the product.

A CONSUMER GRADE could be defined, then, in a broader sense as any grade applied to a product in the form in which it is sold to the consumer and which identifies qualities of interest to the consumer.

This definition would include the earlier category of products that are graded and also sold to the consumer under that grademark. It would also include another category of products which are graded specifically in the form consumers eventually buy, but which are for one reason or another not sold to consumers under the grade identification.

Examples of this latter type of grading use would be many brands of frozen fruits and vegetables, poultry products, and dairy products.

THREE SITUATIONS, therefore, must be considered when we talk about Federal-State grading:

• Consumer grading without labeling. This involves packing to meet a specific U.S. grade but not using the grade designation on the consumer package. The practice is common for some food products, particularly those merchandised under established brand names. The commercial firm, in such instances, does not wish to distract attention from its brand name by also using the U.S. grademark on the package.

• Consumer grading with labeling. The U.S. grademark is used to lend sales appeal to the product or guide the consumer's choice of product. For example, the Government grademarks "U.S. Choice" beef or "U.S. Grade A" eggs have the effect of increasing consumer appeal in the food stores as well as serving as a designation of quality.

• Commercial grading. This is grading for the use of commercial firms in buying and selling among themselves on the basis of U.S. grade standards, even though these standards are not used at the retail level. Wholesale trading in some products is based largely on U.S. grades, but they are not used in retailing the finished product. For example, most peanut butter manufacturers buy peanuts from shellers in terms of U.S. grades with Government inspection certificates required. However, the manufacturers do not use a U.S. grade standard in selling their different brands of peanut butter. In many more cases, the U.S. grades and Government grading services are used in commercial marketing, but no

301

Asparagus being canned at a California plant under continuous USDA inspection.

evidence of their use is found in retail stores in the form of U.S. grade designations on the food packages.

QUALITY CONTROL PROGRAMS—industry's way of insuring a continuous level of quality in its products—can also be served by Government grades and grading programs, which provide a basis for quality control activities of either the producer or the marketer.

The grades (like U.S. Choice) become quality control goals which should be met by the producer if he is to realize the most from his investment. Today, about 70 percent of "fed cattle" grade out as U.S. Choice beef—since producers and feeders have set the "Choice" grade as a goal in their production.

Quality control—as a purpose for grading—is also a means of reflecting the needs of consumers to the marketers and producers. If consumers want Choice beef, this desire—all other factors being equal—will eventually be communicated economically back into

the production and marketing strata. Grades serve as a common language for quality control.

Also useful in quality control activities of marketers are the various voluntary inspection programs, operated by the grading services of the Consumer and Marketing Service. These programs, known in the trade as continuous inspection or in-plant inspection, serve the food marketing industry and the public by providing unbiased inspection for wholesomeness and quality for some foods not covered by mandatory inspection laws.

VOLUNTARY inspection programs also help provide a "language for the marketplace." But where grading identifies several levels of quality, voluntary inspection certifies that a product meets the "minimum standard" required. This official certification helps to identify the product in the marketplace.

The official USDA shield and grademark may be used only on products

302

packed in approved plants operating under continuous inspection.

Examples of these marks are shown on the right.

Continuous in-plant inspection and grading services are used most widely by plants producing canned and frozen fruits and vegetables, egg products, and dairy products.

BEFORE THE Agriculture Department will start continuous inspection on a contract basis, a survey inspection of the plant is made to determine whether the plant and methods of operation are adequate and suitable. The buildings and the equipment must be properly constructed and maintained in a sanitary condition.

AFTER A PLANT is approved for continuous inspection, one or more inspectors are assigned at all times when it is operating to make continuous in-process checks on the preparation, processing, and packing operations. The Government inspectors observe preparation of raw materials; observe plant conditions under which the product is being prepared; make frequent line checks of product quality; and examine the final product to determine and certify the U.S. grade standard which it meets.

The inspectors provide a quality control service by means of daily—or more frequent if necessary—reports on the grade of the product being packed, as well as on plant sanitation conditions.

ON THE BASIS of these reports, plant management can correct problems before they become serious and can protect the quality of their product.

This in-plant inspection and grading service was provided to more than 800 plants during 1965.

This does not include meat and poultry plants where the grading service relies on mandatory inspection—required by the meat and poultry inspection acts—for assurance that a graded product is wholesome and fit for human consumption.

The wholesomeness of all other foods

303

shipped between States is protected by provisions of the Federal Food, Drug, and Cosmetic Act. Food and drug inspectors are not stationed in plants, like meat and poultry inspectors are, but enforce their regulations by periodic examination of the plants and by picking up samples of the products for testing.

AGRICULTURE DEPARTMENT inspectors stationed in the fruit and vegetable, egg, and dairy products plants make every reasonable check during plant inspections and finished product examinations to determine, in addition to the grade, that products are wholesome and are free from objectionable substances.

In-plant inspectors are backed up by well-equipped laboratory facilities. Bacteriological, chemical, and other special analyses are performed to determine wholesomeness of products and assist in product quality control. A USDA certificate of acceptable quality and condition is not knowingly issued on a product which would fail to comply with any Federal food and drug requirements.

THE FEDERAL-STATE grading services and FDA work very closely together in carrying out their respective assignments.

A Memorandum of Understanding was developed and signed in 1953 setting forth the principal working arrangements adopted in the interest of each agency in discharging its responsibilities as effectively as possible.

The Agriculture Department clears all new or revised grade standards with FDA prior to issuance. The Department furnishes FDA with a list of all processing plants operating under continuous, in-plant inspection contracts.

THE FDA INSPECTOR requests the Department inspector on duty at the plant to accompany him during his inspection of the plant. FDA advises the Department whenever it finds objectionable conditions in a processing or packing plant where USDA grading

304

service is being provided. And FDA does not start seizure action on a USDA graded product without first reviewing and considering Department findings.

FEDERAL MARKETING order programs make up another phase of Federal-State grading services.

Producers of fruits, vegetables, and nuts are authorized by the Agricultural Marketing Agreement Act of 1937 to organize and operate industry-wide marketing plans, under supervision of the Agriculture Department. The growers in an industry, voting in a referendum, must approve such a Federal marketing order.

These orders, issued by the Secretary of Agriculture after a public hearing and referendum, are then binding upon all handlers of the commodity in a producing area.

Under terms of the marketing orders, shipments may be regulated to bring about better marketing practices and thus improve returns to producers.

ONE OF THE forms of regulation most commonly adopted is to prohibit the shipment in normal domestic trade channels of products which fail to meet specified standards for grade, size, or maturity. Coupled with such quality regulations is a further requirement that all shipments must be inspected by a third party, impartial grading service, usually the Federal-State service, to determine that shipments meet quality standards established under the marketing plan.

IN 1965 there were 48 Federal marketing agreement or order programs in effect for fruits, vegetables, and nuts. During the year, grade, size, or maturity regulations were in effect and official inspection was required on the following commodities:

Oranges and grapefruit produced in Florida, Texas, California, and Arizona; lemons from California and Arizona; limes and avocados from Florida; apricots and cherries from Washington; peaches from Georgia, Colorado, Washington, and California; fresh prunes from Idaho, Washington, and Oregon; plums from California; Bartlett pears from California and winter pears from California, Washington, and Oregon; potatoes produced in Idaho, Oregon, Washington, and California; onions from Idaho, Oregon, and Texas; carrots, lettuce, and tomatoes from Texas; and all peanuts, almonds, walnuts, filberts, dates, raisins, and dried prunes.

FOR A NUMBER OF YEARS many producers of commodities subject to Federal marketing orders were concerned that their efforts to improve domestic marketing conditions were being impaired or offset by imports which failed to meet the quality or size specifications that have been established for domestic shipments.

In response to producer requests, Congress in 1954 amended the Agricultural Marketing Agreement Act to require that whenever certain commodities produced in the United States are being regulated as to grade, size, quality, or maturity under a Federal marketing order, imports of those commodities must meet the same grade, quality, and maturity specifications that apply to domestic shipments. Furthermore, there is mandatory inspection of such import shipments at point of entry by the Federal-State grading service.

These import regulations apply only during periods when regulations on domestic shipments are in effect.

During all or part of 1965, imports of tomatoes, Irish potatoes, onions, oranges, grapefruit, limes, avocados, walnuts, and dates (other than dates for processing) were required to be inspected for quality at point of entry under this program.

The major use of our U.S. grade standards for food products is in commercial transactions.

An estimated 90 to 95 percent of all food products graded in 1965 was for commercial firms and the remaining 5 to 10 percent was for hospitals, schools, military agencies, and for other governmental agencies.

Industry orientation is inevitably a vital element in voluntary grading programs. Commercial firms apply for the service and pay the fees which cover the costs.

THESE COMMERCIAL FIRMS use the U.S. grade standards and employ the grading service only if it helps them in marketing their products.

The buyer and seller may mutually agree to designation of a particular U.S. grade as part of their contract. The seller may decide entirely on his own initiative to process or pack his product in accordance with U.S. grades. The buyer may specify delivery of a U.S. graded product.

In any event, either the seller or the buyer or both have to conclude that it is advantageous to make use of the Government grading service.

TO RETAIN their usefulness, grade standards need constant revision to keep them current with changing marketing conditions and with changing buyer, seller, and consumer values. Keeping grade standards up to date is a challenging task.

Fortunately, voluntary grade standards cannot be maintained unless a reasonably successful job is done in making them retain their usefulness. Otherwise, the grade standard goes into bankruptcy and dies because it ceases to be used.

Serving the interests of the consumer has proven to be compatible with the principle of grading on a voluntary, industry-supported basis. A primary reason for this lack of conflict of interest is that the U.S. grades simply indicate the different levels of quality.

GRADING plays an important function in today's highly organized but complicated marketing system. At the same time, grading plays a vital role in translating the consumer interests and preferences into recognizable standards of quality for common use in preparing and merchandising many of our food products.

PUBLIC HEALTH PROGRAMS

EDWIN L. RUPPERT and FRANK W. MACKISON

THROUGHOUT history food has been one of man's major concerns. Of the essentials of life, none is more vital. Yet over the years mishandling of food—whether from ignorance, carelessness, or for other reasons—has often led to illness and sometimes even to death.

To protect himself, man has had to protect his food. This is why since the early pages of history there have been rules, regulations, and laws to safeguard our food supply and public health. Many were based on religious mores. And all reflect, of course, the medical knowledge of the time.

In the United States, one regulatory effort goes back even before our Nation was founded, although other efforts came much later. As early as 1764 the Massachusetts Bay Colony adopted sanitary requirements for slaughterhouses.

The State of Massachusetts, in 1856, passed the first law in this country prohibiting adulteration of milk. In 1884 Illinois adopted State laws for food sanitation, and in 1881 the State of New York passed the first effective food and drug law.

ADVENT OF THE GERM theory of disease in the middle 1800's was soon followed by recognition of the role of food in communicable disease.

At the turn of the century, the part played by milk in the spread of disease was intensively investigated.

ONE OF THE tasks of the Public Health Service (PHS), an agency of the U.S. Department of Health, Education, and Welfare, is to help guard the public against health hazards in food. In 1906 PHS, through its predecessor, the Marine Hospital Service, investigated typhoid fever cases in the District of Columbia.

The investigation identified milk as the transmission agent in 10 percent of 866 typhoid cases studied. This and other studies by the Service established

* * *

Edwin L. Ruppert is *Chief*, Milk and Food Branch, Division of Environmental Engineering and Food Protection, Bureau of State Services, Public Health Service, U.S. Department of Health, Education, and Welfare.

Frank W. Mackison is *Food Consultant*, Division of Environmental Engineering and Food Protection.

that milk can be a vehicle for the transmitting of disease.

As a result of these findings, a more effective and easier method of milk pasteurization was developed.

IN 1923, THE STATE of Alabama requested PHS assistance in developing a statewide milk control program. Research and investigational activities, field studies, and demonstrations conducted by the Service resulted in a highly effective program for preventing diseases associated with milk.

Knowledge and experience gained provided the basis for much of the present approach to preventing and controlling foodborne illness.

The Alabama work centered around a cooperative effort to unify milk control methods throughout that State by means of legislation designed to prevent outbreaks of milkborne diseases like typhoid fever, diphtheria, and septic sore throat.

A study of existing milk ordinances showed little or no uniformity of requirements. In some instances, requirements were diametrically opposed. The need for a single uniform ordinance, which would apply to all communities, became obvious.

This led to development in 1924 of what was to become known as the Standard Milk Ordinance, later as the Milk Ordinance and Code, and today as the Grade "A" Pasteurized Milk Ordinance—1965 Recommendations of the U.S. Public Health Service.

DEVELOPMENT OF the Standard Milk Ordinance illustrates the method used today in developing PHS recommended ordinances and codes.

Although the Alabama studies emphasized the need for uniform legislation, it soon became evident that even if communities adopted the same milk ordinance, interpretation and enforcement of the ordinance were far from uniform.

To meet this problem, the Public Health Service Milk Code was developed. The code took up the Standard Milk Ordinance item by item, setting forth in each case the preventive steps needed for protecting the milk supply, the reasons for them, and how satisfactory compliance would be determined.

To gain the advantage of review by a large number of groups and individuals, drafts of the Standard Milk Ordinance and Code were referred to the public health and dairy organizations for their study.

A Milk Sanitation Advisory Board was appointed to assist. This board made available to PHS the know-how of experts in various phases of public health control of milk.

RESEARCH WAS UNDERTAKEN where needed to provide a scientific base for provisions of the original ordinance and code, and subsequent revisions.

This research through the years has included studies on the effectiveness of commercial milk pasteurization equipment in destroying disease-producing bacteria. Findings led to the recommendation that pasteurizing equipment be capable of heating every particle of the milk to not less than 160° F. and holding it at that temperature for 15 seconds.

Subsequent investigation has shown a need to increase this temperature to 161° F. to prevent the transmission of Q fever through milk.

OTHER INVESTIGATIONS involved bactericidal treatment of milk utensils and containers; preventing contamination of milk in the regenerator section of a high-temperature short-time pasteurizer after pasteurization; effectiveness of valves to prevent the contamination of pasteurized milk with raw milk; nutritional value of pasteurized milk; methods for assuring proper treatment of foam in pasteurizing vats; and, more recently, a method for removing strontium 90 from milk.

While PHS made most of these milk investigations itself, some were conducted with State or local health agencies, institutions, with other Federal agencies, and the dairy industry.

New editions of the Milk Ordinance

307

and Code have been published to keep pace with new techniques in fluid milk processing and sanitation. Thirteen editions have been issued to date. The first edition was published in 1925, and the latest revision completed in 1965.

These sanitation criteria are widely used throughout the United States. Effectiveness of the measures outlined in the ordinance and code has been demonstrated. While milk was once a major factor in transmission of disease, a single case of any illness attributed to properly pasteurized milk is extremely rare at the present time.

In 1925 a typhoid fever outbreak, involving over 1,500 cases and 150 deaths, was traced to consumption of contaminated oysters. In response to requests from State and local health officials and from the oyster industry, PHS developed criteria for public health protection of these shellfish during growing, harvesting, and processing.

THE SERVICE'S PROGRAM for preventing foodborne illness was broadened in the 1930's to give guidance to States and municipalities on sanitary control of food service in public eating places and for frozen desserts.

PHS sanitation standards have since been developed for food and beverage vending machines, poultry processing, and ice manufacturing. Many of the standards have been adopted by State and local agencies.

The Milk Ordinance and Code is currently the basis of the milk sanitation laws or regulations of 37 States. Almost 110 million people live in these particular States.

PHS RECOMMENDATIONS for food service establishments are currently the basis of sanitation laws or regulations in 43 States and the District of Columbia. In addition, over 1,100 local health jurisdictions have adopted laws and regulations based on the recommendations. Over 161 million people live in these areas.

The Service is presently cooperating with the Bureau of Commercial Fish-

eries of the U.S. Department of the Interior in developing sanitary guidelines for the fish-smoking industry, and with the American Academy of Pediatrics in developing sanitary standards for processing commercial baby formulas. Sanitation standards are being developed for processing eggs and egg products, and for convenience foods. Publication of all these guides is anticipated in either 1966 or early 1967.

State and local health agencies are involved in these cooperative efforts, since PHS furnishes copies of proposed standards to State and local health agencies for review and comment, as well as to other agencies and industries.

PROGRAMS FOR CERTIFYING interstate milk shippers and interstate shellfish shippers in which PHS exercises the leadership role are examples of cooperative efforts between Federal, State, and local regulatory agencies and industry. These voluntary programs have been initiated at the request of the State and local regulatory agencies. They provide information about the sanitary quality of fluid milk and fluid milk products and fresh or frozen oysters, clams, and mussels from distant sources. The programs have fostered a high sanitary quality in these foods which are moving within a State or in interstate commerce.

INSPECTION and laboratory control of milk and shellfish sources are performed by representatives of States and municipalities, using uniform procedures approved by PHS. A numerical rating is given for sanitation and for program enforcement.

The ratings are reported to the Service, which then publishes a list of names and ratings of certified shippers. The lists are widely distributed to States and communities on request.

The Service periodically checks the certified shippers and the work of each participating State, including its laboratory program. Currently more than 1,400 interstate milk shippers in 46 States and the District of Columbia, and over 1,200 interstate shellfish shippers in 23 States, are listed as certified shippers by PHS.

THE INTERSTATE shellfish shippers program involves governmental cooperation at the Federal level.

The Interior Department is charged by the Fish and Wildlife Act of 1956 with responsibility at the Federal level for matters primarily relating to fisheries. It thus is concerned with shellfish production. PHS has responsibility for preventing transmission or interstate spread of communicable disease by shellfish.

So that both agencies can fulfill their responsibilities and prevent a duplication of effort, they have an agreement whereby the Interior Department's Fish and Wildlife Service provides advisory assistance to the PHS. The Fish and Wildlife Service (FWS) also makes available to PHS information helpful in preparing technical guides or in research on shellfish sanitation.

CONVERSELY, PHS consults with FWS on the technical guides and shellfish research.

FWS, through its industry contacts, disseminates information on the shellfish certification program.

In addition, PHS coordinates with FWS any control measures needed to combat an outbreak of disease which is attributed to fishery products other than shellfish.

FOOD PROTECTION PROGRAMS, to be successful, must be based on technically sound procedures practical in their application.

The programs must be checked out through research, field studies, and by demonstrations.

PHS food protection research and investigational activities are conducted primarily at two locations—the Robert A. Taft Sanitary Engineering Center in Cincinnati, Ohio, and the Communicable Disease Center in Atlanta, Ga.

In addition, the Service supports research on food protection problems through grants to universities and colleges, State and local health agencies,

public and private nonprofit agencies, and to individuals. Recently, significant contributions have been made through these grants on problems related to foodborne illness attributed to the Salmonella and botulinum organisms.

FORMAL AND IN-SERVICE type training programs are conducted at PHS training centers, the Robert A. Taft Sanitary Engineering Center, and the Communicable Disease Center. This training helps State and local regulatory officials and industry personnel keep abreast of new developments in food protection and technology.

Training courses are conducted in other locations at the request of State and local agencies.

Courses of instruction of 2 to 10 days' duration are offered periodically on such topics as epidemiology of foodborne disease, milk pasteurization controls, pesticide residue analysis of food, food microbiology, radionuclides in foods, institutional sanitary food service, and the laboratory examination of dairy products.

During the fiscal year 1965, more than 2,000 trainees attended these courses.

IN COOPERATION with national health-related groups, and the industry involved, PHS participates in developing standards for sanitary design and construction of food equipment. It is obvious that properly designed and built equipment is much more easily kept clean and sanitary.

Among the industry and private groups with which the Service cooperates in developing equipment standards are: The Baking Industry Sanitation Standards Committee; the Automatic Merchandising Health-Industry Council; the National Sanitation Foundation, for food equipment; and the 3–A Sanitary Standards Committees, for dairy equipment.

PHS also issues publications, visual aids, and other materials to inform the industry and the public about recommended procedures for preparing, processing, and serving food, both in the home and in commercial establishments as well.

An example is the publication "From Hand to Mouth," which explains the need for good food protection and describes methods for preventing foodborne illness. Thousands of copies of this publication have been distributed.

THE SERVICE's food protection functions are authorized by the Public Health Service Act of 1944, Public Law 410.

In meeting its responsibilities under this act, the Service acts chiefly in an advisory, stimulative, and research capacity.

Its food protection program goals are to promote establishment of an effective food sanitation program in each State; to stimulate adoption of adequate State and local control legislation; to encourage uniform enforcement; and to induce industry to support and comply with State and local food protection programs.

The Service has no regulatory responsibility for protecting food, except for enforcing Interstate Quarantine Regulations dealing with the sanitary quality of food served on interstate conveyances and American flag vessels.

TRANSLATION of public health food protection measures into consumer benefits is effected largely by the State and local agencies.

Today all States and most local health agencies have milk and food protection programs which follow closely PHS recommendations.

To have a legal basis to operate on, the States enact laws and adopt regulations setting up the minimum sanitary standards which food establishments must comply with in order to carry on business.

Minimum standards are usually set for milk and food processing plants, warehouses, retail food establishments, and food service and related businesses. These standards are enforced through inspection.

To help assure compliance, most of the States use educational measures to improve sanitation levels within food establishments.

Court action can be taken as a last resort to obtain compliance.

Many States have delegated authority for protection of public health—including prevention of foodborne disease—to cities, towns, counties, and other local governments.

Local governments usually regulate the sanitary control of food through ordinances. In a number of States, however, local governments have been designated to act as an agent for the State in enforcing specific State food protection laws.

Although a variety of agencies at both the Federal and State levels of government are involved in food protection activities, the great bulk of these activities are administered by only two agencies at each level.

At the Federal level, these agencies are the Department of Health, Education, and Welfare (HEW) and the U.S. Department of Agriculture.

At the State level, food regulation activities are generally vested in either the State department of health or the State department of agriculture. There may be some sharing of responsibility between these agencies in some States.

Programs for the sanitary control of food do not always follow a uniform pattern, nor are they always enforced with equal effectiveness.

A degree of coordination, however, has been developed between Federal, State, and local programs which permits close cooperation on problems of mutual concern.

Those arrangements include the exchange of technical information, exchange of information upon seizure of food products and other enforcement actions, cooperative inspections, appearances as expert witnesses, and assistance in training.

Investigation of disease outbreaks is another very important part of a food protection program.

These investigations often reveal conditions which call for modified preventive measures.

In addition, there are occasional out-

310

breaks of disease of unknown cause associated with food. Studies of these outbreaks offer the possibility of identifying the causative agent and determining how the food had become contaminated.

PROMOTION OF UNIFORM local regulations within the State and providing technical and consultative services on food sanitation problems to cities, towns, and counties are activities that States have found of prime importance. Uniformity of regulations facilitates communications between those enforcing the regulations and those who must comply with them.

States strengthen food protection programs by training local personnel in enforcing State and local regulations. This training is necessary for uniform interpretation and application of regulations on a day-to-day basis.

THE STATES, by appraising local food protection programs, assist local agencies in determining how well food protection goals are being achieved.

The States also obtain information which is useful in planning for new preventive measures.

Application of food protection measures in local jurisdictions varies with the administrative pattern of the State and the size of the local jurisdiction. Sometimes a large municipal health agency conducts a more comprehensive program than the State itself, while rural communities may carry on only a limited program or none at all.

STATE AND LOCAL health agencies assist management in training employees in sanitary food-handling practices. This includes on-the-spot demonstrations as well as formalized training.

All State and many local agencies have laboratory facilities for both routine and special analyses of foods. These analyses may be to gain information on the bacteriological quality of market foods, or the effectiveness of methods for cleaning and sanitizing food equipment.

Local agencies that don't have their own laboratories, or have only limited facilities, usually arrange with the State public health laboratory for examination of food samples.

Special analyses, perhaps involving outbreaks of foodborne illness or suspected food adulteration or contamination, may be performed by both the State laboratory and a Federal laboratory.

Paralleling the food protection programs of official health agencies are comprehensive programs of the food industries. Some of these industries have initiated sanitation and quality control programs.

These programs, generally developed with assistance from official agencies, familiarize industry personnel with food protection techniques and the requirements of food protection laws and regulations. Some segments of the food industry train personnel in the proper methods of food handling and food protection.

ONLY A FEW food industries have begun industrywide sanitation programs like that of the milk industry. However, a number of industries, through their national organizations, associations, and institutes, provide direct services to their members by quality control, plant inspection, product research, and supplying technical information.

In addition, some national food organizations participate with health agencies in developing food protection standards, standards for sanitary design and construction of processing equipment, and educational programs.

PUBLIC HEALTH PROTECTION of food is a responsibility shared by all levels of government and industry.

Public health agencies of Federal, State, and local governments have set up sanitation criteria and methods to prevent or minimize foodborne illness.

Through its cooperation with the health agencies, the food industry has been able to maintain and improve the quality and wholesomeness of food for the American consumer.

NATHAN KOENIG

FOOD

STANDARDS

FOR

THE WORLD

Nathan Koenig was formerly *Special Assistant* to the Administrator of the Consumer and Marketing Service, and was U.S. delegate at the first three sessions of the Codex Alimentarius Commission. He is now retired from the U.S. Department of Agriculture but is serving as a consultant on U.S. participation in the Joint FAO/WHO Program on Food Standards which is carried out through the Commission.

A WORLDWIDE unified movement is now underway to bring about a meeting of minds on protecting the interests of consumers in safe and wholesome food, promoting fair trade practice in food, and facilitating international trade.

This is spearheaded by the Codex Alimentarius Commission, which was set up by two agencies of the United Nations, the World Health Organization and the Food and Agriculture Organization.

Objective of the Commission is to develop international and regional food standards, and publish them in a Codex Alimentarius—or food code.

Work of the Commission is carried out through committees—each chaired by an individual country. The Commission may also undertake development of food standards on a joint basis with other organizations, as with the Economic Commission for Europe. Or it may request another group, which usually is an international body, to carry on a particular assignment in its own specialized field.

The concept of an organization that would provide leadership in developing international food standards dates back to mid-1953. Dr. Hans Frenzel, a former Minister in the Austrian Government, advanced the idea of unifying European food legislation at a meeting of the Research Group of the German Food Industry.

Numerous lectures were subsequently delivered by Dr. Frenzel to explain his proposal for unifying European food legislation through establishment of a unified food code, or Codex Alimentarius. As a result, in June 1958 the European Council of the Codex Alimentarius was established in Vienna. Dr. Frenzel was elected as the first president.

At the time the Council was organized, some governments felt that functions relating to the Codex Alimentarius could be absorbed into the activities of existing international organizations, particularly the Food and Agriculture Organization (FAO) and the World Health Organization

(WHO). For this reason, the statutes of the Council were drafted so as to permit eventual absorption of its activities by one or more general international organizations.

THE PROBLEM of developing, coordinating, and harmonizing food standards activities came to the fore during 1960 at the first FAO Regional Conference for Europe in Rome.

Out of the deliberations came this statement by the conference:

". . . a valuable step forward would be achieved if the Director-General of FAO, in collaboration with the Director-General of WHO and after consultation with the international governmental and nongovernmental organizations active in this field, could submit to the 11th session of the Conference proposals for a joint FAO/WHO program on food standards and associated requirements, with particular reference in the first instance to the principal foodstuffs offered for sale on the European market."

Acting on this suggestion after discussions with the European Council of the Codex Alimentarius, the FAO Director-General submitted to the 11th session of the FAO Conference, held in Rome in 1961, a proposal for a joint FAO/WHO program on food standards. This proposal was endorsed by the Conference.

THE PROPOSAL as endorsed involved establishment of a Codex Alimentarius Commission. Commission operations were to be financed from a special trust fund to which all interested member nations were urged to contribute.

A Joint FAO/WHO Conference on Food Standards was held in Geneva, October 1–5, 1962.

Representatives from 44 countries and observers from 24 international organizations attended. That Conference endorsed establishment of the Codex Alimentarius Commission and developed guidelines for the work of the Commission.

Subsequently, WHO approved the proposal for establishment of the Codex Alimentarius Commission. Thus, with the earlier adoption of the resolution by the FAO Conference, this food standards program began as a joint undertaking of FAO and WHO. The Commission's work is guided by statutes developed by FAO and subsequently endorsed by WHO. All member nations and associate members of FAO and WHO are eligible to become members of the Commission.

THE FIRST SESSION of the Codex Alimentarius Commission was held in Rome in 1963 with some 120 participants, including representatives from 30 countries and observers from 16 international organizations. The Commission adopted rules of procedure and allocated preparatory work on draft standards either to existing outside specialist bodies or to designated ad hoc Codex Committees chaired by member governments. The second session of the Commission was held in Geneva during 1964.

THE THIRD SESSION of the Commission was held in Rome, October 19–29, 1965. This session was attended by 137 registrants, including representatives and observers from 37 countries and observers from some 24 international organizations.

The decisions reached made several fundamental contributions to the future success of the Joint FAO/WHO Program on Food Standards. Among them was adoption of the General Principles of the Codex Alimentarius which had been developed by a special committee to simplify and more clearly define the purpose and the scope of the food standards program.

UNTIL 1966, operating expenses of the Commission were defrayed from the special trust fund originally provided for in the Commission statutes. This fund was administered by FAO on behalf of both FAO and WHO.

From the beginning at the 11th session of the FAO Conference in 1961, the United States—along with some other countries—opposed financing the

313

The U.S. delegation at the 1965 session of the Codex Alimentarius Commission in Rome.

work of the Codex Alimentarius Commission through the trust fund arrangement.

The U.S. delegation indicated that even though there was much interest in the proposed food standards work, a contribution to the trust fund from the U.S. Government was "unlikely since Congress did not look with favor on special grants over and above the already substantial amounts contributed to the regular budgets (and technical assistance operations) of many international organizations."

Since a U.S. Government contribution was unlikely, the delegation pointed out at the time that any financial support from the United States "would no doubt be from private sources."

The first contributions to the trust fund were made in 1962. The U.S. contributions in 1962, 1963, and 1964 amounted to $15,000 for each year supplied by the Food Law Institute on behalf of private industry. The next

highest contributor has been the United Kingdom with an annual contribution of $14,000.

For 1965, contributing countries were requested to double the contributions made in the previous year. As a result, the U.S. contribution in 1965 totaled $30,000 obtained by the Food Law Institute from industry sources.

Provision was made in the 1966 regular budget of WHO for the Commission's food standards work, and in the FAO budget for 1966 and 1967, which eliminated the trust fund method of financing.

THE CODEX Alimentarius Commission represents a new and a vital influence in the sphere of international food standards.

Never before in history was there the multitude of international, regional, and other bodies concerned with promulgation of standards in the food field functioning in different parts of the world that existed when the idea of a Codex Alimentarius Commission was initially discussed.

In 1962, for example, FAO listed 135 organizations and instrumentalities other than governments as working on international food standards and on related problems. And FAO pointed out at the time that this was not a complete list.

The standards work of these 135 bodies alone ranged through the entire food field and included every aspect from standards that cover sanitation, sampling, analysis, additives, and pesticide residues to standards of food product identity and quality.

DEVELOPMENT OF trading areas throughout the world, improved transportation, new food technology, and changing economic conditions have all accelerated the pace of world trade in food and intensified the need for various safeguards. Moreover, local terminology in trade and production practices differs vastly from one country to another.

Consequently, there arose a new urgency for establishing standards that would facilitate international trading and set acceptable levels of sanitation, quality, and other factors important in protecting consumer health and insuring fair practices in the food trade.

WHILE A LARGE NUMBER of organizations and groups came into being to meet expanding needs for food standards, this great buildup resulted in much duplication, confusion, and conflict. Moreover, besides scientific aspects of the problem, there long had existed a need to overcome misuse of food standards. Countries had established internal limitations or requirements under one legitimate guise or another in order to protect their products from the competition of imports and to thus restrict the international food trade.

To meet the growing demand for corrective action, the Codex Alimentarius Commission provided the instrumentality through which greater simplification and harmony could be brought into international food standards activities.

FUNCTIONING through assignments to its own Codex Committees or in cooperation with other international organizations or specialized bodies, the Commission had underway at the beginning of 1966 a program of work that involved development of a wide range of international standards which relate to foods.

The United Kingdom chaired a Codex Committee on Fats and Oils responsible for developing worldwide standards for oils and fats of animal, vegetable, and marine origin. It also chaired a Codex Committee on Sugars responsible for developing draft international standards covering all types of nutritional sweeteners.

SWITZERLAND chaired a Codex Committee on Cocoa Products and Chocolate to develop draft standards for a large variety of cocoa products significant in international trade.

A Codex Committee on Food Additives was chaired by the Netherlands. The Committee was to develop draft lists of acceptable additives and wherever possible to designate proposed maximum levels of use for them in individual foods. This involved both intentional and unintentional additives.

The Netherlands also chaired a Codex Committee on Pesticide Residues. This Committee was to survey, and propose where possible, tolerances for pesticide residues in individual food products.

THE UNITED STATES chaired a Codex Committee on Processed Fruits and Vegetables with responsibility for developing draft international standards for all types, including dried products and jams and jellies.

Also chaired by the United States was a Codex Committee on Food Hygiene with responsibility for promulgating draft hygiene standards for foods other than meat and milk and milk products.

Hygiene standards for meat are the responsibility of the Joint FAO/WHO Panel on Meat Hygiene, since it is the Commission's advisory body on this subject. Questions concerning milk hygiene come under the Joint FAO/WHO Committee of Government Experts on the Code of Principles concerning Milk and Milk Products. This joint committee is treated as a Committee of the Whole of the Commission.

The United States chaired a Codex Committee on Poultry and Poultry Meat Products.

The Committee had two goals. One was to develop worldwide standards of identity and quality for fresh, frozen (including deep and quick frozen), and otherwise processed poultry and poultry meat products. The second goal was to work up definitions, labeling provisions, and other requirements for such poultry and poultry meat products as the Codex Committee might think was desirable.

A CODEX COMMITTEE on Food Labeling was chaired by Canada. This Committee had responsibility for drafting provisions on labeling applicable to all foods as well as products given priority by the Commission, and for studying specific labeling problems assigned by the Commission itself.

France chaired a Codex Committee on General Principles. This involved development of the General Principles of the Codex Alimentarius, including defining terminology and the purpose and scope of the Codex, and the nature and type of standards to be covered.

A CODEX COMMITTEE on Fish and Fishery Products functioned with Norway as the chairing country. The Committee was given responsibility for developing worldwide standards for fresh, frozen (including deep and quick frozen), or otherwise processed fish, crustaceans, and mollusks.

The Federal Republic of Germany chaired a Codex Committee on Methods of Analysis and Sampling. This Committee was to select or develop procedures for use in the analysis or sampling that might be prescribed in a food standard, or might be necessary in connection with its application.

The Committee's goal was to give recognition to the analysis and sampling methods which would yield identical reproducible results when they were used anywhere in the world.

A CODEX COMMITTEE on Meat and Processed Meat Products also was under chairmanship of the Federal Republic of Germany. It had responsibility for developing proposals for classifying and grading carcasses and cuts of beef, lamb, mutton, pork, and veal. The Committee also was to develop definitions, labeling, and other requirements for such processed meat products as it might deem desirable, excluding both poultry and processed poultry products.

Development of standards for milk and dairy products on an international basis was first undertaken in 1958 with establishment of the Joint FAO/WHO Committee of Government Experts on the Code of Principles concerning Milk and Milk Products.

WHEN THE Codex Alimentarius Commission was established, it was decided that this expert group would serve as a Committee of the Whole of the Commission, with exclusive competence for all questions concerning milk and milk products. Therefore, decisions of this Committee—membership in which is already open to all member countries of FAO and WHO— would be decisions of the Commission in the specific field of milk and milk products. However, in certain cases the decisions made by the Committee could be reviewed by the Commission before acceptance.

One of this Committee's achievements has been development of a Code of Principles, to protect the consumer of milk and milk products and to assist the dairy industry on both the national and international levels. By the beginning of 1966 this Code of Principles had been accepted by 66 countries.

JOINT FAO/WHO FOOD STANDARDS PROGRAM

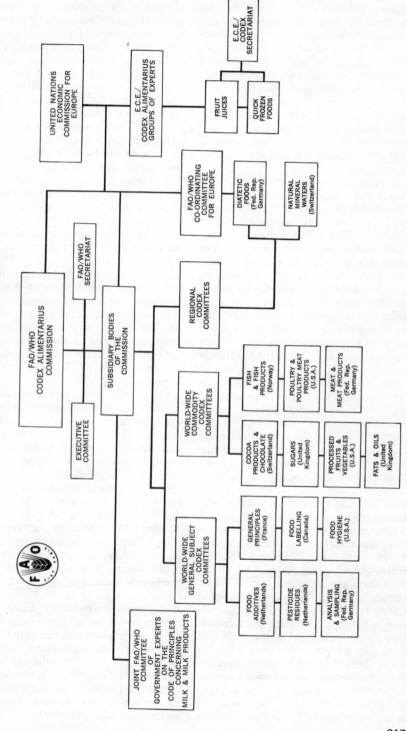

In addition, 55 countries had accepted international standards developed by the Committee for dry milks, and 30 to 45 countries had accepted the standards for butter, anhydrous butterfat, and condensed and evaporated milks, as well as the standards for sampling and analysis.

ASSIGNMENTS HAD BEEN MADE by the Commission for developing, on a regional basis, standards for dietetic foods, for natural mineral waters, and for wild edible fungi.

A Codex Committee on Dietetic Foods was established to function under chairmanship of the Federal Republic of Germany. Development of dietetic food standards on a regional basis was to be a first step towards promulgation of worldwide standards. Standards work on natural mineral waters was assigned to a Codex Committee under the chairmanship of Switzerland. Leadership for developing standards for wild edible fungi was assigned to Poland.

Development of international standards for fruit juices was underway through a joint arrangement between the Economic Commission for Europe and the Codex Alimentarius Commission. This work, in the hands of the Joint ECE/Codex Alimentarius Group of Experts on Standardization of Fruit Juices, was the first undertaken on this basis between the two organizations.

ESTABLISHMENT OF international standards for frozen foods was the second combined effort and was the responsibility of the Joint ECE/Codex Alimentarius Group of Experts on Standardization of Quick Frozen Foods. A draft standard for quick frozen strawberries had been developed to provide a format for standards that might be promulgated for various quick frozen food items, primarily in the fruit and vegetable field.

The International Organization for Standardization, a nongovernmental body with a widely ranging competency in the standards field, was cooperating with the Commission in developing information on methods of sampling for physically similar food product groups and, where necessary, specific methods for important food products. In addition, it was surveying work being done by various organizations on methods of sampling and analysis of wheat and all other cereals which were important from an international standpoint.

When a draft worldwide standard is developed by a Codex Committee or other body to which an assignment has been made, it is first circulated by the Commission among its member governments and interested international organizations for their comments. Subsequently, in the light of comments received, it may then be modified by the originating group.

THE DRAFT is next submitted to the Commission with a view to adoption as a draft provisional standard. Once accepted by the Commission it is then sent for comment to all the member governments and to appropriate international organizations. The resulting comments may provide the basis for further modification.

The next step is the consideration of the draft provisional standard by the Commission for possible adoption as a provisional standard. In the form then adopted it is next sent to the member governments and interested international organizations.

At the final stage, members of the Commission are requested to indicate their acceptance of the provisional standard. When the Commission determines that a sufficient number of the members have accepted, it is printed in the Codex Alimentarius finally as a worldwide standard.

A MODIFIED procedure is followed in developing regional standards. While all member governments may submit comments on any draft regional standard, take part in debate within the Commission, and propose amendments, only a majority of members of the region which is concerned can amend and adopt the draft.

There is no compulsion to use a food standard developed through the Commission's procedures and published in the Codex Alimentarius other than that which a government may place upon itself. Under the General Principles of the Codex Alimentarius, acceptance of standards is to be governed as follows:

"A Codex Standard so defined may be accepted by a country—in respect of trade and distribution of the food within its territory—in its entirety, or accepted with a declaration of more stringent requirements, or accepted as a target which will be put into effect after a stated number of years.

"Acceptance in its entirety or target acceptance would imply an undertaking by the importing country not to hinder within its territorial jurisdiction the distribution of food which conforms to the standard by any legal provisions relating to the health of the consumer or to other food standard matters."

PROCEDURES FOR developing worldwide and regional standards may seem complex, but they are essential. All member governments have an opportunity to comment on any standard proposed. This gives all of the governments an opportunity to review—a safeguard which is not provided by any other instrumentality in the field of international food standards.

THE GENERAL PRINCIPLES of the Codex Alimentarius adopted by the Commission provide that the Codex "is to include standards for all the principal foods, whether processed, semiprocessed or raw, for distribution to the consumer." Materials for further processing into foods are to be included to the extent necessary. "The Codex Alimentarius is to include provisions in respect of food hygiene, food additives, pesticide residues, contaminants, labeling and presentation, methods of analysis and sampling."

The nature of Codex Standards is also set forth in the General Principles as follows: "Codex Standards contain requirements for food aimed at ensuring for the consumer a sound, wholesome food product free from adulteration, correctly labeled and presented."

A CODEX STANDARD may specify in whole or in part the following criteria:

"(a) *Product designation, definition and composition.* These should describe and define the food (including its scientific name when necessary) and cover compositional requirements which may include quality criteria.

"(b) *Hygiene requirements.* These should include such factors as specific sanitary and other protective measures and safeguards to assure a sound, wholesome, and marketable product.

"(c) *Weight and measure requirements,* such as fill of container, weight, measure or count of units based on an appropriate method or criterion.

"(d) *Labeling requirements.* These should include specific requirements for labeling and presentation.

"(e) *Sampling, testing and analytical methods.* These should cover specific sampling, testing, and analytical procedures."

THE GENERAL PRINCIPLES which guide the work of the Commission became effective on their adoption at its third session in Rome, in October 1965.

The most important gain was agreement that there should be a single type of food standard known as a Codex Standard. This single standard would replace the "trading" and "minimum platform" standards which had hitherto constituted the type of food standards that could be promulgated by the Commission.

Such a Codex Standard could be developed and accepted according to the circumstances on a worldwide, regional, or a group of countries basis.

IN SOME INSTANCES, a Codex Standard setting forth only hygiene requirements to assure the wholesomeness of a food might be entirely adequate. Or, in the case of a particular food item, a standard consisting only of such components as product designation and definition, hygiene requirements, and labeling requirements would be fully adequate and most practical. For some other foods more may be required, including quality criteria.

In promulgating a Codex Standard that is to include quality criteria, the Codex Committee responsible for the work usually finds it desirable first to develop a standard which will incorporate those characteristics for a product of minimum acceptable quality in the international food trade.

ESTABLISHING and reaching an agreement among the various countries only on such minimum quality requirements in a standard can be done with far less disagreement than providing for a minimum quality and, in addition, making provision for a range of qualities above the minimum. However, where a standard provides only for a minimum quality the use of the standard will be limited, since there usually also is a buyer and consumer demand for qualities above the minimum.

For most foods, however, it probably is best first to develop standards on the basis of minimum quality for the product. But the door should not be closed against the subsequent development of standards which incorporate provisions for higher quality levels. For some food items, development of standards including higher ranging quality levels might be done at the same time that standards containing the minimum quality levels are being promulgated.

UNDER CERTAIN circumstances, like unfavorable weather conditions, crop growth could be so adversely affected as to make it quite impossible for the resulting food products to meet even the minimum quality requirements of a standard.

Therefore, consideration would need to be given to providing in the standard for marketing these products with appropriate labeling to show they are below minimum quality while meeting the other requirements.

Since one of the chief purposes of a Codex Standard is to provide means for assuring a wholesome food product, each individual commodity standard providing for quality criteria and for other requirements would have to specifically set forth the hygienic and wholesomeness requirements.

GENERALLY this can be done by a reference in the standard to the hygiene requirements developed for the Commission by the Codex Committee on Food Hygiene. On the other hand the particular Codex commodity committee may choose to develop its own hygiene requirements for food covered by the standard.

Likewise, labeling requirements can be incorporated in the standard by reference to those developed for the Commission by the Codex Committee on Food Labeling. Any desirable or necessary labeling requirements peculiar to the particular product, not covered by those developed by this Committee, could be specified in the individual food standard. Normally these would be optional labeling provisions.

SAMPLING PLANS for lot acceptance and suitable test methods applicable for many products can be handled in the food standard by reference. Sampling procedures for evaluating and classifying the product in individual containers need to be described in the standard.

As a general rule, a Codex Standard should be self-contained and not require reference to outside documents except for those concerned with application of standard methods and procedures or uniform requirements accepted by the Commission.

Moreover, food standards necessarily must be written in clear and simple language and in sufficient detail to maintain uniformity in interpretations under all circumstances.

PROPERLY DRAFTED food standards are the cornerstone of effective protection of consumers by enabling them to know what they are buying and by providing safeguards against fraud

320

and deception. Likewise, the honest producer, processor, and distributor is protected from unfair competition. Such standards are in effect a yardstick for the buyer, the seller, and the enforcement official alike. Thus, they provide the basis for confidence in the food trade.

Therefore, standards must set forth appropriate and practical requirements, including levels of quality which producers are capable of meeting, and which those engaged in international trade are willing to use as a basis for buying and selling.

THE CONSUMER wants to be assured that a food product is clean and wholesome, and seeks a product of a quality, style, and type that will fill his needs. The standards must, therefore, set forth the requirements and make the provisions to meet consumer demands.

In fulfilling their basic objectives and purposes, Codex Standards should permit the use of wholesome ingredients consistent with good manufacturing practices to achieve the physical or taste characteristics which are desired for the food product.

Codex Standards should also provide appropriate safeguards against adulteration and deception.

Food standards should not be tools of trade restriction. They should aim at assuring the market and the consumer of wholesome food products, correctly labeled and presented in order to enable the buyer and consumer to exercise individual judgment in selection.

MANY COUNTRIES, particularly developing nations, have practically no food standards while the fully developed countries have many standards ranging upward from the minimum. Codex Standards may be designed primarily for international or regional use, but the developing countries can adapt them to internal needs.

On the other hand, in the fully developed countries Codex Standards offer an opportunity to simplify and bring into closer harmony food standards of concern on an international basis, or on a regional or a group of countries basis.

STARTING WITH the 1962 Joint FAO/WHO Conference on Food Standards, when the decision was made by representatives of 44 countries to establish a Codex Alimentarius Commission, the United States has provided strong leadership and support. The objective was to bring into being and maintain a policy that food standards generally should meet international needs in safeguarding the interests of consumers and facilitating trade.

The United States held the chairmanship of the Commission during its first three sessions and was represented by effective delegations with but little turnover in membership since the very start. This provided urgently needed continuity in both leadership and participation.

Also, the United States takes part in the work of all Codex Committees and has sent some of its best technical experts to participate in practically every meeting that has been held.

THE USUAL representation from this country to a Codex Committee meeting has been one person from the appropriate government agency who serves as spokesman at the session, and two individuals from industry who serve as advisors.

U.S. delegations to Commission sessions have also included personnel from both the government and industry.

U.S. Government agencies, particularly the U.S. Department of Agriculture, have had to gear themselves to new demands growing out of the Commission's program. Besides, a considerable amount of consultation has been necessary with agriculture and industry in a two-way street of communication. As a result of all of this, the United States has been able to participate effectively in the Commission's program and work, and to provide sound guidance along with the positive leadership that has won recognition and support from other participating countries.

MONITORING FARM USE
OF PESTICIDES

JOSEPH W. GENTRY

MORE and more insecticides, fungicides, herbicides, and other pest control measures will be needed to give us more and better food. At the same time, this could contribute to contamination of our environment and might harm some beneficial animal and plant life.

The same technology that can develop effective pest controls, however, can develop materials and methods that will not cause detrimental side effects yet still assure us a plentiful supply of wholesome and safe food.

Monitoring activities, which were being initiated on a broad scale in 1965, will point out ways to avoid possible hazards from pesticide use.

Problems relating to pesticide usage received a full appraisal in a report issued by the President's Science Advisory Committee in May of 1963. Since then, each Federal Department with a responsibility for the use of pesticides, or interest in the effects of pesticide use, has increased emphasis on its activities in the field. One of the major actions which the President's Science Advisory Committee report

recommended was a monitoring system to give "an assessment of the levels of pesticides in man and his environment. . . ."

The U.S. Department of Agriculture recognized its broad responsibility in the use of pesticides since it registers these materials and issues suggestions for their effective and safe use. The Department, therefore, needed a monitoring program to determine effects of the normal use of pesticides and to feed back information for guidance in decisionmaking. Especially needed was a program to give data to serve as a basis for developing the materials and methods of use that would avoid pesticide residues in the environment or hold them at a safe level.

Such a monitoring project was started on a pilot basis in the Mississippi River Delta in the spring of 1964

*   *   *

Joseph W. Gentry is the *Chief Staff Officer*, Survey and Detection Operations, Plant Pest Control Division, Agricultural Research Service. For 2 years he was staff specialist in charge of pesticide safety and monitoring for the Division.

by the Agricultural Research Service (ARS). This region was chosen because large amounts of insecticides had been used in cotton production for many years. The rice-growing areas of Arkansas were included because of interest in the possible contamination of water from the use of persistent pesticides as a seed treatment.

A TEAM OF ARS scientists—biologists, chemists, soil and water specialists, and statisticians—designed a broad program to investigate the impact of pesticide use upon farms selected for the study.

Main objectives of the program were to determine:

• Existing pesticide residue levels in soils, water, sediment, crops, livestock, and certain species of aquatic and land animals; and

• The impact of pesticides on nontarget animal and plant life, particularly beneficial insects.

The studies were planned for a minimum of 3 years in this area in an attempt to determine rates of accumulation or depletion of residues in various components of the environment.

FIVE LOCATIONS typical of farming practices in the Delta region were selected. Three locations were in Mississippi and two in Arkansas. Main crops on the Mississippi farms were cotton and soybeans.

Rice, soybeans, and cotton were principal crops in the Arkansas area. Some small grains, forage, and vegetables were also produced.

Each location was made up of two 1-square-mile study areas. Each area contained pastures, water sources like ponds or streams, and some wildlife. Efforts were made to find companion farms with the same makeup in crops but with contrast in their pesticide use practices.

Cooperation of State agricultural officials and the farmers involved was excellent in every case. They realized the importance of this type of a pesticide study and wanted to contribute to its success.

A TEAM LED BY a supervisory biologist was assigned to each location to conduct investigations in the field. First, the investigators laid out each area in plots or blocks for sampling purposes. Maps were diagramed to show where soil, water, crop, fish, and other samples would be collected.

Then with the assistance of the farm operators a detailed history for at least 10 years was compiled upon kinds and amounts of pesticides used on each block since the introduction of DDT and of other chlorinated hydrocarbon insecticides.

Some of the participating farm operators had excellent and accurate records on file; others had to search their memories. A lack of records on pesticide use is quite understandable. Who would have thought that someone in 1964 would be quizzing a farmer on how much DDT he used in 1948 or how much dieldrin in 1955?

In every case, nevertheless, the information obtained was good enough to give a basis for the studies.

Besides the pesticide use history, the biologist and his crew began to record details of every pesticide application made in their areas. This meant keeping complex pest control operations under constant surveillance; recording what was used, why it was used, how it was applied, weather conditions, and possible hazards to nontarget organisms at time of application. They would continue these activities for the duration of the study. In the pest control season that called for being on the job 7 days in each week.

SINCE PESTICIDES are known to move by air and water from one area to another, the biologist visited surrounding farms and cataloged the pesticides which were being used.

He was laying the groundwork or establishing a baseline against which the analytical results could be compared. In other words, to get any idea of the rate of buildup or breakdown of a pesticide in the soil, accurate figures were required on how much of the material had been applied.

WHILE THE FIELD CREWS developed their plans of work, equipment for carrying out the program was arriving at the stations.

It was a collection of strange looking items: Five-gallon water bottles, bright new sample cans, light traps, weather equipment, sweep nets, tick drags, forage cutters, pumps, boots, dippers, sieves, shovels, ice cream cups, portable freezers, jugs of alcohol to be used in insect traps, and plastic bags of all shapes and sizes.

Everything was brand new or sterilized. To work with residues at levels of sensitivity in parts per million and parts per billion, cleanliness is essential.

The central laboratory at Gulfport, Miss., was also gearing up at the same time for one of the largest analytical loads ever undertaken by a chemical laboratory in this country. More personnel, more equipment, and more space were added. Chemical supplies by the barrelfuls were being trucked in instead of the customary quarts and gallons.

SUDDENLY, MAY CAME. Sampling had not yet started. It was time for it. The cotton was up and growing and the soybeans were planted. Some weedkillers had already been used but no insecticide yet. A preseason sampling was needed at once.

The crews went at it. Technicians collected soil cores on a random pattern over each field, pasture, and wildlife area. They used a 2-inch-diameter corer which they plunged into the ground to a depth of 3 inches. Each type of cropland was being sampled separately.

Cores from a field were deposited in a large collecting pail, then rubbed through a quarter of an inch mesh screen. The material was passed through the screen again to insure thorough mixing. Stones, roots, grass, and other debris that would not pass through the screen were discarded. A new, 1-gallon paint container was then filled with the mixed, screened soil and sealed with an airtight lid.

The collector completed a data sheet, identifying the sample, and fastened it to the outside of the container. He cleaned up his equipment thoroughly and moved on to the next field. Soil samples were collected once each month during the first season.

THE ROLE OF WATER as a carrier of pesticide residues is of prime interest to everyone studying the pesticide pollution problem.

Several of the Delta farms contained lakes, ponds, and sloughs which got all their water from runoff from treated fields.

Analysis of the water and the mud in these sources would show the relative amounts of residues in soil, sediment, and water. It would also furnish a base for comparison with levels found in the aquatic life, such as in turtles, frogs, and in fish.

WATER was collected by using a bilge pump with an extended length of hose on the outlet.

This was a two-man job in the larger water sources. One man operated the pump while the other moved the 5-gallon glass carboy and directed the water into the bottle. In deep water a boat was necessary.

Water was taken at several places at various depths over each water source. The bottle was carefully sealed after collection, labeled, and taken to the laboratory as soon as possible for processing in order to prevent breakdown of the residue content.

Water was taken from ponds and other surface sources once each month and whenever a quick runoff occurred after rains. Wells were also sampled each month.

A SEDIMENT or mud sample was taken from the bottom of each pond, slough, or stream each time a water sample was collected. The technician used a modified soil corer for this. He waded out through the water, plunging the corer at random into the bottom until he reached solid matter. The tool was withdrawn, and the mud ejected into a 5-gallon container.

324

Two USDA field team members study a map of a pesticide monitoring area near Utica, Miss. In the background other team members are bringing in a fish trap.

After a representative number of cores were collected, they were mixed by stirring and a 1-gallon portion taken off and prepared in the same manner as the soil sample. An extension was used on the handle of the sampler when sediment was collected from a boat in deep water.

Interspersed with the sampling of soil and water was the collection of plants and animals for residue analysis and insects for sorting and counting.

CROPS WERE SAMPLED at or near harvest. First came wheat, oats, and hay. Later rice, cottonseed, and soybeans would be taken.

Ten pounds of material, made up of plant tissue and seeds, were collected at random over the field; two samples from each field or block. The material was placed in a plastic bag and sealed.

If it was green or perishable, it was quick-frozen and kept frozen until processing in the laboratory. Freezer facilities were provided at each of the field stations.

Forage was being sampled periodically, usually following the pesticide applications in nearby areas.

LAND AND AQUATIC animals were regarded as important components of these studies. It has been demonstrated that certain animals can concentrate residues in their tissues. Other animals preying on them may magnify the residues to an even higher level in their own bodies.

Indicator species of animals were selected to try to learn what effect known amounts of pesticides applied to farms would have on their fish and wildlife complement. Only those species most

325

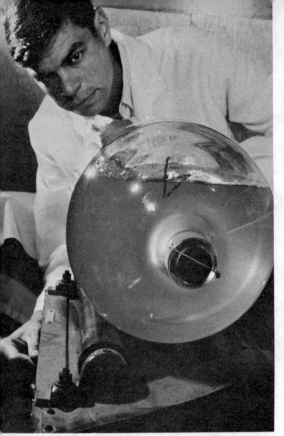

chloroformed, packaged, labeled, and quick-frozen immediately to stop metabolism as quickly as possible.

A limited number of beef cattle was available in these intensively farmed areas. Samples were taken from the carcasses at slaughter.

THE INSECT STUDIES had broad objectives. One was to determine side benefits from use of pesticides on the farms. The other was to find out the impact of treatments on beneficial species.

The biologists carried out many assignments in this phase of the work. They made sweep net counts of grasshoppers, lady beetles, and bumble bees each week. They ran a light trap one night a week, then sorted out 10 indicator species from among a catch of thousands. They made tick drag counts, dipped mosquito larvae from the ponds, and counted chiggers, horse flies, and house flies.

PITFALL TRAPS were made by digging holes and placing ice cream cups half full of alcohol in them. Crawling insects like ants and ground beetles tumbled into the cups and preserved themselves for counting and recording.

Populations of earthworms, wireworms and white grubs were estimated by random digging. Then these soil forms were preserved for laboratory analysis to determine residue content.

Three colonies of honey bees, placed in each area by ARS research apiculturists, were equipped with dead bee traps and pollen traps. Counts and collections were made from these traps each day for residue analysis. Honey and nectar were also collected for analysis. In addition, the welfare of each colony was studied closely.

BY THE END of season, it was decided that little could be gained from most of the insect studies because of the impossibility of establishing true check areas in a region where pesticide use was so widespread.

Statistical examination of the data indicated the pitfall trapping and soil organism study had merit and war-

Water sample is turned on roller to mix it with a solvent solution of redistilled pentane and ether, as part of pesticide monitoring study. The pentane and ether solution absorbs any residues in the water and is drawn off for analysis after mixing.

likely to have lived their entire lives in the 1-square-mile area were chosen.

MICE, rats, cottontail rabbits, snakes, tadpoles, frogs, crayfish, turtles, and pan fish were selected as indicators. Once a month the technicians set out mice, rat, and turtle traps. It was difficult to get representative numbers of the mice and rats but turtles were so plentiful that one biologist reported "they lined up" to get into his traps.

Fish, tadpoles, and crayfish were collected by seining and the rabbits were shot with the assistance of local game officials. Collecting of snakes was left to the option of the individual biologists and technicians. The animals were

Hand-operated corer is used to collect soil samples in pesticide monitoring study.

ranted further study. These phases and the honey bee investigations were the only parts of the insect work which were continued in the study.

As the different kinds of samples were collected they were carefully packaged and stored at each station. A courier truck picked up samples each week and transported them to the Gulfport laboratory.

When the samples reached Gulfport, perishable items like green crops and animals—which had been quick-frozen when they were collected—were rushed into the freezers.

The soil, sediment, and water were placed in the processing laboratory where extraction procedures started immediately. Pesticides have to be extracted from unfrozen samples as soon as possible after collection to prevent breakdown of pesticide content. This is especially true with the organophosphate pesticides like methyl parathion.

As the tons of samples came in each week, water was processed first. Each water sample was transferred to a larger bottle and 1,000 milliliters of redistilled pentane and ether (3 to 1 ratio) were added as solvents. The sample was then put on a rotator and turned for 20 minutes. In this interval if pesticide residues were in the water, they would be extracted by the solvent. The solvent mixture was then drawn off in a bottle and the extract was ready for a chemical analysis.

In processing soil samples, a 300-gram portion was weighed out. This was placed in a half gallon fruit jar and 600 ml. of redistilled hexane and isopropyl alcohol were added. The mixture was rotated for 4 hours on a wheel so that residues, if present, could be taken up in the solvent. The mixture was filtered and the solution washed twice with distilled water.

The extract containing the residues was then drawn off in a small bottle and placed in refrigeration. All samples were processed to the extract stage as soon as possible so they could be held for an indefinite period without significant deterioration or change in residue content.

After a portion of a soil or sediment sample was taken for processing, the remainder of the sample was placed in a separate building, which was especially reserved for this purpose, and held for later reference.

Perishable samples like green crop material and animals were kept frozen until they were extracted. Procedures different from those used for extracting soil and water samples were employed for processing biological samples but the objective was the same: To "fix" the chemical content in an extract solution.

IN THE ANALYTICAL laboratory a sample was subjected to one of several methods to determine its pesticide residue content both qualitatively and quantitatively. The sample was first injected into a highly sensitive gas chromatograph machine and then the findings were confirmed by the thin-layer chromatographic method as needed.

Other methods available in a well-equipped laboratory—like infrared spectrophotometry—were used, depending upon the type of pesticide that was involved.

Water samples were determined down to levels in parts per billion. Soil and other samples were analyzed in parts per million.

Chemical analysis of many different kinds of pesticide residues in many different kinds of samples of environmental media is a very complex and demanding job. If nothing unusual happens, a sample will require about 3 man-hours from the time it starts through the laboratory until the time the amounts of residue it contains are computed out. Whenever a problem sample turns up, which is about 30 percent of the time, more than 2 days is required, on the average, to complete an analysis of the sample.

BY THE TIME more than 3,000 samples had been collected and analyzed in the Delta program, spring had come back again.

Preliminary results pointed out some things in the first year's work in this new field that would not be done the second year. The results also showed the need for strengthening the existing program and the need for expanding the monitoring activities to other areas of the country.

More information was needed on the fate of residues in different types of crop production. So broad-scale studies were set up in new areas.

One of these was at Mobile, Ala., on

farms growing soybeans, potatoes, and other vegetables. A second was started on farms producing cotton, alfalfa, cantaloup, and lettuce at Yuma, Ariz. A third location was established near Grand Forks, N. Dak., to study the impact of pesticides used in sugarbeet and potato production.

IN THE SPRING of 1965 interest continued to grow concerning the fate of persistent pesticides in the environment. The Agriculture Department felt it needed to conduct exploratory surveys in farm areas over the country in addition to those just discussed.

To do this, sampling was conducted in important farming areas in 15 different locations. The work was limited to soil studies only. This would determine need for additional studies on other phases of the environment. Included in the study were fruit and vegetable farms in Florida, South Carolina, Georgia, North Carolina, Pennsylvania, Michigan, Washington, Colorado, Arizona, California, and in Texas.

MORE WORK on pesticides in soils was added to the Department's monitoring program in July 1965. This stemmed from an assignment by the Federal Committee on Pest Control which sponsored a minimum national pesticide monitoring program. The Agriculture Department's part in the broad program was limited to soils. Other Federal Departments designed studies to monitor pesticides in people, food, feed, fish, wildlife, water, and air.

An additional 34 sites involving areas where low amounts of pesticides or none at all had been used were selected for this pilot-scale soils program. These areas were on range and forest lands where periodic outbreaks of insects require control measures, and on wildlands—like game refuges—where pesticides have not been used. By adding the low and nonuse sites to the 21 high pesticide use sites already under investigation, a study of the pesticides in soils was placed in operation in more than 50 locations.

STATE DEPARTMENTS OF AGRICULTURE

GEORGE H. GOLDSBOROUGH

STATE departments of agriculture have a wide variety of programs to protect food from deterioration as it moves through marketing channels from farmer to consumer, and to assure consumers of wholesome food.

Regulatory activities aim primarily at consumer protection and deal mostly with food products moving within a State. Consumer protection programs operated in cooperation with either the U.S. Department of Agriculture (USDA) or the Food and Drug Administration of the Department of Health, Education, and Welfare (HEW) may also cover products moving interstate.

Information and service programs covering food grading, standardization, certification, and quality control may include products moving both between States and within States. Grading programs are generally conducted with USDA's Consumer and Marketing Service and uniform Federal grades are employed. If the State alone is involved, the grades are frequently patterned after existing or recommended USDA grades. In some cases, grading is mandatory by State law or regulation.

CONSUMER PROTECTION regulatory activities by State departments of agriculture include:

• Inspection of raw commodities—red meat, poultry, eggs, fruits and vegetables, dairy products, and seafood;

• Inspection of food handling establishments which process, store, and distribute foods, and of eating and drinking establishments; and

• Inspection for food additives, pesticides, and animal feed medication.

In many States, departments of health administer consumer protection work. In others this is handled by such agencies as the Consumer Protection Department, Livestock Sanitary Board, State Chemical Laboratories, State Egg Board, Agricultural Experiment Station, or Laboratory Department. Agriculture departments handle raw product inspection and food processing establishment inspection. Eating and drinking establishments are most often the responsibility of health departments.

* * *

George H. Goldsborough is *Director* of Matching Fund Programs, Consumer and Marketing Service.

State Agencies Administering Consumer Food Protection Activities

Interest code—other agency:

(1) Fluid milk.
(2) Dairy products.
(3) Meat.
(4) Fish.
(5) Shellfish.

(6) Poultry.
(7) Eggs.
(8) Fruits and vegetables.
(9) Other foods.
(10) Eating and drinking places.

Foods and associated processing and distribution

State	Principal agency	Other agency	Interests of other agency
Alabama	Agriculture	Health	1, 3, 10
Alaska	Health	Agriculture	3, 8
Arizona	Health	Dairy Commission	2
		Livestock Sanitary Board	2, 3
		Agriculture and Horticulture Commission.	8
		Egg Inspector	7
Arkansas	Health	Plant Board	8
California	Health	Agriculture	1, 2, 3, 6, 7, 8, 9
Colorado	Health	Agriculture	2, 6, 7, 8, 9
Connecticut	Consumer Protection.	Agriculture	1, 8, 9
		Health	5
Delaware	Health	Agriculture	2, 6, 7, 8, 9
Florida	Agriculture	Health	1, 5, 10
		Hotel and Restaurant Commission.	10
Georgia	Agriculture	Health	1, 5, 10
Hawaii	Health	Agriculture	3, 6, 8
Idaho	Health	Agriculture	1, 2, 3, 6, 7, 8, 9
Illinois	Agriculture	Health	1, 10
Indiana	Health	University	6, 7, 8
Iowa	Agriculture	Health	(*)
Kansas	Health	Agriculture	2, 7, 8
		Health and Restaurant Board.	9, 10
Kentucky	Health	Agriculture	7
Louisiana	Health	Agriculture	6, 8, 9
Maine	Agriculture	Health	10
		Sea and Shore Fisheries	5
Maryland	Health	Agriculture	2, 7
Massachusetts	Health	Agriculture	1, 6, 7, 8
Michigan	Agriculture	Health	1
Minnesota	Agriculture	Health	10
Mississippi	Health	Agriculture	2, 3, 7, 8
Missouri	Health	Agriculture	2, 7, 9
Montana	Health	Livestock Sanitary Board	2, 6
		Agriculture	2, 3, 7, 8, 9
Nebraska	Agriculture	Health	(*)
Nevada	Health	Agriculture	7, 9
New Hampshire	Health	Agriculture	6, 7, 8, 9
New Jersey	Health	Agriculture	6, 7, 8
New Mexico	Health	Agriculture	1, 7, 8, 9
New York	Agriculture	Health	1, 10
North Carolina	Agriculture	Health	10
North Dakota	Laboratories Commission.	Agriculture	1, 2, 9
		Health	1, 9, 10
		Livestock Sanitary Board	3
Ohio	Agriculture	Health	10
Oklahoma	Health	Agriculture	2, 3, 7, 9
Oregon	Agriculture	Health	10
Pennsylvania	Agriculture	Health	10
Rhode Island	Health	Agriculture	7, 8

*No information available on specific interests.

State	Principal agency	Other agency	Interests of other agency
South Carolina.......	Agriculture........	Health...................	2, 9, 10
South Dakota.........	Agriculture........	Health...................	10
Tennessee............	Agriculture........	Health, Conservation, and Commerce.	10
Texas...............	Health............	Agriculture..............	8
Utah................	Agriculture........	Health...................	10
Vermont.............	Health............	Agriculture..............	1, 7, 8, 9
Virginia.............	Agriculture........	Health...................	1, 2, 4, 5, 10
Washington..........	Agriculture........	Health...................	1, 4, 5, 10
West Virginia........	Agriculture........	Health...................	1, 9, 10
Wisconsin...........	Agriculture........	Health...................	1, 10
Wyoming............	Agriculture........	Health...................	10

Exclusive of any payments to the local governments in support of companion programs performed by counties and municipalities, the State programs for consumer protection during the 1964 fiscal year that ended June 30, 1964, cost $7.6 million for meat and poultry inspection, plus $6.3 million for dairy products inspection, and some $2 million for supervision of eating and drinking establishments.

Expenditures have risen rapidly in the 10 years from 1954 to 1964, ranging from an increase of about 70 percent for dairy products to 93 percent for meats, 133 percent for feeds, and 159 percent for pesticides.

OVER 4,000 man-years were devoted in fiscal year 1964 to consumer protection activities related to food. Some 260 man-years were for administration, 3,200 for inspection, and 756 for laboratory analyses of samples of food which is destined for and moving through the marketing system.

The inspectors assigned to these programs check on industry adherence to laws, regulations, and agency standards where products are produced, processed, stored, offered for sale, or prepared for immediate consumption. These inspectors collect samples of products for field examination or for later laboratory analysis.

In addition, the inspectors explain requirements to regulated establishments and give technical support.

The inspectors also gather information on production, control, and distribution of products and any signifi-

cant developments in the businesses that they review. This information may then be pieced together to pinpoint the needs, identify trends, develop priorities, and adjust programs.

THE STATES have enacted hundreds of laws for consumer protection. These laws fall roughly into two categories. First there are statutes similar in many ways to Federal laws covering meat, milk, food service establishments, feeds, and pesticides.

These statutes and the resulting State programs have been influenced by the Federal laws and by the recommended codes of Federal agencies like USDA and HEW.

The second group of laws gives special recognition to problems or interests within State boundaries.

Measures for regulating native products like maple sirup and establishments like frozen food locker plants and bakeries are typical. And in some cases, the State agencies are tied in with local and municipal groups.

DAIRY PRODUCTS inspection is a key part of State consumer protection work.

Inspectors check dairy farms, receiving stations—including bulk milk tank trucks—processing and pasteurization plants, delivery trucks, and occasionally retail stores and food service establishments.

Products which are inspected include milk, butter, cheese, and ice cream, as well as soft-serve dairy items.

On the farm, inspectors see if cows have been tested for disease and whether the milk handling sanitation meets the requirements.

In the processing plant the methods used are checked and products analyzed for butterfat content, total solids, bacteria, presence of foreign substances like pesticide residues, evidence of pasteurization, claimed vitamin content, temperature, and added water. Labeling practices are also observed.

TECHNIQUES include both direct inspection and sampling for laboratory analysis, with special emphasis on grade A pasteurized milk. The programs emphasize sanitation and product quality.

In the grade A program, sanitation is regulated by agency employees conducting at least the minimum number of inspections recommended by the Public Health Service of HEW.

These recommendations are often written into the State laws and State regulations. Furthermore, product quality is assured by sampling.

ABOUT 15 PERCENT of commercially slaughtered meat and poultry is processed in plants shipping only in intrastate commerce, and is covered by a State service in most States. In November 1965, a total of 37 States had statutes providing various types of red meat inspection service, and 31 of the 37 were actually carrying out some type of meat inspection activity.

A review of State laws on red meat reveals a great variety of requirements. Thirty States require preslaughter inspection of every animal and 30 require examination of all carcasses and viscera.

Thirty-four States provide for supervision of plant and equipment sanitation, 15 for reinspection of meats that may have deteriorated during handling, and 28 for examination of all meat during processing.

Twenty-eight check for false or deceptive labels, and 27 require destruction of meat and meat products unfit for human consumption.

Meat inspection programs are carried on by veterinarians who have lay

inspectors working under their supervision. The principal emphasis is put on wholesomeness of the meat at the time of slaughter. After the meat enters the channels of commerce it then becomes subject to spot checks.

A 1963 SURVEY by the Intergovernmental Relations Subcommittee of the House of Representatives showed that 32 States have laws for poultry processing inspection. Seventeen of these provide for sanitary inspection only, and 15 for wholesomeness inspection of the product. Of the latter, nine programs are voluntary and six programs are mandatory.

Two States—Maine and North Dakota—carry out poultry inspection for wholesomeness in cooperation with the Poultry Division of the Consumer and Marketing Service and under the Federal Poultry Products Inspection Act. Inspection personnel on the processing lines are qualified and licensed by the Poultry Division, but they are State employees.

In all States except the two which are cooperating with USDA, the State inspection system services only intrastate plants.

INFORMAL COOPERATION with USDA exists in many States. USDA inspection personnel assist in training State inspectors and drafting proposed legislation and regulations. A model meat and poultry inspection law has been developed by USDA for the States to use as a guide.

A close working relationship exists between inspection and disease eradication activities in both USDA and State departments of agriculture laboratories. This has helped to combat any disease outbreaks among poultry flocks.

In addition, the State veterinary officials and industry service personnel have been aided in fostering better poultry management practices that have cut producer and processing losses.

Virtually all States have sanitary inspection authority for poultry plants.

Inspectors of other food products visit establishments where food is processed, stored, offered for sale, or in a few cases prepared for immediate consumption. Within this range are retail and wholesale stores, plus warehouses, soft drink manufacturers, canneries, bakeries, frozen food locker plants, and confectioneries.

General food inspectors give their main attention to products and operations not covered by the dairy, meat, and poultry programs, and devote little time to products regulated by other units at State or local levels.

FOOD PRODUCTS are examined and sampled for contamination or adulteration, and labels checked to see if they are both accurate and adequate. Sanitary conditions of the facilities are surveyed. The processes and procedures are checked for adherence to agency standards. Information is also recorded about any new products, practices, and processes.

The health and habits of employees are noted. Occasionally, special investigations are conducted to find out the sources of questionable products such as rejected incubator eggs. A minority of the programs emphasize thoroughness of inspection at the processing stage, with most giving primary attention to sanitation.

FEED INSPECTORS visit farms, farm suppliers, feed mills and mixers, and in some cases retail stores that carry pet foods.

Samples of feed for farm and domestic animals are collected so laboratory analysts can compare ingredients with the label guarantees.

Only a few programs devote much effort to inspection and examination of feed manufacturing or mixing processes. Under stimulation from the Food and Drug Administration, however, techniques are being enlarged to include such inspection, due to processing problems from the introduction of drugs in livestock feed.

WHILE FEED inspection programs of the past were considered mainly for the farmer's benefit, the consuming public has an increasing stake in the newer programs. By devoting more attention to processing, these programs strive to prevent farmers from inadvertently giving medication to their animals which might result in residues in meat, milk, or eggs with potential consumer hazard.

INSPECTION OF food service establishments is another State activity.

Restaurants, taverns, and other facilities where food is prepared for immediate consumption are surveyed. Food handlers, their practices and the facilities they use are checked. Often an attempt is made to determine the source of foods like milk, meat, and shellfish.

Inspectors make periodic on-the-spot inspections but resort only infrequently to sampling; agencies that use swab tests to detect bacterial contamination are the exceptions. Most food service programs are carried on by the health agencies.

STATE AGENCIES rely heavily on laboratory analyses to confirm judgments of compliance in the marketing system.

Every State has one or more laboratories used in analyzing food products. The man-years of analytical staff time add up to about 900 for milk products, meat, poultry, other foods, feeds, and drugs.

The State departments of agriculture possess important powers to regulate commerce in farm products, assist farmers, and protect consumers. The most effective enforcement weapons have been embargoes upon products moving within the State, and condemnation of foodstuffs determined unfit or hazardous. Permit and registration control are also widely used.

THE FACT that the agency represents the power and authority of the State is appreciated by those covered by regulation and is frequently sufficient to influence industry to uphold laws, regulations, and standards.

Over 90 percent of the compliance activities of State agencies are concerned with persuading firms to comply rather than employing disciplinary measures. Educational and preventive programs are used extensively by the States to achieve this purpose.

Agencies tell the regulated operator what is expected and instruct him in proper equipment, plant, and procedures. Once an operator is in compliance, the State inspectors help him to maintain standards.

RESPONSIBILITY FOR consumer protection is diffused among State agencies partly because it is split between several Federal agencies with which the States work closely. Consumer protection activities for meat and poultry shipped in interstate commerce is the responsibility of USDA's Consumer and Marketing Service. Fish is the responsibility of the Bureau of Commercial Fisheries, which is an Interior Department agency.

Fluid milk, shellfish, food service establishments, and interstate carriers

Chef prepares thawed scrambled eggs, packaged in a disposable plastic bag under a quality frozen egg program developed by New York State in cooperation with USDA's matching fund program. With liquid whole eggs packaged this way, volume feeders can prepare 1,800 scrambled eggs in 13 minutes. Preparing the same number of shelled eggs takes 1¾ hours.

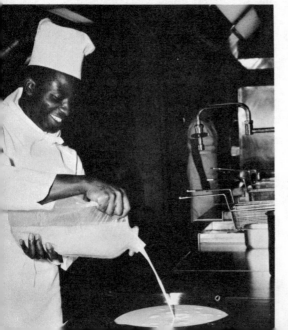

come under the Public Health Service, HEW. The Food and Drug Administration of HEW also has responsibilities in food. Both USDA and HEW have responsibilities in pesticides.

MOST STATE DEPARTMENTS of agriculture are quite active in food grading, standardization, and certification programs—generally in cooperation with USDA. While grading programs are designed primarily to facilitate trading between buyer and seller, they have as indirect benefits reduction in economic loss through deterioration, and consumer protection against spoiled and low quality food.

AS A RELATED EFFORT, many State departments of agriculture conduct special service and informational programs with producers and marketers to put to work their research findings on quality control and maintenance. These services include specialists expert at in-plant quality control and in demonstrating use of grades and standards to marketing agencies and consumers. Producers get advice on the optimum time of harvest to insure the longest possible shelf life.

CONSUMERS are instructed on use of grades in identifying product qualities in the retail store. This is confined, of course, to products that have a grade marking on the package and where the wholesale grades are also suitable for consumer grades. The principal items are eggs, poultry and red meat, and fresh fruits and vegetables.

The State departments of agriculture occasionally engage in experimental work seeking better methods of quality control, although reliance is placed primarily upon researchers in USDA, State land-grant universities, and the food industry.

A SIGNIFICANT PROPORTION of State service and informational work is conducted under the Federal-State Matching Fund Marketing Service Program. The balance of this chapter describes only the matching fund work because of lack of documentation for work carried on with State funds.

Federal payments, as authorized by section 204(b) of the Agricultural Marketing Act of 1946, are made under cooperative agreements between USDA and the State departments of agriculture for any marketing service activities upon a matching fund basis. States contribute at least half the cost; State personnel do the work.

This program spurs improvements in marketing agricultural commodities. It serves to bridge the gap between research and its application, as well as to stimulate the adoption of sound marketing methods and practices.

STATE PROJECTS in the quality field show marketers how to maintain or improve quality of the products they handle so deterioration and spoilage can be reduced and products placed before consumers in the best possible condition. This field embraces such activities as:

• Checking products at various stages in marketing for off-quality condition, finding the cause of the quality loss, and describing what corrective steps should be taken.

• Showing farmers and marketing agencies how to determine the proper maturity of products for harvesting.

• Demonstrating proper methods of picking, packing, handling, and transporting products in order to protect quality and to separate products into quality groups, and encouraging the use of the Federal and Federal-State grades.

• Establishing criteria for State grading of items not covered by Federal or Federal-State grades.

• Assisting on ways to prevent deterioration of products in storage.

• Determining and showing marketing firms what containers will best protect quality.

MATCHING FUND PROGRAMS for fruits and vegetables were conducted during the fiscal year 1965 in 28 States, for poultry and eggs in 24 States, dairy products in 17 States, livestock and

B. P. Holden, operator of a pork barbecue business at Youngsville, N.C., in a converted bus where he once barbecued his meat.

meats in 14 States, and grain and seed in 10 States. Improving and maintaining quality is a continuing task with changes in the emphasis and direction made as any new problems arise and better methods and techniques are developed.

The 37 States carrying on quality improvement projects were: Alabama, Alaska, Arkansas, California, Colorado, Connecticut, Florida, Georgia, Hawaii, Indiana, Kansas, Kentucky, Louisiana, Maine, Maryland, Massachusetts, Michigan, Minnesota, Mississippi, Montana, New Hampshire, New Jersey, New Mexico, New York, North Carolina, North Dakota, Oklahoma, Oregon, Pennsylvania, South Carolina, Tennessee, Texas, Vermont,

Mr. Holden and his wife now operate from this new plant, built with technical assistance provided under USDA's matching fund program in cooperation with the State of North Carolina. They are loading their station wagon to deliver the barbecue product.

Vermont farmer is presented with "good milk flavor rating" by his dairy, as part of a statewide program in cooperation with USDA to improve the flavor of Vermont milk.

Vermont milk truckdriver uses his trained sense of smell to search for any off-odor in the farm bulk milk tank, while farmer pours in milk.

A farmer judges the flavor of a sample of milk from his own herd. To their surprise, farmers sometimes have downgraded their own milk samples.

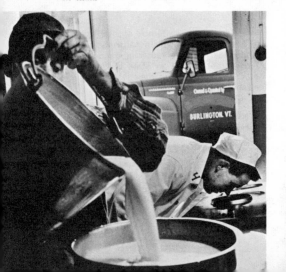

Virginia, Washington, West Virginia, and Wisconsin.

Here are some specific examples of market quality work.

FLAVOR PROGRAMS assist producers and marketers in preventing off-flavor in their milk.

These programs, in existence several years, have developed to where milk handlers have made it a part of their regular procurement program to check flavor and assist producers in overcoming flavor defects. Producers have made significant improvements in their milking facilities and handling practices to protect flavor. Emphasis recently has been shifted from the farm to working with processors and retailers in studying and correcting the adverse effect on milk flavor of new developments in handling, processing, packaging, and distribution.

STARTING IN 1951 the Wisconsin Department of Agriculture undertook,

with matching funds, a very intensive effort to upgrade the quality of the State's butter production by improving the processing facilities, equipment, and handling.

Only about 40 percent of the butter production, as measured by sample inspections, was of Wisconsin grade A and AA in 1951, but by 1964 this had gone up to 79 percent.

SEVERAL STATES conduct quality improvement work on soft-serve and other frozen dairy desserts to assure wholesomeness.

Marketing service personnel collect samples of mixed and finished products from retail outlets, check temperatures and storage conditions, and make chemical, bacteriological, and flavor and odor testing examinations of the samples.

Owners of manufacturing plants and retailers are helped to adjust handling and storage operations. Results of the State project activities are analyzed

IMPROVEMENTS IN THE QUALITY OF WISCONSIN BUTTER, under the Federal-State matched fund program, 1951–1964

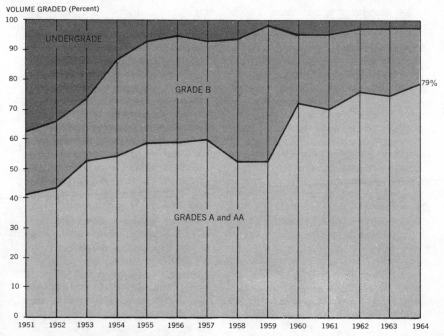

periodically to see whether there is need to revamp laws and regulations for the manufacture, handling, and sale of these popular desserts.

Special studies evaluate the extent of sediment in grade A bulk tank milk and suggest improvements, for cooperating processing plants. Emphasis is placed on methods for drawing samples, frequency of taking samples, criteria for determining degree of sedimentation, and steps to be taken to prevent sedimentation. Results of the work provide guidelines so commercial dairies can set up their own internal procedures for periodic testing of sedimentation in milk received from bulk tank producers.

THE MARYLAND Department of Markets started work in 1960 with Eastern Shore processors to upgrade the quality of broilers being processed.

Specialists help three plants identify causes of downgrading, adopt corrective measures, and install quality control systems to maintain improved performance. Production of grade A broilers increased from 46 percent of the total volume in 1960 to 69 percent in 1964. Similar work is going on in the State of Alabama.

Hawaii conducted a project to improve and standardize flavor in fresh papayas, to insure better consumer acceptance both locally and in export markets. A collection of field data to establish a desirable sugar-acid ratio for the fruit was completed and analyzed. Information was also obtained on consumer preferences for flavor. Based on these findings, recommendations for a regulatory program that covers maturity standards have been developed.

UNDER A quality improvement program, New Mexico encouraged growers and shippers to use official grade standards and the services of the Federal-State Inspection Service for marketing lettuce and onions. In 1964, about 90 percent of the lettuce and 75 percent of the onion crop were being marketed on certified grades, compared to 1963 when 40 percent of the lettuce and a negligible volume of onions were shipped under official inspection.

Projects designed to develop new and expanded markets and promote greater consumption of agricultural products were conducted in fiscal year 1965 by 40 State departments of agriculture.

INCREASE IN PERCENTAGE OF TOP-GRADE BROILERS PRODUCED by three Maryland poultry processing plants under the Federal-State matched fund program on quality control since 1960

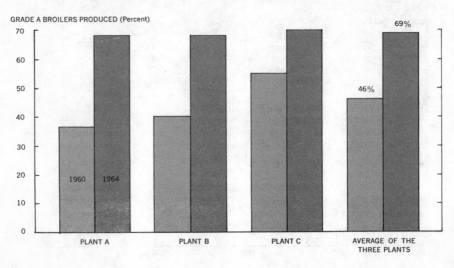

GRADE A BROILERS PRODUCED (Percent)

ARCHIBALD B. PARK

FALLOUT

AND

FOOD

Archibald B. Park is an *Assistant to the Administrator*, Agricultural Research Service. A veterinarian, he has received technical training from the Office of Civil Defense; U.S. Public Health Service; U.S. Army Chemical Corps; and Walter Reed Army Institute of Research.

791–476 O–66—24

NO one likes to think about war and the impact of war on our food supplies, and yet we must. No one would want to undertake the job of planning a food rationing system in these times of abundance, and yet we must. Why do we plan? Why do we prepare? A review of recent world history reveals that to be vulnerable is to invite an attack.

Is it farfetched to relate ballistic missiles and antiballistic missiles to the vulnerability of our food supply? Not at all. We estimate that the blast effects of an all-out nuclear attack on this country may involve approximately 2 percent of the continental landmass. The thermal or fire effects could go as high as 10 percent at the right time of the year.

But the real hazard for most of the population will be radioactive fallout. The estimate of this hazard is as high as 80 percent of the landmass.

The key to the solution is shelter before fallout arrives; sheltered people and sheltered food. Decontamination of people and food is a good countermeasure, but this is a tool that cannot replace preplanned protection.

EVERYONE KNOWS what an explosion is and what a fire is, yet many people have a wrong impression about fallout. Since weapons testing started and even since it stopped we have been subjected to fallout, but very few people have ever seen it.

As a result many consider fallout to be an invisible dust that will invade our homes and even our shelters and kill us. This is simply not true.

We have been subjected to worldwide fallout all these years and this, for all practical purposes, *is* an invisible dust. These ultrafine particles are carried right up to the stratosphere by a nuclear explosion.

But this is not the kind of fallout we are talking about in a postattack situation. Early fallout particles *are* visible. In fact, if we think of this as a housekeeping problem, we can use sand as an example. Actually, some of these particles are larger than sand.

339

It is true, of course, that the dangerous nature of this sand is not detected by our senses, but it is very important that we understand the physical nature of the problem. It takes detection instruments to assess the radiations from these particles, but it does not take special skills to know when fallout is present.

THE RADIATION HAZARD in food from fallout is internal radiation; that is, exposure to the radiation from isotopes that enter the bodies of animals and human beings. These radioactive elements generally enter in food and in water.

At first, the principal source of internal radiation is external contamination of edible plants when fresh fallout drops upon the affected area.

For livestock, this would include primarily forage grasses and legumes. For man, it would include fruits, vegetables, and milk—the last particularly for children.

As time passes and the initially contaminated food and feed have been discarded, the principal source of internal radiation for man and animals is indirect—from the radioisotopes in the soil which are absorbed through plant roots into food and feed crops. When meat and dairy animals eat contaminated feed, some radioactive elements are absorbed into their bodies.

Thus, man's food supply of both plant and animal products can become contaminated with radioactivity.

MANY OF THE radioactive isotopes created by nuclear explosions are of minor concern, in the hazard of internal radiation, because of (1) the small amounts involved; (2) their extremely short half-lives; (3) the fact that the radioisotope is eliminated very quickly by the body; (4) the fact that they are not incorporated into the food chain and hence do not seriously affect man and animals. (The half-life of an element is the time in which half the atoms in a radioactive substance disintegrate and change into another element. This new element may also be radioactive and

340

undergo further disintegration, or on the other hand, it may be stable.)

AMONG THE isotopes taken up in the food chain are barium 140, cerium 144, cesium 137, iodine 131, iodine 133, promethium 147, ruthenium 106, strontium 89, and strontium 90. Of these, the radioactive isotopes of most significance as internal radiation hazards are barium 140, cesium 137, iodine 131, iodine 133, strontium 89, and strontium 90.

Radioactive iodine, because of its chemical identity with ordinary iodine, accumulates in the thyroid gland when it gets into man or animals. However, iodine 131 has a relatively short half-life of 8 days. Iodine 131 will not be an important long-term fallout hazard, but it is the most hazardous internal radiation emitter during the first 60 days after an attack.

When considering the dosage to the thyroid derived from radioiodine in the first few days after attack, it is important to consider both iodine 133 and iodine 131.

Iodine 133 has a half-life of 22 hours but it occurs in sufficient quantity to make a significant contribution to the thyroid radiation dosage.

CESIUM 137 has a long half-life of 29.7 years and is chemically similar to the essential nutrient element potassium.

When cesium 137 is consumed and absorbed, it is found primarily in muscle tissue and can cause several types of cell damage, including genetic damage. But this radioisotope is not retained long in the body. It continually enters and leaves the system just as does potassium.

Strontium 90, however, with its half-life of 27.7 years, is of primary importance. Strontium 89 is chemically identical, but it has a half-life of only 50.5 days.

They both behave much like the calcium in soils, plants, and animals.

Nuclear explosions produce large amounts of radioactive strontium. It is taken up in biological systems, in plants, is secreted in milk, and collects in bones, where some of the strontium 90 remains for years. Radioactive isotopes of strontium deposited in the bone probably can produce serious consequences, such as bone cancer.

CHILDREN are relatively sensitive to radiostrontium. During their early growth period they require larger quantities of calcium than adults. Consequently a greater fraction of the ingested strontium is deposited in their bones, and the concentration of strontium is more uniform throughout their skeletons. And since children have longer life expectancies, there is more time for a slowly developing disease like bone cancer to occur.

BARIUM 140 behaves similarly to strontium 89 and strontium 90 in that it is deposited in the bone.

However, both the proportion of ingested barium 140 that reaches the skeleton and the half-life (12.8 days) are smaller than for radiostrontium, so that barium 140 contributes less to the bone hazard.

Although those radionuclides mentioned above are of special concern in view of their predominance in the food chain, total fission products in fallout have to be considered in the event of food being contaminated directly with the fallout.

While only the group that was described above passes into the bloodstream in significant quantities, the entire material irradiates the gastrointestinal tract as it passes through and can cause serious injury. Results of this damage are among those that appear earliest—nausea, vomiting, and diarrhea which one would expect from an irritant to these tissues.

THE CONCERN in protecting food, feed, and water is to prevent consumption of contaminated materials that would subject man and animals to internal radiation hazards.

However, the immediate problem is to protect a sufficient quantity from fresh fallout to provide for survival during the critical period.

The principle of protecting food, feed, and water from external fallout is simple: Prevent the fallout from becoming mixed or incorporated into these materials. They may be irradiated by the fallout, but if the radioactive particles do not come in actual contact with them—or if the fallout is removed—they will not be radioactive and thus will be safe to eat or drink.

METHODS OF prevention are the same as those for preventing dust from contaminating food or water if the air is heavily dust-laden. Fallout can also be removed in much the same way as dust—by washing, vacuum cleaning, and brushing. Precautions should be taken to avoid inhaling or swallowing particles of the material while engaged in removing it.

Radioactive fallout deposited on agricultural land will contaminate food chains with radioisotopes by way of the soil and crops. Depending upon the radiation intensity level, it may prevent farmworkers from handling their crops properly.

Salvage of unharvested crops like grain, fruits, and vegetables may be impaired by crop contamination, external exposure hazard, and unavailability of fuel and machinery.

If fallout is heavy, ripe fruits may be lost because of the personal hazard in harvesting them.

Fruits that do not have to be picked immediately and that can be decontaminated by washing and peeling before eating can probably be saved. Orchard trees should be maintained as usual and the fruits monitored for any radioactivity.

Consequently, the land contamination problem in heavy fallout zones would be primarily a long-term soil contamination problem. For most crops and soils, about 1 percent of the available strontium 90 in the soil is removed in a single crop. But on sandy soils, some crops may remove as much as 5 percent. However, even at this higher rate of removal, more than 40 crops would be required to achieve 90 percent decontamination of the soil. The succeeding crops only remove 5 percent of what is left.

For example, if 40 percent is left, the next crop will remove 5 percent of 40 which is 2, thus leaving 38 percent still remaining in the soil.

FALLOUT PARTICLES that fall directly on food and forage plants contaminate them by remaining attached to the aboveground parts, or by releasing radioisotopes that are absorbed into the leaves and other plant parts. Rain and wind move these particles from plants to soil, but certain characteristics of the leaves, such as hairiness, waxiness, and roughness, increase retention while smoothness reduces it.

Strontium 89, strontium 90, and ruthenium 106 absorbed into leaves tend to remain there because they do not move readily into other parts of the plant from the leaves. On the other hand, cesium 137 and iodine 131 will move readily throughout the plant from the leaf.

Accordingly, internal contamination by strontium 89, strontium 90, and ruthenium 106 from leaf absorption is greatest in leaves and is comparatively less in fruits, seeds, and edible roots and tubers.

As the season progresses, the fallout contaminants that have accumulated in the leaves, especially strontium 89, strontium 90, and ruthenium 106, may be washed from the leaves to the soil in rain and dew. They may then be absorbed by the roots and distributed throughout the entire plant and thereby increase the total content of contaminants. In arid regions with little rainfall these contaminants are not washed to the soil from the leaves, and any new growth that develops after the fallout thus will be relatively lower in strontium 89, strontium 90, and in ruthenium 106.

VEGETABLES AND FRUITS harvested from fallout zones in the first month after attack will require decontamination before they can be used for food.

First, the exposed parts must be thoroughly washed to remove the fallout particles. Then, vegetables or fruits should be peeled, pared, or the outside otherwise removed in such a way that hands or utensils do not contaminate the parts to be eaten.

It should be possible to decontaminate almost completely such crops as apples, head lettuce, and cabbage by repeated parings, washing hands and washing utensils before each paring.

Since fresh fallout provides only a surface contamination, it should be possible to wash and shell peas and beans or to husk sweet corn in order to remove the contaminated parts.

THIS TYPE OF decontamination could be applied to many human food items in the home immediately after harvest, if possible using well water, or some other noncontaminated water.

It should be remembered, however, that one can wash his hands effectively using dirty water, and that it is also possible to decontaminate most vegetables effectively using radio-contaminated water for washing.

Do not use drinking water for decontamination unless you have more than is necessary for that purpose.

Cooking will not destroy radioactivity, but research has shown that boiling foods, including meat, will leach radionuclides from the food. The food itself may be consumed, but not the water it is cooked with.

SOME FOOD PRODUCTS that have fallout on or mixed in them can be used only after holding the products long enough to allow the radioactivity to decay to a safe level.

Storage of the contaminated material for a period ranging from 2 weeks to many months, depending upon the degree and kind of contamination, will reduce the amount of radioactivity present, usually to a negligible level. Obviously, many food products—including most meat that is not canned—could not be stored for the necessary time.

Fallout on unpackaged meat presents a salvage problem, since it is extremely difficult to remove the outer surface without carrying contamination onto other parts of the meat. Washing is not an effective method of removing this type of contamination. Meat products contaminated with fresh fallout could be canned and then stored until their radioactivity had decayed sufficiently.

MEAT and meat food products in home or commercial storage will be most effectively protected if canned.

For uncanned products, a sealed covering of one of the commonly available plastic films, like polyethylene, will provide adequate protection from contamination by fallout. Even fiberboard and similar tight containers that will exclude dust will be effective. Refrigeration facilities should be maintained as usual to control spoilage.

BECAUSE EARLY radioactive fallout results in surface contamination, the simplest method to protect feed and water is to place a cover over them to prevent direct contact with fallout.

Grain stored in a permanent bin and ensilage in a covered silo are provided with adequate protection against radioactive fallout.

The contents can be safely used as soon as the farmer is able to get into the area to use them. A haystack in an open field can be protected with a covering, like a tarpaulin. The fallout will lodge on the tarpaulin. If the tarp is carefully removed, the radioactive fallout will be removed also.

The hay and the contents of the feed bin and silo would not be radioactive and could be used immediately as safe feed for livestock. Many materials like uncovered haystacks and piles of farm produce may be safely used as food and feed provided that the contaminated outer portions are removed.

WATER STORED outside—as in stock water troughs—should be covered with any material that would normally keep out dust. Larger farm ponds and lakes would be difficult if not impossible to protect against fallout.

As time passes, contamination of ponds and lakes may not be a major problem. Dilution of the radioactive fallout in the water and its adsorption by clay on the sides and bottoms of the pond or lake will be effective in reducing the hazard below that of the surrounding land.

Boiling of water contaminated with radioactive particles will not make it safe, but distillation removes nearly all of the radioactive material.

Water from covered sources like springs and wells would be essentially free from contamination—even in heavy fallout areas—and could be used with confidence for man and animals.

WITH THE BREAKDOWN of refrigeration, which is very likely in a damaged area, it may be impossible to salvage perishable products. But if spoilage is not too great, the perishables may be washed or trimmed and cooked thoroughly before eating them.

Products or containers would very possibly be contaminated by water in the event of firefighting or sewage problems. If perishable products are so contaminated, vitally needed supplies could be partially salvaged by trimming and thorough cooking before consumption.

BOXED PRODUCTS might be similarly handled to provide an emergency supply of meat, and canned goods may be sterilized by washing, dipping in a chlorine solution, and drying. Canned goods must be carefully examined for rust spots, and damaged stocks used promptly following washing. Knowledge of the normal appearance of cans will enable us to determine soundness of the product involved.

Damaged cans should be held at room temperature for a 10-day period, if possible, after disposal of the obviously ruptured cans. The absence of proper incubation temperatures may require longer holding if emergency conditions permit. Any swelling of these cans would indicate bacterial spoilage and prohibit use of the contents as food.

Glass containers will be especially

subject to crushing, and there is also the possibility of a ruptured seal between the lid and container from pressure surges. Radioactive material or contamination from polluted water easily lodges under the screwcaps or friction type lids, and it is very difficult to remove.

In event the contamination is from water only, the contents may be salvaged by sterilization before using.

Meat food product ingredients, like cereal, will cake when damaged by water, and some dry material may be recovered from the inside of bags or drums. Fresh vegetables, like potatoes, carrots, and onions, if not crushed, can usually be salvaged through peeling or by thorough scrubbing.

Unlined cloth or porous paper over a product will not always protect it from radioactive fallout, so the product should be trimmed or portions next to containers discarded. Naturally, such trimming or discarding should be done so that the rest of the product will not be contaminated.

The disruptions brought on by conditions making salvage of food necessary also favor an increase in rats and in other vermin.

Special attention must be given to eradicating vermin and preventing their access to food, since vermin contamination and disease spreading is obviously a more serious threat under disaster conditions.

MOST OF THE MATERIAL discussed to this point has involved what the individual can do to prevent incorporation of radionuclides into food stocks under his own personal control.

It is also important to know what government at all levels is prepared to do with food stocks which have not yet reached the retail level.

It is unthinkable to allow resources like fuel, electricity, and manpower to be wasted on processing food from the farm to the market only to have the finished product unfit for human consumption.

The USDA inspection legend on meat and meat products is a familiar sight to most American housewives. That kind of inspection has become a standard of excellence which the public seems to take for granted.

This is not, however, the case for all food items, even though it is definitely a desirable goal.

UNDER THE CONDITIONS expected to prevail in a postattack environment, a high quality of food inspection no longer remains just a desirable goal; on the contrary, it is mandatory.

The U.S. Department of Agriculture and the Department of Health, Education, and Welfare are responsible for food resources and food, respectively. This does not mean that either agency has the manpower to do the total job, but they are responsible for planning the programs on a national basis. They have the responsibility to assist State and local governments in preparing uniform plans to protect the general public from the hazards of radionuclides which could be incorporated into the food chain.

The actual inspection services will be a combination of all the levels of government working together in the common interest.

But the success of such an undertaking depends upon a thorough preemergency plan along with extensive testing of the integrated plan.

Government at all levels is prepared to shoulder these burdens, but it is obvious that the widest possible dissemination of the necessary information is very important. Certainly the hazards are great and the consequences of ignorance deadly. Nevertheless the rules are logical and easy to follow.

The average housewife can do an effective job of protecting her family in food preparation during the immediate postattack period by following the procedures outlined in this chapter.

Perhaps the most important thing to remember is that lack of knowledge about the radionuclide content of food should never under any circumstances deter anyone from eating. Starvation is never a good solution to the problem of radiation exposure.

344

GOVERNMENT

FOOD

RESERVES

GEORGE H. WALTER

IN nearly every major disaster the Federal Government uses its food reserves to assist local disaster organizations in emergency feeding of disaster victims and workers.

A major share of the foods used for emergency feeding comes from stocks supplied by the U.S. Department of Agriculture.

Plans in case of war likewise assume that food supplied by the Agriculture Department would be used to meet a part of the emergency needs.

AN EXAMPLE OF emergency use of Government food reserves was Hurricane Betsy in September 1965. About 4.9 million pounds of Department-supplied food was used to feed over 318,000 people at temporary shelters in 105 schools and public buildings. This was supplemented with food supplies provided by the military, by the Red Cross, and others.

One advantage of having Government-owned food reserves is the speed

with which they can be made available to meet disaster requirements.

The idea of food reserves is not new. The Bible refers to Joseph building up food reserves in the years of plenty to supply the Egyptians and their friends in a period of famine which followed.

In our own country, when the late Henry A. Wallace was Secretary of Agriculture he developed the concept of the ever-normal granary, which is the basis for our present price support programs for food and other agricultural products.

Reserves built up during the late 1930's provided a valuable stock of

George H. Walter is an *Assistant* for Emergency Programs, Office of the Secretary of Agriculture.

food to provide aid to our friends and allies during World War II.

THE VALUE of Government food reserves to assist needy people has received increasingly greater recognition in recent years.

The first Executive order issued by President Kennedy was to augment the distribution of Government-owned foods to needy people in this country. The Food for Peace program was designed to use our food abundance for assistance to needy people in other parts of the world.

IN TIMES OF WAR, Government food supplies have been used to feed our own Armed Forces and the armed forces of our allies, as well as to supplement food supplies in war-damaged and occupied areas.

Food is vital both from a humanitarian standpoint and to help maintain health and order in occupied areas.

Following major wars, food has been a major item in aid and assistance programs. When we have had Government food reserves, these have been used, reducing pressures on the already expanding economy.

If no Government food reserves are available, unusual demands require special production programs to get the needed commodities. It has proved difficult to readjust food production downward once these war-generated demands have been met.

Many people have the impression that the Federal Government owns huge stocks of food of all types.

But compared to commercial food stocks, Government-owned foods are relatively limited, both in terms of quantity and of variety.

The term "Government Food Reserves" as used in this article includes the following types of foods owned by the Federal Government: (1) Foods procured specifically for use in public institutions and welfare programs, (2) civil defense shelter stocks, and (3) inventories acquired as a result of price support operations of the Agriculture Department.

Food for use in public institutions and welfare programs includes that purchased for the school lunch program, food supplies of the military and other Government agencies for their own use, and food for distribution to needy people.

FOOD FOR schools and welfare distribution is provided by the Agriculture Department to State agencies for distribution. Over 2 billion pounds are distributed annually.

At any one time, inventories in the hands of the distribution agency, the schools, or in the Department's warehouses and in transit probably average at least a 2- or 3-month supply for the purpose that was intended.

FOOD STOCKS owned by the military, by the Veterans' Administration and other Federal agencies are for their own use.

Only limited amounts can be diverted from these stocks for other uses. Efforts are made to hold inventories to the minimum needed.

Civil defense shelter supplies include about 318 million pounds of biscuits or crackers plus a small quantity of carbohydrate supplements. These stocks are packaged in cans to provide a long shelf life and protection from contamination. Thus they are intended only as a survival ration and are not available for other purposes.

INVENTORIES of foods acquired as a result of the Agriculture Department price support operations vary widely, depending upon the season and upon crop conditions.

In September 1965 they included over 70 million pounds of butter, around 3 million pounds of cheese, some 201 million pounds of dry milk, and nearly 3 million pounds of dry beans, over 3 million pounds of peanuts and peanut butter, and 1.8 million pounds of honey.

Supplies of grain included about half a billion bushels of wheat and a billion bushels of feed grains.

While these Government food reserves seem large in terms of total pounds, they represent only a few pounds per person. Except for grains, they are also relatively small when compared with commercial food stocks maintained by food processors and by distributors.

But even Government and commercial stocks combined cannot be considered a substitute for continued new production and the distribution of food from the farm through the normal commercial channels to the ultimate consumer.

A MAJOR PART of food made available by the Department of Agriculture to schools and needy families is acquired as a result of price support and through removal of surplusage from the marketplace. Quantities may vary markedly within the year.

These stocks consist only of foods in surplus supply since, by law, price support stocks must be sold whenever a buyer offers the support price plus certain carrying charges.

Food available as a result of price support programs usually includes wheat, corn, and other grains in unprocessed form which are often kept in storage in the production areas.

This food can be processed into cereals, flour, or other items usable in an emergency. But it takes time, and in disasters the immediate need is obviously for ready-to-use food.

Therefore, these grains serve primarily as backup reserves to assure adequate food for a considerable period after an emergency.

Following natural disasters like floods, Government stocks of feed grains are sometimes made available to farmers at reduced prices or donated, to keep livestock alive until local feed supplies are again available.

SOME FOODS acquired as a result of price support operations are in a form readily available and suitable for immediate use in case of a disaster. They include butter, dry milk, cheese, and dry beans. These items can quickly be shipped to the disaster areas either for

Tornado victims eat Palm Sunday dinner in a firehouse at Dunlap, Ind., with food made available by USDA.

use in group feeding operations or for distribution to families.

Generally there are quantities of some or all of these foods in the "pipelines" en route to or in schools or welfare distribution centers. Immediate disaster needs are usually met from the nearest source with the Agriculture Department arranging for resupply from more distant points.

ANOTHER immediate source of foods for disaster use is Commodity Credit Corporation (CCC) price support stocks which have been processed into forms ready for school use or distribution to needy families. Examples are wheat, flour and other cereal products, peanut butter, milled rice, and vegetable oil products.

Processing contracts provide for most of these items to be shipped directly by the processor to a State-operated warehouse from which they move to the school or welfare distribution center. Usually, however, supplies en route from the processor can be reconsigned to meet emergency or disaster feeding needs. In other cases, the supplies are "borrowed" from already donated stocks with the promise to replace them subsequently.

IN CASE OF DISASTER the Agriculture Department also makes available foods it purchases for other purposes.

347

Funds are provided under section 32 of Public Law 320 of the 74th Congress so the Department can purchase foods to encourage an increased domestic consumption. The authorizing legislation says these funds must be devoted principally to perishable items that are not under price support.

THESE FUNDS are used to purchase foods like fruit, vegetables, meat, and powdered eggs. The funds can also be employed for processing and moving the foods to where they can be used.

The foods can be donated for relief purposes, including emergency feeding in disaster areas. They supplement food provided out of CCC stocks and are generally distributed through the very same outlets.

Inventories of foods purchased by the Government as a part of this program are generally only those in transit to school and welfare outlets and small supplies awaiting movement. Consequently, in natural disasters and other emergencies the Agriculture Department relies upon diverting foods already in the school or welfare stocks or that are in transit, and replaces them when new purchases are made.

ANOTHER SOURCE of Government-provided foods that can be used to relieve effects of a disaster are those purchased specifically for the school lunch program, under section 6 of the National School Lunch Act.

Unlike foods procured by CCC or with section 32 funds, school lunch foods cannot be donated for relief purposes without reimbursement or replacement. But although the foods must be replaced, their location in schools where disaster groups can be fed may simplify the operation.

AGRICULTURE DEPARTMENT agreements with State agencies responsible for distributing donated foods to schools, welfare recipients, and other eligible outlets contain an authorization for making the foods available for use in disasters. No special authorization is needed after a disaster. The foods are available immediately to local governments where group feeding becomes necessary.

FOOD FOR PEACE includes several types of programs to provide food to other nations, both for relief following natural disasters and to supplement food production within these nations. The programs include distribution by voluntary agencies, donations to nations, and various sales arrangements.

Food for these programs comes from purchases out of commercial stocks and in large part from stocks acquired by the Agriculture Department as a result of its price support operations.

GOVERNMENT FOOD INVENTORIES are useful in emergency feeding operations but they cannot be relied on as the only source of food.

Such inventories in all areas are limited in total amount since they normally supply only a small part of the total population. Also, they usually include only a few items—not the full complement required for emergency feeding purposes.

Government stocks never include bread, coffee, salt, other seasonings, or sugar. Items highly desirable for emergency feeding like canned pork and beans, soup mixes, and jellies are seldom if ever in inventories.

As a result, the emergency feeding groups must supplement the supplies made available from Agriculture Department-donated stocks with other foods—from regular commercial stocks or in some cases through the feeding of refugees by the military with its own food supplies.

Food stocks acquired through price support are owned and managed by the Commodity Credit Corporation, fiscal agent of the Agriculture Department for national farm commodity programs.

Its grain stocks are stored in more than 10,000 private warehouses, most of them in areas where the grains are produced.

Rice is stored in over 200 privately owned storage facilities.

CCC uses approximately 400 dry and cold storage installations for storing processed foods.

It also stores wheat and feed grains in Government-owned storage bins in the major production areas.

With CCC inventories in so many places, the chances are relatively small that any large part of CCC stocks would be damaged by a disaster.

Even in case of an attack upon this country, dispersion reduces the probable degree of loss and helps in assuring that supplies will be available where needed following the attack.

Most CCC stocks are in structures which provide relatively good protection from radioactive fallout and from other threats of contamination.

In managing CCC stocks, defense needs are a consideration in deciding where food will be stored. However, to keep costs at a minimum, stocks generally are held where acquired until they can be marketed. This results in most food items being stored in production areas rather than close to the major population centers.

IN MANY DISASTERS, the Department of Defense is requested to help local authorities relieve suffering and care for refugees. This often includes feeding people by making use of military food supplies.

In case of war, Defense Department arrangements authorize that military support include food for local civil defense when this is possible without significantly affecting defense operations themselves.

Diversions of military food stocks immediately following a disaster are useful in meeting immediate need but the stocks must be replaced later.

USE OF specially packaged military rations has the disadvantage of being an expensive food source for meeting emergency requirements, and is discouraged if other sources are available.

Military food stocks are generally located at military bases and supply depots but some are kept in commercial storage facilities.

ANOTHER FOOD SOURCE for a defense emergency is the shelter rations the Office of Civil Defense (OCD) has purchased and stocked.

Most of these rations are in shelter areas in large buildings or in OCD warehouses.

They consist primarily of enriched crackers or wafers and are intended as only a subsistence diet while people have to remain in fallout shelters.

PRESIDENT JOHNSON has recognized the need for Government-owned food reserves.

His February 4, 1965, agricultural message included the following about Government reserve stocks:

"It is time to consider our requirements for agricultural commodities in a reserve for national security, for emergency relief purposes, and for domestic economic stabilization.

"The President should be authorized to determine the levels of commodity stocks required and to take actions to insulate these stocks from the market so that they might be preserved for time of emergencies."

The need for legislation authorizing "national security reserves" of foods, feeds, and fibers was stressed in the 1964 report of the National Agricultural Advisory Commission.

The report said Government-owned stocks were needed for use in defense and natural disaster emergencies, to provide commodity price stabilization, and to meet international food problems. The Commission pointed out the advantages of reserves for consumer welfare.

One of the Commission's "goals for farm policy" was to assure "an abundant supply of quality food and other farm products at reasonable prices." And its recommendations included the following:

"The availability of large stocks of several farm products acquired under farm programs of the past has delayed proper attention to the question of reserve supplies needed for national security, assistance to allies abroad, and stability in the domestic economy.

349

"There is urgent need for a determination of the reserve stocks that should be on hand and for policy decisions regarding their management. . . . Here we wish to call attention to the question and to urge that the need for reserve stocks and the costs of providing them be explicitly recognized."

BECAUSE OF THE IMPORTANCE of food in all types of emergencies, there have been many proposals for building up Government food reserves. In part, these proposals reflect the major reductions which have taken place in "surplus" stocks that are held by the Agriculture Department.

At the 1965 National Outlook Conference, Secretary Freeman said it would be the Department's policy "to maintain adequate reserves of food and fiber, as opposed to unneeded surpluses, to respond to any need at home or abroad, and we will preserve the capacity to expand production substantially."

He also indicated the desire to use Government-owned food supplies "as an instrument of American foreign policy and humanitarianism. . . ."

PRIMARY DETERRENTS to establishing reserves are their high cost of acquisition and maintenance and the need for frequent rotation or replacement. For the domestic population, a week's supply of food providing a balanced diet, and packaged to withstand a year or more of storage life, would probably cost well above a billion dollars.

Rotation of such a food stockpile presents unending problems, since there are no easy ways to sell and use many items needed in the stockpile so that they could be replaced with new production.

Even the best packaged foods must be replaced from time to time to assure that quality is maintained. Special packaging can lengthen shelf life but it also increases costs.

The need for special Government food stockpiles for use in emergencies and to stabilize prices is also debated.

Advocates of stockpiles say a nuclear attack would fragment our country and make interarea movement of food difficult or impossible.

They also contend that fallout could seriously limit agricultural production following an attack.

Opponents say a nuclear attack would probably reduce our population far more than our food production. They doubt that transportation would be so disrupted as to drastically reduce shipments of food.

They also cite the food stocks in commercial trade channels and homes and their availability to meet food needs until shipments could be resumed.

HOME FOOD RESERVES vary from little or nothing to supplies sufficient for months, but probably average at least enough for a week, though not necessarily with the normal variety and balance.

Retail store inventories vary, even within the week and among items. But in terms of dollar value they average a 1 to 2 weeks' supply for their usual clients. In addition there are large quantities of food in commercial storage and in processing plants.

In total, all the stocks of ready-to-use foods probably equal over 2 months' supply at normal rates of use. These are replaced by daily processing and by deliveries from farms.

ABOUT TWO-FIFTHS of our foods are continuously produced items like meat, eggs, milk, and flour.

Government wheat stocks assure continued supplies for millers, even in case of a poor crop or of unusual world demand. Government supplies of feed grains likewise assure adequate feed for production of meat, eggs, milk, and other livestock and poultry products. Relatively smaller Government-owned stocks of other foods like dairy products, dry beans, rice, and peanuts help to assure supplies required for an orderly flow through distribution channels and to meet some of the unusual needs for food—as when a disaster strikes.

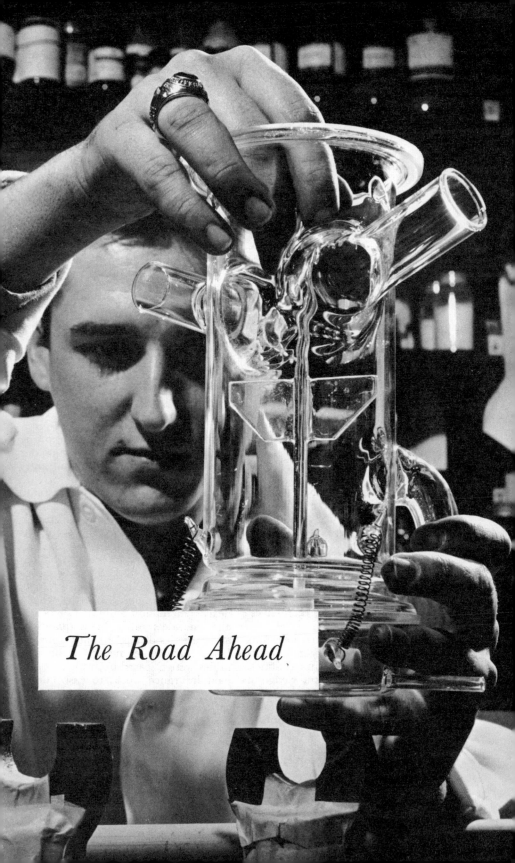

The Road Ahead

CHEMICALS: ONE KEY TO THE FUTURE

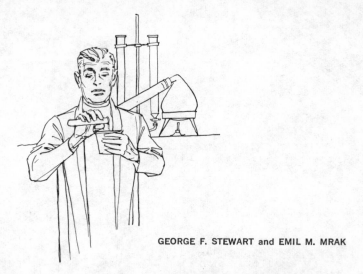

GEORGE F. STEWART and EMIL M. MRAK

MAN must continue to probe the chemical nature of his universe and to rearrange its basic elements if he is to survive.

These life-giving elements are deposited by nature in various ways: In the soil, in rocks and minerals, in water and air, in plants and animals, and in man himself.

Man's natural curiosity and anxiety concerning his environment has many aspects. First, there is the interest in living things and in the millions of processes that go on at once. Then, there is the matter of relationships; that nothing exists by itself, but everything is modified by something else. And finally, the respect for the absolute necessity of change; of things growing, developing, and renewing themselves.

NOWHERE IN THE WORLD are the results of man's intensive curiosity more readily apparent than in the United States. This has led to superior knowledge in the physical and the biological sciences affecting his primary needs of food, clothing, and shelter, and the application of such knowledge so as to produce each year enough raw material to feed and to clothe half of the peoples of the world.

Research and technology have revolutionized U.S. agriculture to a point where in 1965 its crop yield per acre continued to soar and the Nation's cropland to shrink, with the rising level of our agricultural output in contrast to the destruction of our prime cultivated and arable lands and our natural resources through a constantly increasing urbanization.

Fortunately for the United States, the feeding of its people has long been the Nation's major industry. And it has been more than successful, its food stores alone carrying on an annual business in excess of $70 billion.

The 1965 record U.S. harvest produced over 4 billion bushels of corn, more than 1 billion bushels of wheat, nearly 900 million bushels of soybeans, and countless other huge quantities and varieties of food bounty from the land. Meanwhile, needed grain surpluses were released from the Nation's food insurance stocks to ease famine

* * *

George F. Stewart is *Director*, Food Protection and Toxicology Center, University of California at Davis.

Emil M. Mrak is *Chancellor* of the University of California at Davis.

and its resulting tensions in other parts of the world, and stockpiled processed foods were available for the relief of manmade and natural emergencies at home as well.

THE UNPRECEDENTED U.S. wealth is largely attributable to the longstanding and persistent Government support of science and technology, which has consistently returned improved cultural practices, and better crop varieties and livestock breeds.

The principal technological factors in moving the agricultural output ever upward are mechanization and the wise use of agricultural chemicals and food additives. Such factors will continue to protect the food supply, and result in further essential cultural and economic benefits.

And despite the constant radical improvement in the quality, quantity, and built-in convenience of U.S. foods, less than 19 percent of the total take-home pay is spent by today's housewife for meals of higher quality, greater variety, and added nourishment.

CHEMICALS ARE EFFICIENT and versatile tools forged and modified from man's increasing ability to understand the breadth and scope of chemistry. They are used as a sure means for increasing the efficiency of crop and livestock production.

As the result of knowledge gained from continuing research at all levels and from all sources, the U.S. chemical industry has developed the capacity to act quickly to commercialize chemical compounds which perform specific jobs. For example, chemicals are used to protect fruits and vegetables from deterioration and damage during transit and storage, and to hasten the ripening of fruits or to delay the blossoming of trees to avoid frost damage.

In livestock production, the chemical industry maintains research stations, duplicating farm conditions for the development of feed additives and other valuable compounds. Chemicals such as antibiotics are used for getting healthier, heavier poultry, swine, sheep,

and cattle to market in less time, and choline—an essential vitamin—is used for farm animals and man.

Among the recent and numerous introductions to the market are two trace mineralized salt products containing medicants. One is designed to prevent deterioration of cattle hooves, and the other to inhibit development of unsanitary, weight-reducing, cattle-irritating horn flies.

THE BIGGEST VOLUME of chemicals used in agriculture are the fertilizers. Soil chemistry shows there are 16 elements which are essential to plant growth.

Nitrogen, phosphorus, and potash are the primary plant foods that most often have to be added as fertilizers to the soil to produce a variety of highly nutritious raw food materials. And depending upon the crop and its environment, other plant food elements must also be added.

Soil in itself is merely a chemical container of various particles and arrangements. Therefore it is imperative that the chemical nutrients used by the plants be replaced throughout the growing cycle and after harvesting. Chemical fertilizers, then, protect the food supply by guaranteeing a constant source of essential plant foods.

EQUALLY IMPORTANT to replenishing the soil is the protection of the resulting products. Pest control is essential in the production of feed, food, and fiber, and for protecting plants, animals, and man against the ravages of insect damage and disease. Presently, chemical pesticides are mostly used for the control of insects, plant diseases, weeds, nematodes, and rodents.

Insects attack all plant and animal life in every stage of growth, and in storage. They also spread disease. Other enemies of our food are plant diseases; weeds, which reduce both crop yield and quality; nematodes, the microscopic worms that live mainly on plant roots; and rodents and other small animal pests.

Despite these attackers, the major source of the food supply is safely and ably protected by the discriminating use of chemicals, such as insecticides for control of insects attacking crops and livestock; herbicides, fungicides, nematocides, growth regulators, defoliants, and desiccants used on agricultural crops; chemicals to control diseases and other deterioration of fruits and vegetables during marketing; and insecticides used to protect stored-food products by means of insect-resistant housing and packaging.

LABOR SAVINGS from the use of chemicals in agriculture cannot be isolated since they act in conjunction with agricultural machinery, including the airplane.

U.S. agricultural practices, born of sustained basic and applied research, produce abundance at a rate of only 2 man-days of work per acre compared to 400 man-days of work in the Far East to attain equivalent yields.

IN 1913, it took 135 man-hours to produce 100 bushels of corn. Today, it takes about 15 man-hours. The former tedious and time-consuming methods of weed control in corn were eliminated through the application of a pound per acre of a selective chemical herbicide, taking about an hour with a tractor-drawn power-sprayer compared to 100 hours for manual weeding.

Mechanization in cotton harvesting—and cottonseed is an increasingly important feed and food crop—was made possible by the development of chemical defoliating agents.

RECENT ADVANCES in cotton production include the use of chemicals in the form of black polyethylene film—a chemical—as a replacement for the traditional mulches.

Great lengths of film are mechanically placed over the planting rows, followed by a planting machine which simultaneously punches holes in the film and inserts quick-dissolving vermiculite capsules to an exact depth in the soil, each capsule containing seed and meticulously calculated amounts of fertilizer, insecticide, and fungicide.

Protection, warmth, and moisture from the polyethylene film quickly germinate the seed, bringing much faster maturity to the young plant as it emerges through the hole in the film. Weeds between the film strips are chemically controlled, while their inability to grow beneath the film results in weed control savings of approximately $12 an acre.

The film is now used for other crops, such as pineapple.

Here, slip cuttings from the pineapple plant itself replace the seed, but it is mechanically planted along with the chemical-containing capsule and the results are the same.

RESEARCH IS ALSO modifying the airplane so that it becomes a far more efficient agricultural tool.

Its capability for seeding is becoming greater, as are applications of herbicides and insecticides formulated with new water-swellable thickening agents for the control of any drift in airplane spraying operations.

On land, a recently developed citrus fruit handling system provides labor savings while reducing fruit damage. It consists of a truck-mounted frame holding 9 bulk bins with a capacity of 1,600 pounds of fruit each, compared

Strawberries grown through holes punched in polyethylene film are harvested.

with 55 pounds contained in manually handled field boxes.

In the packing plant, a new mechanical process applies an invisible chemical coating to fresh fruits and vegetables that retards spoilage and moisture loss en route to market.

Food chemicals, or food additives as they are commonly called, are used extensively in food processing. They protect food from deterioration before use and, as in the case of the soil, replenish processed foods with the natural chemical elements that they may lose following harvesting, during processing, and in storage.

EVERY CHEMICAL used in food production and processing is designed to improve nutritional value, enhance quality or consumer acceptability, preserve food, or make food readily available to the consumer.

Monosodium glutamate, for example, brings out the flavor in certain cooked foods.

Food processors have matched the progress of agriculture by providing processed products that contain practically all the nutritive quality and appetizing flavor found in both fresh and home-cooked foods.

Foods and chemicals are synonymous. When we eat foods we eat chemicals. Our reason for eating foods is to assimilate the chemicals that they contain.

With the growth of man's knowledge, it became evident that he could utilize to his benefit some of the countless chemicals that make up his environment. Not only could he improve the flavor of his meat, but he could prevent his bread from becoming stale. It became possible to fertilize his crops, protect them from insects and improve their keeping qualities, all through an adroit use of chemicals.

CHEMISTS AND CHEMICAL manufacturers have materially contributed to the protection of the food supply by their amazing ability to first synthesize natural chemicals and then to commercially manufacture them.

Research and product development continues on new and improved types of food colors, for example.

EMPHASIS also is being placed on synthesis and production of aromatic and flavor chemicals, "fine" terpene chemicals—citronella oil, lemongrass oil, bois de rose, and derivatives from these three essential oils used in the manufacturing of vitamins A and E. Heretofore, these essential oils were available primarily in their natural states. But chemists developed methods of synthesizing them from terpenes, thus assuring oils of uniformly high quality at stable prices from our own domestic sources.

Chemists have also synthesized peppermint and spearmint oils, and lemon and lime flavors from terpene raw materials.

From the scientific viewpoint, a manufactured or synthetic chemical is identical to its natural counterpart, possessing the same capabilities and the same purposes for which it was intended by nature. Only nature's methods of synthesis may differ from those of man.

EVERYTHING WE CAN SEE, feel, smell, or eat is chemical in nature. Water, salt, and carbon dioxide are simple chemical compounds. The bulk of our foods—proteins, fats, and carbohydrates—are made up of complex chemical compounds.

Our bodies are very complex chemical organisms, producing heat, energy, and growth of cells as long as we consume adequate chemical raw materials in the form of food.

THIS FOOD is chemically disintegrated by saliva and digestive fluids in the stomach and intestines to form amino acids, vitamins, sugars, and fatty acids. It is these relatively simple chemicals which are absorbed into the bloodstream and nourish our bodies.

Once in circulation they chemically react to build muscles, nerves, fluids, and bones.

Nature is the original and greatest

synthesizer of chemicals. Man is only now learning some of the secrets of chemical syntheses which nature has practiced from time untold.

THIAMINE made in a chemical laboratory is equally as nutritious as the vitamin derived from cereals. The acetic acid in vinegar is identical to the acid synthesized by the chemist.

Processing procedures are governed by chemical and mechanical engineering, and the availability of a wide spectrum of chemicals.

The frozen foods field is making increased use of chemicals for the preservation of foods to bring full flavor and nourishment to the consumer. For example, liquid nitrogen is used to flash-freeze fruits and vegetables to preserve their fresh delicate flavor.

Hydrogen is used to stiffen oils into shortening through hydrogenation.

ANALYTICAL CHEMISTRY and instrumentation are prime tools in the development and application of chemicals with which to produce and protect the Nation's food supply.

Advances in this field have speeded the detection of infinitesimal amounts of pesticide residues in foods. The result: Dramatic elimination of the once tedious and costly methods of analytical determination. Highly technical manpower has been freed for advanced phases of research, and the all-important time factor in finding new materials and processes for food production has been reduced.

Analytical instruments play an unobtrusive but major role in practically every phase of man's environment. They are used to define the structure of new chemicals, identify dozens of components in a food flavor, and unmask the cause of contamination.

There has hardly been an important new material developed in the last 10 years that has not depended in part upon analytical instruments.

One mass spectrometer can literally take the fingerprints of a chemical by analyzing its molecular mass.

Gas chromatographs increase product yield by monitoring and controlling the processing of chemicals through analysis.

A brand new electron microscope makes possible 100,000 times magnification of any surface texture measurement, showing every detail of surface texture.

The microscope then records these on charts for comparative study.

This is an important development in food processing where the flavor and texture are major determinants in consumer acceptance.

AN IMPORTANT BREAKTHROUGH in analytical procedure was recently made by development of a new scanning electron microscope, giving clarity and depth to minute particles never before obtained at such high magnification.

The electronic computer, too, is used with profound effect in both research and service to contract growers.

Individual soil fertilization recommendations are worked out on the computer and sent to growers who submit soil samples for analysis. Analysis findings for a particular field are fed into the computer with such other information as the fertilization history, crop rotation practices, and the desired crop goals.

Accurate recommendations are printed out immediately on the computer.

SUCH ARE THE WAYS of a technological era in which computer programing can make specialized recommendations for a distant, particular tract of land.

These are but a few examples of the fast-growing number of research tools being developed so scientists may continue to discover the pathways leading to the construction of new foods from new materials.

MAN IS THE MAJOR THREAT to his own food supply. Never before has the U.S. consumer been blessed with so great a variety of high-quality, easily prepared foods. These he takes for granted, giving not a thought as to how they come about.

Meanwhile, man places ribbons of

concrete highways across the lands that must sustain him. He contaminates the water that in turn must sustain the land and pollutes the air with the wastes of a society he has helped to create. He bulldozes the hills and mountains whose contours were designed by nature to save the earth from the ravages of fire and flood. He fells the timber which has taken centuries to grow, and removes fruit and ornamental trees without regard for the natural purposes they serve.

In general man dissipates the basic values and resources upon which his very existence depends.

LEGISLATION in itself cannot control man's actions. Only the educated understanding of problems will provide their solutions.

Presently, the natural resources of the United States are fast running out. Scientific research, and in a very large sense research in chemistry and on chemicals themselves, is the Nation's last great frontier.

THE NATION'S agricultural land is decreasing at the rate of several millions of acres a year due in part to the covering over of long-cultivated, highly productive soils for highways, tract homes, industrial complexes, and the like for use by our rapidly increasing population.

The rapid disappearance of these farming areas would have had early and dramatic impact on the public had it not been for the Nation's past investment in agricultural research and, in most part, the judicious use of chemicals in both agricultural practices and in food processing.

While unwarranted attacks have been made by the uninformed on the application of chemicals in food production, the safety of their use has been necessarily monitored by expensive analytical and regulatory procedures.

Stringent regulations, both Government and self-imposed, are placed on agricultural producers, food processors, food package manufacturers, and the chemical industry on the use of chemicals in the total area of food production.

Chemicals cannot be used indiscriminately. Their long-term effect upon the total environment is a subject of constant study. Furthermore chemicals are expensive. So they have their definite limitations.

TWO ADEQUATELY supported research projects are now needed, with these objectives: Conversion of the Nation's desert areas to intensive crop production, and assurance of the highest degree of production efficiency upon our existing agricultural lands.

Chemicals have a big role to play in this research.

Water development and conservation is even more important than development of new land. Problems involving the availability and quality of water are severe, and mounting. Research is needed not only to conserve water, but to recover water as well.

Priceless water is our most wasted resource. It is a major factor in our ability to produce and process foods.

A single ear of corn needs 25 gallons for its development. For each pound of weight, a steer needs 3,750 gallons for himself and the feed he eats. A slice of bread and the growing of its grain has used over 37 gallons, and a single serving of potatoes 1,405 gallons. More than a ton of water is required to produce a single pound of cane sugar.

The average rainfall for the United States is about 30 inches, with some parts of the Nation receiving as little as 2 inches annually.

While some scientists are seeking ways to change the distribution of this water, others are seeking means of protecting our water.

Chemical manufacturers and engineering firms are spending heavily on research in studying the behavior and quality of water. They are rapidly expanding their water treatment facilities. They supply engineering and laboratory services and water treatment chemicals. They are developing chemical feeding equipment and water monitoring and control systems.

As a result, detergent manufacturers are well ahead of their conversion schedule to the so-called "soft detergents" through the development of biodegradables—new chemical materials that are easily decomposed by nature's micro-organisms.

Thus the manufacturers are helping to combat the growing problem of foaming on surface waters caused by residues of household and industrial detergents.

In other areas of water conservation, the chemical industry has developed a number of soluble phosphates for use in various types of water treatment. The search for solutions to modern sanitation problems continues with a new method of inducing sludge digestion for fast, efficient waste disposal coming under close study.

Among recent commercial chemicals is a water-swellable material for protecting the watersheds: A fire control polymer used in aerial sprays to check forest fires.

The food processing industry has a vital stake in the quantity and quality of water, not only as a food ingredient within itself, but in protecting intricate and expensive plant processing systems and equipment against corrosion and contamination.

The industry is meeting the water pollution problem mainly by chemical water treatment, treating both incoming water and plant effluents before they are deposited in streams and in rivers.

Purity of water is of prime concern in all phases of food manufacture. A carbonated beverage, for example, is no better than the water that goes into it, so chemicals are used to produce commercially sterile water.

Huge tanks are filled with local water pure enough for normal consumption. To this, purifying chemical agents like chlorine are added to kill the germs and oxidize organic matter. Balancing agents, such as lime, reduce alkalinity.

The purified water is then put through a sand filter that removes solid matter not previously absorbed. It next enters an activated carbon filter that frees it of chlorine, taste, and odor. Finally, it passes through a paper "polishing" filter.

Food processing "in-plant" controls are also being made more effective. While isolation of contaminants and incineration is used in some plants, others are recovering profitable by-products from waste: Dried spent grains from distilleries are converted into cattle feed; sulphite waste from paper mills is converted to food yeast; and materials recovered from water used in processing certain corn products help manufacture penicillin and streptomycin.

Thus, the removal of contaminants from industrial water wastes recovers both water and ingredients that are important in the food chain.

High density agriculture is the increasing order of the day as agricultural areas are forced to give way to heavy population increases.

The greater use of agricultural chemicals must also follow, because further concentration of agricultural production must intensify hazards from insects, plant pathogens, nematodes, weeds, and animal diseases.

There is no other way to meet the burgeoning demand for food.

This is not to say that chemicals will be applied without regard to human safety and long-term environmental effects.

Research must be strongly supported at all levels of government and industry to protect the Nation against all hazards, including those that are sociological in nature, and to further explore the effectiveness and practicality of biological control, the development of insect and disease resistant plants, and the like.

Changes in food patterns must inevitably follow reductions in agricultural land areas. Simply, the complex system of nature must be scientifically rearranged for long-term survival.

NATURAL SYSTEMS have become increasingly inadequate to support the basic requirements of mounting world populations.

In the near future, the United States may encounter food shortages unless its leaders reevaluate their thinking regarding agriculture and its growing research needs. Scientists will be increasingly charged with making new discoveries leading to new components and sources in the food chain.

Within the next decade, vital edible protein must be found because man will be increasingly competing with his domestic animals for this important chemical nutrient.

While scientists have been amazingly successful in synthesizing a wide variety indeed of other important chemicals in the food supply, the synthesizing of protein is a highly complex and quite formidable problem.

IT IS HIGHLY IMPROBABLE that any control can be made of the rising increase in the U.S. population. It is therefore inevitable that livestock as an intermediary source of protein will have to be minimized.

As a source of protein, domestic animals are wasteful in terms of the protein required to feed them. Only 23 percent of the total protein consumed by the cow is returned for human consumption (as milk), 12 percent by the pig, and only 10 percent is returned by beef cattle.

An acre of land can produce 800,000 Calories in the form of plants, but only 200,000 Calories when these plants are fed to animals. Thus, meat animals use roughly 600,000 Calories from each acre's crop for their own metabolism.

THE MOST LOGICAL approach to the mounting food problem, then, is in the use of legumes that live symbiotically (each helping the other) with nitrogen-fixing bacteria, and efficiently produce protein with less depletion of nitrogen from the soil.

U.S. AGRICULTURE has repeatedly demonstrated that by the judicious use of chemicals, in many forms and for many reasons, crop yields per acre can be increased without producing any detrimental side effects.

Future protein needs must be met by chemically nurtured and protected plant materials. They certainly cannot be met by animal protein. Furthermore, research shows that meat, milk, or eggs are not indispensable to human health and human well-being.

RESEARCH will also find other sources of edible protein. Scientists abroad, for example, recently discovered microorganisms feeding on petroleum residues that are said to synthesize 2,500 pounds of edible protein in 24 hours. A pilot plant is now producing oil-derived protein as animal feed. Rich in B vitamins and lysine, the protein concentrate may well become a promising source of human food.

With the exception of protein, many of the valuable byproducts from livestock production have already been synthesized or replaced by plant oils.

As a result of exploratory research conducted in many areas of science and technology, chemists were able to successfully simulate the qualities of natural leather, which is an extremely complex material.

Interestingly enough, market research revealed that within less than 20 years the world demand for hides would exceed the supply by 50 percent.

AN IMPORTANT CONTRIBUTION to the present status and technology of plant protein foods is a method of processing edible protein. This is done first by solubilizing the material, and then by using textile spinning techniques to orient the molecules in continuous filaments, resulting in food products of spun protein fibers.

Textured soybean protein fiber is being successfully used to simulate chicken, turkey, beef, and ham products. Furthermore, nearly every meat or meat product has been fairly well simulated in experimental prototypes.

A chemical company researcher at Princeton, N.J., begins a test on a new compound to see if it has systemic action on plant leaves. Insects are placed on top of the leaf. If the compound is drawn up through the plant stem and kills insects feeding on the leaf, the chemical will be tested further for safety as well as effectiveness.

Great potential and versatility exist in soya fiber food products, because they can be formulated to any protein, fat, or carbohydrate level. Proteins may be blended to accomplish very favorable amino acid ratios: Synthetic vitamins, minerals, color, and flavor may be added as desired.

HISTORICALLY, food habits change. In the long view, adequately supported research may be able to stem and control the hazard of growing human numbers in relation to the food supply. However, flavor and texture, and familiar shapes and appearance, are of major importance in consumer acceptance of new food concepts.

Tremendous advances have been made in the chemistry of flavor and texture. As further knowledge is acquired on these two important food components it will become virtually possible to construct any of the presently acceptable conventional foods,

through chemistry. Research, then, is the guiding factor in providing food for the future.

RESEARCH and development expenditures in 1964 amounted to about $20 billion. The Federal Government contributed about 75 percent of this amount to the Nation's total effort. Alarmingly, its support of agricultural research is not in keeping with the future problems of food production, the authors of this chapter believe. The problems of today are even more complex than those of past generations.

As a result of expanding research and development (R. & D.) effort, research vistas are rapidly expanding to present ever-increasing challenges. Despite the promising picture, there are problem areas which impede R. & D., particularly in matters of cost.

Costs were among the principal reasons for an assessment and reevaluation of R. & D. in 1964 by the Select

Committee on Government Research of the House of Representatives.

The testimony revealed that the U.S. scientific community had performed a vital job effectively and with reasonable efficiency. It was also brought out that many problems continue to handicap the Nation's scientific potential, among them: The need for clearer definition of national technological goals, for improved methods in planning and evaluating research efforts, and for more emphasis on basic research in developing a greater fund of scientific knowledge.

INCREASED industrial research is vital to the Nation's economy. But such expenditures can only follow a recognition of potentially fruitful areas and a willingness to assume risks, not only on applied research, but on costly development, plant, and marketing commitments preceding profits.

In an age when the future subsistence of the United States must depend in large measure on the use of chemicals and their development, it appears necessary and important that their total impact on the environment be a matter for intensive and continuing study.

Science and technology have successfully determined the structure and capabilities of chemicals to provide an adequate, abundant, and safe food supply to more than presently meet the needs of a growing nation. Yet pressures of these needs have produced certain side effects stemming from the calculated risks which are inherent in maintaining our food supplies.

THE FRAILTIES of human nature make it mandatory that Government agencies regulate the methods of chemical application in agriculture and in food preservation. And if the Food and Drug Administration is to wisely regulate pesticide tolerances, for example, then the Federal Government must provide the means for research-oriented data and analytical methodology for this regulation to be effective.

At the same time, the registration of chemicals and the establishment of tolerances in their use must be dictated only by scientific findings.

A TOKEN STEP toward scientific determination of possible hazards to the total environment due to the application of chemicals was made in 1965 when the University of California established a Food Protection and Toxicology Center on its Davis campus. This was done with the aid of the U.S. Public Health Service.

The center's objective is to provide effective means to monitor the growth and progress of environmental research, identify trends, and define areas for special emphasis in the planning of future programs.

The center seeks to provide effective means for monitoring any environmental change which is due to the imperative use of chemicals in all phases of food production. The monitoring system is designed to detect potential hazards and to define needed areas of research.

Briefly, the mission of the center is to acquire factual knowledge and assemble its findings in an integrated manner on the complete relationships or ecology in which a chemical will move—from the time of its manufacture until it is decomposed, diluted, or removed from the environment. As data are acquired they must be made rapidly available.

CHEMICAL COMPOUNDS have a varying degree of stability or resistance to decomposition. Some intermediates in the decomposition process are also toxic and may be stable.

Ideally, a pesticide would be stable enough to reach the target organism, perform its function, then decompose to innocuous products. At the other end of the stability or persistence spectrum are compounds which continue to exist for many years, regardless of their position in the environment. Here, the chemicals move from the point of manufacture to spread by various mechanisms to great distances and into every part of the ecology.

361

Chemicals can move in a bewildering pattern, and how they are finally removed or how they are restrained from further movement or reaction with organisms, are all matters of continuous monitoring, inspection, and analysis.

While it is highly desirable to use those chemicals, insofar as is practicable, which have short lives and disappear through a decomposition route soon after accomplishing their purpose, it is likely that some pest control programs will best be served by stable, long-lived chemicals.

This, then, demands close attention to industrial and agricultural practices, controlled application techniques, and intensive and continuing research on the mode of decomposition and the toxicity of degradation products.

As THE UNIVERSITY of California center's research and training programs develop and, hopefully, similar facilities are established elsewhere, there should be mounting public confidence and support of scientific research and its motives.

Furthermore, mandatory high-level academic standards will provide a growing and highly competent scientific force dedicated to preserving the beneficial systems within the environment, and to eliminating those that cause destruction, and in the final analysis, famine and disease.

FUTURE FOOD NEEDS will be met only to the extent to which education and fundamental research are supported.

Educational systems must be governed by standards of excellence based on constant analysis. The continued study and reevaluation of the educational capacity of man, who can also move in bewildering patterns, is even more important than the behavior of chemicals in ecology—the science of the relation of the organism to its environment.

It is imperative that man's decisions be based upon values which are derived from education and scientific fact.

If the great majority of people had the educational capacity to understand the extent of a problem, and the capacity to understand the employment of certain means toward solving that problem, there would be no need for legislation.

If man is to survive, he must understand the basic factors upon which his existence depends. It is all too apparent, especially in the field of chemistry, that the U.S. educational system at all levels is in dire need of study and evaluation, for it is this system that must produce the science-oriented manpower which is capable of maintaining and advancing all the branches of research and technology.

THE SCOPE OF RESEARCH and quality control in food production begins with the seed developed by experimentation, and ends with observation of the shelf storage performance of the finished product itself.

In between, there is a range of functions—bacteriological research, engineering research, experimental cookery, food technology research, crop research, nutritional research, product and package development, and quality control standards.

All of these have contributed to the safety and protection of the Nation's food supply and, very importantly, to the reputation of the product and its manufacturer as well.

The research process deals partly with totally new ideas and discoveries, partly with improvement of existing products and systems. But in everything the aim is to pass on some benefit to the consumer.

DESPITE THE phenomenal progress that has been made in understanding the natural systems which bring about such benefits, man is only at the threshold of understanding and applying the ever-widening scientific complex. Therefore, a growing source of talent must be developed to maintain even a modicum of scientific progress, for the complexities encountered in the future will be far greater than those of mankind's past.

Educational systems, then, must be in step with scientific and technological advancement.

Fundamental research is the best investment any nation can make. It always provides excellent dividends.

The oft-maligned stored food surpluses are all products of fundamental research. The day is not too distant when as food demands increase they will provide the all important time buffer needed by the scientific community to develop new food sources, and at the same time maintain the food supply. It is certainly no hardship on our Nation when the U.S. Government must go abroad to conduct its studies on starvation in its quest to discover the most efficient forms of some human food substances, particularly the proteins.

FUNDAMENTAL RESEARCH has hidden and priceless values. It results in such findings as that the female house fly deposits up to 2,500 eggs during a life-span of 2 to 4 weeks. The discovery of this basic fact determined the degree of hazard from this important carrier of disease.

Research is continuing to discover the built-in mechanism by which the fly becomes immune to once lethal insecticides.

An important commercial research development in the agricultural field during 1964 involved a new insecticide which is characterized by a very high toxicity to flies and mosquitoes, but with a correspondingly low toxicity to mammals.

Fundamental research had preceded the hybridization of cotton, brought about with spectacular results because of simultaneous chemical protection against weed infestation and the cotton borer insect.

It also has pointed the way to the development of systemic insecticides, chemical compounds which are absorbed and carried in the sap stream of plants, thus making the plants toxic only to insects.

Scientists working on fluorocarbon refrigerants came across a white plastic

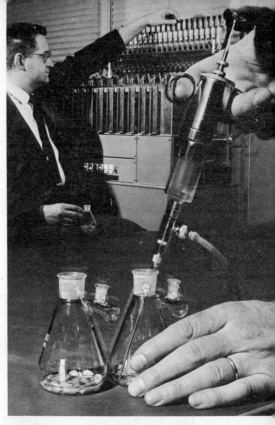

Seed vigor tests at Beltsville, Md. Water is added to special flasks containing seeds, to start germination. Flasks are then placed in mechanical respirometer (rear) that measures their breathing rate and determines if seeds will develop into healthy plants.

substance. Some 25 years later, this chemical compound found extensive uses, among them as a coating for cooking utensils whereby foods could be cooked without fat and without adhering to the pan or the pot.

FUNDAMENTAL RESEARCH provides truth and the paths to freedom from want and suffering.

For example, biochemists are attempting to determine the mechanisms of action of toxins related to food poisoning, and the distribution and effects of staphylococcal enterotoxin in laboratory animals.

This toxin is of interest because of the increasing resistance to antibiotics by bacteria producing the toxin.

363

REGULATION

R. J. ANDERSON

R. J. Anderson is *Deputy Administrator*, Regulatory and Control, Agricultural Research Service.

O F man's basic needs—food, clothing, and shelter—food is an absolute essential. We cannot long survive as individuals or as a nation without adequate food. It is essential to our physical, emotional, and mental health.

Our needs for food appear simple— an adequate and wholesome supply. Abundance is one of America's blessings that is not fully appreciated. It is often taken for granted in the absence of an understanding of the vast amount of scientific know-how that goes into food production, or of the rigid surveillance under which food must be produced and marketed.

Each year a larger percentage of the population of the world depends on others for production of its food.

Yet food supplies in America and the world cannot be taken for granted. They vary according to man's ability to control diseases and other pests of livestock and crops. Our own health and prosperity are related to the ability to control them so we can have food in the first place. And as consumers, we must in addition be protected against some 80 diseases of animals which can be transmitted to man.

PRECEDING CHAPTERS of this book describe the efforts made to protect our food supply against natural hazards like pests and diseases, and possible manmade hazards like chemical residues and food and feed additives.

Manmade hazards are the result of action to prevent losses from pests and diseases during production, and from pests and bacterial contamination during shipment and processing.

Your first question may have been:

Blood samples are taken from tagged animals as part of a plan to screen market cattle for brucellosis.

Can I be sure my food is safe with all the potential hazards that it may have been exposed to?

LET'S TRACE two of our basic food commodities—wheat and beef—from seed to bread and from calf to T-bone steak.

Let's see where each protective mechanism is applied. The earlier benefits are applied for protection during growth, and the second phase to protect during storage, shipment, processing, and marketing.

The wheat seed, having met germination standards, is protected against pests and diseases while in storage and immediately following germination by pesticides that have met Federal and perhaps State standards of safety and effectiveness.

The growing plant is faced immediately with the ravages of diseases and pests, even though it may be a variety which is resistant to some of them. Pesticides that have met rigid require-

ments for safety and efficiency are applied to the growing crop as needed to protect against natural enemies until it is harvested. These pesticides carry instructions for use that will not result in harmful residues on the harvested grain.

As the grain moves into commerce, States and possibly the Food and Drug Administration (FDA) may take samples to determine if it contains illegal chemical residues. Additional samples are taken and tests conducted on the grain prior to milling to assure freedom from insects, filth, and contamination of any nature.

THE FLOUR must also be handled in storage and shipping to prevent vermin contamination.

After the flour reaches the supermarket or bakery, it comes under the control of State or municipal authorities to assure that the final product, when offered for sale, is not contaminated or adulterated.

365

Food additives used in the bread must meet the FDA requirements for purity and safety. The lard or the other animal fats used, if produced in an establishment engaged in interstate commerce, must meet the U.S. Department of Agriculture requirements for wholesomeness.

FULL WEIGHT of local public health requirements are brought into play at local markets, food preparing centers, and restaurants.

Preparation, baking, and delivery of bread to markets and restaurants are regulated to assure a clean, wholesome food item.

Restaurants must also meet local standards of sanitation to assure that bread served is wholesome and safe. Local public health codes require that food handlers meet health requirements and not be a source of disease contamination.

Disinfectants, sanitizers, and insecticides used in the restaurant to control pests and prevent bacterial contamination must comply with the Agriculture Department requirements for safety and effectiveness.

NOW LET'S FOLLOW the newborn calf which is vaccinated soon after birth for protection against many diseases. The vaccine used must meet Agriculture Department veterinary biological standards for potency and safety.

The calf will receive numerous treatments with pesticides to prevent or eliminate flies, ticks, and other pests, many of which are vectors of diseases.

The pesticides have met standards of safety and effectiveness. Directions for use are designed to prevent illegal residues in meat at time of slaughter.

In periods of growth and preparation for market the calf may receive feed additives to stimulate growth and antibiotics to treat diseases. These must meet FDA's standards for safety.

Public livestock markets and transportation facilities used in moving the steer to slaughter in interstate commerce must meet Agriculture Department standards for sanitation and

handling operations so as to prevent exposure to disease.

ON ARRIVAL at a slaughtering establishment operating under the Department's inspection, the calf is given an examination for any evidence of disease. After passing inspection it is then slaughtered in a plant that has met Department sanitary requirements for facilities and operations.

The entire operation—slaughter and processing of the meat—is under Department veterinary inspection.

The carcass is also graded for quality by the Agriculture Department. When it is moved from the plant, it carries two stamps—one assuring wholesomeness and the other establishing quality.

The supermarket, where the meat is cut up, operates under State or local laws governing sanitation and adulteration. It is at this point in marketing that the wheat and the beef come together under local regulations.

THIS IS A BRIEF RÉSUMÉ of the interrelationship of Federal, State, and local regulations that protect our food supply against pests and diseases to assure the consumer his food is safe, unadulterated, and wholesome.

As new knowledge becomes available about how to protect our food better against presently known hazards or as unforeseen hazards arise, regulations will be strengthened or added to provide the protection necessary for our food. The regulations are backed up by actual inspections and tests of the products as marketed to assure that the consumer will have a continued supply of wholesome food.

Basically, regulations are designed to do good. Those providing protection to the Nation's food supply benefit everyone.

By preventing contamination and spoilage of food, persons and firms involved in the producing, transporting, processing, distributing, and marketing of food avoid economic losses. And the consumer benefits from having an abundant, safe, and wholesome supply of food at a reasonable price.

NEW HORIZONS IN RESEARCH

JOHN R. DEATHERAGE

THREE discoveries made almost by chance a century ago touched off a revolution in agricultural pest control. They showed that chemicals can be used against crop insects and diseases.

A poisonous-looking mixture of lime and copper sulfate, sprinkled on grapevines to discourage pilfering, reduced mildew infection. The gaudy paint pigment, paris green, tested to keep beetles off potato plants, killed the beetles. And a compound of carbon and sulfur applied on the ground over grape roots had a hoped-for effect: The fumes killed the phylloxera root louse.

THESE SUCCESSES must have given but small encouragement in the pest problems of the day, which seemed each year to become ever more heavily weighted in favor of the pests.

Our forefathers understood little of the important technology they initiated. But today's technology is to an increasing extent designed through a much better understanding of the organic functions of plants, animals, and their pests. Broad studies of the fundamental nature of living things are providing this understanding. We are thus learning how to exploit the weaknesses of pests and augment natural defense mechanisms of crops and livestock.

The trend, then, is strongly toward a biological type of control technology and—through nature's cooperation—a much improved means of protecting our foods from the pests.

During the 1930's the rearing and releasing of sexually sterile insects in an infested area was proposed as a potential method for eradicating the native population of a pest. In time, atomic science provided a practical method of sterilization by exposure to the gamma rays from a radioisotope.

THE SCREW-WORM FLY, a serious pest of livestock, was chosen for a trial of this theory.

A practical plan was then worked out for mass rearing the fly in sufficient numbers to overwhelm the native population. Radioactive cobalt proved an effective sterilizing agent and did not destroy the screw-worm fly's mating competitiveness.

The cooperative Federal-State eradication of the screw-worm fly population from our Southeastern States in 1958 and 1959 is familiar history. In a more recent campaign in the Southwest, the pest was eradicated from most of the area north of the Mexican border. The melon fly was similarly

* * *

John R. Deatherage was formerly an *Information Specialist* with the Agricultural Research Service. He is now retired.

eradicated from the Pacific island of Rota and the oriental fruit fly from the island of Guam.

The sterility method is also being tested on the codling moth, European corn borer, several tropical fruit flies, and on some other species.

AMONG THE biological control techniques with promise is the rearing and release of insect strains with inferior genetic traits. Someday we may breed and release hybrid insects that produce a preponderance of nonmaturing individuals or of males. Or we may develop genetic strains that are unable to fly during the crop growing season or some other critical period, or unable to enter a resting stage called diapause that conditions the insect for overwintering. A start is being made in exploring these concepts.

SCIENTISTS have now discovered several substances that can chemically sterilize insects. In 1964 and 1965 millions of Mexican fruit flies were reared in the laboratory, treated with one of these chemosterilants, and released in northern Mexico. The huge numbers of sterile flies prevented breeding by wild flies emerging from imported fruits and eliminated their threat. The house fly, mosquitoes, various fruit flies, codling moth, pink bollworm, boll weevil, tobacco budworm, tobacco hornworm, some nematodes, and various other pests have also been chemosterilized experimentally.

Unfortunately the chemosterilants we now have are too hazardous to man and to animals for use outside of the laboratory.

Scientists are searching for safe ones to use around crops, livestock, and in other areas of infestation. They're also trying to develop safer ways to use the present chemosterilants.

CHEMOSTERILANTS would reach their peak of usefulness if combined with another ingenious modern weapon, the selective insect attractant.

Insecticides and traps are already being used with attractants.

Insects will react instinctively and in characteristic ways to certain kinds of light and natural odors like the scents emitted by females to attract males for mating, odors of the species' natural foods, and odors that lead females to suitable egg-laying sites.

By sophisticated chemical techniques scientists have collected and in some cases identified and synthesized the sex attractants of several insect species. A synthetic sex attractant, gyplure, has been used for several years in trapping gypsy moths and keeping check on the area and intensity of their infestation in the Northeastern United States.

RECENTLY a synthetic feeding lure, methyl eugenol, which attracts only male flies, was used with an insecticide to eradicate the oriental fruit fly from the Pacific island of Rota. The males were eradicated and the fly population on the island then died. And the synthetic attractant, butyl sorbate, has been used to trap the European chafer and determine its areas of infestation.

Other attractants, some from normal food sources, have been developed for a number of insect species. Insecticides baited in a spray with a protein hydrolysate feeding lure of the Mediterranean fruit fly eradicated that species from more than 1,000 square miles in Florida during 1956 and 1957.

Egg-laying attractants might be used to cause females to deposit their eggs on incompatible hosts or in exposed places where the eggs cannot hatch or the young cannot survive.

RESEARCH ON insect physiology uncovered the fact that one insect, the cockroach, secretes a hormone that starts sex-lure production and another hormone that stops it. This suggests various possibilities—for example, identification, synthesis, and use of the hormones to upset the normal timing of insect reproduction.

Moths that collect around a lamp are responding to the irresistible attraction of radiant energy. Other kinds of insects, including the tobacco hornworm, are attracted to so-called black or ultraviolet light, which is invisible to human beings.

The tobacco hornworm population in a 113-square-mile test area of North Carolina was substantially reduced by using an average of three black-light traps per square mile and also destroying the tobacco stalks after harvest to prevent the development of late-season hornworms on sucker growth.

THIS TYPE OF lamp is being tested with some success in trapping various other insects. A manufacturer has put a fluorescent powder into a lamp to create the precise wavelength of blue-green light which has been found to be attractive to the cotton boll weevil.

Other lamps can be built to the precise wavelengths to attract additional species when we learn the wavelength responses for these species.

Light not only attracts insects but also affects body functions. For example, photoflashes of less than a thousandth of a second given nightly during the larval stage of one insect, the imported cabbage worm, caused it to develop from a pupa into an adult at a time it otherwise would have entered the dormant stage of diapause. Insects forced to bypass diapause would be unprepared for survival through the winter. This aspect of physiology will be explored for practical applications.

OUR BIOLOGICAL INNOVATIONS have not all been recent or immediately successful. Consider the control of insects with other insects that prey on or parasitize them. That began at least three-quarters of a century ago.

Scientists started collecting from around the world some of the natural enemies of our major crop pests, and through the years they have introduced around 650 species to this country. About 100 are now well established and helping in various degrees to control some 20 major agricultural pests and many minor ones besides.

THE DESIRED CONTROL of pests has seldom been achieved with parasites and predators. Nevertheless, we are spurred on by a number of outstanding successes, like control of the cottony cushion scale of citrus by the vedalia lady beetle in California.

Scientists have also been trying out disease organisms against insect pests and they have recently made excellent progress in the use of bacteria and of viruses as living insecticides.

Geocoris bug feeding on beet leafhopper. Insect predators serve as biological control agents.

Scientists will continue the search for effective disease-producing organisms and parasitic and predatory insects.

INSECTICIDES, sexually sterile insects, attractants, predators, parasites, cultural practices, and other control devices might be integrated to increase the effectiveness of control efforts and to achieve a total population control of given insect species.

Hazards to other forms of life and the costs of control might be reduced in this manner.

Integrated use of insecticides and of sterile males, for example, might be developed for controlling the boll weevil, one of the most destructive of all our pests.

Seven insecticide treatments in the fall, when the pest is particularly vulnerable, might destroy about 98 percent of the weevils. Releasing in the following spring about 100 sterile males to each fertile male in the population would drastically reduce productive matings and the size of the succeeding generation. A followup release of the same number of weevils—about 2,000 sterile males per fertile male in the reduced population—should stop reproduction.

Total population control might be developed similarly for corn earworms, tobacco hornworms, cabbage loopers, sugarcane borers, the European corn borers, pink bollworms, tropical fruit flies, cattle grubs, face flies, and other major insect pests.

MAN'S AGE-OLD PRACTICE of using pest-resistant plants and animals led to exploitation of another natural factor for pest control. For years, breeders have been incorporating into our desirable varieties of plants and breeds of livestock the factors for resistance to insects, diseases, and other pests.

Plant breeders have produced several wheats that are resistant to both the hessian fly and stem rusts, potatoes resistant to potato-X virus, alfalfas resistant to the stem nematode and spotted alfalfa aphid, sugarbeets resistant to the curly-top virus and a cyst

nematode, experimental cottons unattractive to the cotton bollworm and to other important cotton pests.

Animal breeders have taken advantage of the tick resistance found in the Zebu cattle of India and developed the American Brahman, Santa Gertrudis, Brangus, and Charbray breeds of cattle that are resistant to ticks and possibly to other external parasites.

PEST RESISTANCE obtained through breeding has two advantages over chemical control. It does not involve the use of poisons. And the protection often lasts for year after year.

But plant and animal breeding is a slow process. It sometimes requires as long as 25 years to develop a desired plant and much longer for some livestock. However, revolutionary developments in genetics may help to speed up the process.

Discoveries from basic genetic research, which have come with increasing frequency, have accelerated the pace of progress in controlling plant pests.

Plant breeders have learned how to make difficult crosses, some of them between different genera of plants, which could not be made a few years ago. Progress has also been made in livestock breeding methods.

NEW INSIGHTS and revolutionary concepts have been our main sources of recent progress and of optimism—insights and concepts such as mark the work of a flax-breeding team.

Rust-resistant varieties have been a boon to the flax grower. However, the resistance of the new varieties of flax usually succumbs to some new genetic strains or races of the disease-producing organism after a few years.

TO INVESTIGATE why varieties become susceptible, a scientist collected many different strains of the rust fungus and tested them on 25 flax varieties, each with a specific gene affecting the plant's structure, chemical processes, or other functions in a way to make the plant resist the rust fungus. From this investi-

370

gation came the revolutionary concept that for each rust gene enabling the fungus to infect there is a corresponding gene in the host plant determining whether it will be susceptible, resistant, or immune to that rust.

WHAT WAS THE biochemical basis for this gene-for-gene relationship? A team study with the aid of serological procedures demonstrated that there is such a basis but the precise chemistry has not yet been determined.

Plants produce reaction products from infection and some scientists have suspected that these are antibodies. Antibodies are chemical substances that animals produce to tie up invading disease organisms. Antibodies are also produced in response to alien proteins and proteinlike substances.

The antibody response sometimes takes the form of an allergy, as in man's reaction to pollens and to toxic substances of the ivy plant.

Plants resistant to a disease like rust seem to have a local hypersensitive or allergic type of reaction to the pathogen (disease-producing organism), and some scientists believe that antibodies figure in the resistance.

A research team studied the susceptible and resistant reactions of other plants to fungus pathogens. They found that germinating spores on the surface of a susceptible plant alter the chemical reactions of the local cells.

SOME CELL PROTEINS are converted into enzymes that break down those cell walls and otherwise help produce a disease pustule from the contents. The resistant plant, on the other hand, forms a wall of dead cells around the fungus. And nearby cells convert certain of their proteins into phenolic compounds and other substances that are injurious to the fungi.

This doubtless is a mere fraction of the chemistry involved in resistant and susceptible reactions between host and pathogen. When the picture is more complete, we may be able to chemically induce resistant reactions or to inhibit susceptible reactions in plants.

BY FAR THE MOST significant development in genetic research has been discovery of the chemical composition and physical structure of the deoxyribonucleic acid (DNA) molecule in all living matter. This molecule is self-replicating. When a cell divides, its DNA molecules duplicate themselves, providing identical molecules for each new cell.

Each gene carries the coded instruction for its primary function, namely the production of a specific enzyme which in turn can activate additional chemical reactions.

Scientists are deciphering the exact sequence of chemical reactions by which the gene carries out its functions.

The outcome of these studies may place powerful new tools in the hands of the biochemist, the physiologist, the pathologist, and the breeder. Some believe we can eventually learn to identify the chemical code for specific traits like resistance to flax rust.

IF WE KNEW the DNA formula for a particular gene, perhaps we could learn to synthesize the molecule—in other words, to tailor-make a specific gene, which is a self-perpetuating unit of life—and to introduce it into our animals and plants.

A variety with a specific gene conditioning a high type of resistance is a powerful weapon against disease so long as the pathogen does not change. However, this form of protection does not remain effective for very many years against the virulent forms of rust fungi and viruses that arise through genetic changes. The resistance should be fortified by creating lines with more than one gene for specific resistance.

ANOTHER highly desirable type of resistance—called nonspecific, field, or horizontal resistance—allows the plant to survive and reproduce even under severe infection.

Plants having both specific and nonspecific types of resistance are not killed, but produce a fair crop, even when their genes for specific resistance

371

become ineffective. When both types of resistance fail, chemicals are needed for control of the disease.

WE WILL CONTINUE to depend somewhat on chemical pesticides in the foreseeable future, so scientists are trying to improve the ones we use. The main objectives are chemicals that are highly specific against certain pests, low in effect or without effect on other species, noninjurious to man and other warmblooded animals, and nonpersistent in the plant and in the soil and other parts of the environment.

We have already begun to get some of these improvements in the comparatively safe mirex, carbaryl, and highly refined form of malathion insecticides now on the market. Scientists are also working out better timing and other methods to make pesticide usage safer as well as more effective.

Plant physiologists and biochemists are approaching the pesticide problem in another way. While we have much basic information about plants, scientists will try to find out how the susceptible and resistant plants differ in their content of trace minerals and in oxygen intake, enzymatic processes, respiration, and in the performance of their breathing pores.

Scientists will also try to find out what natural attractants and repellents are produced by plants, and what pest species are attracted or repelled. It is hoped that this knowledge will enable us within 5 or 10 years to design chemicals that will control diseases by stimulating specific biochemical changes in the host plant or in the disease-producing organism.

It is difficult to adopt chemical controls for some sporadic pests because of the uncertain needs and the high cost of stockpiling chemicals for long periods. We can avoid stockpiling for some insects and diseases because their outbreaks are predicted, and the pesticides are produced and distributed when needed. Advance warnings have been very helpful, for example, in combating a number of fruit and vegetable diseases. We need a similar prediction system for the cereal rusts and some other intermittent plant diseases.

WE MUST STUDY the weather and other factors that favor the buildup of these diseases and find out just what data we need. Then we can set up a system of continuous reporting and prompt analysis of the data. Scientists are already planning such studies and they hope to develop forecasting for more of our crop diseases.

Despite all our preoccupation with

Microbiologist A. C. Michael surrounded by bee colonies used in developing nonchemical weapons that kill harmful insects but not beneficial ones. The bees, at the USDA Agricultural Research Center, Beltsville, Md., are fed diets containing insect pathogens or disease-causing organisms which may be used to control insects harmful to crops. If bees and other beneficial forms of life are not affected, the control methods can be enlisted in the war on pests.

pesticides, we have not adequately considered the therapeutic value of another class of chemicals, the natural plant constituents that figure in growth.

A VIRUS, for example, robs plant cells of some essential nutrients and disrupts the cell chemistry which supplies others.

Nutrition greatly affects the susceptibility of plants to disease and an adequate reserve of cell nutrients often benefits plants under attack. Studies being started should tell us whether disease injury can be prevented by altering the level of trace minerals in the plants.

Viruses—proteinlike substances that can multiply in living tissue and produce disease—are a special problem in several ways. They live within the plant cells and throughout the plant. It takes a systemic type of chemical—one that is absorbed into and moved throughout the plant—to act on viruses. Systemic chemicals like disulfoton and phorate are effectively controlling the aphids on young cotton plants, and then are changed into nontoxic substances before the cotton is harvested.

CHEMICALS are not promising in virus control because the effective viruscides found thus far injure or kill the plants. However, scientists are trying to discover the chemical factors for absorption and translocation and will try to combine systemic and viruscidal features in noninjurious chemicals.

Genetic plant resistance is still our most effective weapon against viruses. But viruses often mutate. Then it is necessary to combine resistance to both the old and the new strains.

Insects are a very common means of spreading viruses. Entomologists and plant pathologists are cooperatively working out insect controls that should check the spread of viruses.

Viruses sometimes spread through seed and through the vegetative propagation of plants. Recently, aerated steam has been used for small-scale disinfection of certain seeds.

High-temperature treatments offer another way of destroying some viruses in a few plants which could then be vegetatively propagated free of the viruses into commercial quantities. Some viruses do not invade the tip of the plant where rapid growth is occurring, so virus-free tissue at the tip of the shoot can sometimes be removed and grown out on an artificial nutrient to produce virus-free stock.

A number of plants produced at high temperatures will literally outgrow the virus, producing disease-free tips for budding and for grafting.

The possibility of getting the same effect through plant-growth regulators is also being investigated in India under a contract that has been financed through Public Law 480.

BUILDING UP virus-free stocks of many tree crops is so urgent that we may have to resort to increasing the laboratory-made foundation stocks in environments like tropical islands or northern greenhouses far from all sources of the viruses themselves.

These are a few of the hopeful signs for virus control in the next several years, but the real future in virology lies in the less specific region of basic research.

Viruses today occupy a dim place on the scientific horizon. We have just begun to learn the most elementary facts about them.

NEVERTHELESS, only a few years after viruses were first photographed through the electron microscope, we have identified them as ultramicroscopic chemical units. Each is a specific form of ribonucleic acid (RNA) or deoxyribonucleic acid (DNA) surrounded by a protein jacket. A virus without its protein is able to reproduce.

Scientists everywhere understand the significance of this recent knowledge and scores of them are engaged in carefully planned basic studies to penetrate the mystery of these pathogens.

SOILBORNE VIRUSES and other disease organisms, nematodes, and insects account for a significant part of our total

373

losses from pests. The nature of the soil environment and the complexity of the factors which influence soil microorganisms are being studied intensively through research.

THERE ARE MANY questions which remain to be answered.

For example, how does the nutritional balance of the soil affect the balance of the various soil organisms? Can we supply nutrients to favor beneficial organisms that destroy some pathogens? What determines which kinds of spores will germinate? What metabolic processes enable pathogens to grow and produce enzymes? Do some soil pathogens require secretions of other organisms in order to parasitize? What are the main factors for specific pathogen survival?

CULTURAL and nutritional management and perhaps other biological measures seem to be good possibilities in controlling soil pests.

Crop rotation is the oldest and still an excellent means of controlling soil nematodes—minute worms that attack our plants.

Some crops build up a nematode population and other crops reduce it. For example, plant growers can scarcely afford to grow tomato transplants following on a crop of nematode-prone sudangrass; in a test, the yield was only about 28,000 good marketable transplants per acre. But a preplanting of wild marigold sharply reduced the nematodes and made it possible to produce about 302,000 good tomato transplants per acre.

A crop of ryegrass greatly reduces clubroot fungus infection in a succeeding crop like cabbage, and a crop of onions reduces the dry root rot fungus infection in beans.

SOME OF THE HIGHEST costs in crop production are for control of weeds. In addition, weed competition reduces the yield and lowers the quality.

The entire modern technology of chemical weed control has grown up in the past two decades and provides, for the first time, an efficient means of controlling weeds. Some 90 million acres of cropland are treated with herbicides.

The newness and efficiency of this technology does not imply, however, that the weed problem has been solved.

Herbicidal control of weeds hinges largely on the ability of some chemicals to affect only certain plant species. One of the most selective is siduron, which controls annual grasses without killing the perennial forage grasses.

SOME CHEMICALS are effective because they are absorbed and moved throughout the plant. Due to both its selectivity and movability, the herbicide picloram can be used along with a trap crop to destroy witchweed.

Witchweed grows on the roots of various species in the grass family, including sorghum. So sorghum can be grown as a trap crop to make the witchweed seeds germinate and grow. While the young witchweed plants are still developing in the soil, picloram can then be applied to the sorghum without harming it. Picloram will move to the roots and thence into the attached witchweed, killing the latter while it is still underground.

WEED CONTROL in the future will increasingly employ safer and more effective treatment methods and chemicals that are specially adapted to specific crop and weed situations.

For example, delayed planting and precise placement of seed seem to help in reducing or avoiding crop injury following a preplanting application of herbicide. Sometimes less of the chemical can be made to do the job by combining it with oil or a chemical that reduces surface tension of the spray so it can better spread over the plant surfaces.

One study showed that it may be practical to mulch crops before they emerge from the ground with a low-cost, loosely woven cloth that has been pretreated with just the right amount of herbicide.

This could prevent the crop injury and residue problems that sometimes

374

occur from excessive applications. Also, the safety of herbicides and the duration of herbicidal activity has been improved experimentally by covering treated soil surfaces with a petroleum or a wax mulch.

Basic studies of plants will help us understand the species differences in plant physiological response to herbicides, and also to understand how plants translocate systemic chemicals and how plant metabolism is affected by growth regulators.

JUST AS CROP-PEST problems grew with our agricultural expansion, so have the need, difficulty, and costliness of protecting our livestock and livestock products also increased.

Diseases and parasites are a tremendous drain on livestock and animal products, so gains in this field can be particularly rewarding.

Sweeping developments in our fundamental knowledge about animals have laid a solid foundation for a period of truly great advancement in U.S. livestock health.

It is reasonable to expect that the animal sciences will be advanced tremendously by discovery of the role of the chemical DNA in cell function. DNA is the genetic material that specifies reproduction and also specifies the enzymes to be produced, which, in turn, activate additional chemical reactions in the cell. This information seems imminent and would profoundly affect virtually all animal research.

DECIPHERING the riddle of the gene will also tell us much about some disease organisms and how animals react to them, and also lead us away from our historic dependence on drugs. Drugs are not only an imperfect tool, but are often used against a symptom rather than its cause.

With better understanding, we can direct more of the therapy toward supporting the normal defense mechanisms of animals. Indeed, a significant part of our modern protective effort is based upon the defense mechanism of immunity.

Although immunization has been practiced for a long time, animal scientists are still trying to identify the exact chemical substances involved in it.

STUDIES at the animal disease laboratory of USDA on Plum Island, N.Y., are devoted to identifying, isolating, and synthesizing the protein or other true chemical antigen of the foot-and-mouth disease virus—the specific molecule or element that generates antibodies in the host.

With a pure antigen to use in animal studies, scientists would next produce the pure antibody to the disease and isolate and synthesize it free of the side effects of an impure biological product. The scientists could then study antibody effects on animals and identify the metabolic product that actually protects the cells from disease. A number of diseases are being similarly studied.

THE ULTIMATE objective, of course, is pure laboratory-made therapeutics—the same ones nature uses—to reliably and promptly control the pathological diseases in our livestock.

They would supplant our present inexact medicines and today's cumbersome, imperfect procedure of employing animals in the production of the immunological materials.

We know that pests often change and become genetically resistant to established disease or parasite controls. Research scientists will attempt to discover the physiological basis for this resistance and develop countermeasures.

We have been trying to control animal diseases without understanding the true nature of the carrier state and active state of disease. This problem is being attacked through basic research. We are trying to learn what happens to the pathogen as a disease comes and goes, and also what happens to the host itself.

We're interested in the total relationships in biology from the smallest factor, virus, to man.

Carrier animals passively sustain a parasite, enabling it to live and reproduce without producing the disease.

375

For example, a tiny gnat incubates and reproduces in its salivary glands the organism of the bluetongue disease of sheep. Thus, without harm to itself, the gnat can keep the organism alive and deliver it to a new host. Similarly, some cattle carry tuberculosis, anaplasmosis, and other diseases.

Why do the susceptible animals and the carrier animals differ?

Research scientists will try to learn why one species of animal is susceptible to a parasite, another one is nonsusceptible but is a carrier, and a third cannot carry the organism.

Just as we hope to destroy pathogens in susceptible animals, we must also learn how to overcome the compatibility of the carrier animal for the disease organisms.

The human population is expected to increase greatly in the next two or three decades and we will need to raise much more livestock. Keeping more animals on the same area of land intensifies the parasite problem.

IN THE PAST, parasitologists have not had pure parasites to work with but had to tolerate a little contamination. For example, the parasites they worked with might, in turn, carry diseases. While some scientists are trying to develop the artificial culturing of parasites in test tubes, other scientists are developing methods of keeping animals free of internal and external parasites until they are tested.

With those two tools, scientists could study the parasite-host relationships and develop precise immunological programs.

EXCEPT FOR THE limited improvement already mentioned in cattle resistance to ticks and possibly some other external parasites, livestock breeding efforts have largely failed to increase resistance substantially.

This type of research has been slow, costly, and discouraging due to the long time from one generation of livestock to the next. We know that our livestock does have genetic variability as to parasite and disease resistance

which should respond to systematic breeding. Therefore, basic studies will be made with mice in an effort to discover some new genetic principles that would raise the limits for improvement.

The stakes are indeed very high, but the prospects are nevertheless uncertain.

NEW BASIC KNOWLEDGE of livestock diseases is promptly put to use by technicians in supplying the necessary materials for further research. For example, study at the animal disease laboratory on Plum Island, N.Y., has shown how to grow the foot-and-mouth disease virus in tissue culture rather than in live animals. Now technicians can produce that virus in quantity 'for the research scientists to use in their further investigations.

Sophisticated instruments and techniques developed in the past decade or two are even greater factors in the expediting of research.

Quick, accurate methods of chemical analysis are examples.

For some time, we have produced data faster than we could digest it. But the modern data-processing techniques make it possible to feed mass data into machines, and analyze and interpret it promptly.

NOW A RESEARCH SCIENTIST can get as much chemical information in a few days as he formerly would have produced only in a lifetime. He can even retrieve and digest information from old data which it was impractical to analyze exhaustively by the former cumbersome procedures.

Sensitive new methods of biochemical analysis are affecting research in another way. They sometimes detect unsuspected traces of pesticides in animals, animal products, feeds, or in grasses.

INVESTIGATIONS are exploring every aspect of both human and animal health in relation to toxic chemicals. Pesticide practices will, of course, be revised as we discover the need. And safer new pesticides will be developed.

Much of the discussion to this point may have seemed to pertain largely to the raising of crops and livestock. Of course, pest and spoilage problems follow the farm products from the farm even to the point of consumption.

Most of the products continue as living entities, or at least as biochemical systems, throughout transportation, storage, and marketing. They encounter many of the same or similar pest and spoilage problems as before, and likewise some new ones.

OVER THE YEARS, many marketing practices have been developed—temperature and moisture control, aeration, fumigation and other chemical treatments, sanitation, protection from mechanical injury—to protect the food and fiber that has been produced.

Even so, waste and spoilage take about an eighth of the fruits and vegetables produced, and similar proportions of cereal grains and field crops. There are substantial losses in market animals and in animal products, too.

DETERIORATION and damage begin at harvest or even earlier, and when the animals leave the farm.

This calls for protection at every stage—in packing and shipping, in storage, at the terminal market, and in the retail store itself.

METHODS OF PUTTING UP forage have been modernized to reduce damage from weather hazards and to preserve a maximum of the nutrients. Silagemaking has been improved to favor the desirable organisms of fermentation and prevent development of the organisms that spoil or reduce quality.

Mechanical drying has been introduced to reduce the spoilage of grains and oilseeds resulting from excessive moisture content.

Temperature control has been developed to retard the development of the rot, mold, and mildew organisms on perishable products.

Field-warm products like peaches, carrots, green corn, asparagus, celery, and cantaloups are hydrocooled with chilled water. Products like lettuce are vacuum-cooled by evaporating a little of the water which they contain under reduced pressure.

METHODS have been improved for the cooling and temperature control of refrigerator cars, trailers, and cold storage houses to deter the growth of organisms and reduce physical damage from freezing and heating.

Chemical treatments have been developed to control normal but undesirable physiological developments like apple scalding and potato sprouting in storage, and to reduce the microbe count on fresh dressed poultry.

STERILIZATION by radiation to destroy the spoilage organisms is also being investigated currently.

The Food and Drug Administration has permitted unrestricted consumption of bacon which has been sterilized by 4½ million rads of energy from cobalt 60 per gram of product.

Meanwhile, a similar treatment is now being investigated for chicken, ham, and potatoes.

Low-energy radiation (about 200,-000 to 300,000 rads per gram) is being studied with perishables like strawberries, citrus, peaches, and some other fruits and vegetables. Light doses (about 8,000 rads) have been used successfully to prevent sprouting of stored potatoes.

And radiation at 25,000 to 100,000 rads interrupts the life cycle of grain storage insects and could possibly become a practical control.

THE SAME KINDS of basic studies that are being made to discover principles of animal and plant physiology for application in raising livestock and crops will also open the way for specific and effective new methods for protecting plant and animal products through marketing channels. We hope to learn, for example, how browning in apples, core breakdown in pears, pitting in grapefruit, and development of black spots in potatoes occur. Then we can deal with the causes.

CONSUMER RESPONSIBILITY

RUTH M. LEVERTON

SCIENCE and technology have given the United States one of the best food supplies in the world, whether measured in terms of quantity, quality, variety, or availability. Not only do we—as consumers—take this for granted, we make increasing demands on the persons and processes that provide our food.

We expect agriculture and the food industries to put on the retail market an abundant supply of every kind of food we need or want. We expect the food to be nutritious and highly desirable in flavor, color, and texture. We expect it to be clean, unadulterated, and handled under sanitary conditions.

WE EXPECT these qualities even if the food must be transported thousands of miles and stored for long periods in order to give us seasonal foods the year around.

We expect to be able to choose from an almost limitless variety of every kind of food at any stage of preparation. We expect this food to be appropriately packaged in convenient forms and informatively labeled. We expect it to be available to us at any food store where we choose to shop during any hour of a 10- to 12-hour day, or any day of a 6- or 7-day week.

In addition, we want all these products and services for a reasonable price. We don't want to have to wait in line at the checkout counter to pay for it. We even want the option of ordering by telephone and having the food delivered promptly to our kitchen when we choose to.

Foods and related services in the U.S. marketplace meet most of these expectations.

Our dependence on many persons in many places to produce, store, process, and partially or fully prepare our food, places the consumer "a far piece" from the origin of his food. Some consumers view this separation with alarm and are afraid that procedures and materials may be used which will adversely affect the wholesomeness of food.

Occasionally there has been a crisis when some link in the chain of activities to protect food from the time it is

*   *   *

Ruth M. Leverton, a professional nutritionist, is an *Assistant Deputy Administrator*, Agricultural Research Service.

produced until it is eaten has weakened or broken. Occasionally some threat has come from an unknown or unexpected source.

More widespread and dangerous than any crisis, however, are the extremists who try to undermine our confidence in our food supply. They try to discredit the protection that has been given us over the years and the work that is being done constantly to protect and improve our food supply and our health.

GREAT STRESS is being given to the rights of the consumer—the right to safety, to be informed, to choose, and be heard. Equal stress might well be given to the responsibilities of the consumer who enjoys such rights.

Government, through a relatively small number of public leaders, can make decisions and take action to insure a safe food supply, a safe water supply, adequate sanitation, and to keep hazardous food products or processes out of the channels of trade.

Government can provide information to help the consumer make satisfying choices. It can provide opportunities for the consumer to voice his views at public hearings or through correspondence to those who can take them under proper consideration.

But if as a Nation we are to benefit fully from all that is done to protect our food supply, action by the individual consumer is essential.

THE VALUE of almost every protective measure used from farm to table can be erased, deliberately or unintentionally, if the consumer fails to take responsibility for the right action.

Nutritional value and eating quality of any food can be seriously reduced, or a safe and wholesome food can become hazardous, by improper storage and preparation in the home.

Much is done to keep the cost of food down to a reasonable level. This benefit is lost, however, by the consumer who buys food carelessly and allows excessive waste.

Another loser is the uninformed consumer who spends money on food fads and nutrient supplements when customary foods meet nutritional needs.

Our food supply is abundant and varied enough to adequately nourish the Nation. But it is only when we as individual consumers take responsibility for right action—in this case, wise food selection—that we can enjoy and benefit from our abundance to the fullest.

Fortunately, the majority of consumers take personal responsibility for wise food selection, and for supporting and safeguarding all that is done to protect the Nation's food supply.

A consumer examines a product at a Washington, D.C., supermarket.

PHOTOGRAPHERS

Sources of photographs and the photographer's name are listed wherever possible. Photographs with a USDA number may be ordered from the Photography Division, Office of Information, U.S. Department of Agriculture, Washington, D.C. 20250. Please refer to the 1966 Yearbook and give the page number the photo appears on in addition to the USDA number. USDA photos are free to news media. The editor is deeply indebted to Russell T. Forte of the Photography Division for assistance in obtaining photographs. Others in the Division and in USDA agency and State extension photo units were also most helpful.

Front end papers—Left, David F. Warren, USDA BN–22479. Right, Kevin Shields, Consumer and Marketing Service photo, USDA ST 872–3. Half title page (p. 1)—Russell T. Forte, USDA N–50314. Title pages (pp. 11 and 111)—Hermann Postlethwaite, USDA N–33332. viii—Quincy Jensen, USDA IDA–45275. xiv—USDA FS–364931. xvii—Roy M. Clark, USDA BN–20676. xviii—Erwin W. Cole, USDA WIS–1414. xix—Russell T. Forte, USDA ST–117–15. xx—USDA BN–18599. xxi—USDA BN–271. xxii (top)—David F. Warren, USDA BN–19707. xxii and xxiii (bottom)—USDA BN–20761. xxiii (top)—David F. Warren, USDA BN–24367. xxiv and xxv—California Packing Corp., YB–62–12. xxvi—USDA N–19031. xxvii—Lloyd W. Richardson, USDA N–29362. xxviii and xxix—Leland J. Prater, USDA FS–456974 RM. 1—CARE. 4—USDA ES–486. 6—USDA BN–23040. 7—A. Defever, FAO. 11—Roy M. Clark, USDA BN–21303. 13—USDA N–58447. 15—USDA BN–26811. 18—Lloyd W. Richardson, USDA N–39314. 22—Roy M. Clark. 25—Roy M. Clark, USDA ST–826–12. 28—Lewis Riley, Clemson Agricultural College Extension Service, S.C. Cen–301. 32—Top, USDA BN–20853. Center, USDA BN–20856. Bottom, USDA BN–20855. 40—Hermann Postlethwaite, USDA N–38173. 41—Joseph F. Spears. 51—B. Harold Kracht, USDA IND–60559. 53—Rex Gary Schmidt, Fish & Wildlife Service, FWS–4635. 62—Babson Bros. Co., Chicago, No. 5.051, Neg. No. 4060–4. 66—North Carolina Department of Agriculture. 76—Murray D. Lemmon, USDA ST–719–12. 81—David F. Warren, USDA BN–24995. 86—Kevin Shields, USDA ST–327–8. 95—H. J. Heinz Co. 96—J. M. Cross, USDA LA–62624. 97—J & L Engineering Co., Inc., Jeanerette, La. 99—Gentry Co., Glendale, Calif. 105—Hermann Postlethwaite, USDA N–48647. 106—Hermann Postlethwaite. Top, USDA N–44451. Lower left, USDA N–44438. Lower right, USDA N–44439. 120—SEA-LAND. 128—Hermann Postlethwaite, USDA N–44329. 132—USDA N–44050.

134—T. K. O'Driscoll. 136—Murray M. Berman, USDA N–58518. 143—USDA N–58477. 144—Murray D. Lemmon, USDA ST–546–14. 145—USDA BN–26009. 147—William J. Forsythe, USDA N–9881. 159—Gentry Co., Glendale, Calif. 162—Campbell Soup Co. 168—William C. Allen, USDA N–56232. 175—Kevin Shields, USDA ST–870–1. 194—NASA. No. 63—Space Food–11. 207—Hermann Postlethwaite, USDA N–55797. 209—Edwin C. Hunton, USDA N–27726. 211—Extension Service, Rutgers University. 212—John Burwell. 213—USDA BN–20762. 220—USDA BN–20484. 227—David F. Warren, USDA BN–24916. 228—Bottom, Del Deterling, Texas Agricultural Extension Service. 229—Top, William C. Allen, USDA ST–286–11. 230—Del Deterling, Texas Agricultural Extension Service. 250—Kevin Shields, USDA ST–632–15. 253—Kevin Shields, USDA ST–686–6. 260—USDA BN–9599 X. 273—David F. Warren, USDA BN–21637. 276—USDA N–17686. 287—Pete Keay, USDA ST–770–19. 292—Food and Drug Administration, DT #2–F–35. 296—Murray D. Lemmon, USDA ST–743–6. 300—Hermann Postlethwaite, USDA N–54087. 302—William R. Jolley, USDA N–27329. 303—USDA BN–6149 and USDA DN–1358. 325—David F. Warren, USDA BN–23872. 326—David F. Warren, USDA BN–23722. 327—David F. Warren, USDA BN–23908. 334—USDA BN–24588. 335—Murray D. Lemmon, USDA ST–116–10 (top), USDA ST–119–16 (bottom). 336—Top, Vermont State Department of Agriculture, USDA BN–10822. Lower left, USDA BN–12327. Lower right, USDA BN–12328. 347—Murray D. Lemmon, USDA ST–222–9. 351—David F. Warren, USDA ST–876–20. 354—Hermann Postlethwaite, USDA N–31492. 360—American Cyanamid Co., R & D–287. 363—David F. Warren, USDA ST–953–1. 365—Hermann Postlethwaite, USDA N–33304. 369—William P. Nye. 372—Kevin Shields, USDA ST–326–21. 379—Kevin Shields, USDA ST–693–6. Back end papers—Kevin Shields. Left, USDA ST–641–19. Right, USDA ST–691–6.

INDEX

U.S. GOVERNMENT PRINTING OFFICE: 1966 O—791–476